WHITEFORD L. BAKER

PRINCIPAL ENTOMOLOGIST, RETIRED
FOREST INSECT RESEARCH BRANCH
FOREST INSECT AND DISEASE RESEARCH DIVISION
FOREST SERVICE

EASTERN FOREST INSECTS

U.S. DEPARTMENT
OF AGRICULTURE●
FOREST SERVICE

**MISCELLANEOUS
PUBLICATION NO. 1175**

FEBRUARY 1972

THIS PUBLICATION SUPERSEDES "INSECT
ENEMIES OF THE EASTERN FORESTS,"
MISCELLANEOUS PUBLICATION NO. 657

ACKNOWLEDGMENTS

The author gratefully acknowledges the invaluable assistance of many of his colleagues in the Forest Insect Branch of the USDA Forest Service in the preparation of this publication. He is also greatly indebted to the following individuals for their helpful reviews of different sections of it: Dr. A. E. Brower, Maine Forest Service; Dr. R. L. Giese, Purdue University; Dr. D. M. Benjamin, University of Wisconsin; Dr. R. F. Anderson, Duke University; Dr. Jack L. Krall, State University of New York College of Forestry at Syracuse; Dr. R. T. Franklin, University of Georgia; Dr. C. E. Atwood, University of Toronto, Canada; Dr. J. A. Slater, University of Connecticut; Dr. John A. Davidson, Dr. T. L. Bissell, and Dr. F. E. Wood, University of Maryland; Dr. D. L. Collins and Dr J. A. Wilcox, New York State Museum and Science Service, Albany, New York. Finally, he wishes to make acknowledgement to the Connecticut Agricultural Experiment Station, Illinois Natural History Survey, and Duke School of Forestry for the loan of many photographs for illustrations.

LIBRARY OF CONGRESS CATALOG NO. 76–607316

CONTENTS

INTRODUCTION

Interest in the protection of the Nation's forests from insects has grown considerably in recent years. This has come about largely because of increased awareness of the destructive capacities of insects and the heavy toll they take of our dwindling supplies of commercial timber. Interest has been further heightened by the fact that more and more people have come to realize that much of the damage caused by insects need not necessarily happen—that given adequate knowledge of the habits and behavior of injurious insects, it should be possible to either prevent or reduce most of it.

Increased interest in the protection of our forests from insect-caused losses has resulted in increased research to develop cheaper, safer, and more effective methods of control. Much progress has been made in recent years, especially since World War II, in studies of the biology and ecology of many important species, leading to new or improved control methods. Much new information has also been obtained on many other species of potential pests. The results of these investigations appear in many publications, some of limited circulation and more or less inaccessible to the general public.

It is the purpose of this publication, which supersedes U.S. Department of Agriculture Miscellaneous Publication 657 (*167*),[1] to review the literature on eastern forest insects which has been published since 1940, the cutoff date for nearly all of the information contained in M.P. 657. Insects discussed are those which occur either entirely in portions of the United States lying east of the 100th meridian or which occur in both the eastern and western halves of the country.[2] The major portion of the publication is devoted to the identification, distribution, host relationships, and life histories of insects occurring in eastern forests.

This publication includes not only new information obtained since 1940, but also much of the still pertinent information obtained earlier and reported in M.P. 657. The common names of insects preceding the scientific names are approved (*85*); the common names following the scientific names have not been approved.

---

[1] Italic numbers in parentheses refer to Literature Cited, p. 503.
[2] A companion volume covering western forest insects is also available.

INSECTS AND RELATED ORGANISMS

Insects belong to the phylum Arthropoda, one of the major groups of the animal kingdom. In the hierarchy of animal phyla it stands near the top, far removed from the simplest, one-celled organisms in the phylum Protozoa. The phylum also contains many other well-known forms such as crawfish, shrimp, millipedes, centipedes, spiders, and mites. Members of the phylum are distinguished by having the body composed of a series of more or less similar rings or segments joined together and in having some of these segments bear jointed legs. In certain forms, the segmentations of the body may be obscure and not evident from cursory examination. In most instances this is due to a secondary modification of form, a result of adaptation to special modes of life (*152*).

Insects comprise the most abundant and important group of arthropods, but many other members of the phylum are also common and often important. Many of the latter are harmful, either to trees and other vegetation or to wildlife and man. Many are so small they are seldom seen, although enormously abundant; others, larger ones, are easily seen. Some of the latter are also many-legged and wormlike and bear little or no resemblance to insects; others are often mistakenly identified as insects. The arthropods discussed here belong to the Classes Hexapoda (Insects); Crustacea (crawfish, shrimp, crabs); Diplopoda (millipedes); Chilopoda (centipedes); and Arachnida (spiders, mites, and scorpions). Mention is also made of shipworms which belong to the phylum Mollusca.

Class HEXAPODA

Insects

An insect is an air-breathing arthropod with a distinct head, thorax, and abdomen. It has one pair of antennae, three pairs of legs, and usually one or two pairs of wings in the adult state. The majority of species are terrestrial and are found in an almost endless variety of microhabitats on the land. Many other species spend parts of their lives in water.

The majority of insects hatch into wormlike larvae which grow by periodically shedding the outer skin, finally transforming into an inactive pupal stage from which the adult emerges. This sort of development is known as complete metamorphosis. The immature stages of others are very similar in appearance to the adults and are known as nymphs. Members of the latter group are said to have simple or incomplete metamorphosis.

Approximately 900,000 species of insects have been described. This represents 80 to 90 percent of all the known kinds of animals. The actual number of insect species, however, is believed to be much larger and to run into the millions (*628*). Countless numbers feed on plants of all kinds, attacking all parts from the roots in the ground to the flowers and seeds in the tops. Thousands of others feed on other insects or other animals, including man.

Fortunately for man and his interests, the majority of insects are either innocuous or beneficial. The remainder, unfortunately, include some of his most important enemies—not only do they feed on him and other animals and often transmit deadly or debilitating disease organisms, but they also devour his crops and decimate his forests. Because of their abundance, their fantastic reproductive powers, and their remarkable capacities for adapting to changing conditions, they present a continuing challenge to man in his efforts to limit their numbers to tolerable levels.

Several general references to insects are available for consultation: Leonard (454), Brimley (101), Essig (232), Comstock (152), Imms (391), Matheson (510), Brues, Melander and Carpenter (114), Ross (624), and Borror and DeLong (90).

Class CRUSTACEA

Wood Lice

Crustaceans are aquatic organisms, mostly marine. They occur throughout the world, and several species attack the wood of most species of trees when they are placed in salt water. The surface of heavily infested wood may be so completely honey-combed that it resembles a sponge. When this damaged wood is removed by wave action, deeper layers of uninfested wood are exposed. They, in turn, are attacked and the process of destruction is repeated. Continuous infestation may result in the loss of the outer 1 inch of wood per year, Infested pilings often have an hour-glass shape as a result of the erosion of infested portions between low- and high-tide marks. Heaviest attacks occur between mean tide level and low tide, but serious damage sometimes occurs at water depths of 40 to 70 feet or more (9).

Limnoria lignorum (Rathke), commonly called the wood louse, is one of the most destructive species. It has seven pairs of legs, sharp claws for holding onto the wood, and a pair of toothed mandibles for boring into it. Full-grown specimens are 3 to 6 mm. long and resemble sowbugs. This species occurs in clear salt water only and spreads slowly, usually in infested driftwood.

Members of the genus *Sphaeroma* are beetle-like in appearance and are up to 12 mm. long. They occur in both salt and fresh water and may be found in such places as crevices, empty barnacle shells, and in burrows made by molluscan borers. They also damage pilings, usually between tide marks but sometimes all the way down to the mud line. Damage is usually less severe than that caused by *Limnoria,* however, even though the burrows are somewhat wider and penetrate to depths of 3 or 4 inches.

The genus *Chelura* contains the largest of the wood-boring crustaceans. None of these initiate attacks on wood, but they do invade and enlarge burrows made by shipworms. *C. terebrans* is a well-known species along the Atlantic Coast.

Methods for protecting timbers from wood-boring crustaceans are the same as those used against molluscan borers.

3

Class DIPLOPODA

Millipedes

Millipedes are slow-moving, elongate, worm-like organisms, usually with 30 or more pairs of legs. They are usually found under bark, stones, old boards, or in damp rubbish. Their food consists of decaying vegetable matter. The adult has two body regions: (1) the head, which bears a pair of short antennae, usually seven-segmented; and (2) the rest of the body, which consists of a large number of similar cylindrical segments. The first four or five body segments are not fused and each bears a single pair of legs. The remaining segments are fused into ring-like joints, each of which bears two pairs of legs. *Spirobolus marginatus* Say, one of the larger species, is dark brown, narrowly ringed with red, and about 100 mm. long.

Millipedes sometimes become very abundant. At such times they may invade camps, old buildings, and residences in large numbers. Many species emit a fluid with a cyanide-like odor through openings along the sides of the body. Removal of moisture and of accumulations of vegetable matter from infested areas should be helpful in their control. Williams and Hefner (*768*) discuss many of the species occurring in eastern United States.

Class CHILOPODA

Centipedes

Centipedes are worm-like animals, with elongate, flattened segmented bodies. They have 15 or more pairs of strong legs, one pair per segment. The antennae have 14 or more segments, and the appendages of the first body segment behind the head are clawlike and function as poison jaws. The last two pairs of legs at the posterior of the body are directed backward. Centipedes are usually found under bark, in rotting logs, or under stones or boards. They are swift runners and feed on various small animals such as snails, insects, and spiders. All species possess poison jaws with which to paralyze their prey. They will also bite man.

The largest centipedes belong to the family Scolopendridae, some of which may be more than one foot long. The largest species found in the United States, however, is only 125 mm. long. Members of this family are also the most venomous of all centipedes. The bite of the largest ones are not only quite painful but also are occasionally fatal (*90*). The larger and more dangerous species are southern in distribution; those occurring in the North are usually too small to be harmful to man. Bailey (*16*) discussed the centipedes of New York.

The removal of debris used as hiding places is helpful in centipede control.

4

Class ARACHNIDA

Spiders, ticks, mites, scorpions, etc.

The class Arachnida is a large group of air-breathing arthropods in which the body is usually comprised of two regions: (1) the cephalothorax, and (2) the abdomen. They generally have six pairs of appendages (the chelicera, pedialps, and four pairs of legs) but are without antennae.

Order ARANEIDA

Spiders

Spiders are found almost everywhere, both indoors and outdoors, and are so familiar as to need no description (*153*). Objects of fear and revulsion to many people, their presence in large numbers in and around places of habitation or other areas frequented by people, is often considered intolerable. Fortunately, the majority of species pose no hazard to man, even though all have venom glands. Actually, they generally are more beneficial than harmful since their food consists mainly of insects and other small organisms. A few species, however, are poisonous to man and should be avoided (*14*).

The **black widow spider**, *Latrodectus mactans* (Fab.), is probably the most poisonous spider in the United States. Its bite is described as being extremely painful throughout all the muscles of the body, and it occasionally results in death. The black widow occurs from southern Canada southward through the United States, Mexico, Central America, and deep into South America. In the Eastern States it is most common in the South, but also occurs as far north as Maine.

Black widows are usually found in such places as garages, sheds, outdoor toilets, under rocks and old boards, and in hollow logs or animal burrows. The female is shining jet black and bears an hour glass-like red mark on the underside of the abdomen. The body of a full-grown specimen is about 12 mm. long exclusive of the long legs. Males are much smaller and are seldom seen.

Loxosceles reclusa Gertsch and Muliak, the **brown recluse spider**, is also quite poisonous to man, its bite producing a condition known as "North American Loxoscelism." Adults are about 9 mm. long, have long legs, and vary from light fawn to dark brown. A distinguishing mark is a dark fiddle-shaped band on the anterior portion of the carapace, which narrows to a thin center line and extends almost to the abdomen. It is only within recent years that this species has been recognized as poisonous to man. It has been recorded from several Midwestern and Southern States—Oklahoma, Arkansas, Kansas, Texas, Louisiana, Mississippi, Alabama, and Tennessee. It may be found in almost any situation where protection, food, and dryness are adequate, but it probably occurs most commonly inside buildings. Its web is medium-sized and irregular, with a maze of threads extending in all directions without definite pattern or plan (*354*).

It is usually impractical or impossible to eliminate spiders completely. Populations can be reduced, however, by the removal of favorite breeding places.

Order ACARINA

Mites and ticks

The order Acarina contains a large number of important pests of plants and man and animals. The majority are extremely small and seldom seen; others, such as the ticks, are large enough to be seen with the naked eye. Members of this order differ from other Arachinids in having the mouth parts more or less distinctly set off from the rest of the body on a false head and in never having the body so divided that a distinct cephalothorax and abdomen are clearly recognizable (*18*).

MITES.—Numerous species of mites feed on and weaken or kill a wide variety of valuable plants, including trees. Many others attack man and various other forms of animal life, often causing extreme irritation, and sometimes illness and death. A considerable number are either parasitic or predaceous on various species of destructive insects and harmful species of their own kind. Many others feed on dead materials of all kinds on the forest floor.

The family Tetranychidae (*480, 281*) contains a large number of species commonly known as **spider mites,** many of which are important pests of trees and shrubs. These mites vary in color from yellowish, greenish, orangish, and reddish to red, and all are less than 1 mm. long. Infested leaf surfaces are usually covered with a fine netting of silk and spotted with tiny spherical eggs or broken egg shells. Heavily infested foliage may be discolored, disfigured, or killed.

The **spruce spider mite,** *Oligonychus ununguis* (Jacobi), feeds on a number of conifers, especially spruce, cedar, and some of the pines and is widely distributed in the United States. Infested trees may become brownish-gray and appear unhealthy, or they may be completely defoliated. Outbreaks over large forested areas have been recorded. Periods of drought appear to be most favorable for population build-ups. Outbreaks have also occurred following widespread spraying with DDT (*403*). Young nursery stock and recently planted trees are especially subject to serious injury.

Oligonychus milleri (McG.) feeds on pines throughout the South and north to Pennsylvania and the Lake States. Outbreaks covering millions of acres have been recorded during recent years from North Carolina to Florida, in northern Louisiana and southern Arkansas, and in Mississippi and Texas. Young, open-grown, even-aged stands appear to be susceptible to severe attack.

Other important species in the genus *Oligonychus* include: (1) *O. bicolor* (Banks)—long recognized as a pest of oaks, especially shade oaks and sometimes injures beech; (2) the **southern red mite,** *O. ilicis* (McG.)—damages azalea and camellia; (3) *O. aceris* (Shimer)—sometimes a serious pest of maples; (4) *O. letchworthi* Reeves—occasionally seriously injures hop hornbeam; (5) *O. newcomeri* McG.—often seriously infests shadbush; (6) *O. cunliffei* P. & B.—feeds on longleaf pine in Florida; (7) *O. boudreauxi* P. & B.—feeds on cypress in the South; and (8) *O. propetes* P. & B.—feeds on oaks from Washington, D. C. to North Carolina.

The **carmine spider mite,** *Tetranychus cinnabarinus* (Bois.), is a common and widely distributed species that feeds on a great many species of plants, trees, and ornamentals. Several generations are produced during the summer months, often giving rise to tremendous populations. Heavily infested plants may be entirely defoliated, especially during hot, dry weather. *T. ellipticus* Garm. is often abundant on honey locust in the Midwest. *T. homorus* P. & B. feeds on hickory and ash in North Carolina; *T. magnoliae* Boud. occurs on magnolia and yellow poplar in Louisiana; the **four-spotted spider mite,** *T. canadensis* (McG.), feeds on elm, basswood, horse chestnut, osage orange, and poplar throughout eastern United States and southern Canada; and the **Schoene spider mite,** *T. schoenei* McG., infests elm and black locust throughout eastern United States.

The genus *Eotetranychus* also contains a number of common and frequently important species. *E. populi* (Koch) and *E. weldoni* (Ewing) are found on poplars and willows; *E. hicoriae* (McG.) occurs on pecan, hickory, horse chestnut, and various oaks; and *E. matthyssei* Reeves attacks elm in New York. Heavy infestations may cause severe browning and cupping of the undersides of leaves. *E. querci* Reeves has caused severe browning of pin oaks in New York.

Platytetranychus multidigituli (Ewing) feeds on the leaves of honey locust, causing them to turn yellow, and *P. thujae* (McG.) attacks arborvitae, juniper, and cypress. *Eurytetranychus buxi* (Garman) is a serious pest of European boxwood. The leaves of infested plants become bronzed, then wither and sometimes fall prematurely.

The family Eriophyidae contains a number of tree-infesting species (*414*). Many produce open pouch-like or blister-like galls on the twigs and leaves of their hosts. Some cause a rusting of infested leaves, and certain others feed on buds. A few of the more common and important tree-infesting species are discussed here.

The **maple bladder-gall mite,** *Vasates quadripedes* (Shimer), is a common species. It ranges in length from about 1/20 to 1/5 of a mm. and feeds on the under-surface of silver maple leaves, causing the formation of pouch-like or bladder-like galls up to 3 mm. in diameter (fig. 1). At first, these galls are light colored or yellowish green. Later, they are reddish to almost black and look for all the world like miniature green peppers standing on stalks above the leaf surface. Heavily infested leaves are often distorted. The related species, *V. aceris-crummena* Riley, produces slender, fusiform, or spindle-shaped galls about 5 mm. long on the upper surfaces of silver and sugar maple leaves.

A few of the other eriophyids infesting trees and some of their hosts are as follows: *Eriophyes fraxiniflora* Felt—feeds in the staminate flowers of ash. Infested clusters become deformed and remain on the tree as green masses until fall. The **pear leaf blister mite,** *E. pyri* (Pagen)—an introduced pest of pear and apple, has also been recorded on mountain ash and shadbush. It is sometimes abundant enough on mountain ash to cause noticeable injury. *E. parapopuli* (K.)—stunts the growth of poplar by producing woody galls around the buds. *E. caulis* Keifer—causes large, deforming, hairy growths on the petioles of black walnut leaves. The

7

F-506694
FIGURE 1.—Galls of the maple bladder-gall mite, *Vasates quadripedes*, on leaf of maple.

pine bud mite, *Phytoptus pini* Nal.—causes the yellowing and dropping of pine needles. *Aceria phloceoptes* (Nal.)—deforms fruit spurs and produces woody galls on plum. *Nalepella tsugifoliae* Keifer—has been reported damaging hemlock in nurseries in New York. *Trisetaceus cupressi* (K.)—attacks southern red cedars, causing distortion and deformation of young trees.

Mites of the family Sarcoptidae are skin parasites of warm blooded animals. The **itch mite,** *Sarcoptes scabei* (DeG.), is a well-known species. It attacks man and causes severe itching as it burrows into the skin.

The family Trombiculidae contains the notorious red bugs or chiggers. The common **chigger** in eastern United States is the first instar larva of the species, *Eutrombicula alfreddugesi* (Oudermans). In its later stages, it feeds on other insects, snakes, birds, lizards, and rodents. When it attaches itself to the skin of man and insects, it inserts its mouth parts to feed, causing intense itching and sores. Heavy attacks may cause fever, and secondary infections may occur. Chiggers are often abundant in the forests of the Central and Southern States and along the Atlantic Seaboard north to New Jersey.

Many other species of mites occur in association with bark beetles,[3] and some are known to be parasitic. So far, very little information is available on their effectiveness in natural control of the beetles. In some instances, it may be substantial.

TICKS.—Ticks are all parasitic, chiefly on mammals, birds and reptiles. All American species have a number of features in common, such as large size, a piercing hypostome with recurved teeth, and chelicera with lateral teeth on the movable digits. Some ticks are mostly covered by a hard dorsal plate called the scutum; in others this hard plate is absent.

---

[3] Unpublished manuscript by J. C. Moser and L. M. Roton. Mites associated with southern pine bark beetles in Allen Parish, La.

The **American dog tick,** *Dermacentor variabilis* (Say), occurs throughout eastern United States, but is most abundant in coastal areas and in the Mississippi River Valley. The larvae and nymphs feed largely on rodents; the adults feed on dogs, horses, hogs, cattle, and many species of wild animals. Man also may be bitten, but he is not a preferred host (477). Unfed adults are brown, variously marked with white, and about 5 mm. long. Engorged females are bluish gray and sometimes reach a length of 12 mm. Females lay eggs in various places but never on the host; the young seek out their host after hatching. Heaviest infestations are usually found on vegetation along game trails, paths, and roadways. Adults are most abundant during spring and early summer in the North. After August they are usually very scarce. In the South, they occur throughout the year. This species transmits Rocky Mountain spotted fever and tularemia, both serious diseases of man. It also transmits anaplamosis, a disease of cattle.

The **black-legged tick,** *Ixodes scapularis* Say, occurs along the Atlantic Coast. The larvae and nymphs feed on rodents and reptiles, and the adults feed on deer, cattle, sheep, dogs, and other large animals. People are also bitten. This species has long mouth parts and inflicts a very painful bite. Infestations are usually found along game trails, paths, and roadways where the ticks wait on vegetation for people or animals to come by. Adults are most prevalent during fall and early winter. This species transmits anaplamosis to cattle and piroplasmosis to dogs (726).

Order SCORPIONIDEA

Scorpions

Scorpions are fairly common in eastern United States, especially in the South. However, because they are active only at night and usually remain hidden during the day, they are seldom seen. Indoors, they usually hide in such places as closets, attics, folded blankets, shoes, and papers. Scorpions vary considerably in size, ranging from about ½ to 7¼ inches in length. The abdomen is divided into a large anterior portion of seven segments and a long, narrow tail-like posterior portion of five segments. The latter ends in a vesicle which bears a poisonous sting. When a scorpion runs, it holds it large claw-like pedialps forward, and the posterior end, bearing the sting, is usually curved upward.

Scorpions are capable of inflicting painful and sometimes fatal stings. Very young and very old people appear to be the most vulnerable. Scorpions' food consists of a wide variety of animal life including other scorpions, spiders, flies, beetles, cockroaches, grasshoppers, crickets, termites, centipedes, and earthworms. A common species in many parts of eastern United States is *Centuroides vittatus* (Say), the so-called **striped scorpion**. This is a fairly small species, being only about 58 to 60 mm. long. Its sting results in a sharp pain which usually lasts about 15 to 20 minutes. Stings inflicted from late March to early May, however, may remain painful for several hours (15).

Scorpions may be trapped during dry seasons by spreading wet burlap bags on the ground in infested areas.

Order PSEUDOSCORPIONIDAE

False scorpions

False scorpions bear a striking resemblance to their larger relatives, the true scorpions, but differ in having wider, shorter abdomens and in not having terminal poison glands. They are seldom more than 5 mm. long.

Pseudoscorpions may be found in a wide variety of places—in soil cover, under bark, under the wings of beetles, on the bodies of birds and in their nests, in buildings, and in chicken houses and beehives. Their food consists of mites, ants, and various other insects. They have also been reported as biting man but without inflicting appreciable injury. One species, *Chelifer cancroides* (Linn.), is frequently found in association with man. Adults are about 2.5 to 3 mm. long (*360*).

Order PHALANGIDA

Daddy-long-legs

Daddy-long-legs are somewhat similar in appearance to spiders but differ in having small, compact, nearly globular bodies and extremely long legs. They also are rather slow in movement, usually appearing to totter about, and they occur commonly in most parts of the United States. Their food consists chiefly of plant juices or dead insects. Some apparently feed on living insects. When crushed, their bodies give off a disagreeable odor. None are harmful to man.

Phylum MOLLUSCA

Shipworms

Wood submerged in salt water is attacked by several species of bivalve mollusks, commonly known as **shipworms**. Damage to pilings is often severe, especially along the Gulf Coast and along the Atlantic Coast south of the Chesapeake Bay. Boats are also damaged occasionally. These organisms are discussed briefly because the damage they cause is similar to and often confused with that caused by wood-boring insects.

The genera *Teredo* and *Bankia* contain the so-called shipworms. Their bodies are long and soft. They are armed with small, chisel-like shells at the anterior end and there are two siphon tubes at the posterior end. They are free-swimmers in the early larval stage, and during this period the body is protected by a bivalve shell. Free-swimming larvae seek out wood and attach themselves to it near the mud line. Then they bore into the wood leaving very small openings to the outside. Once inside they develop rapidly, enlarging and lengthening their tunnels as they grow. During this period the shell, which is no longer needed for protection, is used as a boring tool. As they develop, shipworms secrete a calcareous material with which they line their tunnels. The openings made by the young larvae are never enlarged. As a result, the only external signs of infestation of a piece of heavily damaged wood are tiny holes in its surface.

Because a single piling may contain several thousand shipworms, it may be literally honeycombed (fig. 2). In such situations, tunnels may be no more than ¼ of an inch in diameter and only a few inches long. Under the most favorable conditions, however, the tunnels may reach a diameter of 1 inch and a length of 4 feet.

The genus *Martesia* also contains a number of destructive species. They differ from the shipworms in being clam-like. The young are also free-swimmers and seek out and attack submerged wood, making small, inconspicuous entrance holes. Once inside the wood, they grow until they are about 25 mm. in diameter and 60 mm. long. As they grow, they enlarge their cavities to accomodate their bodies. Members of this genus are found along the shores of the Gulf of Mexico.

Damage to pilings by shipworms can be prevented by impregnation of the wood with a suitable preservative. Coal tar 1 creosote is recommended for treating waterfront timbers of Douglas-fir and southern pine. Copper naphthenate is usually used for the protection of wood in boats. Coatings of paint and metal are also effective as long as they remain intact.

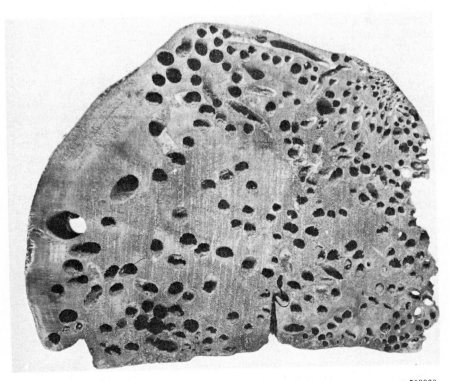

F-519930

FIGURE 2.—Cross-section of a piece of timber riddled with tunnels made by a molluscan shipworm of the genus *Bankia*.

11

FOREST INSECTS

Insects are by far the most numerous of all the forms of animal life inhabiting the forest. They are remarkably well adapted to their surroundings and occupy an incredibly wide variety of ecological niches. They serve many functions in the economy of the forest and are as essential a part of the complex association of organisms comprising it as are the trees themselves (412). While the majority of species are either beneficial or innocuous, many species are exceedingly injurious.

Beneficial forest insects are represented by a great many species, some of which are enormously abundant. Some feed on forest debris and aid in its deterioration; others feed on organic matter in the duff and soil and contribute to improvements in soil fertility. Some contribute to stand improvement by attacking and killing decadent, diseased, or overmature trees and making way for younger growing stock. Many others are parasites or predators of destructive species of insects.

Harmful forest insects are those that are responsible for economic loss. They include (1) species that damage or destroy the flowers and seeds of trees and which are particularly important pests in seed orchards and seed production areas; (2) species that stunt, deform, or kill young trees by damaging or destroying the terminals, laterals, or roots of reproduction and in plantations; (3) species that cause loss of vitality, growth reduction, and often the death of trees by eating the foliage; and (4) species that feed under the bark or in the wood of living trees and girdle and kill them or riddle them with tunnels are important pests in the forest. These are not all: Numerous others that bore into and damage or destroy green logs, storm-felled timber, green-sawn and seasoned lumber, rustic construction, poles, posts, crossties, mine props, and all manner of finished products from flooring to furniture are highly destructive.

Most of our forest insects are native to the continent and are usually distributed throughout the ranges of their hosts. Some are destructive at normal population levels, but the majority normally occur in such low numbers as to be of little or no consequence. A few of the latter, however, are capable of great and rapid increases in numbers when favorable environmental conditions prevail.

Eastern forests are also inhabited by many species of introduced insects, a few of which are widely distributed and extremely destructive. These include the gypsy moth, European pine shoot moth, balsam woolly aphid, European pine sawfly, and the smaller European elm bark beetle. Many species of natural enemies of several introduced pests have also been imported and established in eastern forests.

Conditions conducive to forest insect outbreaks are only partly understood. It appears though that outbreaks are most likely to occur (1) in pure stands rather than in stands of mixed composition, (2) in overmature rather than immature stands, and (3) in plantations rather than natural stands. They may also develop in stands weakened or decimated by hailstorms, flood, wind, drought, tree diseases, fire, or defoliation or during logging operations. Any time a breakdown occurs in the effectiveness of natural control factors, or when changes occur in the genetic composition of populations, or in the age, composition, and density of stands, outbreaks are likely to occur.

Forest insect outbreaks vary greatly in frequency, size, and duration. Fortunately, the majority are small and short-lived, and usually consist of only one or a few "spots" in a stand or region. Unfortunately, some may expand until they encompass hundreds of thousands of acres and last for many years before subsiding. From 1957 to 1966, a total of 154 different species were recorded in outbreak status in eastern forests.[4]

The following general discussions on forest insects are available for reference: Anderson (9); Doane, et al (196); Graham, K. (302); Graham and Knight (309); Thatcher (710); Beal and Massey (41); Beal, et al (40); Becker (50); Houser (381); Kotinsky (437); MacAloney and Ewan (472); MacAloney and Schmiege (473); and Shenefelt and Benjamin (644).

Forest Insect Caused Losses

Insects are among the most destructive agents affecting forest and shade trees. During 1952 (considered an average year), they killed an estimated 1 billion cubic feet of young, growing trees and 5 billion board feet of older, more mature trees of sawtimber size. In addition, they were responsible for a loss in growth of 1.8 billion cubic feet in the young, growing stock and 8.6 billion board feet in surviving sawtimber trees (729). The losses in sawtimber alone were enough to build 1⅓ million homes. Losses incurred during epidemics are sometimes much heavier. Additional losses of a considerable but unknown amount are caused by insects that bore into the wood of living trees or dead and fallen timber.

Insects are not only responsible for the killing of valuable trees and the loss of growth or recoverable volumes from surviving damaged trees, for the weakening or destruction of wood products of all kinds, but also for serious losses of other kinds, both tangible and intangible. Management plans are often upset and fire hazards increased; watersheds and wildlife habitats are impaired or destroyed; water in streams and lakes is polluted; the incidence and severity of floods are increased; and the attractiveness of parks and other recreational areas is reduced or destroyed. Heavy investments in tree improvement programs are also jeopardized or upset by the destruction of seeds and cones or valuable seed trees in seed orchards; stand composition is often changed, leading to the displacement of valuable tree species by others of lesser value; and innumerable shade and ornamental trees around homes, along roadsides, or along the streets of towns and cities are killed or their attractiveness greatly reduced or destroyed.

---

[4] Forest Insect Conditions Annual Reports, 1957–1966 inclusive, USDA Forest Service.

Forest Insect Surveys

It has long been recognized that successful control of forest insect outbreaks depends not so much on the control method used as upon a knowledge of the insect situation on immediate, surrounding areas. When an outbreak is discovered, it needs to be known whether it is increasing or decreasing. It is also important to locate the center of greatest concentration and to determine the direction of spread (*169*). When an outbreak occurs, it is also important to know the value of the resources at stake and the status of natural control factors, before decisions to apply control are made. Of like importance is the possession of a general knowledge of insect conditions throughout a timber type or region. This is helpful in developing plans for the detection of outbreaks in their early stages, a time when they may be suppressed most easily and economically and before heavy losses are incurred. Similarly, it is helpful to have a continuing record of the presence and abundance of the less spectacular, non-outbreak types of insects, to determine if, when, and where their numbers or damage are reaching economic levels of concern. Where intensive management of the forest for timber or other objectives is being practiced, it is also important to have up-to-date information on all destructive pests to allow for their early control where needed. Such knowledge as described above is sought or acquired through surveys.

Forest insect surveys of one sort or another have been made in the United States since the early days of this century (*88*), but prior to the passage of the Forest Pest Control Act in 1947, they were usually conducted on a more or less unorganized basis. Passage of the Act made it possible for the first time to conduct surveys on an organized, systematic basis on forest lands of all ownerships. In part, the Act authorized the Secretary of Agriculture, either directly or in cooperation with other Departments of the Federal Government, with states and other public agencies, and with private organizations and individuals, to conduct surveys to detect and appraise insect infestations before they develop to outbreak proportions; to appraise their potential destructiveness; and to determine the needs for their control. Forest insect surveys are also conducted in Canada. There, the aim is not only to detect and appraise infestations but also to obtain information on the distribution, biology, and cycles of abundance of insect species for taxonomic and other purposes (*481*).

Basically, forest insect surveys are of two kinds, detection and evaluation, and they may be conducted separately or at the same time. Detection surveys, as the term applies, are primarily for the purpose of discovering threatening infestations. Evaluation surveys are usually far more intensive and complex, being concerned with such factors as the intensity and trends of pest populations, the identification and evaluation of natural control factors, the size and boundaries of infestations, the value of the resources at stake, the possibilities of economic loss and an estimate of its magnitude if suppressive measures are not taken.

Many methods and techniques are employed in conducting surveys, the choice depending on many factors, such as the insect species, its life history and habits, the nature of the damage it causes, the forest type and terrain, the size and accessibility of the area, a working knowledge of natural control factors affecting it, and the availability of trained personnel and funds. Aircraft are widely used in detection surveys and to a lesser extent in evaluation surveys. Conditions may be recorded by trained observers riding with the pilot (*3, 339, 341*) ; or by aerial photography (*745, 2, 338, 340, 746, 142*). Unfortunately, evidence of infestation by many insect species is difficult or impossible to detect from the air. Where these insects are concerned, the only recourse is to use ground survey methods. To the extent that it is possible to use them, aerial surveys are far less time consuming and costly than comparable ground surveys.

Ground surveys are not only required to detect infestations of many species but are essential for evaluation purposes. In most cases, they are highly complex and require the services of highly trained personnel. Ground surveys for evaluation purposes present many different sampling problems, such as when, where, and how to sample in order to obtain needed information within desired confidence limits. The choice of procedure is governed largely by the insect species and the intensity and size of the infestation. In addition to insect population density and size, data also may be collected to identify and record the abundance of natural control factors. In all cases information is sought and analyzed to determine two things: what likely will happen if no action is taken to suppress the infestation, and what might be expected to happen if suppressive measures are applied.

Much progress has been made in recent years in reducing the time and cost of conducting surveys, particularly through the use of sequential sampling techniques. These techniques provide for flexibility in sample size in contrast to conventional techniques which usually specify a fixed number of sampling units to be examined. Units chosen at random from a sample are examined in sequence until the sample falls into one or more classes distinguished by specified limits (*743*). Sampling plans have been published for several important forest insect pests (*158, 157, 393, 394, 542, 612, 692*).

Forest Insect Control

The impact of naturally occurring adverse environmental factors on forest insects is so great that the majority of species never occur in sufficient numbers to constitute an economic hazard. Even those insects that become sufficiently abundant at times to be considered "pests" are also subject to control by these factors, though usually to a lesser degree and frequency. Depending on the insect and the value of the forest resources affected, a given degree of natural control may be economically effective.

When natural control factors fail to hold populations to economically tolerable levels, it may be necessary to apply artificial controls. Depending on the insect and its biology and ecological relationships, a wide variety of materials and methods are available for suppressing populations. These may be applied directly against the insect to interfere with its growth or reproduction, or to kill it; or they may be applied to the environment to render it less favorable for the insect either through alteration in food supply, in microclimatic factors, or in the abundance and effectiveness of natural enemies.

The choice of materials or methods in artificial control depends on several things: whether the insect is a native or introduced species; the factors known or thought to be responsible for its abundance; the need for quick and effective reductions in its numbers; and cost. If a native species is involved, the aim usually is not to eradicate it, but rather to reduce and maintain its numbers to a tolerable level; if it is an introduced pest, the aim may be to eradicate it or to slow down or prevent its spread.

Artificial control methods designed to suppress existing outbreaks, usually have short-term effects only; those that are used for the prevention of outbreaks may be long lasting. Control costs vary considerably, depending on the insect and its habits, the methods and materials used, and the size and accessibility of infected stands. It may be limited to only a few dollars per acre where infested stands are treated with aerial applications or insecticides or it may cost several dollars per tree when treatments are made to individual trees. Occasionally, control costs may be retrieved through the salvage and sale of infested timber. Some types of control may be used with complete safety; others, in which hazardous materials are involved, must be used with great care.

NATURAL CONTROL

Natural control results when naturally occurring adverse environmental factors prevent insect populations from reaching or exceeding harmful proportions. It may be effected by a single factor, such as abnormally low winter temperatures, or by several factors working in combination; it never ceases to function entirely, but its impact may fluctuate greatly from place to place and time to time (9, 302, 309).

PHYSICAL FACTORS.—Temperature is one of the most important physical factors affecting forest insects. It not only sets limits to their distribution but also often profoundly affects their abundance. The optimum temperature for many eastern species appears to lie between 75° and 80° F. As temperatures depart from this range, in either direction, activity gradually declines and eventually ceases. When they climb to 120° or drop to around 0° or lower, death results. Rapid changes in temperatures, such as occur in the fall and spring, also may cause mortality even though absolute lethal temperatures are not reached.

Insects react in many ways to escape the rigors of adverse temperatures. During the summer, leaf-feeding larvae may move from the upper to lower surfaces of leaves, or from the periphery of the crowns to the shaded interior to escape excessive heat. Adults find relief from heat by moving into the interior of stands, to the shaded portions of trunks, or to the interior of crowns. During cooler than normal days, they may seek out individual, exposed trees, the sunny side of trunks, or trees along the edges of stands. To escape the effects of winter cold, a species may utilize areas in which to hibernate either in the egg, larval, pupal, or adult stage where the likelihood of lethal temperatures occurring are greatly lessened. Because of physiological changes which occur in the dormant state, many northern species are able to survive temperatures well below 0°. Southern species are much less likely to survive exposure to such temperatures.

Outbreaks of leaf eating insects may be suppressed by late spring frosts which kill the young, tender foliage which the young larvae depend on for food. Late springs may result in greatly delayed emergence from hibernation and cool summers may result in a slow-down in the rate of larval development. Prolonged developmental periods add up to an extended period of exposure to parasites, predators, and disease pathogens, which may lead to unusually heavy losses. The number of generations produced per year is related to photoperiod and the length of the season of biologically effective temperatures. In the South, a species may produce five or more generations per year; whereas in the North, it may produce only one. Outbreaks of such a species often appear to develop with explosive suddenness in the South. In the North, it may require several years for an equivalent outbreak to occur.

Insect populations are also affected by atmospheric moisture and by moisture conditions in host trees and in the soil. For example, various species of wood borers, such as powder-post beetles, breed successfully only in very dry wood; whereas others, such as the ambrosia beetles, require wood with a much higher moisture content. Damage to black locust by the locust borer and to pines by various species of bark beetles may be greatly intensified during or following periods of drought.

A considerable degree of control also may be effected by other adverse weather conditions. For example, heavy, beating rains may dislodge and destroy large numbers of larvae that feed on the foliage of trees; moist weather may result in the development of disease epizootics and the decimation of insect populations.

HOST FACTORS.—Many species of forest insects feed on only one species of tree. Some of the most serious bark beetle pests belong to this group. Many species of destructive wood borers also confine their attacks to a single species or to closely related species. In contrast, numerous other species feed on several to a great many tree species, often in different families. Many leaf eating species belong to this group. The females of some insects deposit their eggs in all manner of places; others deposit them on host trees only. This often leads to heavy losses among newly-hatched larvae, especially where acceptable food is not readily available. Infestations of a single-host species that develop in weak or decadent trees may disappear or be greatly reduced when the ratio of these trees to healthy vigorous trees drops below a critical level in a stand. Populations of multiple-host species, many of which attack trees in all stages of health or vigor, may be held to low levels in mixed stands which contain a low ratio of preferred to non-preferred host species.

BIOTIC FACTORS—Parasites, predators, and pathogenic micro-organisms play important roles in the natural control of insects. Their effects may not always be evident, but they always bring some degree of pressure to bear on their hosts, and it is often severe. Occasionally, as when a virus epizootic develops, the results may be catastrophic. Operating singly or in combination, biotic factors may limit the duration and magnitude of an outbreak, prolong the intervals between outbreaks, or prevent outbreaks entirely. A large number of these control agents have been collected and identified in the forests of eastern America, and new ones are being added to the list each year.

Insect control by biotic factors has several advantages not offered by many of the other approaches to control now available. Where these factors are well established they usually are self-perpetuating, barring natural catastrophies or unwise interference by man; they adjust to changes in the size of host populations; and they operate with practically no adverse side effects.

The majority of the parasites and predators of insects are other insects. Many thousands of species belonging to well over 200 families in 15 orders are known to be either parasitic or predaceous; many of these attack forest insects. The majority of parasitic forms belong to only a few families in the orders Hymenoptera and Diptera. Important predators are found in several families of the orders Coleoptera, Diptera, Neuroptera, Hemiptera, and Hymenoptera.

Parasitic and predaceous insects differ widely in habits and behavior. A parasite usually requires only one host in which to complete its development; a predator usually requires several to many hosts for its development. A parasite usually does not kill its host until it has completed its own development; a predator usually kills its host as soon as it is encountered. Host selection by parasites is a function of the egg-laying female adult only; whereas each individual predator must search out hosts in all of the feeding stages.

Forest insects are also fed upon by many other forms of animal life, principally spiders, mites, birds, and many mammals. Birds, especially woodpeckers, are sometimes effective in suppressing outbreaks. Many other species of birds are also thought to play important roles in control (284, 535). Small mammals such as shrews are often effective in controlling species that spend parts of their lives on the ground.

The literature contains many references to the role of parasites and predators in insect control. A good introduction to the subject is found in publications by DeBach (187), Sweetman (701), Clausen (144), Balch (25), Turnbull and Chant (722), Thompson (714), and Burkner (118).

Many species of forest insects are also subject to a considerable degree of control by pathogenic micro-organisms. Some of the latter, especially the viruses, frequently occur in the form of epizootics and decimate or eliminate outbreaks over large areas. Notable examples are (1) a polyhedrosis virus disease which has played a leading role in the control of gypsy moth outbreaks in the Northeast for many years, and (2) a disease of the same type which caused the collapse of an outbreak of the European spruce sawfly over a region of several thousand square miles in eastern Canada and the Northeastern States during the late 1930's.

Well over 1100 different kinds of micro-organisms, most of which are pathogenic, have been found associated with insects.

18

This total includes 90 species and varieties of bacteria, 260 species of viruses and rickettsia, 460 species of fungi, 255 species of protozoa, and 100 species of nematodes (557). Generally speaking, they gain entry into the insect either by being ingested with food, through wounds or other damaged areas in the integument, or through the integument or trachea. Most of them rely on wind, rain, streams, healthy or contaminated insects, small mammals, or birds for dispersal throughout an insect infestation. Spread is occasionally so rapid that all of the insects in an infestation may appear to be dying at the same time.

Many species of forest insects are particularly susceptible to viruses of the nuclear-polyhedrosis type. Once inside the host these viruses enter the cell nuclei, replicate, and become encapsulated in many-sided, rodlike crystals, known as polyhedra. Invaded cells are soon destroyed, the polyhedra are then released in the body cavity, and the host dies. Diseased larvae usually become sluggish, cease feeding, and in some instances move upward in the trees. After death they may be seen hanging by their forelegs, with the body darkened, decomposed, and liquefied. Eventually they completely disintegrate and dry up on the trees. Some of the more important eastern forest insects, in addition to the gypsy moth and European spruce sawfly, that are subject to polyhedrosis virus diseases are eastern tent and forest tent caterpillars, fall webworm, linden looper, white-marked tussock moth, winter moth, European pine sawfly, red-headed pine sawfly, jack-pine sawfly, Virginia pine sawfly, and *Neodiprion excitans.*

Forest insects are also affected by several other kinds of viruses—cytoplasmic polyhedrosis, granulosis, polymorphic inclusion, and non-inclusion. Generally speaking, these viruses appear to be less effective and less specific in control than those of the nuclear-polyhedrosis type. For further information on viruses the reader is referred to Bergold (*61*), Bird (*67*), Hughes (*389*), Martignoni and Langston (*501*), and Steinhaus (*690*).

Several species of bacteria produce so-called milky diseases in the insect host, the best known being the milky disease of Japanese bettle larvae (*212*). The larvae of many closely related species of beetles are also affected by this disease. Scores of species of Lepidoptera and apparently several species of Hymenoptera, Coleoptera, Diptera, and Orthoptera are susceptible to diseases caused by various crystalliferous bacteria, the best known of which are several varieties of *Bacillus thuringiensis* (*334, 333*).

Some species of fungi occasionally cause significant reductions in insect populations. Aphids are particularly susceptible to attack by species of *Entomophora* (=*Empusa*). The species, *E. megasperma,* was credited with causing a high degree of control of the forest tent caterpillar in Ontario from 1949 to 1952. Another species, *Beauveria bassiana,* reportedly killed over 90 percent of the larvae of the smaller European elm bark beetle in a number of infested elm trees in Connecticut (*195*).

Many species of pathogenic Protozoa are also associated with forest insects. Generally speaking, they prolong the length of the larval stage and reduce the fecundity of surviving adults.

Numerous species of nematodes may be found in the gut, the hemocoel, or in particular organs such as the Malpighian tubules of insects. Some of these kill the host when they emerge; some cause death by initiating the action of lethal microbial disease agents; and some cause injury but not death. Certain bark beetle-infesting species riddle the intestines and gonads of their hosts, block the ducts, and cause the ovaries to shrivel. This may lead to a marked reduction in egg production by infested female beetles and a sharp decline in beetle populations (508). Welch (753) reviewed the literature on the subject.

APPLIED CONTROL

Applied control consists of the regulation by man of insect activities, distribution, and abundance through the use of practices designed to enhance, supplement, or serve as substitutes for natural control. The action taken may be either direct or indirect; i.e., it may be directed either against the insect itself to suppress currently destructive populations or toward the alteration of environmental conditions in such a way that destructive populations cannot develop. Whatever the objective, the aim is to use the cheapest, safest, and most economical methods available.

SILVICULTURAL CONTROL

Insect population density is influenced by the composition and condition of forest stands. Because of this, it is sometimes possible to create unfavorable conditions through the application of carefully designed cultural or management practices. Efforts directed toward this end are commonly called silvicultural control.

Possibilities of silvicultural control occur during the establishment and throughout the lives of stands, by selecting the more resistant tree species for planting, by putting them on sites best suited for them, or by controlling their composition and density. Stand conditions may be created or modified as needed by thinnings or cuttings. Pure stands may be broken up into mixtures of age-classes in small units, with no two contiguous units of the same age-class. Mixed stands may be broken up by cutting in small groups to maintain and promote diversification in species composition and density. Overmature trees may be removed from stands and the stands harvested as soon as they mature. High-risk trees may be removed in sanitation-salvage cuttings (413, 631).

For further discussions of silvicultural control, see Keen (412), Graham and Knight (309), and Prebble (605).

PHYSICAL AND MECHANICAL METHODS OF CONTROL

Many forest, shade tree, plantation, and wood products insect pests are amenable to control by physical or mechanical methods. The method chosen is dictated by many factors, such as the habits and behavior of the insect pest involved, the location and value of the trees or products attacked, and cost.

Trap trees and trap logs are sometimes effective in the control of bark beetles (552). Bands of tanglefoot or similar materials may be placed around the trunks of shade trees to prevent larvae or wingless female adults of several species, such as the fall cankerworm, from ascending the trees to feed or oviposit. Young, newly-planted shade trees may be protected from borers of various kinds by enclosing the trunks in wrapping paper. Bagworms on ornamental trees may be controlled by handpicking. Subterranean termites can be kept out of structures by capping foundations with a 4-inch layer of high grade concrete or with properly applied metal shields, by keeping untreated wood from contact with the ground, by using solid foundation masonry, and by providing good ventilation between the ground and timbers.

The logging and milling of infested timber and destruction of the slabs containing the broods is often effective in preventing bark beetle outbreaks, but this may be feasible only where the trees are of merchantable size, are accessible, and when they can be harvested promptly. Bark beetle broods in or under the bark may also be disposed of by the storage of infested logs in water; by peeling infested logs and burning the bark; by sawing infested trees into short lengths and burning them; by peeling the bark of infested trees and exposing the brood to desiccation and to natural enemies such as ants, birds, and rodents; or by felling infested trees in a north-south direction in the open where the bark is exposed to heat from direct exposure in the sun.

Ambrosia beetle damage to summer cut logs can be reduced or prevented by the quick removal of the logs from the woods, by quickly manufacturing them or storing them in ponds, by quickly drying the lumber cut from them, and by the removal of the bark from rough-hewn pieces.

Ips bark beetle populations which develop in slash following cutting operations can be reduced by limiting small scale cuttings to the fall and winter months, or by continuing large scale cuttings throughout the summer months. In situations where it is necessary to cut on a small scale or discontinuously during the summer, control may be obtained by piling and burning the slash before the beetles complete their development in it. The gathering and burning of severed branches late in the fall or in the winter or early spring when the eggs and grubs are in the twigs is an effective method of controlling twig girdling species.

Wood-borer damage to field-piled pulpwood in the Lake States has been reduced by piling the wood in the shade or by placing it in standard compact piles. *Lyctus* powder-post beetle damage can be reduced by the long storage of susceptible sapwood in water or by steaming it at high temperatures. Bark-beetle damage to bark-covered poles and slabs used in rustic construction can be reduced or prevented by cutting the material during the fall and winter and then seasoning it off the ground and under cover. Damage to young pines by the European pine shoot moth in the Lake States can be reduced by removing the lower limbs. This forces the over-wintering stages of the insect into buds on the upper branches above the snow line where they are killed by lethal low temperatures during the winter.

Regulatory control is aimed at the prevention of entry and establishment of foreign plant and animal pests, or at the suppression, containment, or eradication of such pests as may have become established in limited areas. This form of control became possible with the passage of the Federal Insect Pest Act in 1905 which enabled the Federal Government to regulate the importation and interstate movement of articles that might spread insect pests. It was reinforced in 1912 by passage of the Plant Quarantine Act, which authorized the Secretary of Agriculture to enforce necessary regulations to protect the agricultural economy of the United States by preventing the introduction of insects and plant diseases, and by passage of the McNary-McSweeney Act in 1928, which established a federal policy regarding the use of legislative means for combatting forest insects and diseases. Then, in 1947, passage of the Forest Pest Control Act provided authority for the United States Government to act alone or in cooperation with states, territories, or private timber owners to control destructive forest insects or diseases.

Prior to the passage and enforcement of quarantine laws, many species of forest, shade tree, and ornamental insects, several of which are highly destructive, gained entry into Eastern United States. Since then the rate of entry of additional species has been drastically reduced. The following is a list of species known to have been introduced into Eastern United States.

Order and Species	Country of origin	Principal food plant
Orthoptera		
Gryllotalpa gryllotalpa (L.)	Europe	Nursery stock
Hemiptera		
Stephanitis rhododendri Harv.	Europe	Rhododendron
Isoptera		
Coptotermes formosanus Shiraki	Far East	Wood products
Homoptera		
Adelges abietis L.	Europe	Spruce
piceae (Ratz.)	Europe	True firs
strobilobius Kalt.	Europe	Larch
Asterolecanium variolosum (Ratz.)	Europe	Oak
Cryptococcus fagi (Baer)	Europe	Beech
Gossyparia spuria (Mod.)	Europe	Elm
Matsucoccus resinosae (B. & G.)		Red Pine
Pealius azaleae (B. & M.)	Asia	Azalea
Phenacoccus acericola King	Europe	Sugar maple
Pineus strobi (Htg.)	Europe	Pine
Pseudococcus comstocki (Kuwani)	Far East	Deciduous trees
Quadraspidiotus perniciosus (Comst.)	China	Deciduous trees
Coleoptera		
Amphimallon majalis (Raz.)	Europe	Various plants
Anobium punctatum (DeG.)	Europe	Wood products
Anomala orientalis Waterhouse	Philippines	Nursery stock
Chlorophorus annularis (F.)	Japan, India	Stored bamboo
Chrysomela interrupta F.	Europe	Willow, poplar
crotchi Brown	Europe	Willow, poplar
Cryptorhynchus lapathi (L.)	Europe	Poplar
Crytepistomus castaneus (Roelofs)	Japan	Oak
Heterobostrychus aequalis (Waterh.)	Far East	Oak & mahogany boards
Hylotrupes bajulus (L.)	Europe	Seasoned coniferous wood

Order and Species	Country of origin	Principal food plant
Maladera castanea (Arrow)	Orient	Deciduous trees
Minthea rugicollis (Walk.)	Antilles (?)	Oak flooring
Nacerdes melanura (L.)	Europe	Wooden wharves
Phyllobius oblongus (L.)	Europe	Deciduous trees
Plagiodera versicolora (Laich.)	Europe, Japan	Willow
Polydrusus impressifrons Gyll.	Europe	Poplar
Popillia japonica Newm.	Japan	Wide variety of plants
Pseudocneorhinus bifasciatus (Roelofs)	Japan	Ornamentals
Pyrrhalta luteola (Mueller)	Europe	Elm
Scolytus multistriatus Marsh.	Europe	Elm
Thylacites incanus (L.)	Europe	Pine
Xestobium rufovillosum	Europe	Wood products
Zengophora scutellaris Suffr.	Europe	Poplar
Lepidoptera		
Aegeria apiformis (Clerck)	Europe	Poplar
Anthophila pariana Clerck	Europe	Apple, thorn
Archips rosanus (L.)	Europe	Deciduous trees, privet
Chrysoclista linneella (Clerck)	Europe	Linden
Cnidocampa flavescens (Wlk.)	Asia	Norway maple
Coleophora laricella (Hbn.)	Europe, Japan	Larch
fuscedinella (Zell.)	?	Birch
limosipennella (Dup.)	Europe	Elm
Dichomeris marginellus (D & S.)	Europe	Juniper
Dioryctria abietella (D. & S.)	Europe	Pines
Epinotia nanana (Treit.)	Europe	Spruce
Gracillaria syringella (F.)	Europe	Lilac
Homadula anisocentra Merrick	?	Mimosa, honeylocust
Nepticula sericopeza Zell.	Europe	Norway maple
Nygmia phaeorrhoea (Don.)	Europe	Apple, pear
Orgyia antiqua (L.)	Europe	Deciduous trees
Phalonia rutilana (Hbn.)	Europe	Juniper
Porthetria dispar (L.)	Europe	Oak, etc.
Rhyacionia buoliana (Schiff.)	Europe	Pines
Samia cynthia (Drury)	Asia	Ailanthus, cherry
Spilonota ocellana (D. & S.)	Europe	Apple, oak
Stilpnotia salicis (L.)	Europe	Poplar, willow
Zeiraphera ratzeburgiana (Ratz.)	Europe	Spruce
Zeuzera pyrina (L.)	Europe	Elm, maple
Diptera		
Monarthropalpus buxi (Lab.)	Europe	Boxwood
Oligotrophus betulae (Winn.)	Europe	Birch
Rhabdophaga salicis (Schr.)	Europe	Willow
Hymenoptera		
Acantholyda erythrocephala (L.)	Europe, Japan	Pine
Caliroa cerasi (L.)	Europe	Cherry, shadbush
Diprion frutetorum (F.)	Europe	Pine
hercyniae (Htg.)	Europe	Spruce
similis (Htg.)	Europe	Pine
Fenusa dohrnii (Tisch.)	Europe	Alder
pusilla (Lep.)	Europe	Birch
ulmi (Sund.)	Europe	Elm
Hemichroa crocea (Fourcroy)	Europe	Alder
Heterarthrus nemoratus (Fallen)	Europe	Birch
Neodiprion sertifer (Geoff.)	Europe	Pine
Pristiphora erichsonii (Htg.)	Eurasia	Larch
geniculata (Htg.)	Europe	Mountain ash
Sirex juvencus (L.)	Europe	Pine, fir, spruce
Solenopsis saevissima richteri Forel	South America	General feeder
Trichiocampus viminalis (Fall.)	Europe	Poplar

BIOLOGICAL CONTROL

Biological control is possible because of the existence in nature of a continuing interplay between the abundance of insects and their natural enemies, and because many of the latter are subject to manipulation one way or another. Traditionally, it has consisted of the use of parasites, predators, and disease pathogens to hold populations in check, but within recent years the concept has been broadened to include various other biotic methods for reducing and/or maintaining insect populations at tolerable levels. So far, almost all biological control efforts against forest insects have been confined to the use of parasites, predators, and pathogens.

Generally speaking, biological control efforts against forest insects have been limited to (1) the importation and establishment of foreign parasites and predators of introduced pests; (2) the transfer of parasites, predators, and disease pathogens from one region to another within the country; (3) the augmentation of established parasite and predator populations with field-collected or laboratory-reared individuals; and (4) the use of microbial sprays to control outbreaks.

The majority of importations of parasites and predators were made prior to World War II, with emphasis on enemies of the gypsy moth, brown-tail moth, satin moth (*387, 124*), European pine shoot moth, European pine sawfly, European spruce sawfly, balsam woolly aphid, and larch casebearer. Since World War II, importations have been limited mostly to enemies of the balsam woolly aphid and the smaller European elm bark beetle. Altogether, a total of 156 species of parasites and predators had been imported and liberated against 59 species of introduced and native pests by 1960. Of these, a total of 44 were successfully established (*205*). Since the early 1930's, the Canadian government has also imported large numbers of many species of parasites and predators against a number of pests, many of which also occur in the United States (*484*). Some of these have spread into adjoining areas of the United States. Large numbers of others have been shipped to this country and liberated in infested stands.

A polyhedrosis virus disease of the gypsy moth accidentally introduced into the United States in the early 1900's has since played an important role in the control of outbreaks of its host. Like others of its kind, this virus is most effective in dense populations and is almost unnoticeable in light infestations. Limited field trials have indicated that direct spraying of the virus in water formulations has considerable promise for direct control.

Applications of polyhedrosis virus sprays have been used to suppress populations of the European pine sawfly (*66*), the Virginia pine sawfly (*485*), and the Swaine jack pine sawfly (*654*). Virus epizootics have been initiated in populations of the forest tent caterpillar by disseminating the virus during one generation (*685*).

Viruses are usually applied as sprays, but they may also be applied as dusts if first incorporated with powder. Sprays may be applied by hand-operated sprayers, mist blowers, or aircraft.

Progress has been made in the control of a number of lepidopterous defoliators with *Bacillus thuringiensis*. Aerial applications caused some mortality of the gypsy moth but the results were inconclusive. Higher mortalities of two species of loopers (*Erannis tiliaria* and *Phigalia titea*), which also were present in the sprayed areas, were recorded.

CHEMICAL CONTROL

The use of chemicals to suppress forest insect populations is a method of last resort. It is the policy to use them only when other forms of control, either natural or artificial, fail or threaten to fail in the prevention or control of destructive populations. Depending on the situation, chemicals may be applied to a single tree or to forested areas covering thousands of acres or square miles. The aim, therefore, is usually limited to the suppression of injurious populations to tolerable levels.

Many different types of equipment and techniques are available for applying insecticides (*601*). Aerial applications are made by fixed-wing aircraft (fig. 3) or helicopters to large areas (*29, 214, 57,* and *392*). Individual trees, small groups of trees, and seed orchard trees (fig. 4) may be treated by ground equipment such as mist blowers (*602*) or by knapsack sprayers. Large individual trees may be treated by mist blowers and by hydraulic sprayers. Logs are treated by power sprayers. Fogging machines are sometimes used around resorts and campgrounds. Chemicals may be introduced into the tissues of living trees for bark beetle control (*171, 52,* and *762*). Systemic insecticides may be applied by trunk implantation or injection, by banding or spraying of the circumference of the trunk, by spraying the foliage, by treating the soil around the base of trees, or by dipping cuttings prior to planting (*570, 537, 199, 515, 36,* and *447*).

The effectiveness of chemicals in suppressing many forest insect populations has been amply demonstrated during the past 25 years

F-482299

FIGURE 3.—Airplane spraying for spruce budworm control

FIGURE 4.—Mist blower applying insecticide to pine trees in a seed orchard.

—a period during which a large number of new insecticides and methods of application have come into extensive use, and during which outbreaks covering hundreds of thousands of acres of forest have been suppressed. As effective as insecticidal control has been, however, it has not proved to be an unmixed blessing. It has given rise to many complex problems associated with known or suspected adverse side effects caused by some of the more commonly used chemicals. This stems from the fact that these chemicals, like most other chemicals used as insecticides, are non-specific and can be expected to be harmful to at least some other exposed animal species. The problem is compounded in that some chemical insecticides are very persistent, that all of the material applied in a given environment may not remain in that environment and that free-ranging animals cannot be excluded from sprayed areas. Public awareness of known and possible hazards associated with the use of these chemicals in insect control projects, therefore, has given rise to a considerable degree of concern over their continued widespread use.

Efforts are unceasing to discover and develop new and safer insecticides and to determine the danger points of insecticidal accumulations in the tissues of various forms of wildlife, as a basis for preventing undesirable damage to the biota. Application techniques and equipment are being refined in order to provide better control of the placement of insecticides in the environment and to further lessen the dangers of undesirable side effects. Studies are being made to improve sampling and biological evaluation techniques as a basis for improving the timing of application and to insure that insecticides are applied only when and where they are needed.

The rapid changes occurring in the development and use of insecticides in forest insect control make it inadvisable to include control recommendations in this publication. If you are going to use pesticides, remember: Because some States have restrictions on the use of certain pesticides, check your State and local regulations. Also, because registrations of pesticides are under constant review by the U. S. Department of Agriculture, consult your county agricultural agent or State Extension specialist. For further information on chemical control, in addition to U. S. Department of Agriculture Handbook No. 331, many publications are available. The following are of particular interest: Billings (*65*), Brown (*109*), Brown (*110*), Gorham (*301*), Hickey (*350*), Hoffman, et al. (*363*), Hoffman and Merkel (*362*), Hoffman and Linduska (*361*), National Academy of Science (*555, 556*), Whitten (*761*), and Rudd and Genelly (*625*).

OTHER APPROACHES TO CONTROL

Many conventional methods of suppressing forest insect populations are very effective, but they are all found wanting in many important respects. Insecticides are often entirely effective, but they usually cannot be applied to large areas without endangering other forms of animal life. Furthermore, they usually do not hold pest populations to subeconomic levels for long, nor do they reduce the vulnerability of stands to future outbreaks. Most forms of biological control cannot be depended upon to suppress an outbreak before unacceptable damage has been incurred. They are also incapable of preventing outbreaks, although they may reduce their frequency of occurrence and their magnitude, intensity, and duration. Because of these deficiencies, as well as those of other current methods of control, intensive research is underway to develop new or improved methods which may be used as complements, supplements, or substitutes for them.

Sexual sterilization is receiving much current attention because of its potential use as a new method of control. The effectiveness of releasing males sterilized by gamma radiation was established in the mid-1950's when they were used to eradicate the screw-worm from the West Indian island of Curacao and from the southeastern portions of its range in the United States. Knipling discussed the principal of sexual sterilization in several papers (*425, 428, 426, 429, 427*). Several authors reported the research that led to the method and its use against the screw-worm (*456, 457, 129, 130, 131*). Some progress has also been reported in the sterilization of a few important forest insects by gamma radiation (*300, 401*). Further research must be conducted before the possibilities of using the sterile male release technique for forest insect control can be determined.

Chemically produced sterility also offers promise in control. The appropriate chemicals are called chemosterilants because of their capacity to deprive insects of the ability to reproduce (*89*). Most of the chemosterilants that offer promise for practical control are mutagenic and can be used only in ways that will avoid all contact between them and non-target animals (*557*). Chemosterilants may be administered with the insect's food or by applying them to surfaces to which the insects are attracted. Those mixed with food appear to produce maximum effectiveness and minimum hazard. So far, none are available for use in forest insect control.

Insect attractants are being given increased research attention to improve or reduce the cost of surveys and to open up new opportunities in integrated control of forest insects. Some of these materials are powerful enough to lure insects over considerable distances. Attractants of many kinds are being studied, but those consisting of natural chemicals produced by host plants or the insects themselves are receiving the most attention.

Sex attractants have long been used to some extent in surveys of a few forest insects, particularly the gypsy moth (*151*). For many years, the tips of abdomens of female moths were placed in specially designed traps to capture male moths attracted to them. Research to improve on this technique led to the isolation and synthesis of the attractant material (*398*), and the subsequent synthesis of a closely-related, comparatively inexpensive, highly attractive material called gyplure (*399*). Commercially prepared gyplure is not being used to any great extent in surveys at this time, however, because of the variability in activity of the material in different batches of the finished product. Research is currently underway to obtain a more dependable product.

Many other important forest insects in the orders Lepidoptera, Coleoptera, and Hymenoptera also produce sex attractants. They may be emitted directly from the insect, or they may emanate from the frass or excrement left from insects feeding under the bark (*648*). The material emitted by certain species is enormously attractive. One female of the introduced pine sawfly attracted more than 11,000 males (*161*).

The isolation, identification, and synthesis of the principal component of the attractant produced by the female of the western pine beetle was recently reported (*648*). Also, a synthetic attractant, consisting of three terpene alcohols, originally isolated from male frass, has attracted adults of the California five-spined ips when exposed under field conditions (*792*). For further discussions of sex attractants, refer to publications by Jacobson (*395, 396*) and Knipling (*430*).

Several other approaches to control are also being investigated. These include the selection and breeding of hybrids and varieties of trees resistant to attack by a number of important insects (*522, 286, 663*) as well as the discovery or breeding of more vigorous strains of natural enemies, the introduction of detrimental genetic traits into pest insects, and the identification and isolation of chemicals responsible for host resistance or attraction (*665, 666, 667*).

INTEGRATED CONTROL

Integrated control is defined as a pest management system that in the context of the associated environment and the population dynamics of the pest species, utilizes all suitable techniques and methods in as compatible manner as possible and maintains the pest populations at levels below that causing economic injury. In forest insect control, this would seem to encompass many of the methods discussed in preceding sections on applied control.

Most of the important pest species in eastern forests lend themselves to some form and degree of integrated control. The long life of the forest crop and the fact that many species of commercially valuable trees can withstand some degree of infestation without serious damage provides the opportunity in the majority of cases to utilize different methods of control.

Since the early days of this century, considerable emphasis has been placed on the importation and augmentation of natural enemies of many species of introduced pests. In many cases, the rate of dispersal of these imported enemies has been speeded up by the liberation of colonies in many parts of infested areas. The build-up in numbers after successful establishment of several species has also been speeded up by the liberation of large numbers of field-collected or laboratory-reared individuals.

The presence and abundance of natural enemies is taken into consideration in deciding whether to suppress an outbreak and in planning how to accomplish it. For example, the sudden appearance of a virus disease in heavily infested stands usually portends the imminent collapse of the outbreak. Therefore, when evidence of this disease is encountered during surveys, it is often decided to withhold other methods of control, such as the application of insecticide. Observation of abnormally high percentages of natural control provided by insect parasites and predators may lead to a similar decision. In other situations where insecticidal control is deemed necessary, it is often possible to limit spraying to designated portions of infested areas because of the abundance of natural enemies in other portions (423).

Knowledge of the population dynamics of a pest species provides opportunities for various other means of preventing or reducing losses caused by it, thereby obviating the need for direct, suppressive measures to control outbreaks. Depending on the situation, outbreaks of certain leaf-feeding insects may be prevented or minimized by modifying the composition and density of susceptible stands. It is often possible to prevent or suppress outbreaks of some bark beetles by the removal of infested slash or the salvage of infested trees before the emergence of beetle broods from the bark. The utilization of mature trees growing on poor sites before they begin to deteriorate and become attractive to borers, such as the bronze birch borer, is a recommended control practice. The avoidance of unfavorable sites in planting programs is recommended for preventing damage by certain species (318). Adherence to good construction methods in the building of structures obviates the need for chemical control of termites later on (630). The destruction of elm material suitable for breeding by the smaller European elm bark beetle reduces the need for the use of insecticides in Dutch elm disease control (763).

Some of the new approaches to biological control, many of which are yet to be perfected, may be expected to provide additional opportunities for the integrated approach to control in the next few years. For a discussion of the integrated control concept, see Stern et al. (691). Comprehensive treatments of insect-pest control management and control has also been published (557, 416).

Practical Keys to the Orders and Families of Forest Insects, Based on Types of Injury

The following keys are designed for the use of those unfamiliar with the orders, families, and genera of insects. The insects are first separated into primary divisions according to the portions of trees attacked, the size of the trees, and the timber products infested. These main divisions are in turn subdivided to other groups or subdivisions.

PRIMARY DIVISIONS OF KEY

I. Insects injurious to seeds, seedlings, young plantations, and small reproduction.
    A. To seeds, cones, and fruits.
    B. To seedlings and small reproduction.
II. Insects injurious to large reproduction, forest trees, and shade trees.
    A. Acarina (red spiders).
    B. Defoliators, leaf miners, etc.
    C. Twig and tip damage, etc.
    D. Borers in wood and bark.
    E. Galls, swellings, etc.
    F. Sucking Insects.
III. Insects injurious to forest products.
    A. Defects in green timber.
    B. Insects in round logs.
    C. Insects in lumber.
    D. Insects in material in ground.
    E. Defects in wood in salt and brackish water—marine borers.

DIVISION I

Insects Injurious to Seeds, Seedlings, Young Plantations, and Small Reproduction

This group includes the insects that attack the fruit and seeds of forest trees, also young seedlings in the nursery, plantation, or forest. Insects attacking seedlings more than 4 or 5 years old and somewhat shrubby and woody are discussed under Division II.

A. Insects Attacking Seeds, Cones, and Fruits

1. Larvae without well-developed head capsule; maggot-like:
    With a sclerotized structure like a breastbone near anterior end; in seeds of fir, cypress, birch, and fruit of chokecherry ....**Diptera,** Cecidomyiidae
    Without breastbone; mouth parts well developed; in fruits of cherry, apple, plum, hawthorn; in berries of dogwood, holly, and others; and in walnut husks..........
                       Diptera, Tephritidae
  Larvae with distinct head capsule 2

2. Larvae active; body extended; abdominal prolegs present 3
   Larvae less active; no abdominal prolegs; body curved 4
3. In the shucks of pecans, hickories, and walnuts and in
   acorns .... **Lepidoptera,** Blastobasidae, Olethreutidae
   In cones .... **Lepidoptera,** Phycitidae
   In fruits of wild cranberries and blueberries ....
                                          Lepidoptera, Phycitidae
4. In acorns, walnuts, chestnuts, hickory nuts, and filberts..... 5
   In leguminous seeds .... **Coleoptera,** Bruchidae
   In cones 6
5. First abdominal spiracle vestigal; body spindle-shaped
                                          Hymenoptera, Cynipidae
   First abdominal spiracle normal; body curved like a
   closed finger............................ **Coleoptera,** Curculionidae
6. Cones abnormal and dropping prematurely
                                          Coleoptera, Scolytidae
   Cones maturing; damage to seeds alone
   Larvae legless .... **Hymenoptera,** Chalcididae
   Larvae with true legs .... **Coleoptera,** Anobiidae

B. Insects Attacking Seedlings and Small Reproduction

7. Plants cut off near ground line or stems lacerated and
   shriveled 8
   Plants wilting or fading, easily plucked from ground be-
   cause of severed stem or roots below ground 9
   Gall-like swellings on the stems 10
   Bark gnawed in patches along the stem of conifers 11
   Foliage off-color, yellowish or rusty, and often covered
   with very fine cobweb-like threads or matting
                                          Tetranychidae
   Roots showing small cottony or globular objects at time of
   transplanting .... **Homoptera,** Aphididae
   Leaves or cotyledons cut off and carried away; Southern
   States .... **Hymenoptera,** Formicidae
   Other types of damage. See Division II.
8. Small, tender plants:
   Small, maggotlike larvae causing injury
                                          Diptera, Muscidae
   Large, smooth, dark-colored caterpillars present
                                          Lepidoptera, Phalaenidae
   Larger plants, hardwoods, with woody part tunneled:
   Tunnels longitudinal .... **Coleoptera,** Cerambycidae
   Tunnels across the grain, wood stained
                                          Coleoptera, Scolytidae
   Tunnels irregular, chiefly underground .... **Isoptera**
9. Curved, grublike larvae in the soil
                                          Coleoptera, Scarabaeidae
   Elongate, cylindrical, hard-shelled larvae
                                          Coleoptera, Elateridae
   Small, molelike tunnels usually near the surface of the
   soil .... **Orthoptera,** Gryllotalpinae

10. Bark swollen and gnarled at or just below ground line
                                        Lepidoptera, Phycitidae
    Southern States ....**Homoptera,** Fulgoridae
    Northern States ....**Hymenoptera,** Formicidae
11. Northern, Southern, and Lake States
                                Coleoptera, Curculionidae
    More southern and western States and Lake States
                                    Orthoptera, Acrididae

DIVISION II

INSECTS INJURIOUS TO LARGE LIVING TREES AND TO

SMALL TREES MORE THAN 4 OR 5 FEET TALL

This group includes insects and related organisms which commonly attack living forest and shade trees other than those that attack fruit and seeds or that attack small plants not more than 4 or 5 years old. Insects responsible for damage to wood products, many of which primarily inhabit dead or dying trees or which attack logs, lumber, and other wood products are discussed under Division III.

Injury consisting of discolored, yellowish, rusty, or mottled
  foliage covered with fine cobweblike threads or matting
                                    Tetranychidae   A
Injury consisting of defoliation, leaf rolling, leaf tying, leaf
  and petiole mining, or bast or epidermis miners on green-
  barked stems ....   B
Injury occurring on new growth, twigs, branches, or small
  trees, consisting of mining, pruning, withering, or flagging   C
Injury caused by larvae or beetles boring in the bark, under
  the bark, or in the wood ....   D
Injury consisting of a gall or swelling on stem, branch, or
  leaf ....   E
Injury caused by sucking insects feeding on leaves, twigs, or
  bark surfaces, usually the softer tissues of the plant ....   F

B. Defoliation and Other Injury

1. Injury caused by beetles   2
   Injury caused by larvae   4
   Injury caused by other forms or insect not present   5
2. Adults and larvae associated on the leaves
                                Coleoptera, Chrysomelidae
   Adults only present   3
3. Beetles usually found feeding at night
                                 Coleoptera, Scarabaeidae
   Small, bright-colored, jumping beetles, Flea beetles,
                                Coleoptera, Chrysomelidae
   Dull black, purplish, or gray, soft-bodied beetles, Blister
    beetles ....**Coleoptera,** Meloidae
   Small snout beetles ....**Coleoptera,** Curculionidae

4. Prolegs, usually two or five pairs .... **Lepidoptera**
   Prolegs, usually six or more pairs—or none
   Hymenoptera, Tenthredinidae
   Prolegs inconspicuous; leaf- or bast-mining forms [5]
5. Circular holes cut in the leaves
   Hymenoptera, Megachilidae
   Leaves rolled into a small, compact bundle
   Coleoptera, Curculionidae
   Grasshoppers associated with injury
   Orthoptera, Acrididae
   Walkingsticks associated with injury
   Orthoptera, Phasmatidae

C. Twig Pruning and Other Injury

6. Injured portion hollowed or mined; injury caused by
   larvae or bark beetles, which are usually present   7
   Injury caused by external feeding or ovipositing, which
   removes a portion of the bark or causes a definite
   mechanical injury or a resin-infiltrated scar   13
   Cottony-masses on tips of twigs concealing the insects;
   conifers .... **Homoptera,** Coccidae, Phylloxeridae
7. Injury on two or more whorls of the terminal of conifers;
   inactive, curved larvae under bark or in pupal cells in
   wood .... **Coleoptera,** Curculionidae
   Twigs or brances of hardwoods or conifers containing
   bark beetles or powder-post beetles or a cylindrical
   shotlike hole, usually darkly stained, directly entering
   injured portion
   Coleoptera, Scolytidae, Bostrichidae
   Injury otherwise   8
8. Twigs not mined below fading portion   9
   Twigs mined far below fading portion, tunnel often extending to the ground ...... **Coleoptera,** Cerambycidae
9. Conifers 10
   Hardwoods 11
10. Larvae with prolegs; often pitch masses at point of
    injury .... **Lepidoptera,** Olethreutidae
    Larvae without conspicuous prolegs; usually a spine on
    last segment .... **Hymenoptera,** Tenthredinidae
11. Larvae with well-developed prolegs; usually colored;
    usually in more tender parts of twigs
    Lepidoptera, Olethreutidae, Aegeridae, Cossidae
    Larvae with under-developed prolegs; in woody portions
    of twigs 12
12. Elongate, flat larvae; mines filled
    Coleoptera, Buprestidae
    Cylindrical larvae; mines open
    Coleoptera, Cerambycidae

---

[5] There seems to be no simple and practical method of separating the leaf miners of the four orders that have species with this habit. Those found in conifers are probably either Lepidoptera or Hymenoptera; those on hardwoods may be Lepidoptera or Hymenoptera, or of the families Curculionidae, Chrysomelidae, or Buprestidae of the Coleoptera; or they may be Diptera of the families Agromyzidae or Cecidomyiidae.

13. Obvious scar and pitching of wood at base of injury or along twigs; conifers
    Scale bodies present on twig
                                  Homoptera, Margarodidae
    Scale bodies absent ....**Coleoptera**, Cerambycidae
    Numerous phloem scars on twigs; spittle masses may be present ....**Homoptera**, Cercopidae
    (Hail injury is similar except that the scars are always on top side of branch)
    Twigs slit with a lacerated wound at base of injury or at point of breaking
                    Homoptera, Cicadidae, Membracidae
                                      Orthoptera, Gryllidae

D. Borers in Wood and Bark

14. Borers in the phloem and outer corky bark of living trees rarely scarring the wood 15
    Borers in callous tissue around wounds
    On various hardwoods ....**Coleoptera**, Curculionidae
    On maples ....**Lepidoptera**, Aegeriidae
    On conifers ....**Lepidoptera**, Aegeridae, Phycitidae
    Borers in the dead wood beneath fire scars, turpentined faces, blazes, cavities, and similar wounds 16
    Borers under the bark or in the wood (other than beneath scars or catfaces) of living trees 17
    Bark beetles associated with their larvae under the bark
                                Coleoptera, Scolytidae
    Root borers or mining at base of tree 22
15. White, unpigmented larvae
                                Coleoptera, Cerambycidae
    Highly pigmented larvae
                              Hymenoptera, Tenthredinidae
    Serpentine mines just under the epidermis of chestnut and oak ....**Lepidoptera**, Nepticulidae
16. Ambrosia beetles; wood stained around holes
                    Coleoptera, Scolytidae Platypodidae
    White, fleshy, cylindrical larvae in hardwoods
                    Coleoptera, Cerambycidae, Brentidae
    White, fleshy, flat-headed larvae in turpentined faces in fire scars on conifers ....**Coleoptera**, Buprestidae
    Larvae with heavy, chitinous armature on last segment; chestnut, oak, maple ....**Coleoptera**
17. Larval mines extended under the bark and also deep into the wood in later stages 18
    Larval mines entirely under the bark or only in wood of current annual ring 21
18. Pitch exuding from larval mines; larvae with prolegs present; conifers ....**Lepidoptera**,
    No pitch, but often water and frass exuding 19
19. Head of larvae globular, protuberant 20
    Head of larvae somewhat flattened and embedded in prothorax ....**Coleoptera**, Cerambycidae

34

20. Prolegs absent; last segment often heavily armed
Coleoptera, Tenebrionidae
Prolegs absent; larvae curved, grublike; in willow, poplar, and palmetto ....**Coleoptera,** Curculionidae
Prolegs present; last segment not heavily armed
Lepidoptera, Hepialidae, Aegeriidae
21. Larvae depressed, flat-headed or pestle-shaped
Coleoptera, Buprestidae
Larvae curved, grublike ....**Coleoptera,** Curculionidae
Larvae slender; thoracic segments not noticeably enlarged; cause pitch flecks in wood, birch, etc.
Diptera, Agromyzidae
22. Larvae with prolegs; poplar, willow, alder, ash, persimmon ....**Lepidoptera,** Hepialidae, Aegeriidae
Larvae without prolegs
In hardwoods ....**Coleoptera,** Cerambycidae
In conifers; associated with pitch mass
Coleoptera, Curculionidae, Scolytidae

E. Galls [6]

23. Galls of more or less open, exposed, simple structure, or, when enclosed, the insects maintain permanent openings, or the gall is dehiscent to permit the escape of the numerous insects inhabiting them 24
Gall usually completely enclosing the inhabitant; one or, rarely, several insects to a cavity; occasionally a permanent opening is maintained by the feeding larva 27
24. Mites present having 2 pairs of legs; galls of various shapes but always provided with an opening to the exterior and lined on the inside with hairy or fuzzy growths ....**Acarina**
Galls otherwise 25
25. Insects not fitted for jumping 26
Insects with hind legs developed for jumping
Homoptera, Psyllidae
26. Leaf galls on hardwoods, chiefly elm, poplar, hickory, ash, sumac, and witch-hazel
Homoptera, Aphididae
Conelike galls on tips of spruce twigs
Homoptera, Chermidae
Pitlike galls on twigs of hard pines
Homoptera, Margarodidae
Pitlike galls on twigs of white oak
Homoptera, Asterolecanidae
27. Galls inhabited by larvae with a well-developed head capsule 28
Larvae without well-developed head capsule, maggotlike; white to yellowish or reddish in color:

---

[6] It seems impossible to devise a key that will separate all the varied types of galls into family or order groups. On the other hand, many groups are fairly true to type, and if considered with the larvae or other stages of the insect inhabiting them, you can make a fairly workable distinction.

Larvae with a distinct structure like a breastbone near
anterior end ....**Diptera,** Cecidomyiidae
Larvae without breastbone; mouth parts well de-
veloped ....**Diptera,** Agromyzidae
28. Larvae legless or with only minute legs 29
Legs well developed, also prolegs present 30
29. Woody galls containing plain evidences of mining activity of the larvae; larvae with a well-developed head
capsule and mandibles
Coleoptera, Buprestidae, Cerambycidae, Curculionidae
Larval mines not obvious; white larvae, curved or grublike in form, legless, and with distinct head capsule,
each contained in a specialized cell
Hymenoptera, Cynipidae, Chalcididae
30. On willow ....**Hymenoptera,** Tenthredinidae
On locust, poplar, maple ....**Lepidoptera,** Olethreutidae

F. Sucking Insects

31. Injury or insects present on leaves 32
Injury primarily confined to twigs 33
Injury primarily confined to branches and main stem 34
32. Leaves off-color, yellowish or spotted from feeding punc-
tures of active, jumping insects:
Homoptera, Cicadellidae
Hemiptera, Tingidae
Leaves bearing galls or abnormal spots:
On hackberry ....**Homoptera,** Phyllidae
On elm, poplar, willow, witch-hazel, hickory, oak,
chestnut, etc.
Homoptera, Aphididae, Phylloxeridae
On conifers ....**Homoptera,** Phylloxeridae
Exposed insects on the leaves:
Scalelike, gall-like, or soft grublike insects covered
with wax in the form of powder or tufts
Homoptera, Coccidae
Fringed, scalelike immature forms associated on the
leaves with white 4-winged flies
Homoptera, Aleyrodidae
Soft-bodied insects with long conspicuous antennae
Homoptera, Aphididae
33. Insects surrounded by a conspicuous frothy mass of
spittle; ends of branches and trees slowly dying in
severe infestations; pines ....**Homoptera,** Cercopidae
Injury consisting of ragged slits in the twigs, often
breaking at incision; the tips of the branches hanging
with withered leaves; hardwoods
Homoptera, Cicadidae
Homoptera, Membracidae
Injury consisting of gall-like or gouty swellings on limbs
and twigs of fir ....**Homoptera,** Chermidae
Tips of hard pines flagged (needles yellowing); scales
embedded in pits in bark ....**Homoptera,** Coccidae

Branches and twigs infested with scalelike, gall-like or soft-bodied insects covered with waxy powder or tufts; twigs often dying .... **Homoptera**, Coccidae

Tips of branches swollen forming pineapplelike galls; conifers .... **Homoptera**, Phylloxeridae

Tips of new growth withering, infested with numerous soft-bodied insects with prominent antennae
Homoptera, Aphididae

34. Fir trees unhealthy and dying; trunks infested with masses of soft-bodied insects appearing as a whitish wool .... **Homoptera**, Chermidae

Beech trees unhealthy and slowly dying, with dead areas of bark on stems covered with whitish masses of soft-bodied insects .... **Homoptera**, Margarodidae

Trees infested with scalelike, gall-like, or soft grublike insects, and covered with wax in the form of powder or tufts .... **Homoptera**, Coccidae

DIVISION III

INSECTS INJURIOUS TO FOREST PRODUCTS

This group includes insects causing the type of injury seen in the handling of forest products, i.e., logs and lumber, poles, posts, piling, and manufactured materials, as handles, gun stocks, stored wood, and wood in buildings. Certain types of damage found in green logs or freshly sawed lumber are the result of insects boring in the phloem or wood of the living tree. These are also treated here for convenience. They are usually distinguishable by the more or less stained condition of the surrounding wood, pitch infiltration, or the presence of scar (callous) tissue.

Defects occuring in the wood of green logs or lumber, revealed as the logs are sawed, usually as darkly stained, pitch-infiltrated wood, or scar (callous) tissue .... A

Injury occuring to material having the bark present (lumber excepted), such as round logs after the trees are felled and left either in the woods or at the mill, or logs utilized for rustic work, etc. .... B

Injury to freshly sawed lumber, seasoned lumber, stored and manufactured materials, or wood in buildings C

Injury to materials in contact with the ground, such as cross ties, posts, poles, foundation materials, piling above water, etc. .... D

A. Defects in Green Timber

1. In hardwoods 2
   In conifers 5
2. Holes small, "pinholes," ¼ inch or less in cross section; circular, open i.e., never filled with boring dust 3
   Holes larger, "grub holes," up to ¾ inch in diameter, usually oval in cross section, usually open, not filled with boring dust 4

Pith flecks in wood, birch, maple, etc.
                              Diptera, Agromyzidae
3. Pinholes, about ⅛ inch in size, of uniform diameter
   throughout, wood stained in streaks, in oaks and yellow
   poplar ....**Coleoptera,** Scolytidae
   Holes tapering, several sizes grouped together and origin-
   ating in a wound:
       Holes up to ¼ inch in diameter, in chestnut and
       chinaquapin ....**Coleoptera,** Lymexylidae
       Holes up to ⅛ inch in diameter, in oak and other
       woods ....**Coleoptera,** Brentidae
4. Variable-sized holes grouped and radiating from wounds
   or cavities
       Coleoptera, Cerambycidae, Tenebrionidae, Brentidae
   Large grub holes, up to 1 inch in diameter, usually appearing singly and not associated with wounds
       In hickory ....**Coleoptera,** Cerambycidae,
                                   Lepidoptera, Cossidae
       In poplar and cottonwood
                                   Coleoptera, Cerambycidae,
                           Lepidoptera, Cossidae, Aegeriidae
       In maple
                       Coleoptera, Cerambycidae, Tenebrionidae,
                           Lepidoptera, Cossidae, Aegeriidae
       In ash ....**Lepidoptera,** Aegeriidae
       In persimmon ....**Lepidoptera,** Aegeriidae
       In locust ....**Lepidoptera,** Cossidae,
                                   Coleoptera, Cerambycidae
5. Pitch pockets in the wood
                       Lepidoptera, Aegeriidae, Phycitidae
                                   Coleoptera, Scolytidae
   Holes filled with boring dust, associated with turpentine
   faces or fire scars
       In the South, pines ....**Coleoptera,** Buprestidae
       In the North, pines or other conifers
                       Coleoptera, Cerambycidae, Buprestidae

B. Insects in Round Logs

6. Sawdust exuding from small, round "pinholes" (1/10 inch
   or less in diameter) on the surface of the bark; wood
   usually stained around the holes
                                   Coleoptera, Scolytidae
   Sawdust exuding from larger holes; larvae present under
   the bark or in wood ....**Coleoptera,** Cerambycidae
   Sawdust not exuded; the only evidence of work is the
   presence of larvae or galleries under bark or in the
   wood
       Larvae elongate, cylindrical
                                   Coleoptera, Cerambycidae
       Larvae flat-headed ....**Coleoptera,** Buprestidae
       Larvae curved, legless; only one larva to a burrow
                                   Coleoptera, Curculionidae

Larvae curved, legless; several larvae in a burrow, each usually separated by a pith or clay partition across the gallery
Hymenoptera, Sphecidae, Vespidae, Apidae
Larvae and bark beetles associates
Coleoptera, Scolytidae

C. Insects in Lumber

7. Fine sawdust exuding from small "pinholes" (less than 1/10 inch in diameter) in green lumber; holes usually darkly stained .... **Coleoptera,** Scolytidae
   Sawdust, if exuding, coming from larger holes in drier lumber, cut a month or more 8
8. Damage to lumber with bark present:
   Larvae elongate .... **Coleoptera,** Cerambycidae
   Larvae curved .... **Coleoptera,** Bostrichidae
   Damage not associated with presence of bark on material 9
9. Fine sawdust exuding from circular or oval holes:
   Small, curved larvae .... **Coleoptera,** Lyctidae
   Elongate larvae .... **Coleoptera,** Cerambycidae
   Large, black ants associated with damage; sawdust accumulating in large piles from damp wood
   Hymenoptera, Formicidae
   Damage concealed and sawdust usually not falling from holes 10
10. Larval tunnels packed with sawdust:
    Larvae elongate, cylindrical
    Coleoptera, Cerambycidae
    Larvae elongate, flatheaded
    Coleoptera, Buprestidae
    Tunnels open:
    Irregular cavities following the grain of the wood loosely filled with fine impressed pellets ....**Isoptera**
    Round holes ½ inch or less in diameter, often with cross partitions or cells
    Hymenoptera, Apidae, Vespidae, Sphecidae

D. Insects in Materials in Ground

11. Large, elongate larvae associated with damage consisting of grub holes extending through the wood
    Coleoptera, Cerambycidae, Oedemeridae
    Large irregular cavities eaten in the wood, representing spring wood; usually extending with the grain of the wood; sides of cavities plastered with claylike excrement .... **Isoptera**
    Large, irregular cavities eaten into wood, usually cutting across the grain, surfaces smooth, no excrement, large piles of sawdust accumulating outside; large, black ants associated with injury in moist or damp wood
    Hymenoptera, Formicidae

Important orders of forest insects

The primary purpose of this publication is to list and briefly discuss the more important insects affecting forest and shade trees and wood products. Its secondary purpose is to discuss some of the other insects that are also abundant in the forest, but are not usually thought of as forest insects. Many of these insects are also of economic importance, either as pests of man or of other forms of animal life. Given the ever-increasing use of forested areas for recreational purposes and the growing public concern about our wild life resources, it seems no longer advisable to omit these insects from a discussion of important forest insects.

Order ANOPLURA

Sucking lice

Sucking lice are small wingless insects that live on the skin of various mammals and suck their blood. Their bodies are flattened; the mouth parts consist of piercing stylets; and there is a rostrum with many tiny hooks at the front of the head. The tarsus consists of a single segment with a single large claw. This claw is opposed by a toothed projection on the tibia. The **body louse,** *Pediculus humanus* L., and the **crab louse,** *Phthirus pubis* (L.), attack man, and a number of other species attack various kinds of livestock and other animals. For treatments of the order see Ewing (*236*) and Ferris (*243*). Eddy et al. (*220*) and Cole et al (*145*) discussed the control of species attacking man.

Order MALLOPHAGA

Chewing Lice

Chewing lice are all external parasites of birds and animals. The adults are small, usually flattened, and wingless. They feed on the feathers, hairs, or skin of their hosts. None are known to attack man. The family is divided into six families. Members of the family Trichodestidae attack various species of domestic animals; the other five (Menoponidae, Laemobothridae, Philopteridae, Gyroptidae, and Ricinidae) feed mostly on birds and poultry.

Order SIPHONAPTERA

Fleas

Fleas are small wingless, hard-bodied, jumping insects. The body is strongly flattened laterally and is armed with numerous backward-projecting spines or bristles. There may be no eyes; the mouth parts are formed for sucking; and the legs are long. Adults feed on the blood of birds, wild and domestic animals, and man. The larvae feed on organic matter, their own cast skins, and the feces of the adults. Many species are economic pests. About 75 species of animals and birds in Eastern United States are attacked by more than 50 different species of fleas (*261*).

40

Some of the more important eastern species are as follows: (a) the **human flea**, *Pulex irritans* Lin., (b) the **cat flea** *Ctenocepalides felis* (Bouché), (c) the **dog flea**, *C. canis* (Curtis), and (d) the **oriental rat flea**, *Xenopsylla cheopsis* (Rothschild). The latter species is the principal vector of bubonic plague and may also transmit endemic typhus to man.

Order THYSANURA

Bristletails

Bristletails occur abundantly in the forest in rotting wood and debris, under stones, and among fallen leaves, but none are injurious. They are distinguished by the style-like appendages on some of the abdominal segments, by the two or three tail-like appendages at their posterior ends, and usually by their elongate bodies.

Order COLLEMBOLA

Springtails

Springtails are very small, primitive, wingless insects. The body is covered by a soft exoskeleton and there is a single pair of antennae, each normally consisting of four segments. The mouth is located ventrally, and the mandibles and maxillae are either toothed for chewing, or styliform for sucking. There are three pairs of legs, each typically terminating in one or two claws. The first abdominal segment bears a ventral tube or collophore; there is a pair of small appendages fused basally on the venter of the third segment; and a furcula is appended to the ventral surface of the fourth. The latter operates as a spring and is capable of propelling the insect several inches into the air (*512*).

Springtails are widely distributed and are among the most abundant of insects. They are found in all sorts of places, many unexpected such as on the surface of snow and on the surface of water. In the forest they are found in moist soil, among dead leaves, in dead and decaying logs, under loose bark, and in bark crevices of living trees. The majority feed on algae, fungi, and lichens and other living or dead plant matter. Pollen from conifers is favored by some species in the spring. Some may be attracted in large numbers to decaying fruit and animal matter. Others may be attracted to sap flowing from trees in the spring.

Springtails tend to be beneficial in the forest because of their help in the reduction of litter and in the formation of humus. Bellinger (*54*) published a key to species occurring in eastern America.

Order THYSANOPTERA

Thrips

Thrips are small slender-bodied insects, usually from 0.05 to 5.0 mm long. Adults are either wingless or have four long, narrow fringed wings with few or no veins. The mouth parts are of the sucking type; the antennae are usually short and 6- to 10-segmented; the tarsi are 1- to 2-segmented, with one or two claws, and are bladderlike at the tip.

Thrips are frequently extremely abundant on flowers. Others occur on foliage, fruit, bark, and fungi and in debris. A number of species cause considerable damage to cultivated plants, but only a few have been reported injurious to trees (17).

Liothrips umbripennis Hood became abundant enough on chestnut oak in New Jersey in 1937 to cause the curling of leaves. *Gnophothrips fuscus* (Morgan) has damaged pine seedlings in nurseries in New York and Rhode Island. Jack pine growing in mixed stands on rocky slopes in Ontario has also been slightly damaged. Female strobili of slash pine growing in Florida have been severely damaged (216). Damage to the strobili consisted of punctures and abrasions on the scales and bracts of flowers and conelets. Heavy infestations resulted in shriveled conelets and the death of affected flowers. The **flower thrips,** *Frankliniella tritici* (Fitch), feeds on the flowers and flower buds of hawthorn. This sometimes prevents the buds from opening.

Order PSOCOPTERA

Book lice and psocids

Book lice and psocids are small, soft-bodied, winged or wingless insects, usually less than 6 mm. long. The more typical psocids have well-developed wings and bear a striking resemblance to aphids of the order Homoptera. The wings are held rooflike and almost vertically over the body while at rest. Book lice are either wingless or possess only vestigial wings, and are about 1 mm. long.

Psocids are found under stones, on or under the bark, and on the foliage of trees or shrubs. They are not injurious to trees, but they may be a nuisance, especially when they occur in large numbers around residences or in recreational areas. They feed on fungi, lichens, and probably other vegetable matter.

Book lice occur most commonly in damp, dark rooms, not generally used. They are occasionally found in old books where they feed on the paste of the bindings. Sometimes they are abundant enough to cause serious damage.

Order NEUROPTERA

This order contains a wide variety of terrestrial and aquatic insects. The adults have two pairs of large, membranous, leaflike wings which they hold roof-like over the abdomen while at rest. The antennae are generally long and many-segmented; the tarsi are five-segmented and there are no cerci. The larvae are practically all carbiform and are usually armed with very large, curved mandibles.

FAMILY CORYDALIDAE
DOBSONFLIES

The best-known species of this family is the **dobsonfly,** *Corydalus cornutus* (L.). The adult, especially the male, occasionally reaches a length of 100 mm., has two long curving pincers or mandibles, and has a wing expanse of 100 mm. to 125 mm. Females are similar in appearance except that the mandibles are smaller. The full-grown larvae, commonly known as a hellgrammite, is also large and formidable in appearance. Hellgrammites are found under stones in stream beds, especially where the water runs swiftest. After about 2½ years, they leave the water and construct cells in which to pupate under stones, logs, or other objects on or near the bank of the stream, usually during early summer. The hellgrammites are highly prized as fish bait; otherwise, members of the family are of little or no economic importance.

FAMILY CHRYSOPIDAE
Green Lacewings

Members of the family Chrysopidae are all predaceous in both the adult and larval stages on the bodies of soft-bodied insects. They occur commonly in late summer and fall on the foliage of plants infested with these insects. Aphids and mealybugs appear to be preferred as hosts, but leafhoppers, thrips, mites, and certain species of scale insects are also attacked. The adults are green or yellowish-green and have delicate, lacelike wings. Eggs are usually laid at the ends of gelatinous stalks, 3 to 4 mm. long, firmly attached to the surfaces of leaves. The larvae are elongate, yellow or gray mottled with brown, and taper toward each end. Some species have the odd habit of covering their bodies with packets of trash woven together loosely with strands of silk. The winter is spent usually as full-grown larvae in silken cocoons in bark crevices or in such protected places as piles of leaves on the ground. There are one to several generations per year, depending on climate (*661*). The **golden-eye lacewing,** *Chrysopa oculata* Say, is an important predator of spruce gall aphids in the Lake States.

FAMILY HEMEROBIIDAE
Brown Lacewings

Brown lacewing adults have brown or dark-colored bodies often marked with yellow. Occasionally, the abdomen is pale yellow. Otherwise, they resemble adult green lacewings very closely. All species are predaceous on other insects, principally aphids, but also chermids, mealybugs, white-flies, mites, and occasionally diaspine scales. The larvae are similar in general appearance to the larvae of green lacewings, but they do not carry packets of trash on the dorsum. Eggs are laid on the surface of leaves, and the winter is spent in either the larval, pupal, or adult stages, depending on species. The number of generations per year varies from one to many, depending on species and climate.

FAMILY MYRMELEONTIDAE
Ant Lions

Ant lion larvae, or doodle-bugs, as they are also commonly called, live in tiny, conical pits or craters in the ground, in dry, dusty, or sandy areas. The pits are usually about 1½ to 2 inches wide and from 1 to 2 inches deep. The sides slant sharply from the rim to a point in the bottom. The adults have long slender bodies and two pairs of long, narrow, delicate, many-veined wings; larvae are broad, somewhat flat, taper toward each end, and have long, curved mandibles armed with strong spines and setae. The larva lies hidden under sand at the bottom of its pit and feeds on ants or other insects that fall into the pit.

Order EPHEMEROPTERA

Mayflies

Mayflies are frail, delicate insects, with medium-sized, soft bodies that end in three long threadlike tails, or caudal setae. The wings are membranous and many-veined and are held upright while at rest. The front pair are large and triangular; the hind pair, when present, are small and rounded. The antennae are bristle-like and inconspicuous; the mouth parts vestigial. The nymphs are elongate and cylindrical or flattened, and have leaf-like gills along the sides of the body. In most species the gills have three long tails.

Mayfly nymphs live under stones or among debris on the bottom of streams, where they feed on decaying vegetable matter, algae, and diatoms. When they become full-grown they leave the water and transform to adults on nearby vegetation. The adults occasionally appear in enormous numbers, but they seldom live longer than a day or two. Occasionally, their dead bodies literally pile up along the shore, on bridges, or in the streets of nearby towns (560).

Beyond the occasional nuisance effect created by the presence of piles of dead insects in areas frequented by man and the importance of the nymphs as fish food, which is substantial, mayflies are of no economic importance.

Order PLECOPTERA

Stoneflies

Stoneflies are small to medium-sized, drab-colored insects, with soft, flattened bodies. The wings are membranous and have numerous cross veins. The front pair is rather narrow and elongate; the hind pair is shorter but wider and is usually folded in pleats while at rest. The antennae are long, slender, tapering, and many-segmented. The cerci, when present, are usually long and many-jointed. The nymphs are flat-bodied and somewhat elongate. They have long antennae, long cerci, and branched gills on the thorax and about the bases of the legs.

Stonefly adults occur near streams or along rocky shores of lakes. The nymphs are aquatic and are usually found under stones in the rapids of streams. When they reach maturity, they leave the water and climb up on nearby objects to transform to the adult stage (558).

Stoneflies may be a nuisance at times, especially when they appear in swarms in recreational areas. The nymphs are an important source of fish food.

44

Order ODONATA

Dragonflies and damselflies

Dragonflies and damselflies are relatively large and often beautifully colored insects. The adults have two pairs of elongate, membranous, many-veined wings of about equal size. The head and the compound eyes are large; the antennae are very small and bristle-like; and the abdomen is long and slender. Dragonflies may be up to 75 mm. long and they hold their wings in a horizontal position while at rest. Damselflies are usually somewhat smaller. Their wings are folded along the abdomen or are tilted up while at rest. Adults of both groups feed on various insects they capture while in flight. They are common and often abundant around slow streams and ponds. Dragonflies are particularly noticeable because of their large size and rapid flight, back and forth, over the water.

Dragonfly and damselfly nymphs are all aquatic and feed on various small aquatic organisms. Prey is captured through the use of a modified labrum containing two movable clawlike lobes at the tip. This device is held folded under the head when not in use and is about one-third as long as the body when fully extended. The nymphs breathe by means of gills. In the dragonflies gills are in the rectum; in damselflies gills are three leaflike structures at the end of the abdomen. Mature nymphs crawl out of the water and transform to the adult stage, usually on rocks or vegetation.

Order ISOPTERA

Termites

The order Isoptera consists entirely of termites, one of the oldest and most primitive groups of insects. Termites are social insects and live in colonies. In all but a few species, there is a definite caste system with each caste performing an essential function in the life of the colony. Termites feed on cellulose which they obtain from wood and other plants. Normally, cellulose is indigestible to animals, but termites have single-celled protozoan organisms within their digestive tracts (421) which convert it to simple digestible foods. Many species of fungi are associated with termites (342). Their influence on the activity of the insects is not completely understood, but certain species such as *Lenzites trabea* are known to produce an attractant (231).

Only 40 species of termites are believed to be native to continental United States. Of these, only 15 are known to occur in the eastern half of the country, exclusive of Texas (677).

In addition to these native species, two introduced species, *Crytotermes brevis* (Walker) and *Coptotermes formosanus* Shiraki, also occur in the East. *C. brevis* may have been introduced into southern Florida from a nearby island. *C. formosanus* is believed to have been introduced into the Gulf Coast during World War II.

Termites are small, flat, soft-bodied insects sometimes without eyes. The antennae are moniliform, and in the winged adults, the number of antennal segments varies from 12 to 25 or more. The

45

median ocellus is absent. In certain species it is replaced by a more or less distinct opening of a gland known as the fontanel. The wings are long and narrow and, when folded on the back, extend well beyond the end of the abdomen. In all North American species, the fore and hind wings are similar in form and in the general features of their venation. The abdomen is broadly joined to the thorax.

Termites have very few effective natural enemies. For example, there are no internal insect parasites, and predaceous enemies are largely confined to ants and birds. The predators sometimes consume large numbers of termites during flight periods. This may have some adverse effect on the establishment of new colonies, but it has no effect on the parent colony. Fungi, nematodes, and bacteria usually kill a small percentage of the individuals in a colony. Moulds, occasionally, cause much heavier losses.

In many parts of eastern United States, particularly the South, termites are almost universally present in stumps, dead logs and other woody materials in contact with the ground in forested areas. Termites are largely beneficial in forested areas because of their assistance in the decomposition of dead wood and its reincorporation into the soil. On the other hand, when termites infest wooden structures and other useful wood products, they are often extremely destructive. The extent of the monetary losses they cause is not known, but has been estimated at $400,000,000. to $500,000,000. per year in the United States for damage, repairs, and control.

For further information on termites, the reader is referred to the following (*31, 229, 435, 670, 669, 677, 674, 673, 676, 441*).

Keys to Termites of Eastern United States Based on Soldiers

1. Head long, much longer than broad 2
   Head short, truncated in front 9
2. Mandibles with prominent marginal teeth 3
   Mandibles without prominent marginal teeth 3
3. Hind femora swollen; third antennal segment not equal to
      fourth and fifth .... *Kalotermes approximatus*
   Hind femora swollen; third antennal segment slightly
      longer than fourth .... *Neotermes jouteli*
   Hind femora swollen; third antennal segment equal to
      fourth and fifth 4
4. Anterior margin of pronotum dentate
                                      Incisitermes synderi
   Anterior margin of pronotum not dentate
                                      Incisitermes schwarzi
5. Labrum rounded at tip .... *Prorhinotermes simplex*
   Labrum pointed at tip 6
6. Fontanelle large and tubular; head oval and yellow;
      length of body 5.8 mm. ....*Coptotermes formosanus*
   Fontanelle not large and tubular, sometimes very small,
      circular and distinct 7
7. Gula less than twice as broad in front as in middle
                                      Reticulitermes tibialis
   Gula fully twice as broad in front as in middle 8

46

8. Head 1½ times as long as broad; length 4.6 to 4.9 mm.
                            Reticulitermes arenicola
   Head 1⅔ times as long as broad; length 6 to 7 mm.
                            Reticulitermes flavipes
   Head 1¾ times as long as broad
                            Reticulitermes hageni
   Head twice as long as broad ....*Reticulitermes virginicus*
9. Head cleft and bilobed in front; front of head blackish
                            Calcaritermes nearcticus
   Head not cleft or bilobed in front; front of head blackish
   to dark castaneous behind 10
10. Anterior of head tuberculate ....*Crytotermes brevis*
    Anterior of head not tuberculate
                            Cryptotermes cavifrons

Subterranean Termites

Subterranean termites belong to the family Rhinotermitidae. Because these termites all require a constant supply of moisture, their colonies are found either entirely or partly in the ground. They may, however, feed in wood located some distance from the ground, but they always maintain connection with the ground unless a continuous supply of water is otherwise available. In order to attack wood located away from the ground where a supply of water is not otherwise available, they construct covered passageways, commonly called shelter tubes (fig. 5A).

Regardless of the extent of damage they cause to the interior of wood (fig. 5B), these termites always leave a covering shell intact. Because of this, there usually is no external evidence of infestation, even though the interior of the wood may be destroyed. The first indication of infestation may be the swarming

F-519932-33

FIGURE 5.—Subterranean termite: A, shelter tube on foundation wall; B, damage to a 2 x 4 inch pine stake.

of winged adults, the presence of shelter tubes over foundation walls, or the sudden collapse of the surface of infested wood.

The principal food of subterranean termites is cellulose which they obtain from wood and other plant tissues. As a result, these termites are not only destructive to the woodwork of buildings, telegraph poles, fence posts, and other wood products, but also to paper, fiberboard, and various types of fabrics derived from cotton and other plants. Shrubs, nursery stock, ornamental plants and many kinds of shade trees are damaged occasionally. Trees killed by other insects, fire, or disease, particularly in the South, are attacked and the timber rendered unmerchantable unless it is utilized shortly after being killed.

In attacking wood, subterranean termites feed on the soft spring wood only. As a result their galleries run parallel with the grain. These galleries are characteristically stained on the inside with grayish specks of excrement and earth but are free of pellets like those found in the galleries of nonsubterranean termites.

Subterannean termites occur throughout most of the United States and in southern Canada. They are common throughout most of the eastern half of the United States and along the Pacific Coast. It is considered likely that the native species have occupied their present ranges for millions of years. In recent years, however, there seems to have been an increase in their destructiveness northward. This has probably resulted from the general adoption of central heating plants in structures, from changes in building practices, the wider use of termite susceptible wood in construction, and from the tremendous expansion of suburban homes into forested areas.

The **eastern subterranean termite**, *Reticulitermes flavipes* (Kollar) (fig. 6), one of the most destructive subterranean termites in eastern America, is widely distributed, occurring from the Gulf of Mexico north to Ontario, and from the East Coast to the Great Plains. Infestations normally occur in the forest where the dead wood of practically all species of trees is attacked. Infestations also occur in the woodwork of buildings, in cellulose materials stored therein, in poles and posts, and occasionally in living trees, shrubbery, flowers, and crop plants.

Each colony of the eastern subterranean termite comprises three castes: reproductives or adults, workers, and soldiers. The reproductives (fig. 6A) are soft-bodied and brown or black, have two pairs of long, whitish opaque wings of equal size, and are 10 to 12 mm. long. Workers, (fig 6B) are soft-bodied, grayish-white, and slightly less than 6 mm. long. Soldiers (fig. 6C) are similar to the workers except for their much larger, longer heads, their longer and more formidable mandibles, and their slightly greater length. Winged reproductives are often mistakenly identified as flying ants. They differ from ants, however, in having the abdomen broadly joined to the thorax. The abdomen of an ant is reduced to threadlike proportions where it joins the thorax. The wings of ants are also transparent, and the two pairs are of unequal size.

Colonizing flights occur most frequently after the first warm days of spring, often following a warm rain. They may also occur during the remainder of the warm season and sometimes even in the fall, especially in the South. In heated buildings, flights occasionally occur during the winter. The individuals in these flights are attracted by strong light. When they emerge within buildings they gather about windows and doors. Here they soon shed their wings, which may be found in large numbers even after the termites have disappeared. Soon after shedding their wings, males and females pair off and search for a place to form a new nest. The majority are usually unsuccessful, but some survive and manage to hollow out small cells in or near wood in the ground. They enter the cell, seal over the opening, and mate.

A few days after mating the female lays from six to twelve eggs. Hatching occurs in about 30 to 90 days and the nymphs reach maturity in about one year. Later, both soldiers and reproductive nymphs appear in the colony, and reach maturity in 1 and 2 years, respectively. Mating continues at irregular intervals, and the colony continues to increase in size. The original pair of reproductives live together for life, sometimes for many years. In well-established colonies, there may be hundreds of thousands of individuals. Such colonies may be so widely spread out that it is difficult or impossible to estimate their size or to locate their main parts.

Reticulitermes tibialis Banks, the **arid-land subterranean termite,** is probably the most widely distributed species of *Reticulitermes* in the United States. It is largely confined to the western half of the country, but also occurs eastward into the North Central States as far as the Chicago area. In the latter area, it is found among sand dunes where it infests small pieces of wood partly

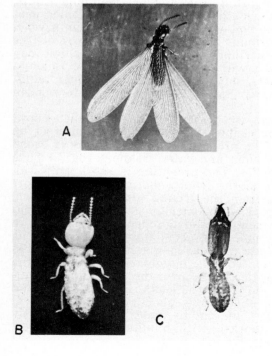

FIGURE 6.—Eastern subterranean termite, *Reticulitermes flavipes:* A, adult; B, worker; C, soldier.

49

buried in the sand. Farther to the southwest, in Kansas and Texas, it occurs in heavily sodded prairies and in hard-packed and often alkali soil. While it is fully capable of damaging buildings, it is not very often injurious to them because of the thinly populated regions in which it occurs. Winged adults are almost entirely shiny black and about 10 mm. long. The tibiae are also blackened and the pronotum is broad.

Reticulitermes virginicus Banks occurs in the southeastern and central western parts of the United States. It is often mistaken for *R. flavipes*, but is smaller. Winged adults are about 8 mm. long, and soldiers 4.5 to 5 mm. long. *R. hageni* Banks occupies about the same territory as *R. virginicus*. Winged adults are yellowish and about 8 mm. long. Soldiers are similar to those of *R. virginicus* except for shorter heads and paler color. These two species are reported to occur more commonly in dry, forested areas than *R. flavipes*. *R. arenicola* Groellnes occurs in the Chicago area and has been found in and under decaying pieces of wood in sandy places near sand dunes. Its habits are similar to those of *R. tibialis* which occurs in the same area. Winged adults have grayish wings and are about 9 to 10 mm. long. Soldiers range in length from 4.6 to 4.9 mm.

The **Formosan subterranean termite,** *Coptotermes formosanus* Shiraki, is an introduced species. Active colonies were first recorded in North America in a shipyard warehouse in Houston, Texas, in 1965. Since then additional colonies have been discovered in Houston and Galveston, Texas; Charleston, South Carolina; and New Orleans and Lake Charles, Louisiana. The species was described from individuals collected in Formosa in 1909. Since then it has been reported from Ceylon, mainland China, Guam, Hawaii, Japan and South Africa. Incipient colonies generally start in or near the soil where moisture and damp wood are available. Nests are normally built in soil near the base of tree stumps, utility poles, or other underground food sources, but may be found almost anywhere with favorable conditions. Colonies have been observed on boats, ships, barges, dredges, water tanks, piers, floating drydocks, in living and dead trees, and in wooden buildings.

Workers are over-all grayish-white. The head is pale yellow, with a white mark in the center and a dark brownish spot on each side of the clypeus. The pronotum is nearly twice as broad as long and the legs are slender and hairy. Soldiers (fig. 7) have oval heads and slender bodies. The pronotum is short, elliptical, and notched at the middle of the frontal margin. A small, short tube-like process extends from the frontal gland and exudes a milky, acidulous secretion. The abdomen is slender, entirely pubescent, and has a 3-segmented caudal appendage. Males have large, hyaline wings, 10.6 mm. long, about three times as long as the abdomen, and about three times as long as broad. The head is hexagonal and brown; the frons is irregularly concave at the center where a globular projection occurs; the pronotum is semicircular and as broad as the head; the legs are short, large, and yellowish-brown; and the abdomen is short, elliptical and yellowish-brown. Females are similar to males but are slightly larger. Their bodies are marked with minute spots, and their wings are 12 to 14 mm. long.

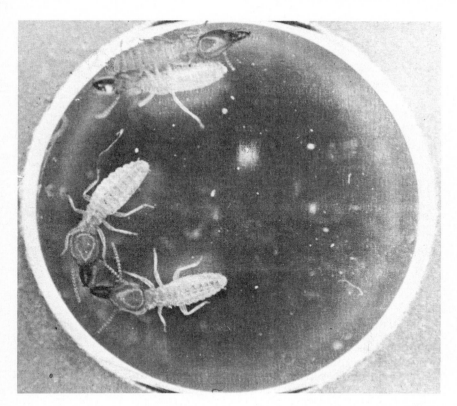

FIGURE 7.—Soldier castes of the Formosan subterranean termite
Coptotermes formosanus.

Formosan subterranean termite nests are constructed from a friable material called carton. It consists of a mixture of masticated wood, saliva, and excrement. A nest may be several cubic feet in size. Tunnels radiate from nests constructed in the soil. They can be found at depths of 10 feet in the earth, and they can extend horizontally to 200 feet. Their walls are lined with essentially the same materials used in constructing the nest and they are nearly impervious to water. Primary queens can lay up to 1,000 eggs per day, and a single colony may contain hundreds of thousands of individuals. Winged reproductives swarm during May and June. They are poor fliers, and the majority drop to the ground within 100 yards of the nest unless carried farther by the wind. First evidence of a colony's presence may be the appearance of these winged adults at swarming time.

Large colonies can cause severe damage in a short time (fig. 8A). In Hawaii, walls of new buildings have been hollowed out in three months' time. Living trees are also hollowed out (fig. 8B) and weakened. Known susceptible trees in the South are the Chinese elm, several species of oak, hackberry, and Arizona ash. Dead trees are highly susceptible. Extensive damage all the way to the top of 70-foot-tall cypress snags has been observed in Louisiana (*43*).

F-519935

FIGURE 8.—Formosan subterranean termite colony and damage: left, carton nest and damaged wood above a window inside a building; right, colony of workers in a cypress log.

Nonsubterranean Termites

Several species of nonsubterranean termites occur in the Eastern States. They are found throughout the state of Florida; also in a narrow strip along the Atlantic Coast as far north as southeastern Virginia, and westward along the Gulf Coast to Mexico. Infestations are found in structural timber and other woodwork in buildings; in furniture; in utility poles; in wooden derricks and piled lumber; in wood pulp or fiber insulation boards; in other products containing cellulose; and in trees and other plants. Because of their ability to live in wood that is frequently moved, nonsubterranean termites are often found in regions far removed from their normal range, including Canada. None of these are able to establish permanent infestations (675).

Nonsubterranean termites fly directly to and enter untreated and unpainted wood at swarming time. They cut across the grain of the wood and excavate broad pockets or chambers, connected by tunnels of small diameter. They feed on both the soft spring wood and the harder summer wood. Their cavities contain compressed pellets of partly digested wood. Some pellets are also pushed to the exterior through small holes and are found in piles on the floors of infested buildings (fig. 9).

Nonsubterranean termite colonies contain only two castes of adults: reproductives and soldiers. Since there is no worker caste, the work of the colony is performed by young nymphs. Winged adults are distinguished by the presence of branches between the upper rim of the wing and the first long vein. These are absent in winged subterranean termites. Soldiers differ from the soldiers of subterranean termites in having their mandibles lined with teeth on the inner edge.

Winged adults usually swarm during the early evening hours of late winter or spring. Unless carried by the wind, they fly for only short distances in search of places to found a new colony. Once they have succeeded, they shed their wings and bore directly into the wood. Then they plug the opening, thereby sealing themselves in. Colonies grow very slowly, are never confined to a single chamber and never contain more than a few thousand individuals. Piles of pellets on the floor may be the first evidence of infestations. Other tell-tale evidence consists of pitted and roughened surfaces of infested floor surfaces, door frames, and other wood.

Nonsubterranean termites usually are less injurious than subterranean species in the United States. However, large public and other buildings in several Florida cities; New Orleans, Louisiana; Savannah, Georgia; Charleston, South Carolina; and less commonly elsewhere, have been seriously damaged (*672*).

Incisitermes snyderi (Light) is the most widely distributed and injurious of the eastern nonsubterranean termites. It occurs from South Carolina to Florida and west to Brownsville, Texas, mainly along the coast. Infestations occur in the woodwork of buildings; in untreated utility poles, and in dead trees, logs, and branches. Winged adults have yellowish heads and are 11 to 12 mm. long. Soldiers are 7 to 8 mm. long and have the anterior margin of the pronotum dentate.

Incisitermes schwarzi (Banks), the **southern dry-wood termite,** occurs in Florida south of Pensacola, where it is the commonest species. Infestations are found in the woodwork of buildings, in the bases and tops of utility poles, and in dead trees, logs, and stumps. Winged adults have yellowish heads and are 15 to 16 mm. long. Soldiers resemble the soldiers of *I. snyderi* except that the anterior margin of the pronotum is not dentate.

Kalotermes approximatus Snyder has been recorded from northern Florida; New Orleans, Louisiana; and southern Virginia. Infestations occur in the woodwork of buildings, in living and dead trees, and in logs and stumps. Winged adults are blackish in color (*349*).

Neotermes jouteli Banks occur in southern Florida, including the Keys. It occasionally occurs in the moist foundation timbers of buildings. In nature, it lives in dead trees and in logs and branches lying on the ground. Adults are yellowish or light castaneous and about 10 mm. long.

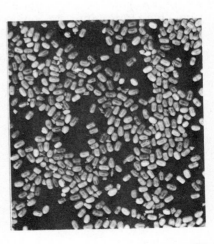

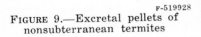
F-519928
FIGURE 9.—Excretal pellets of nonsubterranean termites

Neotermes castaneus (Burmeister) occurs in southern Florida, including the Keys. It has not been found damaging the woodwork of buildings. Infestations have been found in the dead wood of trees, logs, stumps, and branches; also in living citrus trees.

Prorhinotermes simplex (Hagen) occurs in swampy areas of southern Florida where it is found in moist logs. It has been known to attack the woodwork of buildings, but then extremely rarely. Adults are yellowish-brown and about 9 mm. long.

Cryptotermes brevis (Walker), the **tropical rough-headed pow-der-post termite,** occurs commonly in southern Florida and New Orleans, Louisiana. Isolated infestations have also been found elsewhere, including Memphis, Tennessee. This species is found only in the woodwork of buildings and in furniture. It not only destroys these products, but the constant dropping of pellets from infested wood is a source of annoyance to the householder. Winged adults are 10 mm. long. Soldiers have the front of the head black-ish to dark castaneous behind and its anterior margin tuberculate.

Cryptotermes cavifrons Banks, a powder-post termite, occurs in southern Florida where it occurs in dead trees, logs, stumps, and branches. Winged adults are about 8.5 mm. long. Soldiers resemble the soldiers of *C. brevis* except that the anterior margin of the head is not tuberculate.

Calcaritermes nearcticus (Snyder) is also a powder-post ter-mite. It, too, is known only from Florida. Winged adults are small, have smoky wings, and are coarsely punctate. Soldiers have the anterior of the head bilobed. The head is also blackish in front and light castaneous behind.

Order ORTHOPTERA

Cockroaches, grasshoppers and allies

The order Orthoptera contains some of our most familiar in-sects, and many of them are important household or agricultural crop pests. A few species are also injurious to trees.

Members of the order may be either winged or wingless. The winged forms have two pairs of wings, with the front pair gen-erally long and narrow, many-veined, and leathery or parchment-like. The hindwings are membranous, much broader, and are usually folded in fanlike pleats beneath the front wings while the insect is at rest. The body is elongate and cerci are usually well-developed. The females of many species have long ovipositors, often as long as the body.

Many publications have been issued on the Orthoptera: (*82, 275, 329, 330, 331, 332, 546, 274, 730, 613, 770*).

FAMILY MANTIDAE

PRAYING MANTIDS

Praying mantids are large, elongate, rather slow-moving in-sects. The eyes are very large; the head is wider than long and movable; and the prothorax is very long—sometimes nearly as long as the remainder of the body. The front coxae also are very long and the front femora and tibiae are armed with strong spines and fold together to form a pincer. Praying mantids are predaceous and feed on a wide variety of other insects. To capture their prey, they usually lie in wait for it, holding their front legs in an upright position. Once the prey comes within reach, the armed tibiae and femora shoot out with lightning-like speed to grasp it. Because of their habit of holding their front legs in an upright position, these insects are commonly called "praying mantids."

Praying mantids lay their eggs in the fall in paper-maché-like egg cases or ootheca, each of which contains 200 or more eggs. Hatching occurs the following spring; there is one generation per year.

The **Carolina mantid**, *Stagmomantis carolina* (Johannson), is the most common species in the Southern States. It occurs from the Atlantic Coast to New Mexico and north to Nebraska, Pennsylvania, and Illinois. Adults are 75 to 100 mm. long. The male is grayish-brown with smoky-brown outer wings and often with greenish-yellow body and legs. Females are either colored like the males or are greenish-yellow with bright green forewings. *S. floridensis* Davis, a somewhat more slender and longer species, occurs in Florida.

The **Chinese mantid**, *Tenodera aridifolia sinensis* Sauss., an introduced species, occurs in the Eastern States west to Ohio and south to South Carolina. The adults are elongate, robust, and about 100 mm. long (fig. 10). Females are green or greenish-yellow; males are the same color or wholly brown, or brown with margins of the forewings green. The **narrow-winged mantid**, *T. angustipennis* Sauss., also an introduced species, is similar to but more slender and smaller than the Chinese mantid. It is widely distributed in the Eastern States.

Two other eastern species are the **European mantid**, *Mantis religiosa* L., an introduced species (medium sized and greenish-yellow) and *Litaneutria minor* (Scudder). The latter is about 25 mm. long, and occurs on the Great Plains (*316*).

FAMILY PHASMATIDAE

WALKINGSTICKS

Eastern species of walkingsticks are long, slender, and subcylindrical insects. The head is free and nearly horizontal; the antennae are long, and the eyes small; the abdomen is elongate; the legs very long and slender; and the wings are rudimentary, except for one species found in Florida. Walkingsticks are slow-moving insects, and all are plant feeders. The eggs are hard-shelled and are often dropped promiscuously to the ground.

The **walkingstick**, *Diapheromera femorata* (Say), the only species of economic importance, occurs in southern Canada and throughout most of eastern United States west to the Great Plains and Texas. Its preferred hosts appear to be black oak, basswood, elm, black locust, and wild cherry, but it also feeds on white oak, aspen, paper birch, ash, dogwood, and hickory.

Adults are 62 to 87 mm. long and, while motionless, closely resemble the twigs of their hosts (fig. 11). The body color is variable. Some individuals are all brown or green; others are mottled or multicolored with dark or light shades of grays, greens, reds, or brown. Newly-hatched nymphs are pale green, about 8 mm. long, and look like miniature adults. The egg is very hard, oval, seedlike, shiny black or brown, and has a broad white or olive-colored band on one edge. It is about 2 mm. long.

Winter is spent in the egg stage and hatching occurs in May or early June. The nymphs feed at first on shrubs such as sweet fern, blueberry, strawberry, and juneberry. Later, they feed on leaves of the same trees as the adults. Adults emerge in July or August and feed and lay eggs until the onset of cold weather. In heavily infested stands, the sound of falling eggs striking the ground is much like that produced by raindrops in a light shower. In the South most of the eggs hatch the following year; in the North most hatch the second spring following their deposition.

Severe outbreaks occur frequently in the Lake States. They also occur occasionally south of a line drawn from Nebraska to Delaware. Trees may be defoliated twice in the same season during severe outbreaks. Branch mortality sometimes occurs in stands heavily defoliated three or four times; continued defoliation for several years may lead to considerable tree mortality (*304*). The

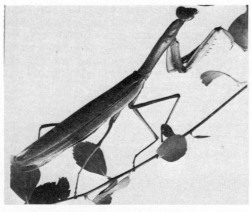

FIGURE 10.—Adult and egg mass of the Chinese mantid, *Tenodera aridifolia sinensis*.

F-504615

FIGURE 11.—Adults of the walkingstick, *Diaphero- mera femorata,* on leaves of oak.

hymenopterous parasite, *Mesitiopterus kahlii* Ashmead; various predators such as crows, robins, and other birds; and dry weather during the period of egg hatch are important natural control factors (*775*).

Several other species of walkingsticks also occur in eastern United States. The **two-striped walkingsticks,** *Anisomorpha bupres- toides* (Stoll.), is found in the Deep South, typically in oak stands growing on excessively drained, sandy soil in Florida. Eggs are laid in groups of 8 to 10 eggs, each in small pits dug in the soil. *A. ferruginea* (P de B.) feeds on various trees and shrubs from southeastern Nebraska and Arkansas through the high country to Georgia and the Carolinas. *Diapheromera velii* Walsh and *D. blatchleyi* (Caud.) feed on grasses and tall shrubs. *D. velii* occurs on the Great Plains; *D. blatchleyi,* from the Great Plains to the Atlantic Coast. *Megaphasma denticrus* (Stal.), the **giant walking- stick,** sometimes attains a length of 150 mm. Its habits are similar to those of *D. femorata,* but it is apparently never abundant enough to be injurious.

FAMILY ACRIDIDAE

SHORT-HORNED GRASSHOPPERS

This family contains most of the well-known grasshoppers, many of which are frequently very destructive to agricultural crops. Ordinarily, they are not very injurious to trees, but they may be seriously damaging during outbreaks. Young trees in nur- series, shelterbelts, and plantations are particularly vulnerable, especially on the Great Plains, in the upper Mississippi Valley, and in the Lake States. The adults are distinguished by their short filiform, or three-jointed, clubbed, antennae; short and in-

57

conspicuous ovipositors; auditory organs on the sides of the first abdominal segment; greatly enlarged hind legs; narrow front wings; and broad, membranous, fanlike hindwings.

The majority of short-horned grasshoppers breed and live in the same general area throughout the year. Certain others may build up in such vast numbers that they are forced to leave their breeding grounds. At such times, they may travel considerable distances. All species have much the same life history. Nearly all lay their eggs in pods at depths of 1 to 3 inches in the soil in late summer or fall, usually in grain stubble, meadows, and along ditchbanks, fence rows, and roadsides. Hatching occurs in the South as early as February; in the Northern States, it usually occurs in May or June. Maturity is reached in 40 to 70 days, after which some adults live and feed until the onset of cold weather. The majority of species spend the winter in the egg stage, but a few overwinter as nymphs or adults, especially in the South.

The following species may be injurious in nurseries, plantations, and shelterbelts during epidemics: (1) The **lesser migratory grasshopper,** *Melanoplus sanguinipes*—the adult is about 2 mm. long and reddish-brown with a distinct patch of black on the neck or collar; (2) The **differential grasshopper,** *M. differentialis* (Thos.)—the adult is 37 mm. long. It is yellow with contrasting black markings; has clear, glossy hindwings; and usually bears yellow and black chevron-shaped bars on the sides of the thighs of the hind legs. (3) The **two-striped grasshopper,** *M. bivittatus* (Say)—the adult is about 30 mm long. It is slighty more robust than the differential grasshopper and is greenish-yellow beneath, with two yellow stripes running the full length of the dorsum. (4) The **red-legged grasshopper,** *M. femurrubrum* (DeG.)—the adult is about 18 mm. long. It is reddish-brown above, yellowish beneath, has colorless hindwings, and has red-tinged hind wings. (5) The **clear-winged grasshopper,** *Camnula pellucida* (Scudd.)—the adult is about 12 mm. long. It is yellow to brown; the front wings are blotched with large brown spots; and the hindwings are clear or pellucid.

A few species of grasshoppers are more closely associated with trees than others. One, *Dendrotettix quercus* Pack., the **post-oak locust,** is widely distributed from east central Texas to the Lake States, Long Island, and southeastern Canada. Oaks are its preferred hosts, but it has also been observed on pines in the Lake States. Several outbreaks have been recorded, some of which covered several square miles. During intervals between outbreaks, it is very scarce. Adults are present from June to September and lay their eggs in the soil in late summer. The nymphs climb the trees to feed. Other tree infesting species are: (1) *D. australis* (Morse)—apparently feeds exclusively on Virginia pine in the Southeastern States; (2) *Melanoplus punctulatus* (Scudd.)—has been observed defoliating young white pines in plantations in Connecticut; (3) *M. bruneri* Scudder—inhabits coniferous forests; and (4) the **eastern lubber grasshopper,** *Romalea microptera* (P de B.)—feeds on shrubs in Florida and Alabama.

FAMILY TETTIGONIDAE

LONG-HORNED GRASSHOPPERS AND KATYDIDS

Long-horned grasshoppers and katydids are mostly large with hair-like antennae, four-segmented tarsi, laterally flattened bladelike ovipositors, and auditory organs sometimes at the base of the front tibiae. The males "sing" by rubbing a sharp edge at the base of one front wing along a file-like ridge on the ventral side of the other front wing. The songs of different species differ in the character of the pulses, the pulse rate, and in the way the pulses are grouped.

Tree-inhabiting katydids are usually long-winged and green, matching in color the foliage on which they feed. Eggs are laid end to end in overlapping rows on leaves or twigs, or are inserted into the edges of leaves. The winter is usually spent in the egg stage and hatching occurs in the spring. Some of the more common species, none of which are very injurious, are discussed below.

The **fork-tailed bush katydid**, *Scudderia furcata* (Brun.), so-called because of the forked appendages at the tip of the abdomen of the male, is widely distributed. It occurs on but is not restricted to trees. The related species, *S. curvicauda* (DeG.), lives commonly on oak.

The **broad-winged katydid**, *Microcentrum rhombifolium* (Sauss.) is widely distributed in the East. Adults are 25 to 35 mm. long and leaf green. The **angular-winged katydid**, *M. retinerve* (Burm.), a smaller species, is more southerly in its distribution. Both species have long, narrow wings, and the vertex is narrowed anteriorally.

Pterophylla camellifolia (F.) is the katydid so commonly heard on summer evenings. The adult is large, green, and robust. The front wings are dark green, leaflike, very broad, concave within, and wholly enclose the abdomen. Infestations occur as small colonies in the dense foliage of trees. Eggs are laid in crevices of loose bark or within the soft stems of woody plants.

Other long-winged species include: *Hubbellia marginifera* (Walker), a large species with green front wings, rarely spotted with brown, which occurs on pines in the Southeastern States, and *Conocephalus brevipennis* (Scudder) which lays its eggs in willow in Canada.

Some members of the family have functional wings and live only on the ground. The most familiar species is the **Mormon cricket,** *Anabrus simplex* Hald. Although primarily western in distribution, it occasionally occurs in destructive numbers as far eastward as the Dakotas and Kansas. It feeds mostly on various trees and shrubs. The ovipositor of the female is sword-shaped and is up to 37 mm. long.

FAMILY GRYLLIDAE
CRICKETS

Crickets are medium-sized insects, usually with long filiform antennae, three-jointed tarsi, spear-shaped ovipositors, and hind legs fitted for jumping. The wings of certain species are fully-developed; in others, they are either abbreviated or absent. They lie flat on the back and bend down abruptly at the sides of the body. The winged forms possess auditory tympanae on one or both sides of the fore tibia. The males also possess sound-producing organs near the base of the dorsal surface of the front wings.

There are several different kinds of crickets, the most familiar perhaps being the common field and house crickets of the genus *Gryllus* (*4*). Tree crickets, however, are the only members of the family that are injurious to trees or shrubs.

Tree crickets are small, delicate, and pale-colored. The tarsi are three-jointed, with the second segment small and compressed. The wings of the male are broad and lie flat over the abdomen, while those of the female are narrow and wrapped closely about the body. Tree crickets feed on other insects such as aphids, tree hoppers, and scales; also on the leaves, flowers, and bark of trees.

The **snowy tree cricket**, *Oecanthus fultoni* T. J. Walker [*O. niveus*], is a common species throughout the United States. Adults are pale green and about 14 mm. long. The wings are transparent with a slight greenish tinge, and each of the first two antennial segments bears a black spot. Adults are found on various trees and shrubs, preferring those growing in the open. Eggs are laid singly in a row of punctures in the bark of twigs or small branches. *O. exclamationis* Davis is similar in appearance, habits, and range to *O. fultoni* except for a black club-shaped mark on the base of the first segment of the antenna. *O. pini* Beut. occurs on pines and lays its eggs in regular rows on the bark. *O. latipennis* Riley occurs commonly on shrubs and low trees, especially on scrub oaks in dry open areas in the Eastern States.

Anurogryllus muticus (DeG.), the **short-tailed cricket**, occurs mainly along the Atlantic Coast from New Jersey to Florida and westward to southeastern Texas. It has been observed damaging newly germinated slash pine seedlings in Louisiana, Texas, and Arkansas. It cuts off the seedlings, pulls them into its tunnels, and eats the tender foliage (*748*).

FAMILY GRYLLOTALPIDAE
Mole Crickets

Gryllotalpa gryllotalpa (L.), the **European mole cricket,** an introduced species, occurs in a number of places along the East Coast. Adults are brownish-yellow tinged with fuscous above and are pale brownish-yellow underneath. They are covered with velvety hairs and are up to 37 mm. long. The front legs terminate in four dactyls which are used for digging. This species feeds at night by tunneling in the upper inch or two of soil. It cuts off the roots of seedlings, eats pits in underground roots and stems, cuts off stems above the ground, and eats seeds. It is occasionally injurious in nurseries.

The **changa,** *Scapteriscus vicinus* Scudder, a tropical species, occurs along the coastal plain of the Southeastern States. The adult is brown above, light brown below, and about 37 mm. long. Its forelegs terminate in two dactyls. *S. abbreviatus* Scudd. occurs in Georgia and Florida. Adults are brownish-fuscous and blotched with yellow. The **southern mole cricket,** *S. acletus* R. & H., occurs from Georgia to Texas. It is pinkish-buff in color and somewhat more slender than *S. abbreviatus.* All members of this genus feed on earthworms, roots, and other insects. They are occasionally injurious in nurseries.

FAMILY BLATTIDAE

COCKROACHES

Several species of cockroaches may be found under the bark and in cavities in dead trees. They feed chiefly on animal and vegetable refuse and, as far as known, are of no economic importance to forestry. The adults are distinguished by their depressed, oval bodies, their nearly horizontal heads, their slender, depressed legs of almost equal size, and the absence of ovipositors in the females.

Order HEMIPTERA

True bugs

The order Hemiptera consists of a large and widely distributed group of insects. The majority are terrestrial in habit, but many are aquatic. Many of the terrestrial forms are phytophagous and feed on a wide variety of trees and smaller plants. Quite a large number are serious pests of cultivated plants. Trees, fortunately, are seriously damaged by only a few species. The order also contains a large number of predatory species, many of which feed on other insects and their eggs. A number of others feed on the blood of man and animals and are decidedly obnoxious or harmful, especially those which transmit disease-causing organisms.

The majority of the Hemiptera have the basal portion of the front wing thickened and leathery, and only the apical portion is membranous. It is from this "half-wing" appearance that the order gets its name. The hindwings are entirely membranous and usually slightly shorter than the front wings. Both pairs of wings lie flat over the abdomen with the membranous distal portion of the front ones overlapping. The mouth parts consist of a bundle of stylets inside a segmented sheath. This slender beak arises from the front part of the head and usually extends backward along the underside of the body, sometimes to the base of the hind pair of legs. Feeding is accomplished by inserting the stylets into the tissues of the plant or animal host and sucking up the juices or blood. The beak sheath folds back beneath the insect as the stylets pierce deeper into the tissues. The antennae are fairly long and consist of four or five segments. Many species have scent glands which give off odors when disturbed. Man usually finds these odors offensive.

Blatchley (*83*) and Britton (*103*) have discussed the Hemiptera of eastern North America.

FAMILY PENTATOMIDAE

STINK BUGS

Pentatomids are commonly called "stink bugs" because of the disagreeable odor they emit when disturbed. The adult is usually a broad, short, slightly convex insect. The antennae are five-segmented and the head and thorax sometimes form a triangle. Many species are brightly colored or conspicuously marked. Green ones may be difficult to detect on leaves. Dark gray ones are also difficult to see when they rest on the bark of limbs and trunks of trees. Most species are plant feeders, but some feed on other insects, and some feed on both.

Tetrya bipunctata (H.-S.) has been recorded feeding on slash and longleaf pine cones in the South. Adults are dark reddish-brown and about 15 mm. long. Because of their coloring, they are not readily noticeable when motionless on a cone. Females lay eggs on needles near cone clusters. The nymphs are gregarious. When they reach the third instar they begin to feed on the seeds within green closed cones. This type of feeding is continued in the adult stage (*188*).

Other plant feeding species and their hosts include the following: (a) *Brochymena quadripustulata* (Fab.)—feeds through the bark of limbs and trunks of elm, oak, and willow. Brownish, hairlike lines running across the grain in the cambial region are evidence of its attack. Adults frequently overwinter in houses. (b) *B. carolinensis* (Fabr.)—feeds through the bark of slash and longleaf pines. (c) *Elasmuche lateralis* (Say)—feeds on the leaves and catkins of yellow birch (also reported feeding on the larvae of *Tetralopha asperatella* in the Lake States). (d) *Pitedia uhleri* (Stal.)—feeds on the larger branches and trunks of white pines in the Lake States.

Predacious species include: (a) the **spined soldier bug,** *Podisus maculiventris* (Say). It has been recorded feeding on more than 30 species of destructive insects, many of which are forest pests. The adult is dull yellow above, with numerous dark brown punctures and is about 12 mm. long. (b) *Stiretus anchorago* (F.) feeds on the larvae of many species, including the gypsy moth and tent caterpillars. Adults are shiny, dark metallic, and 8 to 11 mm. long.

FAMILY TINGIDAE

THE LACE BUGS

Lace bugs, so-called because of their broad gauzelike or lacelike wing covers, are small and usually whitish. They are also flat, oval, or rectangular with reticulated surfaces and are about 5 or 6 mm. long. The head is often hidden beneath a large hood on the front of a greatly modified pronotum, which projects beyond the sides of the body. The abdomen is completely hidden by the wing covers, which are frequently transparent. The nymphs are black and often covered with long spines.

Many species of lace bugs live and feed on the under-surfaces of leaves. A given species usually occurs either on a single host or on closely related ones. The upper surfaces of infested leaves may be either whitened, or brownish, or dead in appearance. The undersurfaces are speckled with eggs, excrement, and cast skins of the developing nymphs. The leaves of heavily infested trees may turn entirely brown and fall off. The winter is spent as adults (under bark scales or other cover on the host tree), or as eggs (cemented to the undersurfaces of leaves or embedded in leaf tissues). Most species have two generations a year.

The **sycamore lace bug,** *Corythucha ciliata* (Say), occurs throughout the Eastern United States (*725*) and in southern Canada. Its preferred host is sycamore, but it also feeds on ash, hickory, and mulberry occasionally. The adult (fig. 12) is white and about 3 mm. long. Overwintering adults emerge early in the spring and deposit their eggs along the ventral surface of the midrib of a leaf. Hatching occurs in 2 to 3 weeks, and the nymphs feed for 5 or 6 weeks. There are two generations per year in the North, probably more in the South. Light feeding causes a stippling of foliage. Heavily infested leaves of sycamore turn white and drop prematurely. During dry weather this may result in severe injury.

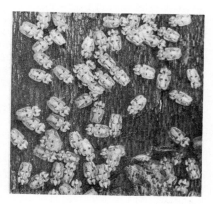

FIGURE 12.—Adults of the sycamore lace bug, *Corythucha ciliata.*

The **oak lace bug,** *Corythucha arcuata* (Say), feeds on white, bur, and chestnut oaks from Alabama and the Carolinas to southern Canada. Connell and Beacher (*156*) discussed its life history and control. The winter is spent in either the egg or adult stage. Infested leaves appear grayish-white. Heavily infested trees may be defoliated, especially during dry weather. Bur oak in shelterbelt plantings is especially susceptible.

The **elm lace bug,** *Corythucha ulmi* O. & D. feeds on American elm in many Eastern States and southern Canada, and on Siberian elm on the Northern Great Plains. It is capable of defoliating its host.

Heavy infestations of *Corythucha mollicula* O. & D. (=*salicis* O. & D.) (=*canadensis* Parsh.) may seriously injure willow, its only known host, throughout the Eastern States. Heavy infestations of the **hackberry lace bug,** *C. celtidis* O. & D., often occur on hackberry in the Midwest. The species has also been reported from Florida. *C. pallipes* Parsh. (=*betulae* Drake=*cyrta* Parsh.)

is often abundant on young yellow birch. Other hosts include white birch, beech, eastern hophornbeam, willow, mountain-ash, and maple. *C. pergandei* Heidemann feeds principally on alder; also occasionally on hazel, elm, and birch. *C. pruni* O. & D. (=*pyriformis* Parsh.) feeds on wild cherry; *C. juglandis* (Fitch) on black walnut, butternut, and linden; *C. elegans* Drake on willow, balsam poplar, quaking aspen, and bigtooth aspen; *C. aesculi* O. & D. on buckeye; *C. associata* O. & D. on wild cherry; *C. bellula* Gibson on hawthorn; and the **hawthorn lace bug,** *C. cydoniae* Fitch, on hawthorn and pyracantha.

The **rhododendron lace bug,** *Stephanitis rhododendri* Harv., an introduced species, occurs from New England to North Carolina and Ohio, and infests rhododendron, mountain-laurel, and azalea. The adult is about 4 mm. long, and has a triangular hood and long, slender antennae. Its wings are rounded at the apex and are nearly twice as long as the abdomen. Winter is spent in the egg stage and there are at least two generations per year. Rhododendron plants infested continuously for several years turn yellow and lose their attractiveness.

The **azalea lace bug,** *Stephanitis pyrioides* (Scott), resembles *S. rhododendri* except for its duskier wings. It feeds on azalea, preferably the evergreen varieties. The leaves of heavily infested plants become almost white and many of them dry out completely and drop. There may be three generations per year.

The **basswood lace bug,** *Gargaphia tiliae* (Walsh), often occurs in large numbers on the undersides of the leaves of basswood. Adults overwinter either under leaves on the ground or in bark crevices. There are two generations per year.

FAMILY REDUVIIDAE

ASSASSIN BUGS

Most species of assassin bugs are predacious on other insects. Others are blood-sucking and frequently bite man. Many species are capable of inflicting painful bites and will do so if carelessly handled. Most species are found on various parts of plants, but a few are found on the ground or under objects on or near the ground. Adults are varicolored, usually black, brownish, green, or orange. They range greatly in size, some being well over 25 mm. long. The head is long, narrow, and cylindrical with the part behind the eyes necklike. The head bears a stout, rigid, three-jointed beak which usually curves downward in the form of a semi-loop, with the tip resting in a groove in front of and between the front legs. The margins of the abdomen are often exposed beyond the edges of the wings.

The **wheel bug,** *Arilus cristatus* (L.), is an important predator of various forest insects. As a young nymph it feeds on aphids; later, it attacks lepidopterous larvae such as the fall webworm, and other insects such as the locust borer. The adult is a large, striking insect, with coglike teeth projecting from a median, longitudinal ridge on the thorax. The female is much larger than the male and may reach a length of 30 mm.

Other species attacking forest insects include: (a) *Sinea spinipes* (H.-S.) which feeds on the fall webworm in the South; (b)

Acholla multispinosa (DeG.), an enemy of the pine webworm; (c) *Zelus exsanguis* Stal., an enemy of the gypsy moth; and (d) *Melanolestes picipes* (H.-S.), an enemy of May beetles and their larvae. Readio (*611*) discussed the biologies of members of the family.

FAMILY NABIDAE

DAMSEL BUGS

Damsel bugs appear to be entirely predatory on soft-bodied plant feeding insects. Adults are usually pale brown to straw-colored and about 8 mm. long. The forelegs are quite slender and fitted for grasping, having the tibiae armed with minute spines and the femora enlarged. *Nabis sordidus* Reuter is a common species in eastern forests. It often occurs in large numbers on rank undergrowth.

FAMILY ANTHOCORIDAE

FLOWER BUGS

The majority, if not all, members of this family of small bugs are predaceous on other insects. The adults may be found on flowers, under loose bark, in leaf litter, or in decaying fungi. *Anthocoris musculus* (Say) (=*borealis* Dallas) feeds on soft-bodied, leaf-feeding insects, principally lace bugs, on deciduous trees in the Northern States. *Elatophilus inimica* (Drake & Harris) feeds on the red-pine scale in Connecticut; it has also been found on pines infested with the pine twig gall scale in Massachusetts. The majority of flower bugs are black with white markings and are only about 3 to 5 mm. long. *Orius insidiosus* (Say) is a common predator of insect eggs.

FAMILY MIRIDAE

THE PLANT BUGS

This is the largest family in the order Hemiptera, with about 1600 species occurring in the United States and Canada alone (*424*). The majority of species appear to be phytophagous. Many others are predaceous and feed on a wide variety of young and/or soft-bodied insects. The adults are 2 to 9 mm. long, and are usually fragile. The antennae and beak are each four-segmented, with the second segment of the beak longer than the head. The tarsi are usually three-segmented. The hemelytra, when fully developed, are separated into a clavus, corium, cuneus, and membrane. In some species, the hemelytra are abbreviated and the membrane is either absent or reduced to a narrow band.

The oaks, ashes, hickories, and birches serve as hosts for many species. *Tropidosteptes amoenus* Reuter [= *Neoborus amoenus* Reuter] has caused noticeable injury to ash seedlings in nurseries in the Lake States; the **tarnished plant bug**, *Lygus lineolaris* (P. de B.), is often injurious to ornamentals and to forest nursery trees. Young, succulent growth of elm is frequently damaged by the feeding of *Neolygus invitus* (Say).

FAMILY COREIDAE

CoreID Bugs

This is a large family of relatively large bugs, some members of which have the legs flattened and leaflike. They are similar to the lygaeids but differ in having numerous veins in the membrane of the hemelytra.

Leptoglossus corculus (Say) occurs commonly in longleaf and slash pine seed orchards in north Florida. First and second instar nymphs feed on the needles and first year conelets; older nymphs and adults feed on the seeds. Adults are reddish-brown to black, have long legs, and average 18 mm. in length. A white zigzag line crosses the wings, and the hind tibiae are flattened and leaflike. Infested cones usually show no external damage symptoms (*188*). The related species, *L. occidentalis* Heidemann, a serious pest of Douglas-fir seed in California (*434*) has been observed feeding on the needles and green cones of Austrian pine in Missouri.

FAMILY RHOPALIDAE

The **boxelder bug**, *Leptocoris trivittatus* (Say), often becomes a pest wherever boxelder is grown as a shade tree in the United States and Canada. In heavily infested areas, it will feed on ash and maple. Adults (fig. 13) are somewhat flattened, brownish-black

F-508517
FIGURE 13.—Adult of the boxelder bug, *Leptocoris trivittatus*, on seed of boxelder.

on top, and about 12 mm. long. There are also three red longitudinal stripes on the thorax; the margins of the basal half of the wings are red; and the abdomen is bright red. Nymphs are wingless but possess wing pads and are dark toward the head. They have bright red abdomens.

The winter is spent in the adult stage in dry, sheltered places, such as the attics of houses. During warm winter days, they become active and come out of hiding, only to retreat again when it turns cold. During the spring, they emerge and fly to their hosts where they deposit eggs on the leaves. Eggs also are occasionally laid on leaves or under the bark of other tree species, on stones, grass, litter, fences, and in doorway crevices. Eggs hatch in 11 to 14 days and the nymphs feed in leaves, fruits, or soft seeds by inserting their beaks into the tissues. Feeding continues throughout the summer, or until the nymphs become adults. In some parts of the country the adults may emerge by midsummer, and give rise to a second generation that matures in the fall.

The importance of the boxelder bug as a pest derives from its habit of invading houses in large numbers in search of shelter. Householders and supervisors of outdoor recreational areas and parks are often concerned. One way to reduce the problem is to remove the boxelder trees, particularly the female seed-bearing trees. The removal or spring burning of leaf litter also discourages the congregating of the insects (791).

FAMILY LYGAEIDAE

LYGAEID BUGS

This is a rather large family, most members of which feed on mature seed. The adults are small insects, about 2 to 18 mm. long. Many are conspicuously marked with spots or bands of white, black, or red. Various plant-feeding species are found on herbaceous vegetation in the forest. One species, *Kleidocerys resedae geminatus* (Say), feeds on the catkins of yellow and gray birch, rhododendron, etc.

FAMILY THAUMASTOCORIDAE

Xylastodoris luteolus Barber, the **royal palm bug,** is the only member of this family known to occur in the United States. It feeds on the royal palm, *Roystonea regia,* in southern Florida. Adults are pale yellow, flattened, and about 2 to 2.5 mm. long. Eggs are deposited on the undersurfaces of leaflet midribs, usually on older trees. Feeding occurs on unfolded leaflets of newly-emerging fronds and to some extent the spike or projecting part of the terminal bud. Fronds exposed to heavy feeding may turn brown (32).

Order HOMOPTERA

Aphids, scales, mealybugs, etc.

The order Homoptera consists of divergent groups, some of which are among the most common and abundant of all insects. Except for the cicadas, they are mostly small and inconspicuous.

A few are brilliantly colored, and many are grotesque in shape. They are closely related to members of the order Hemiptera, but are distinguished by their uniformly-textured wings and by the point of origin of the beak at the back of the underside of the head. The mouth parts consist of four piercing stylets (the mandibes and maxillae). Many species are wingless, at least in the female sex under certain conditions. Where wings are present, they are usually four in number with the front pair longer and the hind pair often wider. The wings do not overlap much at the tip, and their bases are never abruptly thicker than their tips. They usually stand sloping roof-shaped over the abdomen while the insect is at rest. Members of many families are able to conceal themselves beneath various protective coverings such as froth, waxy tufts, hard waxy shells, and the sloughing epidermis of bark. The majority are also able to produce honeydew.

Homopterous insects differ greatly in their biologies; some species produce several generations per year while others may require several years to complete one life cycle. The life history of some species is also very complex, involving both bisexual and parthenogenetic generations, winged and wingless individuals and generations, and sometimes the regular alteration of food plants. However, all species are phytophagous, and they feed on an almost endless variety of plants of all sizes and ages. They feed by inserting their beaks into plant tissues and extracting the sap. A large number of species are injurious both to cultivated crops and to forest, shade, and ornamental trees.

FAMILY FLATIDAE

FLATID PLANTHOPPERS

A number of species of flatid planthoppers feed on trees and shrubs, but they are seldom of economic importance. Members of different genera differ greatly in body and form. Those occurring in this country are usually less than 12 mm. in length, and many have the head greatly modified, with the part in front of the eyes greatly enlarged and snoutlike. A useful characteristic for recognizing them is the position and form of the antennae. The two basal segments are stout, whereas the remainder consist of a nearly pear-shaped basal segment and a segmented, bristle-like terminal part. They also have a few large spines on the hind tibiae. Two fairly common species are *Anormenis septentrionalis* (Spin.) and *Metcalfa pruinosa* (Say). The nymphs, which feed on the undersurfaces and midribs of leaves, resemble small masses of cotton, and are about 6 mm. in diameter. They jump when disturbed. Osborn (*574*) and Van Duzee (*731*) discuss the group.

FAMILY CICADELLIDAE

THE LEAFHOPPERS

This is one of the largest families of insects in the world; all appear to be plant feeders. The adults range in length from about 3 to 15 mm., and come in an almost endless variety of colors. Certain species resemble flatid planthoppers but they differ in having one or more rows of small spines extending the length of the hind tibiae. Because of the nature of their feeding, which consists of piercing plant tissues with their mouth parts and sucking the juices, the damage they cause is usually not recognized or is attributed to other factors. About the only visible effects of leafhopper feeding are the white stippling of foliage or the browning, withering, and curling of leaves. Because of the difficulty in observing or evaluating the damage to trees, very little is known of its magnitude or importance. The probability is that it is grossly underestimated. These insects, in fact, may contribute significantly to the general unproductiveness of many stands of valuable hardwoods in Eastern United States. Many species are also vectors of destructive plant diseases, especially diseases of virus origin.

Some species of leafhoppers spend the winter in the egg stage; others as adults. Overwintering eggs usually hatch in May or June, and the young nymphs feed on new, tender leaves. Overwintering adults emerge during the first warm days in spring and lay eggs as soon as the leaves of their hosts are fully developed. These eggs hatch in about 10 days. As a rule there are one or two generations per year; sometimes, more.

Forest and shade trees serve as hosts for many species of *Erythroneura*, *Empoasca*, and *Typhlocyba* (*189*). Several species of *Idiocerus* feed on willow and poplars. Various species of *Macropsis* feed on poplars, willow, and honeylocust. Certain species of *Scaphoideus*, *Gyponana*, and *Ponana* occur on American elm; oaks are infested by species of *Alebra*, *Eutettix*, and *Penthimia*. This is only a partial listing of genera and species known to attack trees; the total number is far greater.

The most important leafhopper as far as forest and shade trees are concerned is the **white-banded elm leafhopper,** *Scaphoideus luteolus* Van D., the vector of elm phloem necrosis, a virus disease of American elm (*21*). Adults are difficult to separate from those of closely related species, but not so the nymphs (fig. 14). After the second instar, practically all of the nymphs are dark brown with a transverse white band across the dorsum. This band lies just behind the thorax and covers the first two and part of the third abdominal segments. The species is widely distributed in Eastern United States, from New York west to Kansas, Nebraska, and Iowa, and south to Georgia and Alabama.

The white-banded elm leafhopper lays its eggs in the cork parenchyma of elm bark. When the eggs hatch the young nymphs wander in search of leaves on which to feed. The first of these to be found usually are on tiny branchlets growing from the trunk. A dozen or more young nymphs may be found clustered on the undersurface of one of these leaves, where they feed on the midribs or larger veins. Excessive feeding often causes the apical portions of the leaves to turn brown and die. Older nymphs are more widely distributed throughout the crown of the tree (*22*).

Elm phloem necrosis virus is transmitted by the adults which feed first on the leaves of diseased trees and then on the leaves of healthy trees. Studies have shown that a period of several days must elapse after the insect feeds on a diseased tree before it can transmit the virus. All of the details of the life cycle of the species

 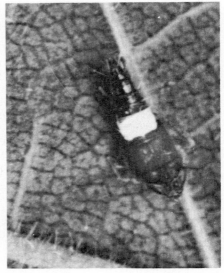

F-519937-8

FIGURE 14.—Adult and nymph of the white-banded elm leafhopper, *Scaphoideus luteolus.*

have not been determined, but it is known that the winter is spent in the egg stage and that there is only one generation per year.

Homalodisca coagulata (Say), *H. insolita* (Wlk.), *Oncometopia orbona* (F.) [= *O. undata*], *Cuerna costalis* (F.), and *Graphocephala versuta* (Say) transmit the virus causing phony peach, a destructive disease of peach trees in the South.

FAMILY MEMBRACIDAE

TREEHOPPERS

Treehoppers are characterized by the prolongation of the pronotum backward and above the abdomen. In some species it not only extends backward but also sidewise and upward, and, in some, it extends to the tip of the abdomen and completely covers the wings. The hind legs are long and adapted for jumping, and the female's ovipositor is long and sawlike. The majority of species apparently live on trees, most often in open stands but also in woods. Only a few species are of economic importance. Osborn (575) discussed the species occurring in Ohio, and Funkhouser (276) listed the species occurring in Connecticut.

The **buffalo tree hopper,** *Stictocephala bubalus* (F.), (=*Ceresa*), is occasionally injurious to young trees such as ash and elm. Injury results from two opposing slits cut in the bark by the female during the act of oviposition. Eggs are placed in the slit and the portion of the stem beyond it often dies. Adults are light green to yellowish and about 9 mm. long. The pronotum is sharply elevated, is widest at the tip, bears two sharply pointed horns which extend at right angles to the body, and ends beyond the tip of the abdomen in a narrowed acute process.

The **three-cornered alfafa hopper,** *Spissistilus festinus* (Say) occasionally damages black locust seedlings in nurseries in the South. Injury results from the feeding of the nymphs on the stems, usually 1 to 2 inches above the base. Gall-like swellings or calluses which develop just above the feeding punctures kill many of the seedlings. Other seedlings are lost when they break at these points. *Stictocephala militaris* (Gibson and Wells) nymphs feed on the veins and petioles of sweetgum leaves in north Georgia. Gall-like enlargements may develop at points of injury on the petioles, or the leaves may die.

Other common membracids and their tree hosts are as follows: *Micrutalis calva* (Say)—abundant on honeylocust; *Telamona reclivata* Fitch— common to abundant on basswood; *T. decorata* Ball —fairly common on aspen; *Vanduzea arquata* (Say)—abundant on black locust; *Thelia bimaculata* (F.)—abundant on black locust; *Cyrtolobus disciodalis* (Emmons)—common on red oak; *Carynota stupida* Walker—sometimes abundant on yellow birch; *Playcotis vittata* (F.)—abundant on oak; and the **two-marked treehopper,** *Enchenopa binotata* (Say)—common on butternut.

FAMILY CERCOPIDAE

SPITTLEBUGS

Spittlebugs are represented in our fauna by 25 species, most of which belong to the subfamily Aphrophorinae (*686*). As a group, the adults are stout-bodied, rarely over 12 mm. long, oval or oval-elongate, and dull colored. The nymphal or immature stages are spent in frothy masses of spittle on their host plants.

The **pine spittlebug,** *Aphrophora parallela* (Say), occurs in southern Canada and throughout most of the eastern states from New England to the Lake States, Arkansas, Florida, and Alabama. Its favorite host appears to be Scotch pine, but it is also known to attack pitch, white, Virginia, jack, slash, loblolly, and Japanese pines; Norway, white, and red spruces; and balsam fir and hemlock. Trees of all ages and sizes are attacked. During outbreaks, infested Scotch pines may be severely stunted or killed (*681*). Adults are tan to dark reddish-brown with two narrow, oblique, light bands, usually bordered by darker bands, on each wing cover, and are about 8 to 11 mm. long (fig. 15).

Eggs are deposited in dead woody tissue or just under the outer bark of twigs during July and August. In the northern parts of its range, the species is known to spend the winter in the egg stage. The eggs usually hatch in May, and the young nymphs feed on the twigs where they soon cover themselves with spittle. As they grow, they usually change locations and form new masses of spittle at each stop. Upon the approach of maturity they move to the main trunk where several may occupy a single spittle mass. When they become full-grown, they migrate to the needles and transform to adults. Adults are present during July and August and feed without producing spittle masses. There is one generation per year.

The fungus, *Entomophora aphrophora,* and high temperatures during the nymphal period occasionally cause heavy mortality of

FIGURE 15.—Adult and nymphal spittle masses of the
pine spittlebug, *Aphrophora parallela*.

the pine spittle bug. The opening up of closed stands and pruning
of dead and dying limbs to reduce the amount of material suitable
for oviposition are recommended as control practices.

The **Saratoga spittlebug**, *Aphrophora saratogensis* (Fitch), occurs in southeastern Canada and eastern United States from
Maine to Minnesota, and south through the Appalachians to
Florida. In the nymphal stage it feeds on a wide variety of herbs
and shrubs. Sweet fern, brambles, prairie willow, and aspen
sprouts are preferred by fourth and fifth instar nymphs. The
adults feed on red, jack, white, Virginia, pitch, and loblolly pines;
white spruce; balsam fir; and tamarack. In the Lake States, red
pine is hit hardest and jack pine ranks second. Heavy infestations
in the Lake States have destroyed entire red pine plantations. The
adult is about 9 to 10 mm. long, light brown to tan in color, with
a light, irregular stripe on the head and pronotum and with
oblique, wavy markings on the wing covers. The abdomen of the
fourth instar nymph is scarlet, edged with black. Fifth instar
nymphs are dark brown.

Adults are active from late June to late September. In the Lake
States, the majority appear in late July. They feed by inserting
their mouth parts into the cortex of new and old shoots of the
host, mostly on two-year-old internodes, and extracting sap. This
causes the formation of necrotic resin-filled pockets in the phloem
and xylem tissues. Damaged pines are characterized by the presence of reddish-brown "flags" of dead foliage, by numerous punctures on the twigs covered with small drops of resin, and by light

72

tan flecks in the wood and inner bark at feeding points. Extensive feeding kills branches, stunts and deforms growing shoots, and may kill entire trees. Mortality usually begins 2 or 3 years after the first flags are seen (235).

On red pine, eggs are laid under the outer scales of buds on the upper part of the tree. On jack pine, they are laid in the sheaths of current year's needles or under the bark of dead twigs. The winter is spent in the egg stage and the eggs hatch in the spring just about the time red and jack pine buds begin to elongate. Young nymphs crawl to the ground and begin feeding at the base of alternate host stems, either singly or in small groups. As they feed they form masses of spittle (fig. 16.). To find these masses it is frequently necessary to brush the litter away from the base of the stem. The nymphs reach maturity in about 40 to 70 days, depending on the weather. Then they climb to the upper parts of their alternate hosts and transform to adults. The adults then fly to the pine hosts and begin feeding on needle bearing twigs. In the Lake States, adult transformation is about 80 percent complete by mid-July.

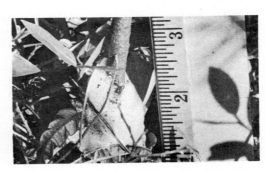

F-489365

FIGURE 16.—Spittle mass of the Saratoga spittlebug, *Aphrophora saratogensis*, at base of sweet fern.

Nymphal populations are often greatly reduced by late spring frosts in the Lake States. Hot, dry weather also kills many young nymphs, especially in open plantations. Insect parasites and predators provide a certain amount of control, but are unable to prevent outbreaks. Recommended preventive control measures include selection of sites for red or jack pine plantations that are comparatively free of hosts favored by the nymphs, dense planting so as to secure early crown closure, and planting on good sites. Methods of direct control are discussed by Wilson and Millers (784) and Wilson and Kennedy (783).

Prosapia bicincta (Say) occurs from Massachusetts to Florida and west to Kansas and Texas. Adults are dark brown and about 9 mm. long. There usually are two distinct bands across the wings and a narrower orange band on the thorax between the humeral angles. Adults have been recorded feeding on holly, redbud, wild cherry, and a wide variety of other woody and herbaceous plants. Infested leaves of holly become distorted, stunted, and discolored and may have necrotic areas at feeding sites.

Clastoptera undulata Uhler nymphs and adults have been observed feeding on the young twigs of Australian pine in Florida. In heavily infested areas, the adults may be attracted to lights in such large numbers they become a nuisance. The **alder spittlebug,**

C. obtusa (Say), a common species, feeds on various shrubs and trees, including hickory, birch, and alder. The **pecan spittlebug, *C. achatina* Germ.**, is occasionally a serious pest of pecan in the Midwest. It feeds on the terminals, sometimes killing fruit-producing shoots. The **dogwood spittlebug**, *C. proteus nigricollis* Fitch, has been recorded on pine. *Omalophora salicis* (DeG.) frequently occurs in large numbers on willow. The **meadow spittlebug, *Philaenus spumarius* (L.),** occasionally feeds on Scotch pine in the Northeast.

FAMILY CICADIDAE

CICADAS

Cicadas are the largest of all of the order Homoptera occurring in the United States. The adults are stocky, heavy-bodied insects with large compound eyes and membranous wings, and some reach a length of 50 mm. There are two common types, (1) the **dog-day cicadas**, often called **harvest flies**, and (2) the **periodical cicada**, also known as 17-year locusts. The dog-day group contains large blackish species, usually with greenish markings. The life cycle lasts from 2 to 5 years but, because of overlapping broods, some adults appear every year. Periodical cicadas differ from the dog-day group in being smaller and in having reddish eyes, reddish legs, and reddish wing veins. The life cycle is 13 years in the South and 17 years in the North.

Cicadas deposit their eggs in the twigs of trees and shrubs and often damage twigs so severely that their terminal portions die. When the eggs hatch the young nymphs drop to the ground, enter the soil, and feed on roots. Here the nymph remains until ready to molt for the last time, years later. Before molting, it emerges from the ground and climbs upon some object, usually the trunk of a tree, fastens its claws in the bark, and molts. The adults of some species live 5 to 6 weeks.

The **periodical cicada**, *Magicicada septendecim* (L.) (fig. 17 A), is widely distributed in Eastern United States and it lays its eggs in more than 70 species of trees and other plants. The most susceptible of the trees appear to be the oaks, hickory, honeylocust, dogwood, apple, and peach; however, many others such as sweet-gum, elm, ash, yellow-poplar, walnut, sycamore, and redbud may also be heavily attacked. Adults are about 40 mm. long. The female is completely black on top, but the male has 4 or 5 orange-brown abdominal segments on top.

The female uses a sawlike ovipositor to puncture the bark and make a pocket in the wood in which she deposits from 24 to 28 eggs in two rows. She may then proceed along the twig and repeat the process until she has deposited about 5 to 20 batches of eggs. Sometimes the punctures are placed so close together that the wounds appear as a single slit up to 3 inches long (fig. 17 B). When the eggs hatch, the nymphs fall to and enter the ground where they feed on suitable roots. Usually they are found at depths of 18 to 24 inches beneath the surface. When they become

FIGURE 17.—The periodical cicada, *Magicicada septendecim:* A, Adults on the bark of a tree; B, oviposition scars in branch of tree.

full-grown they emerge to begin a new cycle, usually leaving the ground during the night. Emergence may begin as early as the last week of April in the South and as late as the last week in May in the North.

A few days after the adults appear, the males begin drumming or singing. During outbreaks the sound is loud and incessant, literally deafening in wooden areas. The chorus begins at dawn and the volume increases as the temperature rises. It ceases at evening.

Cicada adults cause no visible feeding damage. In contrast, the egg-laying habits of the female may cause serious damage, especially to young, transplanted trees in nurseries and orchards. Some damage also results to older trees. Damaged twigs wilt, and some break at damaged points. Methods of control are discussed in U. S. Department of Agriculture Leaflet No. 540 issued in 1966 (*727*).

Magicicada cassini (Fisher) also occurs in Eastern United States. In Kansas, it is found mainly in streamside habitats in lowland forests. *Tibicen canicularis* (Harr.) has been reported causing serious damage in white spruce plantations on poor sites in Quebec.

FAMILY PSYLLIDAE

JUMPING PLANT LICE

Psyllids are very small, about 2 to 5 mm. long, and look very much like miniature cicadas. There is also some resemblance to winged aphids, but psyllids differ in having stouter legs, with the hind pair fitted for jumping. The nymphs of certain species which secrete large quantities of wax resemble woolly aphids. The adults are very active and jump or fly when disturbed.

Hackberry is attractive to many gall-forming species, all of which belong to the genus *Pachypsylla.* Although hackberry (*Celtis*) is cosmopolitan, *Pachypsylla* is known only in North America. Of the five species of hackberry in the United States (*C. laevigata* Willd., *C. occidentalis* L., *C. pallida* Torr., *C. reticulata* Torr. and *C. tennifolia* Nutt.) psyllid galls are recorded for all except *C. pallida,* a spiny bush occurring in the Texas, Arizona, and New Mexico deserts.

Psyllids fall into two species groups, a) the leaf gall makers, and b) the woody gall makers. Adults of the leaf feeding forms emerge from galls in the fall; the wood feeding forms, in the spring. Leaf gall makers are further subdivided into two groups, blister galls and nipple galls.[7]

Pachypsylla celtidisvesicula Riley, the **blistergall psyllid**, forms a small, monothalamous (one psyllid per gall) blister gall. It is believed to occur throughout the range of *Celtis occidentalis* in the United States and is the most abundant of the hackberry psyllids. Fifty or more may infest a single leaf. Adults often become a household nuisance when thousands accumulate on screens in the fall prior to hibernating. Two undescribed species of blistergall psyllids occur on *C. Laevigata* and *C. reticulata.*

Pachypsylla celtidisastericus Riley, the **hackberry stargall**, produces a gall which closely resembles the blistergall formed by the blistergall psyllid, except it has star-like growth on the lower side of the leaf. It can occur on all hackberry tree species except *Celtis occidentalis.*

The **hackerry-nipple-gall maker,** *Pachypsylla celtidismamma* (Riley), is perhaps the best known hackberry psyllid. It produces light green, nipple-shaped galls on the underside of *Celtis occidentalis* leaves. It is monothalamous, although at times it may appear to be polythalamous due to as many as seven galls of *P. celtidisvesicula,* which may be incorporated into a single nipple-gall (*537*). Like the blister-gall psyllid, adults cluster on screens during the fall. The nipple-gall psyllid may disfigure leaves when infestations are heavy (*662*). Methods of control are discussed by Thompson (*713*).

Pachypsylla celtidisgemma Riley, the **budgall psyllid,** occurs throughout the range of hackberry trees in the United States, and may become a pest when populations are high. Adults appear during the latter part of June in the New York City area and lay their eggs on the young leaves. Young nymphs enter the buds and initiate gall formation. The polythalamous galls contain several nymphs, each in its own chamber. The winter is passed in the fifth nymphal instar in the gall (*739*).

---

[7] Riemann, J. G. 1961. A study of the hackberry gallmaker genus *Pachypsylla.* (Unpublished thesis. Univ. Texas, 201 p., illus.)

Pachypsylla venusta (O. S.), the **petiolegall psyllid,** is the largest of the hackberry psyllids, and it forms the largest galls. The galls are polythalamous and usually contain six cells. Sometimes there are as many as 30. These galls may persist on the trees for several years and seriously damage the appearance of shade trees. Distribution of the species is mostly limited to below the 40th parallel.

Pachypsylla celtidisinteneris Mally forms small, inconspicuous, monothalamous galls under the bark of twigs.

Several species in the genus *Psylla* also feed on various trees, shrubs, and ornamentals. Large quantities of honeydew are produced which drip down and cover their hosts. A black mold growing in this material often makes infested plants look unhealthier than they are.

The **boxwood psyllid,** *Psylla buxi* (L.), attacks American and English varieties of boxwood, and probably occurs wherever they grow. The adult is greenish and has transparent wings; nymphs are gray-green and covered with a white cottony or waxy material. The first winter is spent in the nymphal stage. Feeding is resumed in the spring and adults begin to emerge in early May. Infested leaves curl and form cups in which nymphs are concealed. Feeding also results in reduced growth of young twigs. Eggs are laid under bud scales during July and August. Weiss and St. George (*752*) discuss methods of control. Other species of *Psylla* and their hosts include: *P. annulata* Fitch, paper birch and maple; *P. carpinicola* Crawf., birch; *P. floccosa* Patch and *P. galeaformis* Patch, alder; and *P. trimaculata* Crawf., wild cherry.

Trioza tripunctata Fitch has been observed feeding on the needles of pines in ornamental plantings in Connecticut. Damage consists of yellowish or reddish spots which frequently coalesce, causing the needles to die and drop prematurely. The **persimmon psylla,** *T. diospyri* (Ashm.), and *T. magnoliae* (Ashm.) feed on persimmon and magnolia, respectively, in Florida.

Psyllids are attacked by a large number of hymenopterous and dipterous parasites. Jensen (*402*) listed more than 150 species from the United States alone.

FAMILY APHIDIDAE

Aphids, Plant Lice

The aphids or plant lice constitute a very large group of small, soft-bodied insects that feed by sucking the sap from the leaves, stems, and roots of plants and trees. They are pear-shaped, have fairly long antennae, and a pair of tubelike cornicles rise from the top of the fifth or sixth abdominal segment. Winged males are common. The wings are very delicate and membranous, with only a few simple veins, and they are usually held vertically above the body while at rest. Egg-laying females of many species are also winged.

Ordinarily, most of the aphids feed exposed on their hosts. Others feed in sheltered locations such as inside leaves, which they cause to curl or to become distorted, or inside galls. Trees of all kinds, sizes, and ages are attacked, but they normally are not seriously injured. Serious damage sometimes results, however, especially to shade and ornamental trees and young trees in plantations. Honeydew dropping from heavily infested shade and ornamental trees is often a nuisance as it forms a sticky coating on everything below, especially sidewalks, parked automobiles, and park benches. Additional damage may result from the growth of a sooty mold in the honeydew. It not only detracts from the esthetic value of shade trees and ornamentals, but also interferes with the proper functioning of their leaves. Numerous publications have been issued on the identity, distribution, and hosts of aphids (*296, 380, 583, 584, 585, 586*).

Field Key to the Aphids, Based Principally on Host Plants

1. Causing galls or gall-like formations 2
   Not causing galls or gall-like formations 19
2. On conifers 3
   On hardwoods 10
3. On balsam fir twigs, branches, and trunks, causing "gouty" swellings at tips of twigs and stems, often causing leaves to turn red and trees to die. Insects ½ to 1½ mm. long; color dark brown to black, covered with white flocculence .... *Adelges piceae*
   On spruce 4
4. Causing only terminal galls or gall-like formations 5
   Causing galls other than terminal galls 8
5. Terminal galls, compact, small 6
   Terminal galls, larger, composed of entire new growth with needles thickened at base, or loose and on current growth 7
6. Terminal galls conelike, compact; on new growth. On black, Engelmann, red, or Sitka spruce
   Pineus pinifoliae
   Terminal galls small, not conelike; on current year's growth. On spruce, mostly red and black
   Adelges strobilobius
7. Terminal galls comprising entire new growth and causing thickening of needles at base. On black and red spruce
   Pineus floccus
   Terminal gall a loose growth. On Engelmann, Norway, white, black, and red spruce .... *Pineus similis*
8. Causing galls on entire new growth of spruce host. On blue, Engelmann, oriental, and Sitka spruce
   Adelges cooleyi
   Causing pineapple-shaped galls only at base of new growth of spruce 9
9. Galls with very short needles. On white and Norway spruce .... *Adelges lariciatus*
   Galls with longer needles. On white, red, and Norway spruce .... *Adelges abietis*
10. On hickory or pecan, causing green, hollow, bullet-like galls on twigs or leaf stems in June
    Phylloxera spp.
    On other hardwoods 11
11. On elm 12
    On other hosts 15

12. Producing spindle-shaped galls up to 1 inch long. On slippery elm leaves. Insect 1 to 1½ mm. long, reddish
Gobaishia ulmifusa
Galls not spindle-shaped. On various elms 13
13. Causing leaf curl or root swellings ....*Eriosoma*
Causing cockscomb or pouchlike galls on upper surface of leaves 14
14. Pale yellow, translucent, or head greenish-black and abdomen and thorax dark green, covered with white waxy powder. On leaves of slippery and wych elm, producing cockscomb or pouchlike galls on upper surface ....*Colopha ulmisacculi*
Olive green to dark olive brown or reddish-brown; ½ to 1½ mm. long. On leaves, causing only cockscomb galls on upper surface ....*Colopha ulmicola*
15. On apple or serviceberry, causing leaf curl and leaf swellings. About 2 mm. long; yellowish or brown to reddish, usually with white or bluish flocculence
Eriosoma
On other hosts 16
16. On poplar 17
On witchhazel 18
17. Causing convolute galls at tips of branches. Insects 1 to 4 mm. long; head and thorax black, abdomen pale; oviparous female with head, thorax, and abdomen golden yellow ....*Mordwilkoja*
Occurring on leaves and petioles, causing galls at base of leaf, juncture of leaf and petiole, or on petiole. Insects 1 to 3 mm. long; greenish or yellowish-green to greenish-white, head and thorax usually dark; body often pruinose ....*Pemphigus*
18. Causing conical galls on upper surface of leaves. Insects 1 to 2 mm. long, pale yellowish to greenish
Hormaphis
Causing spiny galls from buds on stems. Insects 1 to 2 mm. long, pale yellowish to greenish
Hamamelistes
19. On conifers 20
On hardwoods 29
20. On pine 21
On other conifers 24
21. Small, dark insects covered with white flocculence. Occurring on trunks and branches of Austrian, Scotch, and white pine ....*Pineus strobi*
Insects not covered with white flocculence, at most pruinose. Occurring on twigs, branches or leaves 22
22. Shining black with white powdery spots on sides and white median dorsal line; legs black; body hairy, hairs long and stiff. On branches and twigs of white pine
Cinara strobi
Not as above 23
23. Olive brown, body hairs sparse and spinelike. On leaves of Scotch, ponderosa, shortleaf, and white pine
Eulachnus rileyi

Pale green with white pruinosity. On leaves and twigs
Mindarus abietinus

24. On larch 25
    On other conifers 26
25. Appearing as white woolly masses on the needles, as
    dark individuals on the underside of twigs, or as
    clusters of dark individuals at the base of the leaves
    Adelges strobilobius
26. Nymphs dark green. On Douglas-fir, often causing ab-
    normal foliage drop ....*Adelges cooleyi*
    Not as above 27
27. Cinnamon brown with 4 rows of black spots on abdo-
    men; length about 3 mm.; many specimens covered
    with fluffy white wax above; body hairs long and fine.
    On black spruce branches and twigs
    Cinara abietis
    Not as above 28
28. Brownish-black with a slight pruinosity, legs brown to
    black, antennae pale; length about 5 mm. On branches,
    twigs, stems, and roots of fir and Atlas cedar
    Cinara curvipes
    Pale green with pruinosity, or with white flocculent
    covering when on balsam fir; length about 2 mm. On
    fir and spruce twigs and leaves, causing curling and
    roughening of twigs ....*Mindarus abietinus*
29. Large species, about 6 mm. long; ash gray with triangu-
    lar spots on pronotum; body covered with bluish-white
    bloom:
        On various hosts; common on hickory and sycamore
        Longistigma
    Smaller species, usually 5 mm. or less in length:
        Alder: Causing mottling or dropping of leaves.
        Insects 1½ to 2 mm. long; green or greenish-
        yellow, abdomen uniformly colored or dusky-
        spotted ....*Myzocallis*
        On underside of leaves or on stems. Insects 2 to 4
        mm. long; brownish, covered with white flocculence
        Prociphilus
        Beech: On underside of leaves. Insects 2 to 3 mm.
        long; bluish-white to greenish-yellow, covered with
        white flocculence ....*Phyllaphis*
        On underside of branches or on trunk. Insects 2 to
        4 mm. long; brownish, covered with white floccu-
        lence ....:...............................*Prociphilus*
        Birch: On twigs and leaves; 3 to 4 mm. long; whitish
        to yellow, with or without black stripes on head
        and thorax and dark bands on dorsum of abdomen
        Calaphis
        On twigs and leaves; 2 to 3 mm. long; light green,
        with or without dark patch on abdomen; hind
        tibiae pale with distal part and tarsi black or with
        dark brown stripe ....*Euceraphis*
        Boxelder: On leaves and twigs; 2 to 2½ mm. long;
        yellowish-green marked with brown on thorax and

abdomen or with head, antennae, thoracic lobes, sternal plates, and cornicles black or yellowish to apple green; antennae rather hairy

Periphyllus

Butternut: On leaves; 1½ to 2 mm. long; pale yellow, costal vein yellow or brown, or a brown band extending beyond stigma; antennae ringed with brown ....*Monellia*

Elm: Causing mottling or dropping of leaves; 1½ to 2 mm. long; green or greenish-yellow, abdomen uniformly colored or spotted dusky

Myzocallis

Hickory:

Large species, about 6 mm. long; mostly on branches and twigs; ash gray with triangular spots on pronotum covered with bluish-white pruinosity ....*Longistigma*

Smaller species, 1½ to 2 mm. long; occurring on leaves:

Causing mottling or dropping of leaves; green or greenish-yellow, abdomen uniformly colored or spotted dusky

Myzocallis

Pale yellow, costal vein yellow or brown or a brown band extending beyond stigma; antennae ringed with brown ....*Monellia*

Linden: On underside of leaves; 2 to 3 mm. long; yellow; antennae uniformly yellow or ringed with brown ....*Myzocallis*

Maple:

Brownish, often covered with white flocculence:

Without white flocculence; egg-laying females with 7th and 8th abdominal segments prolonged into ovipositor

Drepanaphis

Usually with white flocculence; 4th antennal segment about one-half or less as long as third segment; length 2 to 4 mm.; always with white flocculence on underside of leaves or on trunks ....*Prociphilus*

Either yellowish, reddish, or shading to green:

On soft maple leaves and twigs; 3 to 4 mm. long; dusky reddish to dark yellowish-green ....*Pterocomma*

On Norway and sugar maple, on underside of leaves; 2 to 2½ mm. long; yellowish-green marked with brown on thorax and abdomen, or with head, antennae, thoracic lobes, sternal plates, and cornicles black or yellowish to apple green; antennae rather hairy ....*Periphyllus*

On Norway, sycamore, or English maple, on underside of leaves; 2½ to 3 mm. long; yellow or reddish to green, with

black markings or bands; legs and cornicles yellow to dark orange
Drepanosiphum

On underside of leaves; 2½ mm. long; olive green or pale sordid green
Drepanaphis

Oak:

Causing mottling or dropping of leaves; 1½ to 2 mm. long; green or greenish-yellow, abdomen uniformly colored or spotted dusky
Myzocallis

On leaves; 1½ to 2 mm. long; pale yellow; costal vein yellow or brown or brown band extending beyond stigma, antennae ringed with brown ....*Monellia*

On underside of leaves; 2 to 3 mm. long; yellow, antennae uniformly yellow or ringed with brown ....*Myzocallis*

Poplar:

On sprouts or tender growth; 2 to 2½ mm. long; yellowish or greenish, with brown mottling; head brown ....*Chaitophorus*

On leaves and twigs; 3 to 4 mm. long; dusky reddish to dark yellowish-green
Pterocomma

On leaves and twigs; about 5 mm. long; ash gray due to white pruinosity over base color of brown, abdomen marked with black spots; large black tubercle on 4th abdominal segment
Lachnus

Sycamore:

Length about 6 mm.; body covered with bluish-white pruinosity ....*Longistigma*

Length 2 to 4 mm.; covered with white flocculence ....*Prociphilus*

Walnut: On leaves; 1½ to 2 mm. long; pale yellow or brown, or brown band extending beyond stigma; antennae ringed with brown
Monellia

Willow:

Length 3 to 4 mm.; dusky reddish to dark yellowish-green ....*Pterocomma*

Length about 5 mm.; ash gray due to pruinosity over base color of brown, abdomen marked with dark spots ....*Lachnus*

The **giant bark aphid,** *Longistigma caryae* (Harris), the largest of all North American aphids, occurs throughout much of Eastern United States and feeds on a wide variety of deciduous trees such as elm, pecan, sycamore, oak, maple, basswood, birch, beech, walnut, and willow. Adults are about 6 mm. long, and are covered with a bluish-white bloom. Males are winged; egg-laying females wingless. Eggs are laid on twigs, a single female laying many. The aphids usually occur in clusters on the undersides of twigs and small limbs. Depending on locality, there may be several generations per year. Heavily infested twigs may be seriously injured or killed.

The genus *Cinara* contains a number of conifer-infesting species, only a few of which are mentioned here.

The **white-pine aphid,** *Cinara strobi* (Fitch), occurs from New England to the Lake States and Carolinas and feeds on white pine. Winged forms are almost 6 mm. long. The body is shiny dark brown, with a white stripe down the middle of the dorsum and white powdery spots on the sides, and it bears long stiff hairs. During the fall, winged females lay up to 5 or 6 eggs each, in straight lines on white pine needles. Hatching occurs in the spring and wingless females produce living young which live in colonies up to 3 or 4 inches long clustered around a branch or the leader. Several generations later, winged females are produced which migrate and also produce living young. Toward fall, winged males and females mate, and a new crop of overwintering eggs are laid. Young trees or individual branches of large trees may be killed by heavy infestations or their growth may be seriously reduced.

Cinara sabinae (Gill. & Palm.), a small, reddish-brown species about 3 mm. long and covered with a white powdery secretion, feeds on red cedar in Eastern United States. Colonies are usually found on twigs and small branches. Heavily infested trees often become unsightly as a result of black mold developing in honeydew on the foliage. The related species, *C. canadensis* Hottes & Bradley and *C. juniperivora* (Wilson), also feed on red cedar.

Cinara pini (Linn.) is a large reddish-brown species with numerous dark specks and a pair of large spots behind the cornicles. It has been recorded feeding on young Scotch, shortleaf, and Virginia pines and seriously injuring them. Additional pine-infesting species of *Cinara* include: *C. carolina* Tissot—loblolly, shortleaf, slash, longleaf, pond, and Virginia pines in the South; *C. taedae* Tissot—loblolly and Virginia pines; *C. watsoni* Tissot—loblolly, shortleaf, slash, spruce, and pond pines in Florida and red, pitch, Scotch, and Virginia pines in Pennsylvania; and *C. atlantica* (Wilson)—various pines in the Southeast.

Other pine-infesting aphids include the following: *Eulachnus rileyi* Williams—Scotch, red, pitch, Virginia, shortleaf, and white pines; *E. agilis* (Kaltenbach)—red and Scotch pines; *Essigella pini* Wilson—loblolly, slash, and pond pines in Florida (has also been recorded from Maryland and Pennsylvania); *Schizolachnus piniradiatae* (Davidson)—jack and red pines in the Eastern States; *S. lanosus* Hottes—loblolly pine in Maryland; and *Prociphilus bumeliae* (Schrank)—roots of white pines.

Several other aphids have also been recorded from other conifers. For example, *Cinara abietis* (Fitch)—various firs; *C. tujafilina* (Del G.)—arborvitae, cypress, and other species (heavy infestations have been reported in nurseries in Florida and Delaware); and the **balsam twig aphid,** *Mindarus abietinus* Koch—wide variety of hosts including balsam fir, Siberian fir, Alpine fir, white spruce, juniper, and Fraser fir (damaged needles curl, and the bark of heavily infested twigs becomes roughened).

The **boxelder aphid,** *Periphyllus negundinis* (Thomas), feeds on the leaves and twigs of boxelder wherever it grows in the United

States and Canada. Its body is usually yellowish-green with brownish marks on the thorax and abdomen. Walks, benches, or cars parked beneath infested trees are often badly soiled. The related species, the **Norway-maple aphid**, *P. lyropictus* (Kessler), often completely defoliates Norway and sugar maple trees. Honeydew dripping from infested leaves is a nuisance. *P. americanus* (Baker), *Drepanaphis acerifoliae* (Thomas), *D. carolinensis* Smith, *D. nigricans* Smith, *D. sabrinae* Miller, and *Drepanosiphum platanoides* (Schrank) are also found on maples.

Numerous species of *Myzocallis* such as *M. bella* (Walsh), *M. alhambra* Davidson, *M. discolor* (Fitch), and *M. melanocera* Boudreaux and Tissot feed on various oaks. Other common members of the genus and their hosts include *M. alnifoliae* (Fitch) — alder; *M. tiliae* (L.)—native and introduced lindens; the **crapemyrtle aphid**, *M. kahawaluokalani* Kirkaldy—crapemyrtle; the **black pecan aphid**, *M. caryaefoliae* (Davis)—hickory and pecan; and the **elm leaf aphid**, *M. ulmifolii* (Mon.)—elm.

Many other species of free-living aphids also occur commonly on various deciduous trees. These include *Monellia caryella* (Fitch), *M. costalis* (Fitch), *M. microsetosa* Richards and *Monelliopsis nigropunctata* (Granovsky)—hickories; *Chaitophorus stevensis* Sanborn, *C. populicola* (Thomas) and *Pterocomma populifoliae* (Fitch)—poplars; *P. smithae* (Monell)—poplars and willows; *P. salicis* (L.)—willow; *Macrosiphum liriodendri* (Monell)—yellow-poplar; *Aphis craccivora* Koch—black locust seedlings; *Calaphis betulaecolens* (Fitch)—birch (often in large numbers); *C. betulella* (Walsh)—birch and beech; *Euceraphis betulae* (Koch)—various birches, especially yellow birch; *E. lineata* Baker—gray birch; and *E. mucidas* (Fitch)—river birch.

Three species of woolly aphids are commonly found on elms in Eastern United States. The **woolly apple aphid**, *Eriosoma lanigerum* (Hausm.), feeds on new terminal leaves, causing them to curl or appear in the form of rosettes (It also attacks apple, pear, hawthorn, and mountain-ash. Damage to elm is not especially severe.). The presence of large numbers of distorted leaves on shade trees is unsightly. The **woolly elm aphid**, *E. americanum* (Riley) has elm as a primary host and shadbush as an alternate host. It feeds at the edges of young elm leaves in the spring, causing them to swell, curl, and roll inward from the edge. Two generations are produced on elm. Then, members of the second generation fly to shadbush and attack its roots. The summer is spent here. During the fall, a winged generation develops which flies back to elm where it lays a crop of overwintering eggs. *E. rileyi* Thomas, the **woolly elm bark aphid**, attacks American and slippery elm. It occurs in dense woolly clusters on the limbs and trunks, causing knotty growths to form at the sites of injury. Heavily infested trees may be seriously injured. Hawthorn is infested by the closely related species, *E. crataegi* (Oest.). It occurs in dense colonies on twigs and branches and is occasionally injurious to ornamentals.

Several other woolly aphids are also found on various species of hardwoods. The **beech blight aphid**, *Prociphilus imbricator* (Fitch) feeds on the trunk and undersides of leaves and branches of beech from New England to Georgia and Illinois. Its body is covered with a white, cottony substance that strings out in fairly long threads and forms a tuft at the rear end. Heavy infestations occasionally develop on forest-grown trees. The **woolly alder aphid,** *P. tessellatus* (Fitch) is often abundant on alder and silver maple. *P. fraxinifolii* Riley feeds on ash and *P. corrugatans* (Sirrine) on shadbush.

Certain species of aphids produce galls by their feeding. The **elm coxcomb-gall aphid,** *Colopha ulmicola* (Fitch), is probably the most important tree-infesting species. It occurs throughout, most of the United States and Canada, wherever its hosts, American, rock, and slippery elms, grow. It feeds on leaves, causing the formation of galls up to 25 mm. long and 6 mm. in height. The gall is irregular in shape and resembles a rooster's comb. The winter is spent in the egg stage on elm, and there are six generations per year. Damage is not severe, but when large numbers of galls occur on the leaves of young trees and ornamentals the trees may become unattractive. The related species, *C. ulmisacculi* (Patch) produces pedunculated, bladder-like galls up to 25 mm. long on the upper surfaces of elm in New England.

The **poplar vagabond aphid,** *Mordwilkoja vagabunda* (Walsh) feeds at the tips of twigs of cottonwoods and occurs from New England to Utah, causing the formation of convoluted galls (fig. 18) up to 5 inches in diameter. These galls may occur singly or in clusters of three to five galls each. The winter is usually spent in the egg stage in old galls or in nearby bark crevices (*390*). Other gall producing aphids and their hosts include *Hormaphis hamamelidis* (Fitch)—conical galls on the upper surfaces of witch-hazel leaves; *Hamamelistes spinosus* (Shiner)—causes galls to form on the stem buds of witch-hazel; and *Gobaishia ulmifusa* (Walsh and Riley)—spindle-shaped, saclike galls on the leaves of slippery elm.

F–506747
FIGURE 18.—Galls of the poplar vagabond aphid, *Mordwilkoja vagabunda*, on poplar.

FAMILY PHYLLOXERIDAE

Members of this family resemble those of the family Aphididae but differ in that eggs are laid by both sexually perfect and imperfect females. The majority of important eastern species feeds on the needles, twigs, limbs, and trunks or in galls on coniferous trees.

The **eastern spruce gall aphid,** *Adelges abietis* (L.), an introduced species, occurs in southeastern Canada and the Northeastern and Lake States. Its preferred hosts appear to be Norway and white spruce, but it is also found occasionally on red and Colorado blue spruce. The winter is spent as small nymphs under coverings of waxy threads at the bases of buds on the undersides of twigs (*765*). The nymphs molt in the spring and become stem mothers which lay eggs on the needles. Hatching occurs in about 2 weeks and the young nymphs crawl to the bases of expanding buds. Here they feed, causing the formation of pineapple-shaped galls (*597*) in which they live and continue their development (fig. 19). During late August to October the galls open and the full-grown nymphs or "pupae" emerge. These transform to winged adults in a couple of days and, although they can fly, many remain on the tree. The females insert their mouth parts through the bark, deposit upwards to 60 eggs each and then die. These eggs hatch within 16 days and the young nymphs immediately crawl to overwintering sites. There is one generation per year.

FIGURE 19.—Galls of the eastern spruce gall aphid, *Adelges abietis*, on spruce.

The eastern spruce gall aphid is a serious pest in nurseries and Christmas tree plantations and on park and other ornamental trees. Its damage is limited primarily to a reduction in the esthetic value of the trees.

The **Cooley spruce gall aphid**, *Adelges cooleyi* (Gill.), occurs from coast to coast in northern United States and throughout the range of white spruce in Canada. Its primary hosts are recorded as white, Colorado blue, Sitka, Engelmann, and big-cone spruce. It also has an alternate host, Douglas-fir.

The Cooley spruce gall aphid winters as immature stem-mothers under bark scales near the terminals of twigs of spruce. The female becomes mature in early spring and deposits a large number of eggs under a mass of white, cottony wax. The eggs hatch in about a week and the nymphs settle down to feed at the bases of young needles. Galls (fig. 20) begin to form immediately and develop rapidly, enclosing the nymphs. Young galls are green or purple in color; older ones are reddish-brown. They vary greatly in size, from about 25 to 75 mm. in length and 12 to 18 mm. in diameter. When the nymphs become mature, the galls open, allowing the nymphs to escape and crawl to the needles. Here they

F 519584
FIGURE 20.—Galls of Cooley spruce gall aphid, *Adelges cooleyi*, on blue spruce.

transform to winged adults and fly to Douglas-fir, if present. Eventually, a winged generation is produced on this host, and it returns to spruce (*179*). Where spruce and Douglas-fir do not occur close enough together for the aphid to move back and forth from one to the other, generations may be produced continuously on either species.

The Cooley spruce gall aphid is not usually considered an important pest in the forest. However, it may be troublesome where spruce and Douglas-fir are growing close together. Ornamental spruce and young spruce trees in Christmas tree plantations are often seriously damaged by excessive numbers of unsightly galls.

The **balsam woolly aphid**, *Adelges piceae* (Ratz.), an introduced species first recorded in North America from Brunswick, Maine, in 1908, now occurs throughout the Maritime Provinces, Canada, and the Northeastern States (except the northern parts of Maine and New Brunswick Province). Infestations also occur over much of Newfoundland, in the Gaspé Peninsula, in the southern Appalachians, and in the Pacific Northwest. Its hosts are balsam and Fraser firs in eastern America. Full-grown aphids are roughly spherical in shape, less than a millimeter long, and almost invisible to the naked eye. Because of a covering of white wax threads, however, they appear as dots of white "wool" (fig. 21).

Eggs are deposited in late spring and early summer, each egg being attached to the bark behind the female's body by a silken thread. Newly hatched larvae crawl rapidly over the bark until they find suitable feeding places. When these are found, they insert their feeding stylets, become stationary, and turn black except for fringes of white wax plates around the edges of the body and down the dorsum. After a short period of rest they develop into the second generation. Adults of this generation deposit eggs during midsummer. Hatching soon occurs and all stages are found until late fall. The winter is spent as a first-instar larva. In the spring these larvae resume activity and reach maturity by the time the buds begin to swell. New adults appear by mid-April in the southern Appalachians and in early May in the Northeast. There are two generations per year in the Northeast; in the

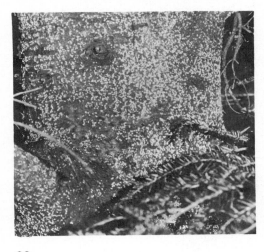

F 519571
FIGURE 21.—Infestation of the balsam woolly aphid, *Adelges piceae*, on trunk of Fraser fir.

southern Appalachians two and occasionally three generations are produced (*24, 5*).

The balsam woolly aphid feeds at any point on the tree where it can reach the parenchyma of the cortex with its mouth parts. During feeding, it introduces an irritating salivary substance into the tissues which causes an abnormal multiplication of cells and excessive growth in the vicinity of the point of attack. Infested twigs and small branches become swollen and distorted. Swellings are particularly noticeable at nodes and around buds. Branchlets may thicken, twist irregularly, and bend down at the ends. The main stem tapers rapidly toward the top. The tip becomes bent or flattened and is usually killed. This results in a condition commonly known as "gout." The wood of infested trees becomes hard and brittle and its surface is usually marked with dark, reddish-brown blotches. This type of wood, which resembles "compression" wood, is produced in greatest amount on moderately infested fast-growing trees. Trees suffering from heavy stem attack may be killed in 3 or 4 years (fig. 22).

The balsam wooly aphid is subject to a considerable amount of control by low winter temperatures, especially in the northern portions of its range. Tree resistance is also an important control factor, some trees being less favorable for multiplication of the insect than others. So far, no insect parasites of the aphid have been found in North America. Quite a large number of predators have been recorded, however, but they have proved incapable of preventing outbreaks. A few species of introduced predators, such as the derodontid beetle, *Laricobius erichsonii*, offer promise of greater benefits in control in the future (*7, 27*).

Outlying infestations of the balsam wooly aphid may be controlled by clear cutting infested stands, especially if this is followed by burning. The spread of infestations may also be checked by the prompt salvage of infested stands during the winter. Short rotation and cutting cycles, combined with silvicultural methods of reducing the balsam fir content of stands, have helped in reducing infestations in New Brunswick (*28*).

Adelges strobilobius (Kalt.), an introduced species, occurs in southern Canada and south and west in the Eastern States to Washington, D. C. and the Lake States. Its hosts are recorded as larch and spruce, principally red and black. Infestations on larch appear as white wooly masses on the needles and as clusters of aphids at the bases of needles. Infestations on spruce may be recognized by the presence of small galls at the tips of new growth. A related species, *A. lariciatus* (Patch), occurs on larch and Norway spruce. It produces galls similar to those produced by the **eastern spruce gall aphid**. Cumming (*180*) discussed its life history.

The **pine bark aphid** *Pineus strobi* (Htg.), an introduced species, occurs over most of the United States wherever white, Scotch, and Austrian pines grow. It is small, dark, and covered with flocculent wax. Infestations may be recognized by the presence of spots and patches of white cottony material on the smooth bark of the trunks and limbs (fig. 23) or at the bases of needles on twigs, or on buds. The trunks of heavily infested trees often appear as if whitewashed.

F-519567

FIGURE 22.—Fraser fir killed by the balsam wooly aphid, *Adelges piceae*.

COURTESY CONN. AGR. EXPT. STA.

FIGURE 23.—Infestation of the pine bark aphid, *Pineus strobi*, on the trunk of pine.

Eggs are laid in the spring by overwintering females and the eggs hatch into both winged and wingless females. The wingless forms remain on the pine host and reproduce repeatedly. Some of the winged ones may fly to spruce where they settle on the needles, lay eggs, and die. Nymphs hatching from these eggs also soon die. Five generations per year have been recorded as far north as the Lake States (619).

Trees in parks and recreational areas, ornamentals and small nursery stock may be seriously damaged by the pine bark aphid. The needles turn yellow, and small trees may be stunted or killed. Large forest trees are usually not seriously injured.

The **pine leaf chermid**, *Pineus pinifoliae* (Fitch), occurs in both Eastern and Western United States. Its range in the East coincides with that of its primary hosts, red and black spruce, where they grow close to its alternate host, white pine. The adult is scalelike, about 1.5 mm. in diameter, and bears a fringe of white hairs.

The life cycle takes two years to complete. During part of this time, including the first winter, infestations are found entirely on spruce; during the remaining time, including the second winter, they are found on pine.[8]

Infestations on spruce result in the production of terminal compact galls which have the appearance of true cones and contain a single aphid in each chamber. These galls are of minor importance except on ornamentals where they may be undesirable. Heavily infested white pines, especially young pines in plantations, may be severely injured. Needles turn yellow; growth is reduced; deformities are produced; and occasionally the trees are killed. Several outbreaks have been recorded since 1900, some of which spread over large areas before subsiding.

Pineus floccus (Patch) feeds on spruce and pine, spending 1 year of its 2 year life cycle on each. It produces loose, terminal galls on spruce. On pine, its effects are similar to those caused by the **pine leaf chermid**. Heavy infestations on spruce may kill the tips of branches, or they may cause an over production of laterals which lead to bushy, deformed trees. Damage to pine is usually not serious.

Pineus similis Gillette produces terminal cone-shaped galls on Norway, white, red, black, Colorado blue, and Engelmann spruces. The galls are shorter and thicker than those produced by the **Cooley spruce gall aphid** and the chambers are intercommunicating. Small white spruce growing in the open in Canada has been severely infested. *P. coloradensis* (Gillette) has been observed feeding on the needles of red and pitch pines in Connecticut.

The genus *Phylloxera* contains several species which produce galls on hickories and pecan. These aphids do not produce waxy threads as do many other members of the family, but some of them may be covered with a waxy powder. Their galls vary from small disklike or buttonlike swellings, with central openings guarded by plantlike hairs or processes, to large, hollow, globelike structures up to 18 mm. in diameter.

---

[8] Lowe, J. H. 1965. Biology and dispersal of *Pineus pinifoliae* (F.). (Unpub. PhD. thesis, Yale Univ., 104 p. illus.)

Phylloxera caryaecaulis (Fitch), the **hickory gall aphid**, is a common species that produces almost spherical galls, 16 to 18 mm. in diameter, on the twigs and leaf stems of hickory. The galls are green when first formed; later, after the aphids vacate them, they turn brown or black. The **pecan phylloxera**, *P. devastatrix* Pergande, and the **pecan leaf phylloxera**, *P. notabilis* Pergande, produce galls on pecan. *P. rileyi* Riley is found on white and post oaks, and *P. nyssae* Pergande infests blackgum.

FAMILY ALEYRODIDAE

WHITEFLIES

Members of this family are very small mothlike insects, usually less than 2 or 3 mm. in length. The adults all have four wings each. The wings, covered with a white powdery wax, are whitish in appearance. The larvae are very small and scalelike and are usually found, surrounded or covered with a waxy secretion, on the undersides of the leaves of the host plant. Whiteflies are most abundant in tropical and subtropical regions, but a few species have been recorded as far north as New England.

The **mulberry whitefly**, *Tetraleurodes mori* (Quaint.) feeds on mulberry, dogwood, azalea, hackberry, holly, mountain-laurel basswood, maple, and sycamore. The larvae are less than 1 mm. long, jet black, and ringed around with a white fringe. Adults are active from June to September. The **rhododendron whitefly**, *Dialeurodes chittendeni* Laing, an introduced species, feeds on rhododendron. The adult is pale yellow; the larvae and pupae greenish-yellow. Infested leaves have a yellow, mottled appearance, and their margins curl. The **azalea whitefly**, *Pealius azaleae* (Baker & Moles), feeds on azalea as far north as Rhode Island and Ohio, and sometimes causes severe defoliation. *Aleurochiton forbesii* (Ashm.), feeds on maple, and the **citrus whitefly**, *Dialeurodes citri* (Ashm.), feeds on chinaberry and on crapemyrtle in Florida.

SUPERFAMILY COCCOIDEA

(SCALE INSECTS)

Scale insects are among the most destructive agents of shade trees and ornamentals. At times they may also cause serious damage to forest growth. Injury results either from the withdrawal of sap or the production of galls while feeding.

Male scale insects are usually winged but the females are entirely wingless. Adult females also either have no appendages, or they are atrophied. As a result, the body is either scalelike or gall-like. It is also covered with wax, either in the form of powder, tufts, or plates or as a thin layer covering the insect. Females usually appear formless because of the difficulty of separating their bodies into head, thorax, and abdomen.

Some scale insects are highly specific in their selection of hosts; others feed on a wide variety of hosts. Because of their habit of feeding on many different parts of plants, many species have been widely distributed by shipping nursery stock or cuttings (*500, 719*).

Field Key to the Genera of Scale Insects Based Principally on Host Plants

1. Restricted feeders on specific host plants 2
   General feeders found on a variety of plant hosts 4
2. On conifers 3
   On hardwoods (see appropriate host).
       Beech branches and trunks; mature female oblong, 1 mm. or less, yellow, body covered with white, wooly wax .... *Cryptococcus*
       Celestrus or euonymus leaves and stems, female oblong, broadened posteriorly, dirty gray to nearly black, small white male scales usually abundant and conspicuous in clusters on leaves
                                               Unaspis euonymi
       Elm bark, branches and stems; mature female oval, about 2 mm., red-brown body with white waxy fringe about margin .... *Gossyparia*
       Horse chestnut twigs and branches, mature female oblong, 1 to 2 mm., dark gray to black with lighter border .... *Aspitiotus,* in part
       Magnolia twigs and branches, mature female round or slightly oblong, about 1 cm. in diameter, rich dark brown, very convex .... *Neolecanium*
       Maple:
           On leaves. Mature female 4 mm. or more:
               Dark purplish, large white egg sac with 2 longitudinal grooves and several transverse ridges .... *Pulvinaria*
           Yellow, body covered with large white cottony mass of wax thread. On sugar maple
                                     Phenacoccus
           On stems and branches (Southern States).
               Mature female round to oval, about 2 mm. gray, dark nipple concentrically placed
                                 Chrysomphalus
       Oak:
           Mature female gall or berrylike in shape, 3 to 4 mm. in diameter, brown with mottling. On twigs and sometimes on leaves .... *Kermes*
           Mature females nearly round, 1 to 1½ mm. in diameter, reddish-brown, body covered with translucent greenish wax "test," causes small craterlike or pitlike galls on twigs, branches, and stems. Various species of white oak group
                                 Asterolecanium
       Pecan branches, stems and fruit in Southern States, not producing red coloration under infested bark; mature female round to oval, about 2 mm., gray, nipple concentrically placed .... *Chrysomphalus*
       Yellow tulip twigs and branches, sometimes on magnolia and poplar; mature female hemispherical, 5

to 8 mm. in diameter, dark brown
Toumeyella, in part

3. On pines:
   Hard pines at base of needles on new growth during summer; mature female oval, woolly, wax covering 1 cm. or more, white woolly covering
   Pseudophilippia
   Scotch, jack, lodgepole, and other hard pines on twigs and branches; mature females oval, 5 to 7 mm., reddish-brown, dorsal surface very convex and pitted or irregular .... *Toumeyella*, in part
   Hard pines on new shoots and under bark scales, mature female long oval, 2 to 4 mm., dark brown to black, produces long, flat white egg sac under bark scales of branches and trunk; immature instars causes small pit galls in epidermis of new growth, new growth dying in July, August, and September
   Matsucoccus
   Pine leaves, various species; mature female pear-shaped, 1½ to 3 mm., dirty white to dirty gray
   Phenacaspis
   Pine, various species, and Douglas-fir leaves; mature female oval, 1 to 2 mm., dark gray, concentric nipple orange .... *Aspidiotus*, in part
   On other conifers:
   Arborvitae twigs; mature female round to oval, 3 to 4 mm., reddish or reddish-brown, sometimes mottled; dorsal surface very convex
   Lecanium, in part
   Hemlock leaves and twigs; mature female oblong, 1 to 2 mm., dark gray to black with lighter border .... *Aspidiotus*, in part
   Juniper leaves and twigs; mature female nearly circular, about 2 mm. in diameter, light gray to white, central or concentric nipple yellow
   Diaspis
   Spruce, various species at base of buds on new growth; mature female round, 3 to 4 mm. in diameter, light brown, dorsal surface very convex .... *Physokermes*

4. Body of adult female covered by a "scale" made up of secreted matter, plus the cast skins of the two larval stages 5
   Body of adult female otherwise: naked, covered with waxy or woolly secretion, enclosed in a secreted shell, never covered by a scale as described above 7

5. Scale of adult female elongated, narrowed anteriorly with the larval cast-skins terminal, broadened posteriorly 6
   Scale of adult female circular to oval with exuviae central or subcentral .... *Aspidiotus*, in part

6. Scale of adult female white or dirty white
   Chionaspsis, in part
   Scale of adult female dark, usually dark brown
   Lepidosaphes

94

7. Body small, not exceeding 2 to 3 mm. in diameter, enclosed in a thin transparent shell with a fringe of secretion around margin ....*Asterolecanium,* in part
   Body not enclosed in a shell, mostly considerably larger, 4 mm. or more 8
8. Adult female at maturity with body remaining soft, fringed at hind end with a large ovisac showing conspicuous flutings ....*Icerya*
   Body at maturity becoming hard and eventually brittle; ovisac, if present, loosely formed, not fluted 9
9. With a short, stout posterior ovisac .... *Pulvinaria*
   Body naked at maturity, eggs deposited beneath it
   Lecanium

FAMILY MARGARODIDAE

MARGARODID SCALES

Margarodid scales occur throughout most of the earth and vary greatly in their habits. Some species feed in exposed positions on their hosts; others beneath the bark or in gall-like pits on the leaves, branches, trunks, or roots. Some species have only one or a few hosts; others have many. Eggs may be deposited in an internal pouch or marsupium; in a posterior ovisac; within a gall-like pit or heavy-walled tent in which the female develops; or in loose cottony materials beneath the female's body. Morrison (*544*) published a classification of the family.

The **red-pine scale,** *Matsucoccus resinosae* Bean and Godwin, probably an introduced species, was first recorded in North America at Easton, Connecticut, in 1946. Since then it has spread slowly and now also occurs on Long Island, in southeastern New York, and in northern New Jersey. Red pine is its only known native host. Other recorded hosts are three species of imported ornamental pines: Chinese, Japanese red, and Japanese black (*322*).

Eggs of the summer generation are laid in May in bark crevices or under bark scales and hatch by the first of June. First-stage larvae move around for a brief period and then settle down under bark scales until they become full-grown (fig. 24). Adults emerge in early August and lay eggs in late August or early September. Hatching occurs soon thereafter. The winter is apparently spent as first-instar larvae. Growth is resumed in the spring, and adults emerge by May (46).

The red-pine scale is one of the most destructive insect pests of red pine in the Northeast. Thousands of trees ranging in size from nursery stock to mature trees have been killed, and many more have been severely injured (44). The foliage of infested trees turns olive green, then yellow, and, finally, brick red when the trees die. The bark on the branches and trunks of heavily infested trees appears swollen and cracked and there is a patch of dead tissue beneath each feeding scale.

Several species of predators attack the scale but none have been effective in control. Low winter temperatures of −10° F. are almost entirely fatal to the species. This may prevent its spread

COURTESY CONN. AGR. EXPT. STA.
FIGURE 24.—Masses of male cocoons of the red-pine scale, *Matsucoccus resinosa*, on lower side of branch axil.

much farther northward than its present range. The cutting and removal of infested trees is effective in reducing the rate of local spread.

Matsucoccus gallicola Morrison, the **pine twig gall scale**, is also an important tree-infesting species. Its hosts include pitch, short-leaf, table mountain, Virginia, ponderosa, loblolly, and spruce pines. It has been recorded from New England to Florida, and west to Ohio and Missouri. Trees of all sizes, from three-year-old seedlings to mature specimens, are attacked.

Mature females are generally much flattened and about 2 to 5 mm. long. They deposit their eggs under bark scales on the larger branches and trunks. Heavy infestations may be quite injurious, especially to young trees. Damage appears to have been most severe to pitch pine in the Northeast (*579*).

Matsucoccus alabamae Morrison has been observed feeding in cracks and crevices of heavy bark on pines in Alabama; and *M. matsumurae* (Kuw.) infests Virginia and pitch pines on Long Island.

Xylococculus betulae (Perg.) occurs in eastern Canada and from New England to Virginia. Its hosts are paper and yellow birches and beech. Adults are orange-red, about 4 mm. long, and covered with white wax. Females live and deposit eggs in cells in the bark. Young larvae crawl from these cells into lenticels and roughened spots on the bark to feed. Here, they lose their legs and produce a mass of wax around themselves, forming pearllike cells (*645*). Honeydew is excreted through hairlike tubes up to 2 inches long. Large necrotic areas develop in infested areas on birch. Damage to beech consists of roughened or swollen spots of bark up to 2 inches in diameter. These spots dry out as they age, and additional cracks form around them. Damaged spots may be found over the entire trunk, but they usually occur in narrow longitudinal strips, starting at old branch stubs.

FAMILY KERMOCOCCIDAE

Kermes pubescens Bogue is often a serious pest of oaks in the eastern half of the United States, especially in the Midwest (*476*). Adult females are light brown, almost spherical, and about 2.5 mm. in diameter. Eggs are laid on new growth from late June to late July. Newly-hatched larvae migrate to the trunk and larger limbs where they hide, in cracks or beneath loose bark. They remain here without much growth until the following spring, at which time they crawl to the new growth and resume feeding. Heavy infestations on petioles and midveins may cause the distortion or death of leaves and twigs. On heavily infested trees, the flagging of terminals may be so severe by late July that the beauty of shade and ornamental trees is greatly reduced. *K. galliformis* Riley, *K. kingii* Ckll., *K. pettiti* Ehrh., and *K. trinotatus* Bogue are also fairly common on oaks in the Eastern States but they are seldom injurious (fig. 25).

FAMILY ERIOCOCCIDAE

The **beech scale,** *Cryptococcus fagi* (Baer.), an introduced species, was first recorded in North America in Nova Scotia around 1890 and in the United States at Boston, Massachusetts, in 1929. It now occurs throughout the beech-growing areas of New England, eastern New York, Pennsylvania and New Jersey, and the Maritime Provinces of Canada. Its hosts are American and European beech and their varieties. Female scales (no males have been found) are circular-shaped, 0.5 to 1 mm. long, and covered with a woollike wax.

Young larvae overwinter and their development is completed in the spring. Egg laying begins in early June or later, depending on location, and continues into July. Hatching begins by August 1 in some areas. The young larvae crawl over the bark until a suitable feeding site is found. There they insert their stylets, become quiescent, excrete a white, wooly wax and eventually spend the winter. There is one generation per year.

F-519574

FIGURE 25.—Female scales of *Kermes* sp. on white oak twigs and leaves.

The first sign of infestation is the appearance of isolated, minute, white wooly dots on the bark, usually near the base of the tree. As the infestation increases, the dots appear in the form of thin vertical lines and then as solid patches. On heavily infested trees the trunks (fig. 26) and lower sides of branches may be completely whitened.

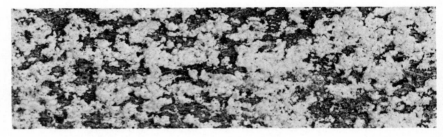

F-502240

FIGURE 26.—Infestation of the beech scale
Cryptococcus fagi, on the trunk of beech.

Light infestations are not particularly injurious but when they increase to an intensity of about 100 scales per square inch the outer layer of bark is killed and turns brown. Depressions or pits form in bark tissues around these wounds and are frequently numerous on young trees. The death and shrinkage of groups of cells within feeding areas also causes ruptures in the bark. However, this usually does not happen until 2 to 5 years of infestation. A fungus, probably *Nectria coccinea* var. *faginata*, also probably introduced, gains entry through these ruptures (*223*). It penetrates to the cambium and sapwood, killing tissues and interfering with the conduction and storage processes of the tree. Red fruiting bodies produced by the fungus become so abundant on severely infected trees that large areas on the trunk turn red. This leads to death of irregular-shaped areas of bark. Individual fungal lesions also coalesce and girdle the trunk, leading to crown deterioration and finally, the death of the tree. The fungus is entirely dependent on the scale for its incidence and spread.

Enormous quantities of beech have been killed and the only known way to prevent such losses is through the cutting and removal of infested trees (*646*). This is true despite the fact that some degree of natural control is provided by the twice-stabbed lady beetle and that winter temperatures of −35° F. are highly effective in the control of infestations exposed above the snow line.

The **European elm scale**, *Gossyparia spuria* (Mod.), an introduced species, occurs over most of southern Canada and the United States, wherever its hosts, native or European elms, grow. The adult female is oval and olive green to reddish-brown, has a white, waxy fringe along the body margin, and is about 1¼ to 1½ mm. long. The males, some of which are winged, are much smaller. Trees of all ages are infested.

The winter is spent in bark crevices on the trunk and large branches. Eggs are laid from spring to midsummer, and newly-hatched larvae are quite active. Some crawl to the undersurface of leaves where they settle down and feed; others settle down on twigs and branches. During late fall those on the leaves migrate back to the bark and settle in crevices where they spend the winter. There is only one generation per year.

The European elm scale is often very injurious, especially to young or transplanted elms. Heavy losses have been reported from many communities in the Midwest. Sooty mold developing in honeydew secreted by the scale also reduces the beauty of surviving trees. Thompson (*712*) discussed methods of control.

FAMILY PSEUDOCOCCIDAE

MEALYBUGS

Members of this family are known as mealybugs because of the mealy or waxy secretions that cover their bodies. Females are elongate-oval and have segmented bodies and well developed legs. Some species lay eggs; others give birth to living young. Mc-Kenzie (*490*) discussed the taxonomy and biology of the group.

Phenacoccus acericola King, the **maple phenacoccus,** an introduced species, occurs throughout the Northeastern, Central, and Lake States. Its preferred host appears to be sugar maple, but it has also been found on hornbeam, basswood, and horse chestnut. Adults are about 5 mm. long and are covered with masses of cottony wax. Evidence of infestation is the presence of cottony masses on the undersides of leaves during the summer. The winter is spent as a partly grown nymph in a hibernaculum beneath a flake of bark. There are three generations per year. This species is usually not very important, although it may damage shade trees. Other tree-infesting species in the genus include *Peliococcus serratus* Ferris which feeds on birch in the Northeastern States and *P. dearnessi* King which occurs on hawthorn in the Lake States.

Dysmicoccus cuspidatae (Rau.) attacks all species of *Taxus* in the Northeast and Midwest. Infestations have also been recorded on basswood, cedar, maple, and rhododendron. Females are 9 to 10 mm. long and 5 mm. wide and are covered with white wax through which reddish body fluids show in longitudinal lines. The winter is spent in the first nymphal instar in bark crevices or under waxy secretions left by previous year adults. There appears to be only one generation per year (in New York State). The branches and trunks of heavily infested trees are often completely covered with these insects and their white, waxy secretions. Continuous heavy infestations stunt the growth or kill *Taxus* in nurseries and ornamental plantings.

An infestation of *Dysmicoccus obesus* (Lob.) was reported in a 15-year-old ornamental planting of loblolly pine in Delaware. Infested trees were spindly, short, and the foliage was sparse and off-color. Conspicuous white powdery deposits occurred in cracks and crevices of the bark on the lower four feet of the trunks of infested trees (*534*).

Spilococcus juniperi (Ehrh.) [=*Pseudococcus juniperi* Ehrh.] is a serious pest of native red cedars in ornamental plantings in

Kansas, Indiana, and Oklahoma. The lower and inner branches are usually attacked first. The foliage of heavily infested trees turns brown and drops. Entire trees are sometimes defoliated. The **long-tailed mealybug,** *Pseudococcus adonidum* (L.), a widely distributed species, feeds on many ornamental plants. Females are oval 2.4 to 3 mm. long, grayish to light yellow, covered with a fine, powdery, waxlike whitish secretion, and bear two unusually long fringe-like filaments at the tail end. *Oracella acuta* (Lob.) feeds on the tips of loblolly pine terminals in Florida. Infestations have also been observed on shortleaf pine in Pennsylvania.

The **grape mealybug,** *Pseudococcus maritimus* (Ehrh.), a widely distributed species, feeds on all species of *Taxus* in Ohio; also on grape, euonymus, and sycamore. The first winter is spent as a first-instar nymph mostly near the main stem in the interior of the plant. The nymph may be found in a mass of white waxy threads produced by the female or beneath webbing, bark scales, and other debris webbed together. During early spring the young nymphs migrate to the twigs to feed. Adults emerge by mid-June and the female deposits her eggs in masses of white fibrous material. When the eggs hatch, the young nymphs migrate to the foliage to feed. There are two generations a year. Damage to *Taxus* in nurseries may be serious enough to warrant control (*562*).

The **Comstock mealybug,** *Pseudococcus comstocki* (Kuwana), an introduced species, occurs throughout most of the Eastern States and feeds on a wide variety of trees such as apple, peach, catalpa, boxwood, holly, horse chestnut, maple, mulberry, osage orange, *Taxus,* and poplar. Full-grown females are 2 to 5 mm. long, and covered with a white waxy material. Short, soft, spines project from the edges of the body forming a sort of fringe. The two posterior spines are three or four times longer than the others. The winter is spent in the egg stage under white cottony masses in bark crevices, under bark scales, and in the axils of twigs and leaves. There are several generations per year. Adults feed at pruning scars and in splits in the bark, causing the formation of knotlike galls. Important parasites include the hymenopterons, *Pseudaphycus malinus* Gahan, an introduced species from Japan, and *Allotropa convexifrons* Muesebck. The latter is often very effective in the Northeast.

Heavy infestations of the **striped mealybug,** *Ferrisia virgata* (Ckll.), have been observed on azalea in Maryland (*351*). It has also been recorded on azalea in Pennsylvania and Virginia and on magnolia in Alabama. The adult is covered with flossy threads, much longer than the body. Young nymphs feed on tender growth, such as flower buds; later, on all parts of the plant except the main stem and roots.

FAMILY ASTEROLECANIIDAE

PIT SCALES

Pit scale insects are small and elongate-oval in shape. Their legs are either vestigial or lacking, their antennae are short and 4- to 6-segmented, and their bodies are either covered by a tough waxy film or embedded in a waxy mass. The genus *Asterolecanium* contains a number of species that are often destructive of forest, shade, and ornamental trees. Females are smooth and shiny, light yellowish to brownish, and about 1 to 3 mm. wide. Males are unknown in most of the species occurring in this country. Morrison and Morrison (545) published on the subfamily. Asterolecaniinae. Russell (617) published a classification of the genus *Asterolecanium*.

The **golden oak scale,** *Asterolecanium variolosum* (Ratz.), is one of our most important species of pit scale insects. It feeds almost exclusively in small pits on the twigs, branches, and trunks of white oaks, and probably occurs wherever its hosts grow in this country. English oak appears to be favored above all other species. In its absence, chestnut oak is preferred (580). Females give birth to living young which move rapidly over the surface of twigs and branches. Once they settle down and begin to feed, however, they never move again. Small pits develop as they feed and the scale appears to be embedded in the bark. Thse pits remain after the scale dies. As a result, the twigs and small branches of heavily infested trees become quite rough. Adults overwinter, and there is one generation per year in the Northeastern States. Heavy infestations may kill young trees and the branches of larger trees (578). Heavily infested mature trees are killed during periods of dry weather.

Asterolecanium quercicola (Bouché) feeds in pits on the twigs branches, and trunks of white, swamp white, red, chestnut, and English oaks from New York to Ohio and North Carolina. Heavy infestations kill twigs, branches, and occasionally entire trees. *A. luteolum* Russell, the **yellow oak scale,** and *A. minus* Lindinger attack several species of oaks in Pennsylvania and Ohio. The **holly scale,** *A. puteanum* Russell, attacks two species of holly (*Ilex vomitoria* Ait. and *I. opaca* Ait.) and *Bumelia* sp. from Delaware and Pennsylvania to Alabama and Florida. *A. arabidis* (Sign.), the **English ivy scale,** occurs on green ash from Massachusetts and New Jersey to Ohio. The **oleander scale,** *A. pustulans* (Ckll.), feeds on *Acacia* spp., the marmalade tree, magnolia, mulberry, and many other species. It is sometimes quite injurious. *A. bambusae* (Bdv.), the **bamboo scale,** is a common and injurious pest of bamboo in the Southern States. *A. miliaris miliaris* (Bdv.) and *A. miliaris robustum* Green also feed on bamboo.

FAMILY COCCIDAE

SOFT SCALES

Soft scale females are either bare or enclosed in waxy or cottony secretions; hence the common name, soft scales. They may be recognized by an anal cleft running anteriorly from the posterior apex of the abdomen. The anal opening lies at the top of this cleft and is covered by two small triangular plates. Forest, shade, and ornamental trees are attacked by many species, several of which are serious pests.

The **cottony maple scale,** *Pulvinaria innumerabilis* (Rathvon), an important pest of shade tree maples, occurs throughout much of the United States and Canada. Its favored host is silver maple, but a large number of other deciduous trees are also attacked, such as other species of maple, basswood, white ash, boxelder, dogwood, honey and black locusts, hackberry, sycamore, beech, elm, willow, and poplar. The female is pale to dark brown, bare, convex to oval in shape, has a more or less distinct median ridge, and is about 4 to 6 mm. long. They are most conspicuous during the summer when large, white, cottony egg sacs extend from the rear. Males are flat, winged, and much smaller than the females.

Eggs are laid from April to June in cottonlike masses under the female. These masses are several times the size of the scale. As a result, the rear of the scale is often elevated at an angle to the twig (fig. 27). Hatching occurs in June and July in the more northern States. Young larvae crawl to the undersurfaces of leaves and feed on the principal veins. They become mature in August and September and mate. The fertilized immature females crawl back to the twigs and small branches where they overwinter. Development is resumed in early spring and the females become mature by April.

F-504123
FIGURE 27.—The cottony maple scale, *Pulvinaria innumerabilis*, on twigs and leaves of soft maple.

Damage to heavily infested maples may be severe. Branches are killed, the foliage turns a sickly yellow, and the vigor of the tree is reduced. Such trees are then frequently attacked by other species of insects and further damaged. Honeydew dripping from infested shade trees on sidewalks, automobiles, or people is often a nuisance. Sooty mold developing in the honeydew also detracts greatly from the attractiveness of the trees. Fortunately, trees are seldom attacked heavily for two successive years. Insect predators, including the dipteron, *Leucopomyia pulvinarie*, larvae of the lepidopteron, *Laetilia coccidivora*, and the coccinellids, *Chilocorus bivulnerus* and *Adalia bipunctata* sometimes play a primary role in the suppression of heavy populations.

Pulvinaria acericola (Walsh and Riley), the **maple leaf scale,** feeds on soft and sugar maples throughout most of the Eastern States and in southern Canada. Female scales are dark purple, have a brownish-yellow mid-dorsal stripe and three rows of small waxy spots on each side, and are about 5 mm. long. The body usually bears tiny tufts of white, cottonly filaments and a long cottony egg sac at the posterior end.

Partly grown nymphs spend the winter on the branches of the host. Growth is completed in the spring. Males appear first and fertilize immature females. During May the females migrate to the undersides of leaves and complete their development. A mass Eggs deposited in the sac hatch in June. The nymphs feed on the of white cottony threads is secreted which forms the egg sac. leaves until late fall and then migrate to the branches where they spend the winter. There is one generation per year (*13*).

Pulvinaria floccifera (W.) feeds on *Taxus* in the Northeast and Midwest. Adult females are pale yellow above and reddish-brown or brightly ochreous below. The undersides of branches of heavily infested plants become covered with irregular, white, cottony masses. Damage is occasionally severe in the Northeast.

The **magnolia scale**, *Neolecanium cornuparvum* (Thro), occurs throughout Eastern United States and feeds almost exclusively on various species of magnolia. This is one of the largest and most conspicuous scale insects found in the United States. Adult females are about 12 mm. in diameter; elliptical; dark, shining brown; convex; smooth; and covered with a white waxy bloom (fig. 28). The nymphs are small, flat, and blackish with a waxy bloom. The winter is spent as a first-instar nymph on the newer wood. Females become mature by late July and early August as far north as Ohio and give birth to living young. The latter move to the current year's twig growth where they settle down and feed. Sometimes they are abundant enough to cover many branches of the tree. There is one generation a year. Heavily infested trees may be seriously weakened, and, if infested continuously for several years, are killed. Heavily infested trees are also rendered unsightly by sooty mold developing in honeydew secreted by the scale.

The **tuliptree scale**, *Toumeyella liriodendri* (Gmelin), occurs from New York and Connecticut to Florida and westward to the Mississippi River Valley. It has also been recorded in California. Yellow poplar is the preferred host (fig. 29), but the scale also attacks basswood, native and cultivated magnolias, persimmon, loblolly-bay, buttonbush, catalpa, and walnut. Mature females are dark brown, about 8 mm. in diameter and approximately hemispherical when not crowded. Males are small, inconspicuous, dark brown, and two-winged. Young scales are very small and range from gray to black.

Winter is spent as a second-instar larva in regions as far north as Pennsylvania and Ohio, and in all developmental stages in the Deep South. Male scales emerge first in the spring and mate with partially grown females. The female gives birth to living young in the fall. Newly-hatched larvae are very active and crawl over most of the host. During the winter they are usually found on the less exposed areas of branches and on the trunks of saplings, usually on wood less than 4 years old.

The lower branches of mature trees and entire trees up to 5 inches in diameter may be killed by heavy infestations. The terminal shoots of surviving saplings are often killed, leading to crooks which makes the trees worthless for future use as veneer or lumber. Black sooty mold developing in honeydew excreted by the scale detracts from the attractiveness of shade trees (*200*).

The **pine tortoise scale**, *Toumeyella numismatica* (P. & McD.), occurs in southeastern Canada and from New York and New

FIGURE 29.—The tuliptree scale, *Toumeyella liriodendri*, on yellow-poplar.

FIGURE 28.—The magnolia scale, *Neolecanium cornuparvum*, on magnolia.

Jersey to Nebraska and the Dakotas. Its favored hosts appear to be Scotch and jack pines, but it also feeds on several other pines. Austrian pine is fairly commonly attacked. Infestations have also been found on red pines growing among or adjacent to heavily infested jack pines. Mature females are reddish-brown, oval, very convex, and about 6 mm. long. Males are tiny, fragile, and winged (*469*).

Partly-grown females spend their first winter on twigs. Growth is completed by June or earlier of the following year, and each female deposits about 500 eggs under her body. Hatching occurs in June or July, and the young larvae begin feeding on the twigs immediately. A white, powdery substance develops on the margins of the larvae. Male adults emerge in about 3 weeks and fly in search of immature females with which they mate. A few days later, the males die. The female continues to develop slowly until late fall, then goes into hibernation. There is one generation per year.

Pole sized stands of pine are occasionally severely infested, but seedlings and young saplings usually suffer the greatest damage. Heavy feeding may result in considerable branch mortality or the death of entire trees. Damage in Christmas tree plantations in the Midwest is often severe. In heavy infestations, a large percentage of the trees may die following one or two seasons of attack.

Heavy infestations of the pine tortoise scale are frequently wiped out by various species of coccinellid beetles. *Hyperaspis congressis* is especially effective. Several other species including *Hyperaspis signata, Chilocorus bivulnerus* Muls., *Scymnus lacustris,* are also important in different parts of the scale's range. The larva of the moth, *Laetilia coccidivora,* is also effective at times.

Toumeyella sp. near *numismaticum* feeds on Virginia pine in Pennsylvania, West Virginia, and Maryland; *T. pini* (King) has been recorded feeding on mugho and Scotch pines in Pennsylvania, Connecticut, Michigan, and Florida; and *T. parvicornis* (Ckll.) has been observed feeding on pines in Alabama.

The **terrapin scale,** *Lecanium nigrofasciatum* Perg. occurs in southern Canada and over most of the eastern part of the United States. Its preferred hosts appear to be the maples, sycamore, boxelder, and hawthorn; however, it also attacks many other forest and shade trees such as ash, mulberry, birch, cottonwood, redbud, basswood, and live oak. Mature females are convex, oval, and about 2 mm. in diameter. The body is dark reddish-brown, smooth and shining, and has 10 or 12 dark radiating bands extending from the high center of the dorsum to the crimped or fluted edges of the body. Males are two-winged and about 1 mm. long.

Partly grown females overwinter attached to branches. Growth is completed in the spring and the female gives birth to living young from early June to mid-July. The young scales migrate to the leaves and settle on the midrib or larger veins on the undersurfaces. They remain here for about 6 weeks and then move back to the branches. Male adults emerge and mate with immature females. The latter continue their growth until cold weather and hibernate. There is one generation per year.

The terrapin scale is most important as a pest of shade trees because it frequently appears in great numbers and seriously reduces the vitality of affected trees. The twice-stabbed lady beetle exerts a considerable degree of control.

The **European fruit lecanium,** *Lecanium corni* (Bouché), also commonly known as the **brown elm scale,** is widely distributed in the United States and southern Canada. It feeds on a wide variety of forest, shade, and fruit trees. Important species include elm, maple, yellow-poplar, white and black oaks, sycamore, beech, basswood, hickory, mulberry, walnut, black and honey locusts, hackberry, poplar, ash, magnolia, aborvitae, and juniper. Mature females are dark brown to reddish, circular to oval, strongly convex, 3.5 to 6 mm. in diameter, and often covered with whitish powder. Living specimens are soft and plastic; at death the body becomes a hard, brown shell loosely attached to the bark.

Eggs are laid in early summer. Newly-hatched larvae crawl to the undersurfaces of leaves and congregate near the veins. They remain here until late summer and then they migrate to the bark of small branches where they spend the winter. Two generations per year have been recorded as far north as Pennsylvania. Damage to shade trees, especially elm, is often severe. Small branches are sometimes killed and weakened trees become subject to attack by various species of boring insects or bark beetles.

The **Fletcher scale**, *Lecanium fletcheri* Ckll., is widely distributed in eastern and midwestern United States and Canada. Heavy infestations have been observed on *Taxus*, juniper, and arborvitae in nurseries in Ohio, Indiana, and Connecticut, and on arborvitae in North Dakota. Because of its prevalence on and injury to *Taxus*, it is sometimes called the **taxus lecanium.** Eggs are laid in late May and hatch by early July. Adult females are light yellowish-brown, almost globular, and about 3 to 5 mm. in diameter. Foliage on the inner portions of heavily infested plants is often blackened by the sooty mold growing on the honeydew excreted by the scales. The **oak lecanium,** *L. quercifex* Fitch, attacks many species of oaks throughout the Eastern States and southern Canada. *L. caryae* Fitch occurs commonly on beech, birch, hickory, elm, oak, willow, and walnut. This is one of the largest members of the genus—mature specimens are up to 12 mm. long. *L. quercitronis* Fitch is occasionally abundant on oaks in the South.

The **spruce bud scale,** *Physokermes piceae* (Schr.), feeds on Norway spruce in the Northeastern States and southern Canada. Mature scales are about 3 mm. in diameter and usually occur in clusters of 3 to 5 at the bases of branchlets. The body is reddish-brown with irregular flecks of yellow, and is covered with a delicate coating of powdery wax. The winter is spent as immature individuals clustered about terminal buds and there is one generation per year. Heavily infested trees are weakened and rendered unsightly by black mold developing in the honeydew which the scale excretes.

Pseudophilippia quaintancii Ckll., the **woolly pine scale,** feeds on young trees of several species of pines from New England to Florida and Louisiana. It forms white, wooly masses at the base of needles of new growth (*240*).

FAMILY DIASPIDIDAE

ARMORED SCALES

The family Diaspididae contains more than one-half of all species of scale insects. Members of the family live under scales composed of cast skins of earlier stages held together by waxy excretions of the insects. The terminal segments of the body are fused and strongly chitinized. Adult females are small, flattened, dislike, and legless. The scale coverings vary from long and threadlike, to oyster shape, to circular. The females of some species lay eggs; others give birth to living young. Adult males and their scale covers are usually elongated. Various trees and shrubs are the principal hosts. Kosztarab (*436*) discussed the species occurring in Ohio.

The **San Jose scale,** *Quadraspidiotus* (= *Aspidiotus*) *perniciosus* (Comstock), a probable introduction from China, was first recorded in North America at San Jose, California in 1880. In 1893 it was also found in Virginia. It now occurs throughout the United States and southern Canada. Its hosts include a wide variety of forest, shade, ornamental, and fruit trees. Some of its most important forest and shade tree hosts are: elm, ash, poplar, linden, willow, redbud, magnolia, and mountain-ash. Female scales are flat, circular, 1 to 2 mm. in diameter, and have a slightly raised, dark or yellow central area or nipple (fig. 30). Immature scales are small, nearly black, and have a black nipple surrounded by a grayish ring. Male scales are oblong-oval and nearly twice as long as wide.

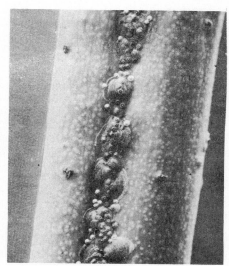

FIGURE 30.—San Jose scale, *Quadraspidiotus perniciosus.* Note large number of immature scales.

The winter is spent as a partly grown larva. Mature males appear in May and mature females in June. Fertilized females give birth to 200 to 600 living young each. Young larvae or "crawlers" swarm over the tree before settling down to feed. The bark of heavily infested trees may be literally coated with a grayish crust.Male scales reach maturity in 3 to 4 weeks; the females in about 7 weeks. There are one to several generations per year, depending on locality.

For many years after it spread over the United States, the San Jose scale was considered one of the most serious pests of orchard, shade, and ornamental trees in the country. In recent years it has generally been less troublesome. Two species of parasites, *Prospaltella perniciosa* Tower and *Aphelinus proelia* (Walker), have been quite effective in its control in the Northeast.

The **walnut scale,** *Quadraspidiotus* (=*Aspidiotus*) *juglansregiae* (Comstock) has a wide variety of hosts including walnut, ash, maple, boxelder, horsechestnut, cottonwood, buckeye, and linden. Female scales are flat, circular, pale grayish-brown, and about 3 mm. in diameter. The exuvium is subcentral and reddish-brown. Young scales usually settle down around the female in a regular formation. Infestations heavy enough to kill twigs and branches have been observed in the South. There are two or more generations per year. The related species, *Q. forbesi* (Johns), has been observed feeding on cherry and *Q. gigas* (Thiem & Gerneck) on poplar and willow.

107

The **Putnam scale,** *Diaspidiotus* (=*Aspidiotus*) *ancylus* (Putnam), occurs in southern Canada and throughout most of the United States. Silver maple and linden seem to be its favored hosts, but it also feeds on several other important forest and shade trees such as elm, ash, hackberry, poplar, dogwood, black locust, and beech. Female scales are circular and about 1 to 1.5 mm. in diameter. They are dark gray to nearly black and have an off-center, brick-red nipple. Otherwise, they closely resemble females of the San Jose scale.

Winter is spent as an immature scale, and growth is resumed and completed in the spring. Eggs are laid over a period of several weeks in early summer, and there is one generation per year. Ordinarily, this scale is not very injurious; although, it may kill small twigs and branches on heavily infested trees.

Diaspidiotus liquidambaris (Kotinsky) feeds on the leaves, twigs, and buds of sweetgum in the South and Midwest. Infestations have also been observed on magnolia and red maple. During the summer it occurs primarily in pockets on the lower surfaces of leaves. Small, discolored galls occur on the upper surface close to the pockets. Damage has been serious in nurseries in Missouri. *D.* (=*Aspidiotus*) *aesculi* (Johns) has been observed on horse-chestnut.

The **hemlock scale,** *Abgrallaspis* (=*Aspidiotus*) *ithacae* (Ferris) feeds on hemlock, fir, spruce, and pine in Eastern United States. It is small, oblong, dark gray or nearly black, and is usually found attached to the undersides of needles. The needles of heavily infested twigs and branches may drop prematurely. The related species, *A. townsendi* (Ckll.), has been observed feeding on yellow-poplar.

The **gloomy scale,** *Melanaspis* (=*Chrysomphalus*) *tenebricosa* (Comstock), occurs from Maryland to Ohio, Florida, and Texas. It is often quite destructive of soft maples in the South. Other hosts include sugar maples, elm, boxelder, and hackberry. Female scales are gray and almost the same color as the bark. They resemble San Jose scales except for their more concentrically placed nipples (*517*).

The **obscure scale,** *Melanaspis obscura* (Comstock) (=*Chrysomphalus obscurus*), occurs from Massachusetts to Florida and Arkansas and feeds on a wide variety of forest and shade trees, including oak, maple, elm, hickory, willow, dogwood, hackberry, and pecan. Female scales are dark gray to blackish, almost circular, and about 3 mm. in diameter. The first exuvium is subcentral, nipplelike, and shining black with a white ring. Damage to pecan is often serious in the South. Chestnut and white oaks are injured, and, in Maryland, willow and pin oaks are severely damaged.

The **elm scurfy scale,** *Chionaspis americana* Johnson feeds on elm and hackberry throughout most of Eastern United States. Female scales are 2 to 3.2 mm. long, oystershell-shaped, and almost pure white. Twigs, branches, and small trees may be killed in heavy infestations, and large trees, seriously weakened. There are two generations per year in the North, but in the South there are probably more.

The **scurfy scale,** *Chionaspis furfura* (Fitch), feeds on the leaves, branches, and trunks of a wide variety of trees in southern Canada and the United States. Important forest and shade tree hosts include elm, ash, maple, hickory, walnut, aspen, willow, mountain-ash, and horse chestnut. Female scales vary from pure white to dirty gray, are somewhat pear-shaped, and are from 2 to 3 mm. long. *C. lintneri* Comstock feeds on willow, birch, dogwood, and other trees and shrubs in southeastern Canada and the Northeastern States. *C. corni* Cooley often damages ornamental dogwoods in the Midwest.

Chionaspis salicisnigrae (Walsh), the **willow scurfy scale**, occurs across the Northern States and in southern Canada. Willow appears to be its favored host, but it also feeds on several other trees such as dogwood, poplar, yellow-poplar, and shadbush. Female scales are white, elongate-oval, convex, and about 3 to 4 mm. long. Infestations are often heavy enough to cover completely the twigs and branches of its hosts. These may seriously injure young trees.

The **oystershell scale**, *Lepidosaphes ulmi* (L.), occurs in southern Canada and throughout the United States. Its hosts include more than 100 species of forest, shade, fruit, and ornamental trees. Important species of forest and shade trees include white, European, and black ash, beech, silver maple, elm, willow, poplar, birch, and lilac. As its common name indicates, this scale resembles a miniature oystershell (fig. 31). The female is chestnut brown or darker and about 2.5 to 3 mm. long.

Eggs overwinter under the protective covering of female scales. Hatching occurs in early June, or late May, or even earlier, depending on location. Newly-hatched nymphs wander over the bark for a short time, then settle down to feed. Eggs are laid during early summer in the South, and during late summer and early fall in the North. There are two generations per year in the South but only one in the North.

The oystershell scale often occurs in such large numbers as to form a crust on the trunk or branches of its host. Damage to ash has been severe during past years. According to some reports, entire forest stands have been killed. Lilac and silver maple are also subject to serious injury. A related species, *Lepidosaphes yanagicola* Kuwana, first found and identified in Ohio in 1950, feeds on Euonymus.

The **pine needle scale**, *Phenacaspis pinifoliae* (Fitch), occurs in southern Canada and throughout the United States. Its hosts include various species of spruces and the following species of eastern pines: white, red, Scotch, Austrian, Virginia, slash, loblolly, and mugho. Mature females are white, have a yellow pellicle attached to the anterior end, and are about 3 mm. long. They are usually widest toward the posterior end. The shape tends to vary, however, depending on the shape and width of the needles on which they live. Males are white and slender and not more than half as long as the females.

Eggs spend the winter under the dead scale covering of the female. Hatching occurs about the time the new needles appear and the newly-hatched larvae crawl to green needles to feed. They become mature in early July and the new females produce new batches of eggs. Offspring of this generation reach maturity by fall and lay eggs which overwinter. There are two generations a year as far north as Ohio.

F-504093

FIGURE 31.—Oystershell scale, *Lepidosaphes ulmi*, on bark of poplar.

COURTESY CONN. AGR. EXPT. STA.

FIGURE 32.—Pine needle scale, *Phenacaspis pinifoliae*, on needles of red pine.

Pine needle scale infestations (fig. 32) are occasionally so heavy that infested trees present a gray, unhealthy appearance. Heavy infestations cause the needles to turn yellow and may kill parts of branches or entire young trees. Damage is particularly noticeable and troublesome on ornamental plantings in or near towns and cities. The twice-stabbed lady beetle is an important enemy of the species.

The **black pine-leaf scale,** *Nuculaspis californica* (Coleman), occurs over most of North America and feeds on many different species of conifers. Mature female scales are yellowish-brown to black and almost circular in shape. They are about 1.5 mm. in diameter, and there is a small elevated nipple in the center. Their first winter is spent as partly-grown females attached to the needles. "Crawlers" appear in late spring and move to the old needles to feed. A second generation appears in midsummer and feeds on needles of the current season. Damage has been serious in nurseries and plantations and to natural reproduction in the Lake States. Heavily infested needles become desiccated and die. The twice-stabbed lady beetle is an important enemy in the Lake States.

The **juniper scale,** *Carulaspis* (=*Diaspis*) *carueli* (Targ.), occurs in southern Canada and throughout the United States. It is primarily a pest of juniper but also feeds on arborvitae, incense-cedar, and cypress. The female scale is white with a yellow center, circular and slightly convex, and about 1.5 mm. in diameter. Male scales also are white, but are long, narrow, and smaller than the females. Only fertilized females overwinter. Egg laying begins in May and hatching occurs during June. Newly-hatched larvae or "crawlers" migrate to feeding sites. Once they begin to feed they never move again. There is one generation per year.

The juniper scale is also a serious pest of ornamental evergreens. It feeds on many different parts of its hosts including the needles, twigs, and cones. Heavily infested plants make poor growth and become grayish-brown in appearance.

The **euonymus scale,** *Unaspis euonymi* (Comstock), a common and serious pest of deciduous and evergreen Euonymus, probably occurs wherever its hosts grow in the United States. Mature female scales are grayish-brown, roughly pear-shaped, and from 1.6 to 2 mm. long. Males are snow white, somewhat narrower than the females, and have three longitudinal ridges. Mature females overwinter. First brood larvae appear from early to late spring; a second brood appears in July. There are two to three generations per year, depending on locality. Plants are often heavily infested, the stems and leaves being practically covered by the scales (fig. 33).

The **camphor scale,** *Pseudaonidia duplex* (Ckll.), a probable introduction into Louisiana from Japan around 1920, is now known to occur also in Texas, Mississippi, and Alabama. Its hosts include more than 200 species of plants, but the camphor tree is the most seriously injured. Uncrowded female scales are nearly circular, convex, have a subcentral nipple, and are about 1.5 mm. in diameter. There is no well-defined hibernation period, and egg laying probably begins as early as January. There are three generations per year.

Fiorinia externa Ferris has been recorded from New York, Massachusetts, Connecticut, Rhode Island, New Jersey, Maryland, Virginia, Pennsylvania, and Ohio. Its hosts are listed as Canadian, Carolina, and Japanese hemlocks, also fir, spruce, and yew (*703*). All developmental stages of both sexes are present throughout the year. Two generations per year have been reported from Maryland and Connecticut. Infested hemlock takes

F-519580

FIGURE 33.—The euonymus scale, *Unaspis euonymi,* on Euonymus.

on a mealy, whitewashed appearance in the spring and fall. Needles drop prematurely and twigs and branches are killed on heavily infested trees. The related species, *F. theae* (Green), a serious pest of camellia in the South, occurs on holly also.

Lecanodiaspis tessalatus (Ckll.), the **persimmon scale**, a large hemispherical species, feeds on persimmon in the South. The surface of heavily infested limbs and trunks become rough, lumpy, or wartlike. The **white peach scale,** *Pseudaulacaspis pentagona* (Targ.), feeds on ash, dogwood, chinaberry, and lilac; *Chrysomphalus dictyospermi* (Morgan) feeds on holly (in Virginia); and *A. hederae* feeds on chinaberry.

Order COLEOPTERA

Beetles

The beetles comprise the largest order of insects. Over a quarter of a million species have been described, and over 26,000 of this number occur in the United States. They can be distinguished from all other insects, except the earwigs, by the structure of the forewings, these being horny "wing covers" or elytra which meet in a straight line along the middle of the back (152). They cover the membranous hindwings when the latter are present. Beetle larvae vary considerably in form in different families. The majority are campodeiform or scarabaeiform, but some are platyform, some are elateriform, and a few are vermiform. All beetles have complete metamorphosis, and all have chewing mouth parts. The life cycle varies greatly in length, from 10 or more generations per year to one generation in many years.

Beetle larvae and adults present a wide range of habits. Some species are aquatic, but the majority are terrestrial. Some feed on vegetable matter; others on animal matter. Many are phytophagous, many are predaceous, some are scavengers, some feed on mold or fungi, and a few are parasitic.

Many species of the phytophagous beetles are external feeders on the foliage, and many others feed under the bark. Some feed in the wood or fruit, on parts of blossoms, as miners in leaves, or on the roots of their hosts. Some of the predaceous species feed both as larvae and adults on free-feeding lepidopterous larvae and various sucking insects; others feed on various insects in the leaf litter and under logs, or on the immature stages of bark beetles and wood borers in their burrows in wood. A few of the parasitic species feed on the egg masses of grasshoppers or in the nests of bees.

The order Coleoptera contains many of the most destructive forest insects. The adults of many leaf-eating species cause extensive defoliation and damage. Many others kill valuable timber or shade trees by introducing blue-staining fungi or other lethal pathogens as they bore into their hosts. The larvae are generally most destructive, however. For example, enormous losses of standing timber are caused each year by phloem-feeding larvae; severe losses in timber degrade and to forest products are caused by the larvae of various woodboring species. Young trees in nurseries and plantations as well as natural reproduction are severely damaged or destroyed by the larvae of other species.

For more extended treatment of the Coleoptera, the reader is referred to the following works: Blatchley (81), Boving and Craighead (91), Bradley (94), Leng (461), and Leng and Mutchler (452, 453). Dillon & Dillon published a manual of species occurring in eastern North America (193).

Key to the Families of More Important Beetle Larvae

1. Legs apparently 6-jointed, the 5th bearing 1 or 2 distinct movable claws 2
   Legs either 5-jointed with tarsus and claw fused into a single claw-shaped terminal joint, or less than 5-jointed or absent 6

2. Hypopharynx and ligula strongly chitanized; soft-bodied, wood-boring forms 3
   Hypopharynx soft; ligula soft or vestigial; mandibles falciform, fitted for grasping 5
3. Ninth abdominal segment armed with 1 or 2 chitinous processes; mandible with large grinding molar structure 4
   Ninth abdominal segment unarmed; mandibles of grasping type .... Rhysodidae
4. Ninth abdominal segment dorsally produced into a straight process .... Cupesidae
   Ninth abdominal segment bearing a dorsal and ventral process, curved toward each other .... Micromalthidae
5. Body fusiform, usually developed for active motion, no abdominal hooks .... Carabidae
   Body fleshy digitate; dorsal surface of 5th abdominal segment bearing 2 or 3 pairs of hooks; larvae living in earthen burrows in the soil .... Cicindelidae
6. Ninth abdominal segment bearing 1- or 2-jointed, movable appendages or cerci 7
   Cerci rigid or absent 9
7. Mandibles of the grasping type without a grinding or molar structure at base; gula reduced or represented by a line, the sides of head meeting ventrally 8
   Mandibles of the biting type; gula present .... Silphidae
8. Spiracles bifore; cardo and stipites fused .... Histeridae
   Spiracles annular; stipites articulate on cardo
   .... Staphylinidae
9. Curved, grublike larvae with strong well-developed legs; mandible with a large grinding structure; lacinia and galea usually distinctly divided; spiracles usually cribriform; no cerci 10
   Form variable and not having the above combination of characters 11
10. Gula present separating submentum from prothoracic skin; lacinia 2-jointed .... Byrrhidae
    Gula absent; submentum and prothorax continues in a soft skinlike connection .... Lamellicornia
11. Gular region or a median gular suture present 12
    Gular region fleshy, i.e., submentum and presternum of prothorax continuous in a skinlike connection 40
12. Parasitic; soft-bodied, swollen larvae with head and body white; mandible without molar structure 13
    Not parasitic; head and body normally chitinized 14
13. Mouth parts protracted .... Cucujidae
    Mouth parts retracted .... Colydiidae
14. Labrum absent or fused with clypeus into a nasale 15
    Labrum distinct 17
15. Head structures reduced and specialized; body usually much depressed; wood borers, the larvae cutting galleries across the grain of the wood 16
    Head structures not so modified .... Elateridae
16. Legs short, 5-jointed .... Throscidae
    Legs absent or vestigial .... Eucemidae
17. Maxillary articulating area indistinct 18

114

46. Mentum bearing a shieldlike plate; labial palpi absent or rudimentary; feeding in the seeds of plants
    Bruchidae
    Mentum without such plate; labial palpi rarely lacking ....Chrysomelidae
47. Adults usually associated with the larvae and boring characteristic galleries in the wood or under the bark of shrubs, trees, or lumber.......Platypodidae, Scolytidae
    Larvae and adults not so associated 48
48. Abdominal segments with 2 transverse folds; larvae often found in a compacted roll cut from a leaf
    Curculionidae
    Abdominal segments with 3 or 4 transverse folds 49
49. Larvae boring in the moist sapwood of dead trees or occasionally in beams of buildings, powder-posting the material ....Curculionidae
    Habits of larvae variable; not working like powder-post beetles ....Curculionidae

FAMILY CARABIDAE

Ground Beetles

This is a large family, containing hundreds of species, nearly all predaceous on other insects. There is considerable variation among species in size, shape, and color, but most of them are dark, shiny, and somewhat flattened. They are commonly found under stones, logs, leaves, debris, or bark, or running about on the ground. The larvae of bark-inhabiting species are white and thin-textured, and the legs are five-jointed with a movable claw or pair of claws on the fifth joint.

A number of species in the genus *Calosoma* Weber are important predators of tree-defoliating lepidopterous larvae. The adults are brilliantly colored, are about 25 mm. long, and emit a disagreeable odor when handled or disturbed.

Calosoma sycophanta (L.), a large bluish-black species with golden-green elytra, and from 24 to 30 mm. long, (fig. 34) was introduced from Europe against the gypsy moth in 1906. It became established rather quickly and has since spread over most of the gypsy moth infested area and beyond. Both the adults and larvae climb trees and feed voraciously on the larvae and pupae of their hosts. Large gypsy moth larvae and pupae are especially attractive, but they will also feed on many other species of insects. Adult beetles spend the winter in the ground and emerge about June 1. Eggs are laid in the ground, and when the larvae hatch, they climb trees in search of food. When they become full-grown, they return to the ground to pupate. Adults live up to 4 years. Populations of this species tend to increase rapidly during gypsy moth outbreaks (*122*).

Several native species of *Calosoma* also feed on lepidopterous larvae and pupae, sawflies, and other insects in the Eastern States. *C. frigidum* Kirby, *C. willcoxi* LeC., *C. scrutator* (Fab.), and *C. calidum* (Fab.) (fig. 35) are widely distributed in the region.

Many other members of the family are also associated with insects attacking trees. *Chlaenius erythropus* Germ., *Dicaelus purpuratus* Bon., *Agonum* spp., and *Tachys* spp. are frequently

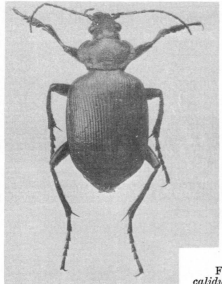

FIGURE 34.—Adult of
Calosoma sycophanta.

FIGURE 35.—Larva of *Calosoma
calidum* feeding on a gypsy moth larva

found in association with bark beetles under the bark. *Galerita
janus* F. and *G. bicolor* Drury are often found under loose bark
of logs or under stones in the forest. The adults are about 20 mm.
long and quite colorful. The thorax is red, the wingcovers bluish-
black, and the long legs red. *Geopinus incrassatus* (Dej.), *Har-
palus* spp., and *Scarites subterraneus* F. frequently feed on and
damage young seedlings.

FAMILY CICINDELIDAE

TIGER BEETLES

Tiger beetles are of no particular importance as forest insects,
but their appearance and habits are such as to arouse the interest
and curiosity of almost anyone when they are encountered. The
genus *Cicindela* L. contains the majority of species. The adults
are mostly metallic green or bronze in color, with bands or spots
of yellow. They are strong flyers and fleet of foot, and are most
often seen along sandy beaches of streams or along woodland
trails on bright, sunny, summer days. Tiger beetles and larvae
are predaceous on other insects. The larvae live in vertical burrows in the soil.

FAMILY CUPESIDAE

Cupesid beetles have flattened bodies and are densely scaly.
Cupes concolor Westwood is a common eastern species. Adults are
grayish brown and from 7 to 11 mm. long. Full-grown larvae are
about 25 mm. long; each leg is armed with a movable claw; and
the ninth abdominal segment ends in a short spine. The adults
feed on decaying and often moist wood, and are usually found in

118

basement timbers of pine, oak, and chestnut in old houses. They are of no economic importance because the infested wood is already more or less destroyed by decay organisms.

FAMILY SILPHIDAE

CARRION BEETLES

Carrion beetles are mentioned here because they are so often seen on animal excrement or around the bodies of dead animals in the forest. Many of the more common species are brightly colored, and their bodies are usually soft and somewhat flattened. The larger and more conspicuous species belong to the genera *Silpha* and *Nicrophorus*. Several small species are also found under the bark of logs and dead trees where they probably act as scavengers. *Agathidium oniscoides* Palisot commonly occurs in the galleries of bark beetles in hardwoods.

FAMILY HISTERIDAE

HISTER BEETLES

Hister beetles are rather small, sluggish, and hard-shelled. The body is often very flat and the wing covers are usually cut off square at the tip, exposing the last one or two segments of the abdomen. Many are shining black; others may be bronzed, greenish metallic or marked with red, yellow, or orange. The larvae are soft-bodied and sluggish and may be found in decaying organic matter, in fungi, or under the bark of trees. Those of *Plegaderus* spp. feed on the eggs and larvae of bark beetles.

FAMILY BYRRHIDAE

Members of this family are oval, convex beetles about 1 to 10 mm. long. The head bends downward and is concealed from above, and the hind femora are wide and extended to the elytra. A few species live under the bark of trees, but the majority occur in sandy areas where they may be found under debris or at the roots of grass and trees. Several species of the genus *Byrrhus* occasionally injure young trees in forest nurseries and plantations. Adults of this genus are about 5 to 10 mm. long, black and grayish in color, and densely covered with hairs.

FAMILY PASSALIDAE

PASSALID BEETLES

Passalid beetles are better known by some people by other common names, such as betsey bugs, betsey beetles, bess bugs, and patent-leather beetles. Three species are known to occur in the United States, only one of which, the **horned passalus**, *Popilius disjunctus* (Ill.), is found in the eastern part.

Horned passalus adults are large, shining black beetles, from 30 to 40 mm. long. The plates of the antennal club are rigid and incapable of being opened or closed; there is a short, forward bending horn on the top of the head; and the elytral striae are deep and finely punctured. There also are roughened areas on the undersides of the wings and on top of the abdomen. When disturbed, the adult rubs these areas together, producing squeaking sounds or the so called "bess" notes. The larvae are bluish and from 30 to 40 mm. long. The anal lobes consist of two large lateral pads, and there are stridulatory organs on the third pair of legs. The species lives in colonies in large, rough galleries excavated in damp rotten logs or stumps, each colony consisting of a male and female and their progeny. The larvae feed on the wood but not until after it has been reduced to pulp and treated with digestive secretions by the parents (*311*).

FAMILY OSTOMATIDAE

Ostomatid Beetles

This family contains several important enemies of destructive forest insects. The adults are rather flattened, elongate or oval, blue, green, or black beetles. The antennae are 11-jointed, the last three joints forming a loose club; the thorax is narrowest behind; and the fourth joint of the five-jointed tarsus is very long. The larvae are similar to clerid larvae except for the ventral mouth parts. The latter are retracted below the point of attachment of the mandibles in ostomatid larvae.

Temnochila virescens (F.) adults are bright, irridescent, bluish-green; there is a pair of recurved hooks on the ninth abdominal segment; and each is about 10 to 18 mm. long. They feed on wood borers in their tunnels, on bark beetles crawling about on the bark surface, and on bark beetle eggs and larvae in the bark. This is one of the most important insect enemies of the southern pine beetle.

Other predaceous ostomatids occurring in eastern forests and their insect hosts include the following: *Tenebroides corticalis* (Melsh.) and *T. dubius* (Melsh.)—feed on bark beetles; *T. bimaculatus* (Melsh.)—feeds on *Agrilus* larvae in oaks; *Corticotomus* (*Nemosoma*) *cylindricus* (LeC.) and *Airora cylindrica* (Serv.)—feed on ambrosia beetles and cossonids.

FAMILY MELOIDAE

Blister Beetles

Blister beetles are most commonly seen on forest vegetation; they are fairly large, soft-bodied, sprawling, and loose-jointed. The head narrows abruptly behind to the neck; the elytra are soft; the abdomen is often large and swollen; the tarsal claws are cleft or appendaged; and the color is either green, gray, brown, or black. The adults are plant feeders and often defoliate their hosts. The larvae are parasitic of grasshopper eggs or in the nests of bees.

Several species, including the **striped blister beetle,** *Epicauta vittata* (F.), and *E. pestifera* Werner, *Macrobasis fabricii* (LeC.), *M. unicolor* (Kby.), *Pomphopoea aenea* (Say), and *P. sayi* LeC. defoliate seedlings in nurseries and in ornamental plantings in the Midwest. The **ash-gray blister beetle,** *Epicauta fabricii* (LeC.)

E. subglabra (Fall), and *Lytta muttalli* Say defoliate *Caranga* in the Great Plains; *Epicauta torsa* (LeC.) defoliates holly in Florida and mimosa in Florida and Oklahoma; *E. cinerea* (Forst.) defoliates black and honey locusts and hornbeam in Arkansas; and *Pomphopoea polita* (Say) feeds on the pollen of shortleaf pine in the South. Horsfall (*379*) discussed the biology and control of common species.

FAMILY NITIDULIDAE

SAP BEETLES

Sap beetles are elongate or oval, usually less than 25 mm. long, and often of contrasting black, red, and yellow colors. The antennae are 11-segmented and club-shaped; the sides of the thorax and elytra are often margined; and the elytra are shorter than the body, leaving the end of the abdomen exposed. The larvae are nearly white, flattened, and moderately elongate. The head is broad and projecting with deeply retracted mouth parts. Paired and forked horny armatures are often found on the ninth abdominal segment. Connell (*155*) published keys to the species occurring in Delaware.

Both the adults and larvae feed on decaying fruit, on fermenting juices under bark, and on sap exuding from freshly cut logs and stumps or wounds on living trees. Patches of cambium are often killed by bark infesting species. When these dead areas dry up and heal over, they remain in the wood as "bark pocket" defects and lower its value. A number of species also appear capable of penetrating the bark of oak in the absence of injuries. When this happens, the larvae feed in the cambium region and destroy patches up to 2 inches across (fig. 36). Several members of the family are also likely candidates as vectors of the oak wilt fungus, *Ceratocystis fagacearum*. In studies conducted in West Virginia, they occurred abundantly in and on moist wounds on wild-infested trees and on mycelial mats of the fungus beneath the bark (*201*).

FAMILY COCCINELLIDAE

LADY BEETLES

More than 500 species of lady beetles occur in the United States, by far the greater number of which feed on aphids and scales, or on the eggs and larvae of larger insects. As a group they are among the most beneficial of all the insects. Being quite common, they are also among the most widely recognized of all species. The adults are small, usually less than 5 mm. long. The body is round or hemispherical and extremely convex. The surface is shining and often brilliantly marked with black, white, red, or yellow spots. The larvae are alligator-shaped, black or gray in color, or spotted or checkered with bright colors, and covered with warts or spines. Eggs are light yellow and are laid in clusters on the leaves or bark of a plant or tree. The winter is spent in the adult stage, sometimes in enormous congregations of beetles. A few of the more important species feeding on forest

F-519925-6

FIGURE 36.—Evidence of nitidulid attacks on oak: A, scars of overgrown attacks; B, pockets in the wood beneath scars shown on A.

insects in eastern United States are discussed. Stehr (*689*) published keys to the identification of species occurring in Minnesota.

The **two-spotted lady beetle**, *Adalia bipunctata* (L.), an introduced species, is an important predator of the pine needle, juniper, beech, and terrapin scales in the Northern States. Adults are about 3 to 5 mm. long. The head is black with two yellow spots between the eyes; the thorax is black with yellow margins; and the wing covers are red with black central spots.

The **twice-stabbed lady beetle,** *Chilocorus stigma* (Say), occurs in the Northern States and feeds commonly on the pine needle, beech, terrapin, and juniper scales. The adult is shining black and about 4 to 5 mm. long. The ventral segments are red, and there is a round red spot on the disk of each elytron.

The **convergent lady beetle,** *Hippodamia convergens* Guer. feeds on aphids and scales throughout most of the United States. Adults are 6 to 8 mm. long. The head is black except for a pale transverse center spot; the thorax is black except for pale margins and is marked with two discal bars; the elytra are reddish with a black scutellar spot and 12 more or less distinct black spots; and the venter and legs are black. In some parts of the country this species hibernates in clusters of tens of thousands of beetles.

Hyperaspis congressis Watson is widely distributed in eastern United States and is an important enemy of the pine tortoise scale. Adults are black, strongly punctate, shining, and about 2.5 mm. long. There is a rather large, yellowish spot on the middle of the elytra, and often a fainter one on their tips.

Anatis 15-punctata (Oliv.) feeds on a wide variety of forest insects, including the larvae of the gypsy moth and cankerworms, in eastern United States. Adults are yellowish and about 8 to 10 mm. long. There are two pale spots enclosed in a black disk on the thorax, a single spot on the scutellum, and seven black spots on each elytron.

Coccinella novemnotata Hbst., the **nine-spotted ladybird,** is a common and widely distributed species that feeds on aphids and scales on both conifers and hardwoods. Adults are 5 to 7 mm. long. The body is pale yellow above and black beneath. Each elytron bears four black spots, and there is one black spot on the elytral suture. *C. transversoguttata* Fald. feeds on scale insects infesting pines in the more northern States. Adults are reddish, nearly hemispherical, and about 6 to 7.5 mm. long. The wing covers may be spotless, or each one may be marked with a long, transverse subbasal spot, a shorter transverse spot near the middle, and a third near the tip.

Several species of coccinellids have been imported against the balsam wooly aphid in recent years. The European species, *Aphidecta obliterata* (L.), is now firmly established in infested Fraser fir stands in North Carolina (6). Eggs are laid on the needles or trunks of infested trees, and the larvae and adults feed on all stages of the aphid except the first larval instar. Attempts to establish it in New Brunswick were unsuccessful (112). *Scymnus* (*Pullus*) *impexus* (Muls.), one of the most important enemies of the aphid in Central Europe, has been liberated in infested stands of balsam fir in New England. The adults and larvae feed on second and third instar larvae of the aphid.

Other important species of native coccinellids include *Scymnus lacustris* LeC., an enemy of the pine tortoise scale in the Lake States; *Microwesia misella* (LeC.), a minute species less than 1 mm. long that feeds on various species of scale insects; and *Cleis picta* (Rand.), which often occurs in large numbers on pines infested with the red pine scale in the Northeast.

FAMILY DERODONTIDAE

Derodontid adults are small brown or dullish-brown beetles about 2 to 6 mm. long. Only about one-half dozen species have been recorded from the United States.

Laricobius erichsonii Rosenh., a predator of the balsam woolly aphid, has been imported from Europe during recent years and released in aphid infested stands of fir in Canada, New England, North Carolina, and the Pacific Northwest. The adult is an elongate oval beetle about 2.2 to 2.4 mm. long. The body is covered with yellowish to brownish to black hairs; the head is usually hidden from above; and the central portions of the elytra, the antennae, and the legs are reddish brown. The larvae are covered with flakes of the aphid's wool and small bits of bark.

Eggs are deposited deep within aphid egg clusters or under lichens on the bark. The larvae feed on the host eggs until full-grown at which time they drop to the ground and pupate in cocoons of compacted soil particles. Adults are active on warm, sunny days (*113*).

FAMILY CUCUJIDAE

Flat Bark Beetles

Members of this family are rather small and extremely flat, yellowish, brownish, reddish, or black beetles. The larvae, also often very flat, are usually found under the bark of unhealthy trees or newly-felled trees and logs. The majority are scavengers, but a few are parasitic or predacious on mites, small insects, wood boring larvae, or Hymenoptera.

Catogenus rufus (Fab.) is a common eastern parasite of borers in sugar maple. Adults are elongate, reddish brown and up to 12 mm. long. The larvae are soft-bodied and white, with recurved hooks on the ninth abdominal segment. They are usually found beneath the bark in the pupal cells of their host. *Cucujus clavipes* F. is another conspicuous eastern species. The adult is bright red, exceedingly flat, and about 10 to 14 mm. long. The larvae are usually found under the bark of recently dead trees, especially ash and poplar.

FAMILY COLYDIIDAE

This family consists of small, elongate, slender beetles rarely over 5 mm. long. They are reddish brown to nearly black and beautifully sculptured. The larvae of certain species, some of which are found under bark in association with bark beetles, are scavengers. Others, such as those of *Nematidium filiforme* LeC., *Bitoma carinata* (LeC.), and *Colydium lineola* Say, feed on the larvae of ambrosia beetles, cossonids, and certain other borers in their tunnels.

FAMILY MELANDRYIDAE

Adults of this family are small to large, usually elongate to oval, loosely jointed beetles. The thorax is margined at the sides; the antennae are filiform; the front coxal cavities are open behind; and the hind tarsi are four-jointed. Adults are seldom seen but the larvae occur commonly under the bark or in the wood of dead logs, usually with wood-decaying fungi.

Some of the more common species are: *Melandrya striata* Say— occurs in many different hardwoods in association with black lines of decay; *Orchesia castanea* Melsh.—occurs in oak, maple, tulip poplar, sycamore, and hickory; *Hypulus concolor* (LeC.) — occurs in rotting sapwood of pines; *Serropalpus barbatus* (Schall.) and *Eustrophus tomentosus* Say—occur in various conifers; and *Dircacea quadrimaculata* (Say) and *Holostrophus bifasciatus* (Say)—occur in various hardwoods.

FAMILY OEDEMERIDAE

Adult members of this family are usually slender, flattish, and soft-bodied. Their color varies from pale to black, with red, yellow, or orange markings, and they range in length from about 5 to 25 mm. The elytra are rather soft and are sometimes covered with fine silken hair; the next-to-last segment of each leg is dilated and bears a dense, hairy pad beneath; the middle coxae are very large; and the hind tarsi are four-jointed. Adults are usually seen on flowers or on old logs or stumps; the larvae feed in dead and rotting wood.

The **wharf borer**, *Nacerdes melanura* (L.), the only economically important member of the family, is widely distributed, occurring along both the Atlantic and Pacific Coasts and around the Great Lakes. Adults are reddish-yellow and vary from 7 to 12 mm. length in the males to 10 to 15 mm. in the females. There is a dark patch on the head and two dark patches on the thorax. The tips of the elytra are also black. The larvae feed almost entirely in very moist wood and occasionally are very destructive of pilings under wharves and under buildings near the water. Boardwalks along the shore and wood floors in damp basements are seriously damaged at times. Adults occur outdoors from April to July. Inside buildings they may be found during the winter.

FAMILY TENEBRIONIDAE

Darkling Beetles

This is a large family of beetles, and many species occur in the forest. The adults are hard-shelled, usually dark brown or black in color, and many are clumsy and slow-moving. The larvae are long and slender, and are covered with tough, horny skins. The majority of forest species feed as scavengers on dead vegetable matter. They are commonly found under the bark of dead and dying or rotten trees or logs, and occasionally in the galleries of bark beetles. A few species in the genus *Strongylium* bore into the wood of living trees at stubs or wounds.

FAMILY LYMEXYLONIDAE

Timber Beetles

Timber beetles are slender and elongate; the head is deflexed and narrows behind the eyes to form a neck; the eyes are large;

and the legs are slender. Larvae are also elongate and slender; the head is globular; the ninth abdominal segment is conspicuously armed; and the tenth segment is ventral.

The **chestnut timberworm,** *Melittomma sericeum* (Harr.), once a destructive pest of chestnut, is now found chiefly in white oak. Adults are brown, clothed with fine, silky hair, and about to 11 to 15 mm. long. Eggs are laid in cracks on the surface of the wood. The larvae bore deep into the wood, enlarging their tunnels as needed. Pupation occurs in cells constructed near the surface.

The **sapwood timberworm,** *Hylecoetus lugubris* (Say), tunnels under the bark and across the sapwood of various hardwoods such as poplar, birch, tulip-poplar, basswood, buckeye, and black walnut. Eggs are laid from April to July in the crevices of bark on dying trees or on green logs left lying in the woods. Damage is caused by pin hole defects. Each larva has a slender, barbed spine on the ninth abdominal segment.

FAMILY MORDELLIDAE

Tumbling Flower Beetles

Members of this family are commonly called tumbling flower beetles because they are usually found on flowers and because of their speed in running, jumping, or tumbling. They are usually dark-colored, wedge-shaped, long legged, and from 3 to 14 mm. long. The larvae of certain species are predaceous on other insects.

Powder-post Beetles

A number of species of Coleoptera belonging principally to the families Lyctidae, Anobiidae, Ptinidae, and Bostrichidae are commonly known as powder-post beetles. The term powder-post, in its broadest sense, is used to designate the type of damage in which the interior of wood is reduced to a flour-like powder, some of which is easily jarred from the wood in handling (40). It may occur in the sapwood or heartwood of either hardwood or softwoods. Damage results from tunneling by the adults of certain species and by the larvae of all species. Surface holes made by emerging beetles also mar the surface of the wood. These holes range in diameter from less than 1 mm. to several millimeters, depending on the species involved.

A few species of cerambycids, buprestids, and curculionids also have the powder-posting habit. They are discussed in the sections devoted to these families. Members of families Lyctidae, Anobiidae, Ptinidae, and Bostrichidae, which are discussed below, comprise the majority of destructive species.

Key to Genera of More Important Powder-Post Larvae

The four families and their more important genera, into which powder-post beetle larvae are usually divided, are characterized and separated in the following key. The genera and species are not described, because they have not been thoroughly worked up and are difficult to characterize on the basis of present knowledge.

1. Head almost entirely protruding from the prothorax; mandible usually dentate; terga usually hairy or asperate 3

   Head deeply embedded in prothorax; cutting edge of mandible gougelike, rarely toothed; terga never asperate 2

2. Last abdominal spiracle much larger than all others; mandible with a fleshy process on dorsal inner edge
   Lyctus

   Last abdominal spiracle not abnormally large; mandible with or without fleshy lobe ....Bostrichidae 12

3. First spiracle pushed forward into anterior margin of prothorax; terga without asperities; usually found in stored plant material, seed, etc. ....*Ptinus*

   First spiracle between prothorax and mesothorax; terga usually asperate 4

4. Chitinization between labium and mentum narrow and U-shaped or lacking; mala divided 5

   Chitinization arrow-shaped and pointing posteriorly; mala simple, no inner lobe; spiracles large, annular without spoutlike projection from side ....*Ptilinus*

5. Inner lobe of mala consisting of a strong, curved spine
   Xestobium

   Inner lobe of mala fleshy, usually with several smaller spines or setae 6

6. Inner lobe of mala smaller than outer. Spiracles with a short or long, spoutlike process 7

   Inner lobe of mala about as large as outer; spiracles with a short spoutlike process 9

7. Claw short and curved; a fleshy lobe at base; feeding in stored plant products and seeds ....*Lasioderma*

   Claw usually slender, no lobe; wood borers 8

8. Spiracles with long spoutlike process; mandible with 3 lateral teeth on dorsal edge ....*Anobium*

   Spoutlike process on spiracles only indicated; each side of prothorax curved rodlike impression. Mandible with 3 lateral teeth ....*Hemicoelus*

   Mandible with 2 lateral teeth ....*Microbregma*

9. Labrum about twice as wide as long ....*Ernobius*

   Labrum about as wide as long 10

10. Tergal asperities in about 2 transverse rows ....*Xyletinus*

    Tergal asperities in about 4 transverse rows 11

11. Posterior tergal fold with long, soft hairs ....*Nicobium*

    Posterior tergal fold densely beset with short, spinelike hairs ....*Trichodesma*

12. Mandible with a large, grinding lobe and a soft, fleshy lobe on upper inner margin; no impressed line on side of prothorax; tarsi all bearing chitinized claws 13

    Mandible without chitinous or fleshy lobe; a curved impressed line on side of prothorax, usually only first tarsal claw chitinized 16

13. Prothorax bearing a chitinized tubercle in front of spiracle; no ocelli; cutting edge of mandible entire 14

    No tubercle; ocelli present; cutting edge of mandible dentate 15

14. Inner edge of molar lobe of mandible smooth

    Polycaon
15. Six ocelli; breeds in conifers .... *Stephanopachys*

    Breeds in bamboo .... *Dinoderus*
16. Maxillary mala without projecting style or spine on
    inner edge; labrum trilobed 17

    Maxillary mala with a free projecting style or spine on
    inner edge; labrum entire 18
17. Chitinization of labium broken in middle; prothoracic
    spiracle larger than antennal ring

    Dendrobiella; Xylobiops

    Chitinization of labium continuous across middle; pro-
    thoracic spiracle smaller .... *Scobicia*
18. Spiracle with a spoutlike process; style shorter than
    lacinia .... *Lichenophanes*

    Spiracles without process; style longer than lacinia

    Amphicerus

FAMILY LYCTIDAE

POWDER-POST BEETLES

This family contains the most injurious of the powder-post beetles occurring in North America. According to some authorities their destructiveness to wood and wood products is exceeded only by that of termites. The family has been revised by Gerberg. Keys to all 12 genera in the world and to all 35 species in the new world were also published (*285*).

Lyctid beetles are small, slender, elongate, reddish-brown to black, and about 5 to 6 mm. long. The head is prominent, slightly deflected, and constricted behind the eyes. Mature larvae vary in size but are usually less than 5 mm. long. The body is small, curved, and enlarged at the thorax.

The larvae of North American species bore in the sapwood of seasoned hardwoods, making small tunnels up to 0.6 mm. in diameter. Second growth ash, hickory, and oak which has been seasoned and stored in the same place for 2 or more years are most seriously damaged. Many other hardwoods such as elm, maple, poplar, cherry, persimmon, sycamore, and walnut are also infested. Because starch is an important component of the larval diet, dry seasoned wood of high starch content is damaged most seriously. The same wood may be infested repeatedly, and the interior may be nearly reduced to powder, and rendered useless. Damage is common in stored lumber, the interior woodwork of buildings, furniture, tool handles, pallets, tent stakes, mallets, mauls, and many other stored hardwood products. This is particularly true of wood that is left unfinished until it is placed on the market or in use.

Lyctus spp. are attacked by several species of insect parasites and predators; however, they cannot be relied upon to keep these pests under control (*671*). The clerid, *Tarsostenus univittatus* (Rossi) is a common predator of both adults and larvae. Various species of predaceous mites also destroy large numbers at times.

The genus *Lyctus* Fab. is represented in the United States by 10 species, all of which feed in the sapwood portions of hardwoods. The wood of ring-porous species is more susceptible to attack than that of diffuse-porous species. Oak, hickory, and ash are highly susceptible. Other species often attacked include walnut, butternut, pecan, elm, sycamore, black locust, poplar, sweet gum, wild cherry, and osage orange. The extent of infestation and subsequent damage is proportional to the starch content of the wood. Since heartwood is practically free of starch it is immune. Wood infested for the first time may show very little external evidence of attack, even though the interior is seriously damaged; whereas the surface of older infested wood is perforated with small, round pin holes (fig 37.). Any slight jarring of the wood causes a fine flour-like powder to sift through these holes. The presence of small piles of this powder beneath infested timbers is evidence of infestation.

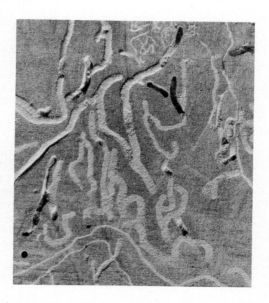

F-519936, F-519929
FIGURE 37.—Lyctus powder-post beetle damage: A, frass packed tunnels in plywood; B, adult exit holes in arm of the frame of an upholstered piece of furniture.

The **southern lyctus beetle**, *Lyctus planicollis* LeC., is one of the most common of the destructive powder-post beetles in this country. It is widely distributed, but is most injurious in the Southern States. Adults are usually black or almost black, have a wider-than-long prothorax with distinctly separated punctations on the disk, and are from 4 to 6 mm. long (fig. 38). The elytra are almost three times as long as wide, bear straight lines of fine long hairs, and are marked with double rows of elongate punctures. Seasoned or partially seasoned wood of oak, ash, and hickory are especially subject to attack. Freshly cut wood is not attacked.

Eggs are laid in the open ends of pores of longitudinal vessels in the wood, at depths of 4 to 7.5 mm. Hatching occurs within a week or two. The larvae burrow through the wood; their tunnels run parallel with the grain and are filled with fine powdery dust.

129

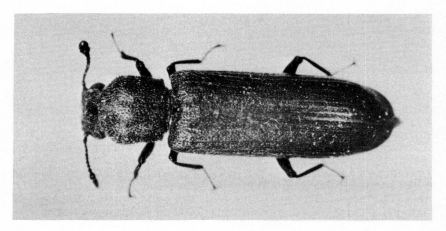

FIGURE 38.—Adult of the southern lyctus beetle, *Lyctus planicollis.*

Full-grown larvae are yellowish-white and about 3 to 5 mm. long. Usually there is only one generation per year, but under certain conditions, a generation may be completed in 3 to 4 months or less. Heaviest emergence and egg laying usually occur during late winter or early spring. Winter is spent in the larval stage (*139, 795*).

Lyctus linearis Goeze, probably an introduced species, occurs throughout the United States. In the eastern half of the country it is commonly encountered in commercial hardwood products, especially in seasoned hickory, oak, ash, and walnut. It is often quite destructive. The adult is brown or reddish-brown and about 2.5 to 5 mm. long. The pronotum is almost square; the elytra are wider than the pronotum and are almost three times as long as wide. The interspace is composed of a single row of large, ovoid punctations, separated by single rows of fine hairs on the carinulae. There is a fringe of fine hairs on the fifth sternite in both sexes.

Other species of *Lyctus* frequently encountered in eastern United States include *L. cavicollis* LeC.; the **western lyctus beetle,** *L. opaculus* LeC.; and *L. brunneus* (Stephens), the **Old World lyctus beetle.** The following distinguishing characteristics should be helpful in identifying them: (1) *L. cavicollis*—elytral striae composed of two rows of punctations. A triangular patch of hairs on each side of median line of apical portion of fifth sternite of female. (2) Western lyctus beetle—two or more rows of punctations separated by carinulae bearing fine hairs in the elytral interspace. The fifth sternite of the male rounded, with a broad fringe of short hairs on the apical margin. (3) Old World lyctus beetle—all carinulae of the elytra bear single rows of fine sparse hair with longitudinal rows of hairs between interspaces. The fifth abdominal sternite of the female bears a "pencil" of hairs.

The genus *Trogoxylon LeC.* is represented in eastern United States by three species. The adults are similar to those of the genus *Lyctus.* They differ in having the femur of the metathoracic leg enlarged and the pubescense of the elytra confused (*285*).

Trogoxylon parallelopipedum (Melsheimer), a common and destructive species, occurs throughout the United States. The adult resembles the adult of the southern lyctus beetle, except that it is somewhat smaller in average size and usually reddish in color. It is distinguished by the prominent, acute, anterior angles of the pronotum; a rounded, depressed postclypeus; and an abruptly expanded antennal club. It breeds in the same type and species of wood as the southern lyctus beetle.

The winter is spent in the larval stage. Heaviest adult emergence and egg laying occurs in the spring. Adults of a second generation emerge in late summer or fall and lay the overwintering supply of eggs. The adults crawl much more rapidly than do those of the southern lyctus beetle. Large numbers of adults once were observed on lumber sawed from green logs only two weeks earlier. Others were observed emerging from lumber that had been sawed from green logs only four or five months earlier (*139*). The related species, *Trogoxylon aequale* (Wallaston) and *T. caseyi* Lesne, have been recorded from Texas.

Minthea rugicollis (Walker), a cosmopolitan species largely confined to the tropics, has been recovered at many points in the United States from wood products imported from abroad.

FAMILY ANOBIIDAE

DEATHWATCH AND DRUGSTORE BEETLES

Members of the family Anobiidae breed in old dry sapwood and heartwood of both hardwoods and coniferous trees. In the forest, many species breed in twigs, while others attack large limbs and trunks. Many species also attack finished timber products, such as the girders, beams, and supports of old houses. Some also infest wooden furniture and other wood products in homes. Sometimes timbers in structures that have escaped attack for more than 20 years become heavily infested and practically destroyed. Other materials in buildings are also attacked, including drugs and groceries. Certain species are known as deathwatch beetles because of the ticking sounds they make as they bore through the wood.

Anobiid beetles are usually reddish brown to black, covered with fine yellow hairs, and from 1.5 to 8 mm. long. The head is hidden by the pronotum; the antennae are inserted on the sides of the head in front of the eyes, and are 11-segmented with the last three segments enlarged; the coxae of the front legs are small; and the tarsi are five-segmented, with the first segment longer than the second. Full-grown larvae are grub-shaped, whitish and about 8 mm. long. The tops of some or all of the segments are roughened with small points or hooks; the thoracic segments are enlarged; and the body is covered with long hairs. White (*760*) discussed the taxonomy of the species occurring in Ohio. Simeone (*651*) discussed the distribution of several species.

As the larvae feed, they excrete small pellets of partly digested wood. These pellets differ from those excreted by drywood termites in being smaller and in tapering toward each end. Pupation occurs in cells in the wood, and the adults emerge through small, usually oval holes about 1.3 to 3 mm. in diameter. Pellets usually drop out through these holes when the wood is struck. The life cycle may require anywhere from 1 to 10 years for completion, depending on the moisture and fungus content of the wood (*460*).

The **furniture beetle**, *Anobium punctatum* (DeG.), an introduced species, occurs in southeastern Canada and in the Northeastern States near the Coast. It has also been found in scattered locations south to the Gulf Coast of Texas and along the west coast of California. Adults are dark brown and about 2.7 to 4.5 mm. long. The metasternum is abruptly excavated in front and the elytra bear linear rows of punctures. Infestations occur in furniture and in the frames and flooring of buildings. Eggs are usually laid in slits, cracks, or crevices in the wood surface, or in old emergence holes. Damage appears to be most serious in old, partly decayed wood, or in old wood such as in antique furniture. The life cycle requires from 1 to 3 years.

Xestobium rufovillosum (DeG.), commonly known as the **death-watch beetle**, is also an introduced species. It is now widely distributed in the Northeastern States where considerable damage has been reported in many old buildings. Adults are robust and dark brown, mottled with patches of yellowish pubescence, and are about 6 to 7.5 mm. long. Both the sapwood and heartwood of hardwoods and softwoods are attacked. Poorly ventilated oak timbers in old buildings are especially subject to attack. The life cycle requires from one to several years.

Hemicoelus carinatus (Say), sometimes known as the **eastern death watch beetle,** is widely distributed in the Northeastern and North Central States, but appears to be most abundant in New England and New York. It also occurs in southeastern Canada. The adult is about 3.4 to 6.8 mm. long. Infestations have been recorded in ash and basswood flooring in Ohio and Michigan, elm floor joists in Minnesota, maple and birch in Indiana, and in sills and flooring in Connecticut. Damage resembles that caused by *Lyctus* spp., but differs in that the emergence holes are larger and the frass coarser. *H. gibbicollis*, the **softwood powder-post beetle,** infests flooring and beams in buildings, and *H. umbrosus* Fall. is sometimes a pest of furniture.

Xyletinus peltatus (Harris) occurs from northern New York to Michigan, southeastward to Florida and southwestward to Arkansas. It attacks both the sapwood and heartwood of seasoned hardwoods and conifers. Adults are reddish-brown to brown and from 3.4 to 6.3 mm. long. Eggs are deposited in cracks or depressions in the wood surface or under small splinters or pieces of debris.[9] Damage is similar to that caused by *Lyctus* species except that it occurs in both the sapwood and heartwood. It is usually confined to the springwood of each annual ring. Damage to joists and flooring in damp buildings is occasionally serious. In North Carolina it is the commonest species found infesting pine floor joists in buildings. In closed, unoccupied buildings, it may be so severe it causes the floors to collapse. *X. lugubris* LeC. has been observed in dead oak twigs in Ohio.

---

[9] Moore, H. B. 1964. Observations on the biology of *Xyletinus peltatus* (Harris) (Coleop.: Anobiidae) with notes on morphology. Unpub. PhD Thesis, Entomol. Dep., North Carolina State Univ.

Ernobius mollis L., an introduced species, has been recorded from southeastern Canada and southward to Florida and Texas. It breeds in coniferous trees. The larvae usually feed under the bark, but may bore into the wood where the bark is thin. Bark-beetle weakened trees are particularly susceptible to attack. Adults are reddish brown and about 3.5 to 5.5 mm. long. *E. tenuicornis* LeC. has been reported from many Eastern States and has been reared from loblolly pine twigs in North Carolina (*40*). Adults are uniformly yellowish brown and are about 2.5 to 3.5 mm. long. *E. granulatus* LeC. occurs in several Eastern States and has been reared from pine twigs and cones. Adults are reddish brown and from 2.5 to 4.5 mm. long.

Petalium bistriatum bistriatum (Say) occurs from Massachusetts and New York to Ohio and south to the Gulf of Mexico. It breeds in the twigs of various hardwoods such as oak, dogwood, walnut, and buckeye (*40*). Adults are about 1.5 to 2.3 mm. long; the head, pronotum, and undersurface are reddish black to black; the elytra black; the legs reddish; and the antennae yellow. *P. seriatum* Fall. has been observed breeding in the dead twigs of pine, oak, and bittersweet. Adults are reddish brown to nearly black and about 1.5 to 2.5 mm. long.

Ptilinus ruficornis Say is a rather common and injurious pest of woodwork in houses and stored products. Adults are about 2.8 to 4.8 mm. long. Males are either completely black, or black with brown elytra, and have reddish-brown to reddish-yellow appendages. Females have the pronotum bright reddish-brown, the elytra reddish-brown to reddish-black, and the appendages reddish-brown to reddish-yellow. *P. pruinosus* Casey has been recorded on cottonwood in Ontario, Canada; Indiana; and Ohio. Adults are similar in size and appearance to those of *P. ruficornis*. *P. pectinicornis* (L.), an introduced species, was first recorded from North America in New York in 1950 (*650*). Infestations were found in joists of beech and in sugar maple timber. Female adults are about 3.9 to 4.7 mm. long. The head, thorax, and abdomen are dark brown.

Trichodesma gibbosa (Say) occurs from New Hampshire to western Ontario in the North and southward to Florida and Texas. Infestations have been found in sweet gum joists and in studding in old historic buildings in Tidewater Virginia. Adults are about 4.5 to 6.8 mm. long and covered with grayish-white to nearly white pubescence.

Microbregma emarginatum emarginatum (Duft.) is generally present throughout the Northeastern States where it breeds in the outer bark of pines and hemlock. Adults are brown to dark brown and about 4 to 5 mm. long. *Trypopitys sericeus* (Say) occurs from Nova Scotia and southward to Florida, Texas, and Arizona. It breeds in the dead branches of oak, cherry, and hickory, and occasionally in flooring, sills, and furniture in buildings. Adults are reddish-brown and about 5 to 6 mm. long.

Coelostethus notatus (Say) occurs in southeastern Canada and southward to North Carolina and Mississippi. It has been recorded feeding in dead oak branches in Ohio. Adults are dark reddish-brown and about 3.2 to 4.3 mm. long. *Eucrada humeralis* (Melsh.) larvae feed beneath the bark of dead oak and beech trees. It occurs from Quebec to Michigan in the North, and south-westward and southeastward to Iowa and South Carolina. *Nicobium castaenum* (Oliv.) a European species, is known to occur in Virginia, South Carolina, and Louisiana. Certain species of *Tricorynus* (=*Catorania*) have been found attacking stored pine cones in the South; others have been reared from twigs of pine and sweet gum. *Platybregmus canadensis* Fisher attacks maple and basswood flooring and elm timbers in buildings. It is known to occur in New Jersey and Ohio.

FAMILY BOSTRICHIDAE

FALSE POWDER-POST BEETLES

The family Bostrichidae contains many species, the larvae of which bore in wood and cause typical powder-post damage. The majority of species breed in the sapwood of hardwoods, but a few attack conifers. Some attack freshly cut and partially seasoned woods with the bark on; whereas others infest wood that has been cut for sometime. Damage consists of circular holes 3 to 9 mm. in diameter and irregular longitudinal tunnels filled with frass or coarse dust.

Bostrichid beetles are reddish-brown to black and about 3 to 6 mm. long. They resemble adults of the family Scolytidae but differ in having a tuberculate and rasplike pronotum, five-seg-mented tarsi, and straight rather than elbowed antennae. The antennal club is three- or four-segmented; the thorax is usually hood-like and covers the head; and the posterior portion of the elytra is frequently tuberculate. The femora and tibia are broad and the latter are frequently toothed on one margin (*254*).

Xylobiops basilaris (Say) is a common species in the Eastern and Southern States. The adult attacks recently felled or dying trees, logs, or limbs with the bark on. Hickory, persimmon, and pecan are most frequently infested, but several other hardwoods also are attacked. Healthy trees growing in close proximity to heavily infested trees are occasionally attacked, but almost al-ways without success. The adults (fig. 39A) are basically black and about 3 to 5 mm. long. The basal part of the elytra is dull reddish or yellow and the posterior end is concave, with three spines or tubercles on each side.

The adult bores through the bark and into the sapwood of its host. Then it constructs a tunnel across the grain just under the wood surface. These tunnels may completely girdle limbs and trunks of small diameter. Eggs are deposited at intervals along the sides of the tunnel. The larvae feed mostly in the sapwood, but also to some extent in the heartwood. Their mines run parallel with the grain and are packed with fine, white, powder-like dust (fig. 39B). Feeding may continue until the wood is quite dry. As a result, adults often emerge after it has been processed. The winter is spent mostly as mature larvae. Hickory and persimmon wood used in the manufacture of small wood products such as shuttle blocks, mallets, and mauls, is occasionally seriously damaged.

F-480474, 480481

FIGURE 39.—*Xylobiops basilaris*, a false powder-post beetle: A, adult; B, larval damage (note openings to frass-frilled larval tunnels in cross-section of a persimmon log).

The **bamboo powder-post beetle**, *Dinoderus minutus* (F.), a very destructive pest of bamboo in the West Indies, occurs in Florida and Louisiana. Adults are reddish-brown to brownish-black and about 2.5 to 3.5 mm. long. The wing covers are often redder than the rest of the upper surface. The female bores into bamboo culms at breaks in the rind, usually at cut ends and trimmed nodes, and then bores a tunnel across the grain. Eggs are deposited in the exposed ends of tubular vessels of the fibrovascular bundles. The interior of infested material is often reduced to masses of powdered wood and fibers. This species is also intercepted frequently in infested bamboo at ports of entry in this country.

In 1967, a heavy infestation of the Oriental bostrichid, *Heterobostrychus aequalis* (Waterhouse), was discovered in oak and mahogany boards in a mill yard in Florida (*728*). This is the most common of the larger bostrichids known to attack packing cases, boxes, plywood, and sapwood in furniture in India. It is widely distributed in southeast Asia and has been recorded attacking the wood of more than 35 species of trees. The adult is reddish-brown to black, shiny, and from 6 to 13 mm. long. The elytra are densely, deeply, and coarsely marked with rows of punctures. Eggs are deposited on the rough surfaces of lumber or logs, in cracks or holes, and in short tunnels made by the female. The larvae, some of which may attain a length of 11 mm., excavate winding tunnels up to 6 mm. in diameter and one foot in length in both hardwood and softwood timber. The life cycle requires from 1 to 6 years.

Stephanopachys rugosus (Oliv.) occurs in eastern United States, mainly east of the Mississippi River, and attacks freshly cut or recently milled pine. Adults are reddish-brown, have roughened and dull, rusty-appearing bodies, and are about 3 mm. long. The larvae normally reach maturity in one year, but may require up to 5 years in seasoned wood. Infestations are occasionally found in floor joists with the bark on in recently constructed buildings. *S. substriatus* (Payk.) occurs in most of the Northern States. It attacks Douglas-fir, hemlock, and all species of pines and firs. Infestations have been reported in furniture and in lumber used in buildings. Oak and hemlock tanbark is also subject to attack and damage. *S. densus* (LeC.), *S. cribratus* (LeC.), and *S. hispidulus* (Casey) breed in pine.

The **apple twig borer**, *Amphicerus bicaudatus* (Say), breeds in dying wood such as large prunings, exposed roots of maple, and diseased and dying branches of most shade and fruit trees. It occurs throughout most of the eastern half of the United States.

A number of other species of Bostrichids are also found in eastern United States. *Lichenophanes armiger* (LeC.) breeds in various hardwods, chiefly dead and dying oak. *L. bicornis* (Web.) has been recorded breeding under dead bark and in the dead wood of sycamore, hackberry, oak, pecan, hickory, apple, beech, and elm. Lumber and other stored stock of oak, hickory, sycamore, and black locust are also infested occasionally. *Scobicia bidentata* (Horn) commonly infests freshly cut wood and lumber of hickory, elm, oak, chestnut, hackberry, and sassafras in the Midwest.

Polycaon stoutii (LeC.), a destructive western species, is frequently shipped to the Eastern States in infested wood. It is especially injurious to veneer plywood which is infested while in storage. Adults are coal black, broad-headed, and from 12 to 25 mm. long. *Dendrobiella aspera* (LeC.), *D. sericans* (LeC.), and *Xyloblaptus quadrispinosus* (LeC.) are frequently encountered in hardwoods shipped to the Eastern States from the southwest.

FAMILY PTINIDAE

SPIDER BEETLES

The beetles in the family Ptinidae are small, spider-like, and from 2 to 4 mm. long. The head and pronotum are much narrower than the elytra; the legs are long; the antennae are long, filiform, and inserted on the front of the head; and the elytra are usually very convex and shiny. The majority of our native species breed in old grass roots or in the bark of dead twigs of trees. Certain other species are destructive in warehouses and museums where they attack collections, to seasoned wood or logs left lying in the woods too long, to wood in old buildings, and to stored products.

The **white-marked spider beetle**, *Ptinus fur* (Linnaeus), a cosmopolitan species, is frequently found damaging dried vegetable and animal materials in warehouses and museums. Infestations also occur in pine and oak woodwork in these structures.

The **brown spider beetle**, *Ptinus clavipes* Panzer, attacks pine boards in old buildings.

FAMILY BRUCHIDAE

Seed Beetles

Members of the family Bruchidae are distinguished by their compact and usually oval bodies, their small heads which are prolonged into beaks, and their short wing covers which leave the tip of the abdomen exposed. The larvae are quite small and feed almost entirely in the seeds of plants.

Amblycerus robiniae (F.) is occasionally a pest in eastern United States. The female deposits her eggs on the pods of honey locust and the larvae feed on the seeds within the pod. Adults are reddish-brown and about 7 mm. long. The body is clothed with grayish-yellow hairs and there are five rows of black spots across the elytra. *Gibbobruchus mimus* (Say) breeds in the seeds of redbud and *Caryobruchus gleditsiae* (L.), in palmetto.

FAMILY CHRYSOMELIDAE

Leaf Beetles

The leaf beetles comprise one of the larger families of Coleoptera, with more than 1300 species occurring in the United States alone. The adults usually are medium-sized or small, short-bodied, and more or less oval. The legs are generally short; but in some species the femora of the hind pair are enlarged. There is great variation in coloring and markings, occasionally even within a species. In some species the entire body, elytra, and legs may have a bright metallic sheen. Some are hairless; others are pubescent or covered with scales or scale-like hairs.

Leaf beetle larvae are usually soft-bodied and frequently have highly pigmented or well-chitinized sclerites on the integument. They vary greatly in shape, depending on their feeding habits. The head usually protrudes, except in the leaf miners, and is bent downward for feeding. The body varies greatly in shape from short and compact to depressed cuneiform, depending on whether the larva is free living or a leaf miner, casebearer, or root feeder.

All members of the family feed on the foliage of plants as adults or larvae, or both. The adults are diurnal and are usually slow moving. Species that are exposed in the larval stage feed

137

gregariously, whereas leaf mining larvae usually feed singly, each within its own mine. Adult feeding is characterized by the presence of holes eaten all the way through the leaf, or by skeletonization usually of the lower surface of the leaf. Free-living larvae either fasten themselves to the surface of a leaf to pupate, or move to the ground to do so. Leaf mining larvae pupate either within the mine, or they vacate it and pupate in the ground. This family has been treated by Leng (451), Leng & Mutchler (452, 453), and Wilcox (264). A few of the more common eastern species are discussed.

The **cottonwood leaf beetle,** *Chrysomela scripta* F., occurs throughout the United States and Canada and feeds on the leaves of poplar, willow, and alder. Adults are about 6 mm. long. The head and thorax are black and the margins of the thorax are yellow or red. The wing covers usually are yellowish with black stripes, but are sometimes almost pure golden to black. Mature larvae are blackish and about 12 mm. long. There are two whitish spots on each side. They are located at the site of the scent glands, one on each side of each segment except those on the prothorax and the last two on the abdomen. The scent glands emit a pungent odor when the larvae are disturbed.

Winter is spent in the adult stage under loose bark or debris or in clumps of grass. Emergence begins in early spring and the adults feed on unfolding leaves or on tender bark at the tips of twigs. Eggs are deposited in groups of 15 to 75 eggs each on the undersides of leaves. The young larvae are gregarious and, feeding side by side, skeletonize the leaves. Later, they feed separately and consume the entire leaf, excepting the larger veins. At maturity they attach themselves to leaf surfaces, the bark, or to weeds and grass beneath the trees to pupate. There are several generations per year. Severe infestations occur occasionally and cause considerable damage.

Chrysomela interrupta F. and *C. crotchi* Brown occur commonly throughout the Eastern States. The adults and larvae of *interrupta* feed on the leaves and at times on the tender bark of alder; adults and larvae of *crotchi* feed on poplar. *C. knabi* Brown feeds on poplar in the Northeastern States. It has also been observed feeding on willow in Tennessee.

The **elm leaf beetle,** *Pyrrhalta luteola* (Mueller) (fig. 40), an introduced species first recorded in North America at Baltimore, Md. well over a century ago, now occurs throughout most of the United States. Its hosts are all species of elm. In the Northeastern States, American elm is often severely attacked and seriously damaged. Farther west, Chinese elm is also frequently heavily attacked. European elms are especially subject to injury. Adults are about 6 mm. long and yellowish to dull green, with a black stripe along the sides of the wing covers. There is also a short, dark spot at the base of each wing cover. Full-grown larvae are dull yellow, with two rows of black spots on the dorsum, and are about 12 mm. long. The head, legs, and tubercles are black and there is a broad yellow stripe down the middle of the dorsum. Pupae are bright orange-yellow with a few black bristles and the pupae are about 5 mm. long.

ELM LEAF BEETLE

A, Undamaged elm leaf.
B, Elm leaf showing
typical feeding damage,
skeletonization, and perfora-
tion; a., egg mass; b,
larvae; c, pupa; and
d, adult elm leaf
beetle. (All about two and one-half
times natural size.)

FIGURE 40.—Elm leaf bettle, *Pynhalta luteola.*

139

Elm leaf beetles spend the winter in sheltered dry places. In the Northeastern States most of them hibernate in house attics, barns, and sheds. During periods of warm weather in the winter many of these become active and cause considerable annoyance by crawling into living quarters or onto windows. Spring emergence begins about the time the buds of elm begin to swell, and the adults fly to nearby elms and feed by chewing holes in the unfolding leaves. Egg laying begins late in May or early June, each female laying from 400 to 800 eggs (725). Hatching begins in about one week and the larvae feed for 2 or 3 weeks on the undersurfaces of the leaves. Only the veins and upper surfaces are left, and the leaves soon dry out and turn brown. Full-grown larvae crawl down the tree and pupate in bark crevices or at the base of the tree. In the eastern United States there may be one or two complete and a partial third generations. Usually the first generation is the most injurious. Beetles maturing in the summer begin entering hibernation quarters on or near the tree on which they fed as early as August.

Shade tree elms are often heavily defoliated, whereas those growing in the forest are usually not seriously infested. The native parasite, *Tetrastichus brevistigma* Gahan occasionally exerts a considerable degree of control in the Northeastern States (62). During damp weather the fungus, *Sporotrichum globuliferum*, is also occasionally effective in control. Some degree of direct control of beetles hibernating in attics can be obtained locally by trapping them as they are leaving their hibernation quarters in the spring. Most of the openings that admit light should be covered with black paper. The remaining openings should be covered with tightly stretched cellophane attached to wooden frames. The inner surface of the cellophane should be covered with a sticky substance such as Tanglefoot.

Pyrrhalta cavicollis (LeC.) occurs in southern Canada and in the Eastern States southward through the Alleghenies and Appalachians to North Carolina and westward to the Rocky Mountains. Its preferred host is pin cherry but it also feeds on plum, other cherries, and peach in heavily infested areas. The adult is red, shining, coarsely punctured, and about 5 mm. long. Larvae are dark brown, with black and yellow spots, and are about 6 mm. long.

The winter is spent in the adult stage. In the spring, eggs are deposited in the soil at the base of the tree, or on the trunk near the base. The larvae climb the tree and feed on the foliage. Full-grown larva return to the ground and pupate in the leaf mold or soil. There is one generation per year. *P. decora decora* Say and *P. tuberculata* (Say) feed on willows.

The **elm calligrapha**, *Calligrapha scalaris* (LeC.), has been reported from eastern Canada and from several widely distributed points in eastern United States. Its preferred and probably only host is elm. Adults are elongate-oval, creamy-white beetles from 8 to 10 mm. long. The head and thorax are dark, metallic green. Each elytron bears from 10 to 14 metallic green spots, a dark green, boot-shaped spot at the base, and a dark, metallic green, irregular stripe along the inner edge. Full-grown larvae are hump-shaped and have yellow heads. The abdomen is light yellow or cream-colored with a black line down the middle of the dorsum.

The winter is spent in the adult stage in bark crevices, in sheltered places around the base of the tree, or in the top 1 or 2 inches of soil. When the adults emerge in the spring, they chew oval or circular holes in the leaves. The larvae devour entire leaves except the veins. When they reach maturity, they crawl down the trunk in search of places to pupate and spend the winter. In heavy infestations, they frequently occur by the thousands on the trunk or under the larger limbs. American elm is sometimes heavily defoliated and damaged in the Midwest (*186*).

Calligrapha multipunctata bigsbyana (Kby.) sometimes completely defoliates willows over large areas in the Northeastern States. It is also a common species in the Midwest. The adult is a somewhat bronzed, metallic green beetle about 6 to 8 mm. long. The antennae and legs are reddish, and the margins of the pronotum and most of the elytra are pale yellow.

The **larger elm leaf beetle**, *Monocesta coryli* (Say, occurs throughout most of the eastern United States from Georgia and Alabama northward to Pennsylvania, Ohio, Indiana, and Illinois and westward to the Plains States (*8*). Its hosts are recorded as native and Japanese elms, river birch, pecan, hawthorn, and hazelnut. Slippery elm is especially favored. The adult is about 12 mm. long. Its color is dull yellow to dark brown, with large greenish patches at the ends of each elytron. Full-grown larvae are reddish-brown, metallic lustered, and about 20 mm. long.

Winter is spent as a full-grown larva in a cell a few inches below the surface of the soil. Pupation occurs in early spring, and adult emergence begins in late May. The adults fly to the tops of their hosts, and feed on the leaves for several days. Eggs are deposited in masses on the undersurfaces of leaves; the larvae are gregarious and skeletonize the foliage; and there is one generation per year. Outbreaks occurred in river bottoms in Piedmont sections of the Carolinas and Alabama in 1964.

The **basswood leaf miner**, *Baliosus ruber* (Weber) (=*B. nervosus* (Panzer), occurs in Canada and throughout most of the eastern United States. Basswood is the favored host, but oak, maple, willow, birch, hop hornbeam, apple, and cherry are also subject to attack. The adult is broad, flat, wedge-shaped, reddish-yellow, and from 4.5 to 7 mm. long. There are indistinct markings on its sides and on the apical half of the elytra. Full-grown larvae are about 6 mm. long. The head and thorax are brownish-red; the rest of the body is white.

The winter is spent in the adult stage under leaves and trash on the ground beneath infested trees (*357*). In the Lake States, the adults emerge in the spring about the time basswood leaves begin to unfold. They feed on these leaves, skeletonizing them. Eggs are deposited singly at the edges of skeletonized areas on these leaves about mid-June, and the larvae feed by mining the leaves (fig. 41). Trees heavily infested for 2 to 3 years are characterized by thin crowns and the presence of dead branches; some trees may be killed. There is one generation of miners per year.

The **alder flea beetle**, *Altica ambiens* subspecies *alni* Harr., occurs in southern Canada and from Maine to Minnesota and New Mexico. It is sometimes a pest of alders growing along roadsides and in parks and other recreational areas. The adult is cobalt blue

F-506746
FIGURE 41.—Leaf of basswood mined by the basswood leaf miner, *Baliosus ruber.*

to greenish-blue above, bluish-black beneath, and about 6 mm. long. Full-grown larvae are dark brown to almost black above, dark yellow beneath, and a little longer than the adult. In Maine, over-wintering adults emerge in early spring and feed for a short time by eating small holes in the leaves before laying their eggs on the lower surface of the leaves. The larvae feed on both leaf surfaces and become mature in about 5 weeks (*794*). In the North there is one generation per year; in the South there may be two. The related species, *A. carinata* Germ. feeds on elm and *A. subplicata* (LeC.), on willow.

The **pine colaspis,** *Colaspis pini* Barber, occurs from Maryland to central Florida and westward to east Texas. It feeds mostly on southern pines but also occasionally on cypress and ornamental spruce. The adult is an elongate-oval, convex, rusty yellow or brown beetle with green reflections, and it is about 4.5 mm. long. Full-grown larvae are sparsely covered with short hairs. Small clusters of longer hairs occur at the lower, outer edges of each body segment.

The winter is spent in the larval stage in cells in the soil. Pupation occurs in the spring and adults begin to emerge by early May. They feed on the needles of the host, chewing from the edges into the midrib. In light infestations, feeding is generally limited to the needles on new growth; whereas in heavy infestations needles over the entire crown may be attacked and entirely consumed. Where this occurs, infested stands appear as if scorched by fire. The larvae feed on the roots of grasses and herbaceous vegetation until fall, and then move deeper in the soil where they spend the winter. Infestations tend to occur on pines growing along the edges of stands bordering on grassland, or on isolated groups of pines growing in fields or yards. Severe infestations have been recorded in pine plantations in Florida, Georgia, and the Gulf Coast States. Nichols[10] discussed the biology of the species in Louisiana.

---

[10] Nichols, H. W. 1962. The biology, distribution, and insecticidal control of pine colaspis (*Colaspis pini* Barber) in Louisiana. (Master's thesis, Louisiana State Univ.)

142

The **locust leaf miner,** *Odontota* (=*Xenochalepus*) *dorsalis* (Thunb.), occurs in southern Canada and throughout most of eastern United States. Its favored host is black locust, but several other tree species such as apple, birch, beech, wild cherry, elm, oak, and hawthorn are also attacked occasionally. The adult is an elongate, flattish beetle about 5 to 6 mm. long. The head is black and the thorax and most of the wing covers are bright orange. The inner edge of each elytron is black, with the blackened area widening posteriorally. The elytra are also deeply pitted, and each elytron bears three longitudinal ridges. A full-grown larva is yellowish-white, somewhat flattened, and a little longer than the adult.

The winter is spent in the adult stage in bark crevices or under debris on the ground. Overwintering adults emerge in the spring, about the time the leaves begin to unfold, and feed for a short time on the leaves, skeletonizing the lower surfaces and eating holes in them. Eggs are deposited on the lower surfaces of leaves in groups of three to five eggs each. They overlap like shingles on a roof, are glued together, and are covered with excrement. All the larvae from a given group of eggs bore into a leaf and feed in a common mine. Later, they separate, and each larva feeds in its own mine. Before reaching maturity, a single larva may mine several leaves. Pupation occurs in the mine, and there is one generation per year.

Outbreaks of the locust leaf miner occur practically every year somewhere within its range and black locust trees on tens of thousands of acres are often defoliated. The defoliated trees are seldom killed, however, unless the damage is incurred during poor growing seasons. At such times trees may be killed in large numbers (*381*). The eulophid parasite, *Clostocerus tricinctus* Ashmead, is reported to have destroyed over 50 percent of the pupae in West Virginia infestations (*747*). Direct control is seldom attempted in the forest, but is sometimes desirable in parks and other recreational areas.

The **imported willow leaf beetle,** *Plagiodera versicolora* (Laich.) (fig. 42), an introduced species, was first reported in this country from Staten Island, New York in 1915 (*366*). It is now widely distributed in the Eastern States and southern Canada (it has also been reported from Alaska) where it feeds on several varieties of willow and poplar. The adult is moderately stout, oval, and about 3.5 to 4.5 mm. long. It is metallic blue or greenish-blue in color, and sometimes tinged with red or bronze. Full-grown larvae are almost jet black and about 5 mm. long. Rows of protuberances run both transversely and longitudinally across and along the body.

The winter is spent in the adult stage under the bark, or in debris or tufts of grass around or near the base of trees. The beetles emerge in April or May and feed for a short period by skeltonizing the leaves or by cutting holes through them. Then the female lays irregular masses of eggs on the leaves. Hatching occurs in about a week. The larvae are gregarious and feed in groups or in rows on the leaf surfaces which they skeletonize. Three and a partial fourth generations per year have been recorded in Massachusetts. Additional generations probably occur

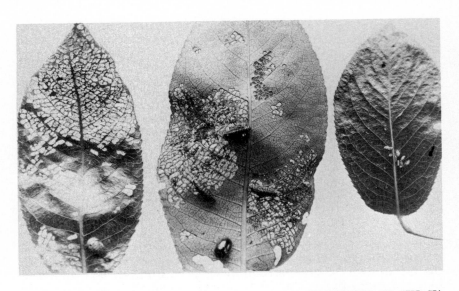

FIGURE 42.—Adults, larvae, and pupae of the imported willow leaf beetle, *Plagiodera versicolora*. Note skeletonization of leaves by larvae and holes eaten in leaves by adults.

farther southward. Heavily infested trees may become entirely brown as early as mid-June. A considerable degree of natural control is exerted by the imported pupal parasite, *Schizonotus sieboldi* (Ratzeburg) (*203*). Extremely cold winters are also fatal to adults not well protected.

Systena marginalis (Ill.) feeds on oak in the midwest and on cypress in northern Florida and southern Georgia. The adult is dull pale yellow in color except for two black lines along the front margin of the elytra and a single black line along the hind margin. The wing covers are densely and coarsely punctate. Adults are present from mid-June to late August and feed by gouging out linear-shaped punctures in the leaves. This usually causes part or all of a cypress leaflet to turn red and die. The beetles occur in large swarms which tend to move about, spending only one to three days in any one place. A single swarm may encompass more than a dozen trees.

Zengophora scutellaris Suffr., an introduced species, feeds on cottonwood and other poplars from New York and New Jersey to Montana and New Mexico. The adult is about 4 mm. long. The head, prothorax, and legs are yellow; the tarsal claws are toothed; there is a prominent tubercle on each side of the prothorax; the elytra are coarsely punctate; and the abdomen is black. The remainder of the body is yellow. Adults feed by skeletonizing the lower surfaces of leaves. The larvae feed singly in the soft inner tissues, chiefly against the upper surface of the leaf, making large black blotch mines. When they become full-grown they vacate their mines and drop to and enter the ground. Here they construct cells several inches below the surface in which to pupate. Trees heavily fed on by both larvae and adults may be completely defoliated.

Glyptoscelis pubescens (Fab.) occurs primarily east of the Mississippi River from Canada to Georgia and feeds on various species of pines and, reportedly, spruce and hemlock. The adult is oblong-oval, robust, broadly rounded posteriorally, dark brown with a brassy or golden sheen, and is from 7 to 10 mm. long. It is also sparsely clothed with an intermixture of white and brownish hairs. Adults feed on the edges of pine needles, causing them to turn brown. Damage has been reported in seed orchards of Virginia, shortleaf, and white pines in North Carolina. *G. barbata* (Say) feeds on hickory and related trees from Connecticut to Pennsylvania. The adult resembles the adult of *G. pubescens* except that it is smaller and its upper surface is shining brown. Krause *(440)* reported on the genus *Glyptoscelis* in the United States and Canada.

Many other chrysomelids also feed on various species of trees in the eastern United States. A few of these and their hosts are as follows: *Pachybrachys peccans* Suffr.—hickory and birch, *P. tridens* (Melsh.)—willow, *P. othonus* (Say)—ash and elm, and *P. carbonarius* Hald.—oak; *Anomoea laticlavia* (Forstr.)—honey and black locusts, elm, live oak, and mimosa; *Tymnes tricolor* (Fab.)—oak, walnut, and ironwood; *Bassareus lituratus* (F.)—hickory; *Derocrepis aesculi* (Drury)—buckeye; *Plagiometriona clavata* (Fab.)—sycamore, basswood, and oak; *Chlamisus platani* Brown—sycamore; *Xanthonia decimnotata* (Say)—oak, beech, and elm; *Paria sexnotata* (Say)—red cedar; *P. quadrinotata* (Say)—walnut and mountain ash; and *Syneta ferruginea* (Germ.)—birch and oak.

FAMILY LUCANIDAE

STAG BEETLES

Stag beetles are distinguished by their very large mandibles which, in the males of certain species, are branched like the antlers of a stag, and by the plates of the antennal club which are rigid and cannot be opened or closed. They are usually found in or beneath rotting logs or stumps. The larvae feed on the juices of rotting wood.

The **giant stag beetle,** *Lucanus elaphus* Fab., the most familiar species, infests dead stumps in the South. Adults are large, fearsome insects, up to 60 mm. long. Male mandibles are branched and are more than half as long as the body. *Pseudolucanus capreolus* (L.) is also a common species. It breeds in the trunks of old, partly decayed trees such as apple, cherry, willow, and oak. The adults fly at night and are frequently attracted to lights. Other eastern species include *Platycerus quercus* Web., *Ceruchus piceus* (Web.), *Dorcus parallelus* Say, and *Sinodendron rugosum* Mann. The first three breed in moist, almost completely decayed logs. *S. rugosum* breeds in decayed alder, willow, and poplars.

FAMILY SCARABAEIDAE

SCARABS

The family Scarabaeidae is represented in the United States by more than 1400 species, the majority occurring in the eastern half of the country. Depending on their feeding habits, members of the family fall into two distinct groups. One group comprises the so-called dung beetles, the larvae and adults of which are saprophytic, feeding on such materials as dung, carrion, decomposing plants. The second group consists of species whose larvae feed on the roots or juices of living plants, decaying vegetable matter, rotten wood, leaf mold, and sometimes manure. The adults feed chiefly on the foliage of plants. They are commonly referred to as lamellicorn leaf chafers. Many of the plant-feeding species are important pests of nursery, plantation, woodlot, shade, and forest trees. The adults of most of these are nocturnal and are strongly attracted to lights.

Scarab beetles have stout bodies, the last 3 to 6 or 7 segments of the antennae are leaflike and capable of being opened or closed. Their front legs are fitted for digging. The larvae or grubs are usually thick, white or yellow, enlarged posteriorally, bent in the shape of a crescent, and they have well-developed legs.

The genus *Phyllophaga* Harris is represented in the United States and Canada by more than 100 species, the majority of which occur in the eastern part of the continent (*462*). The adults, commonly called May or June beetles, are robust, oval, light straw to very dark brown, and from about 12 to 25 mm. long (fig. 43 A). The wing covers are smooth and shiny or are covered with short hairs. The antennae are lamellate and end in 3-jointed clubs; the tarsal claws are armed with a small tooth near the middle. The larvae, commonly called white grubs, are milky white, strongly curved, and about 25 mm. long at maturity (fig. 43 B). The head is brownish; all of the hind parts are shiny; and body contents are visible through the skin.

The adults of certain species are most abundant in the spring, usually in May; others reach peaks of abundance in June or July (*616*). They tend to stay out of sight under stones, leaves, or trash, or in the soil during the day; and to fly, mate, and feed at night. Eggs are laid in masses in the soil at depths of 3 to 7 inches, each egg being placed in a cavity in the center of a ball of dirt. Newly-hatched larvae feed on organic matter; then they move to tender roots of seedlings and other plants to feed. The winter is spent in the larval stage at depths determined by temperatures and frost levels. Pupation takes place in the soil at depths of a few inches to a foot or more. In the South, the life cycle is completed in 1, 2, or 3 years; in the Central States 2 to 3 years are required; farther North, from 3 to 4 years are needed (*684*).

Phyllophaga larvae, or white grubs, have caused heavy losses in forest nurseries and plantations in the South, East, and Central and Lake States during the past several years. Also, here and there throughout the region, many trees are lightly to heavily defoliated by the adult beetles every year, especially in woodlots and around the edges of forest stands. A few of the more common and important species are discussed briefly below:

Phyllophaga drakei (Kirby) occurs throughout most of eastern United States and southern Canada. Adults are dark brown, shiny, and about 25 mm. long. They feed on the leaves of beech, birch, dogwood, maple, basswood, elm, and willow. The larvae are important pests in forest nurseries and plantations in the Lake States and Canada.

A

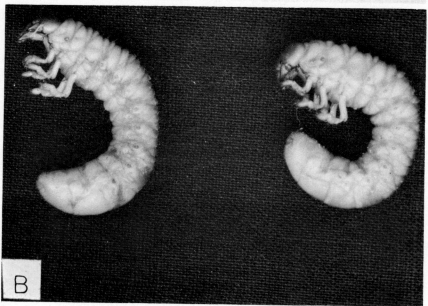

B

F-494655, F-494654

FIGURE 43.—*Phyllophaga species*: A. adult; B, white grubs.

Phyllophaga luctuosa (Horn) occurs primarily along the Atlantic and Gulf Coasts in sandy, oak-pine regions, but also farther
north and inland to Tennessee, Oklahoma, and Iowa. Adults are
dark-brown to black, moderately shiny, and about 21 mm. long.
They feed on persimmon, mulberry, tupelo, walnut, willow, beech,

147

birch, and loblolly and longleaf pines. The larvae are often destructive in nurseries and, probably, plantations.

Phyllophaga tristis (Fab.) occurs throughout eastern United States and in southern Canada. Adults are light or dark yellowish brown or slightly reddish, and about 12 mm. long. They seem to prefer the foliage of oaks but also feed on maple, persimmon, hickory, elm, and willow. The larvae have caused serious losses in nurseries in the Lake States.

Phyllophaga prununculina (Burm.) occurs in the South Atlantic and Gulf Coast States. It is especially common in the Sand Hills of South Carolina. Adults are reddish-brown to black, with the surface shining and slightly pruinose, or dull smoky and are 12 to 18 mm. long. They feed on pines, preferably loblolly and longleaf, and sometimes oaks and persimmon. The larvae have caused serious losses in pine nurseries and plantations in South Carolina.

Phyllophaga rugosa (Melsh.) occurs mostly in the Northern States and southern Canada. Adults are reddish-brown to black, shiny, and from 18 to 25 mm. long. They feed on a wide variety of hardwoods. The larvae are often destructive in coniferous nurseries in the Lake States.

Phyllophaga crenulata (Froel.) occurs throughout eastern United States. Adults are brown, with a covering of short, recumbent hairs, and are about 17 to 20 mm. long. They feed on a wide variety of hardwoods, preferably persimmon, hickory, basswood, willow, birch, and horse chestnut. The larvae are often serious pests in coniferous nurseries in the Lake States.

Phyllophaga forsteri (Burm.) occurs generally throughout eastern United States. Adults are reddish-brown and shiny, have dusky heads, and are about 16 mm. long. They feed on a wide variety of hardwoods such as beech, birch, elm, magnolia, maple, tupelo, walnut, and willow. There are also reports of their feeding on pine. The larvae are often destructive in nurseries in the South.

Phyllophaga prunina (LeC.) occurs throughout the central part of the United States east of the Rocky Mountains. Adults are chestnut-brown to black and about 18 mm. long. They feed on various hardwoods such as beech, elm, walnut, basswood and willow. Feeding on pine has also been observed. The larvae are sometimes injurious in nurseries in the Lake States.

Phyllophaga implicta Horn occurs mostly in the Mississippi and Ohio River Valleys. Adults are orange-brown to brown (with the head and thorax darker), shining, and about 14 to 18 mm. long. They feed on beech, dogwood, elm, sycamore, tupelo, walnut, willow, basswood, maple, and other plants. The larvae killed millions of seedlings in nurseries in Iowa in the thirties.

The genus *Polyphylla* Harris is represented by a number of species in eastern United States, a few of which are sometimes injurious. The beetles are somewhat larger than those of the genus *Phyllophaga*. A few species are entirely brown while the remainder are brown- or white-striped. They are distinguished further by their massive antennal clubs, which consist of six or seven extremely long thin, flat, parallel, leaflike plates.

The larvae of *Polyphylla variolosa* Hentz have caused heavy losses in coniferous nurseries in the Northeast. The larvae of *P. occidentalis* (L.) have been observed feeding on the roots of pine seedlings, but they prefer the roots of grasses. They would appear to be potentially harmful in nurseries and plantations. *P. hammondi* LeC. occurs in the western part of the Central States and has the interesting habit of depositing its eggs in rotten wood.

The genus *Serica* MacL. contains a number of species, the adults of which closely resemble those of the genus *Phyllophaga* except for their much smaller size and their regularly spaced, elytral striae. They are usually less than one-fourth as large as May beetles. The adults are sometimes abundant enough to cause noticeable defoliation in hardwood stands. The larvae have also been known to cause damage in heavily infested nurseries, but they are usually not very destructive. Adults emerge from mid-May to mid-August but are usually most abundant in June. The life cycle requires 2 to 3 years. Common species include *S. sericae* (Ill.), which is often abundant; *S. tristis* LeC., which has been known to defoliate spruce in plantations in southern Canada; and *S. vespertina* (Gyll.) and *S. intermixta* Blotch.

The genus *Dichelonyx* Harris is represented in eastern America by many species. The beetles are small, about 6 to 12 mm. long, and are often brightly colored. A distinguishing characteristic is the presence of two spurs on each middle and hind tibia. The larvae are grubs, which never exceed 18 or 20 mm. in length. Adults are most common in June and July, and the life cycle requires 2 to 3 years. Saylor (*633*) revised the genus.

Dichelonyx albicollis (Burm.) is a well-known species. It has been recorded from New Jersey, Michigan, and Ontario and feeds both during the day and night on the needles of pine, preferably jack pine. The adult is greenish, shiny, and about 12 mm. long. *D. elongata* (F.) occurs from New England and New Jersey to Oklahoma and Kansas. The adults feed at night on the leaves of various hardwoods, especially black birch and alder. The adult is smaller and somewhat darker than the adult of *D. albicollis*. A third species, *D. subvittata* LeC. has been recorded feeding on oak, hazel, and pine from New England to the Lake States and in southern Canada.

The genus *Diplotaxis* Kirby contains a number of species that feed mostly on conifers, preferably pines. The beetles are usually brown or reddish-brown and, except for having five visible ventral abdominal sternites, resemble members of the genus *Phyllophaga*. The exoskeleton is also quite hard and rigid. *D. sordida* (Say) occurs commonly on red and jack pines in the Lake States, and the larvae have caused serious damage in nurseries and plantations in New York. The adult is slate-colored with yellowish hairs on the pronotum, and it is about 10 to 12 mm. long. *D. liberata* (Germ.) also occurs commonly on pines in the Lake States. The adult is blackish, hairless, and about 12 mm. long.

The **Asiatic garden beetle**, *Maladera castanea* (Arrow), an introduced species first recorded in North America in New Jersey in 1921, is now widely distributed in the Eastern States south to South Carolina. Adults are usually cinnamon-brown and about 6 to 12 mm. long. They fly at night and feed on more than 100 species of plants, including forest and shade trees such as maple, horse chestnut, willow, boxelder, and Ailanthus. Young pines, hemlocks, and yews in nurseries are defoliated occasionally and seriously injured. The roots of rhododendron and azalea are damaged occasionally by the larvae.

The **rose chafer,** *Macrodactylus subspinosus* (F.), is widely distributed in eastern United States. Adults are tan to reddish-brown, densely covered with dull yellow scales or hairs, and have long, reddish-brown legs. They feed on a wide variety of hosts, including many species of forest and shade trees (fig. 44). In heavily infested areas, they appear in swarms in late May or early June and feed first on the opening buds. Later, they attack the flowers, fruit, and foliage. The larvae feed mostly on the roots of grasses but may also attack the roots of tree seedlings where they are abundant.

The **European chafer,** *Amphimallon majalis* (Raz.), an introduced species first recorded in New York in 1940, now occurs in several Eastern States and southern Ontario. The adult is oval-shaped, light brown or tan, and about 14 mm. long. A distinguishing characteristic is its toothless, uncleft, hind tarsal claw. During the peak of the flight season they are often seen swarming around various trees and tall shrubs. The larvae feed on the roots of a wide variety of plants, including the seedlings of such tree species as spruce and Douglas-fir.

The **pine chafer,** *Pachystethus oblivia* Horn., occurs from New York to the Lake States and south to Georgia. Male beetles have the head and pronotum greenish-bronze and the elytra dark tan. They are about 6.5 mm. long. Females are light tan in color and

COURTESY CONN. AGR. EXPT. STA.
FIGURE 44.—Birch leaf skeletonized by the rose chafer, *Macrodactylus subspinosus.*

about 9 mm. long. They feed mostly on the new needles of various pines, eating notches in them just above the sheath and causing the ends to die. Heavily infested trees become brownish or scorched in appearance. Needle browning was recorded in several thousand acres of young loblolly pines in southeastern North Carolina in 1959 and 1960. The base of the damaged needle usually survives, however, and the needle grows to about one-half its normal length. The winter is spent in the larval stage several inches deep in the soil. Pupation occurs in the spring, and the adults emerge in June or earlier. Eggs are deposited in the soil near their pine hosts. Hatching occurs in 10 to 15 days and the larvae feed on the roots of various plants, including trees, until the onset of cold weather. There is one generation per year.

Infestations of the pine chafer tend to occur in open pine stands and plantations. Numerous outbreaks have occurred in the Lake States and South during recent years. The majority were short-lived and limited in size, but several were quite extensive and lasted for several years. *Pachystethus lucicola* (F.), occurs from New England to the Lake States and Kentucky. It severely damaged larch seedlings in a nursery in New York.

The **Japanese beetle,** *Popillia japonica* Newm., an introduced species first recorded in North America near Riverton, New Jersey in 1916, now occurs in all or parts of at least 14 States from New Hampshire and Vermont to North Carolina and Ohio. Spot infestations have also been recorded in many other States and in Ontario and Nova Scotia, Canada. The adult is broadly oval and nearly 12 mm. long. The body is a bright, metallic green; the legs, a darker green; and the elytra, a coppery brown. There are two small tufts of white hairs just behind the wing covers and five patches of white hairs on each side. The wing covers are shorter than the abdomen. Full grown larvae are about 25 mm. long, typically grub-shaped, and have the last two rows of spines on the underside of the last abdominal segment arranged in the shape of a V.

The Japanese beetle feeds on the foliage, flowers, and fruits of a wide variety of plants. Many species of forest and shade trees are subject to defoliation, especially Japanese and Norway maples, horse chestnut, sycamore, gray birch, walnut, Lombardy poplar, basswood, mountain-ash, and American, English, and Chinese elms. Feeding is usually confined to young, tender leaves. Damaged leaves may be skeletonized or they may also have large, irregular holes chewed out. In heavily infested areas, the trees may be almost entirely defoliated. The larvae may also seriously damage the roots of ornamental nursery stock.

The winter is spent in the larval stage in the soil. Pupation occurs in early spring, and the adults emerge from late May to early July. They are gregarious and are often found feeding in masses on certain plants, while nearby plants are uninfested. Female beetles enter the soil to depths of 1 to 4 inches to deposit their eggs. Moist, loamy soil covered with closely cropped grass is a favorite site. There may be two generations per year in the southern parts of the species' range. Farther north, the life cycle may require two years.

Disease pathogens, especially the bacterium, *Bacillus popilliae* Dutky, often destroy large numbers of the larvae. Several introduced parasites, *Tiphia vernalis Rohwer* and *T. popilliavora* Rhower in particular, also exert a considerable degree of control (*255*).

Cotalpa lanigera L., the **goldsmith beetle,** occurs throughout eastern United States and feeds on the foliage of various hardwoods, such as aspen, oak, and willow. The adult is broadly oval, convex, and from 20 to 26 mm. long. It is a brightly colored beetle, the elytra being lemon yellow, and the head and thorax burnished golden. The venter is greenish to copper colored and covered with whitish wool. The legs are reddish-yellow. Full-grown larvae are about 43 mm. long. The head is tan and the underside of the last abdominal segment is thickly covered with hooked spines. Adults emerge in late spring and the females deposit their eggs in the soil. The larvae feed on the roots of various plants, probably including young conifers. Adults have been observed fairly commonly in nurseries in the Lake States. The life cycle requires from 2 to 3 years for completion.

The **green June beetle,** *Cotinis nitida* (L.), one of the most widely recognized members of the family, occurs throughout much of eastern United States, most commonly in the Atlantic and Gulf Coastal States and in the Mississippi River Valley. The adult is usually velvety green above, with the margins orange yellow, and is about 10 to 25 mm. long. The under-surface is shining green and orange yellow, and the head is armed with a hornlike process. Full-grown larvae are up to 50 mm. long and have the interesting habit of crawling on their backs.

Adults are most numerous during June and July, and the females deposit their eggs in soil rich with organic matter. The larvae feed on the organic matter during the remainder of the season and then enter hibernation. In the spring, they move close to the surface and feed on both dead vegetation and the roots of living plants. Lawns and golf courses are often damaged severely. Seedlings in forest nurseries are sometimes injured.

The genus *Dynastes* Kirby, which contains the largest known beetles, is represented in eastern United States by only one species, the **eastern hercules beetle,** *D. tityus* (L.). It has been recorded from New York, Indiana, and Arkansas south to the Gulf of Mexico and breeds in decayed hardwood stumps and logs. It is also found occasionally in cavities in the bases of living trees. The adult is very large, from 40 to 60 mm. long and is usually greenish-gray or tan, except for mottlings or blotch-like areas of black. The male is armed with a large pronotal horn which projects forward and almost meets another horn which projects upward from the front of the head. Females are somewhat smaller than the males and are without horns. The habits of the adults are not well understood; however, they have been observed feeding on sap oozing from wounds on ash trees.

The genus *Xyloryctes* Hope is represented in eastern forests by 3 or 4 species, one of which, the **rhinoceros beetle,** *X. jamaicensis* (Drury), is common in hardwood stands in the South. The adults are robust, shiny beetles, about 28 mm. long. They are dark chestnut to blackish-brown above, and paler and thickly clothed with reddish hairs below. The male has a single, large curved horn on top of the head. In the female, a large tubercle replaces the horn.

152

The larvae are usually found in leaf mold on the forest floor. Adults are usually found in the vicinity of ash trees.

At least four species of the genus *Pelidnota* MacLeay occur in eastern forests, one of which, *P. punctata* (L.), is fairly well known. The larvae are usually found in decayed hardwood stumps but sometimes in decaying roots and logs. The adult is about 20 mm. long and reddish-brown above, with three black spots on each wing cover and one on each side of the pronotum. The base of the head, the scutellum, and the entire underside of the body are deep bronzed green. The species is not injurious.

The genus *Polymoechus* LeC. is represented in eastern forests by several species. The most common and widely distributed one is *P. brevipes* LeC. The larvae are found most commonly in decayed hardwood stumps, roots, and logs. Adults are blunt, convex, dark chestnut brown, and about 16 mm. long. The species is not considered to be injurious.

The genus *Osmoderma* Serville is represented in eastern forests by at least four species, two of which, *O. eremicola* Knoch and *O. scabra* (Beauv.), are fairly common. The larvae feed in decayed cavities of dead or dying trees or logs. The adults are broadly oval and depressed dorsally and have heavy leathery elytra; *O. eremicola* is dark chestnut brown, smooth and shiny, whereas *O. scabra* is bronzy-purple black and rough in texture. They are approximately 25 mm. long. When handled, they emit a strong leather-like odor.

The genus *Trichiotinus* Casey contains several species, the adults of which are frequently seen around flowering trees and shrubs, wild cherry in particular. They are variegated, the body is densely pubescent; the elytra are almost as wide as long; the legs are long and slender; and they range in length from 9 to 15 mm. The larval stage is spent in dead logs and stumps.

FAMILY ELATERIDAE

CLICK BEETLES

Click beetles are so-called because of the presence of a spine on the prothorax which snaps into a groove on the mesosternum with an audible click. This mechanism enables an adult lying on its back to throw itself into the air and land on its feet. The larvae are known as wireworms because of their long, narrow, fusiform, tough-skinned bodies. Forest-inhabiting species are predominantly phytophagous, but a few are predaceous on other insects, such as wood borers. Vegetable feeding species usually confine their attacks to dead and often well-decayed wood and are of little economic importance. Dietrich (*192*) reported on the species occurring in New York State.

The **eyed click beetle**, *Alaus oculatus* (L.), is a voracious feeder on various species of borers in hardwoods and the related species, *A. myops* (F.), on borers in pines. Adults of *A. oculatus* are grayish-black, with two large eyelike spots on the prothorax, and are 25 to 50 mm. long. Adults of *A. myops* are more slender and darker, and are only about 20 to 40 mm. long. They also have eye spots.

Other predaceous species include *Lacon discoidea* (Web.) and *L. avita* Say which are found in pines, and *Hemicrepidus bilobatus* (Say) which occurs in hickory. *Ctenicera triundulata* (Rand.) and *C. nitidula* (LeC.) have been observed feeding on cocoons of the European spruce sawfly in Canada *(541)*.

FAMILY CLERIDAE

CHECKERED BEETLES

This is one of the most important families of insect predators attacking injurious forest insects. The adults are active, antlike, brightly-colored, hairy beetles about 3 to 13 mm. long. They feed on adult beetles. The larvae live in the galleries and tunnels of bark beetles and wood borers and destroy the immature stages of these insects.

Adults are distinguished by their 11-jointed and generally serrate antennae, the outer joints of which are longer and form open or compact clubs. The tarsi are five-jointed and the first four joints bear membranous appendages. Larvae are soft-bodied, elongate and parallel-sided, frequently highly colored though often white and thin-textured, and are from 9 to 13 mm. long.

Most species spend the winter in the larval stage. Others overwinter as pupae or as adults in pupal cells in the bark. The larvae travel down the tunnels of their hosts eating one larva after another. Some are capable of consuming several times their own weight of these larvae *(91)*. A few of the more important predators of forest insects are discussed below.

Chariessa pilosa (Forst.) is one of the most common species in eastern forests. Its known hosts include several species of borers in hardwoods, and the smaller European elm bark beetle. The adult (fig. 45) is a wedge-shaped, flattened beetle about 6 to 13 mm. long. The thorax is red with two black stripes and the wing covers are black with dense, fine punctures. The larva is fairly robust, widest at the middle, and of a bluish tinge. Adults are often observed feeding on insects attracted to freshly cut logs during the summer.

Thanasimus dubius (Fab.) is one of the most important predators of destructive bark beetles in eastern United States. The adult is a brightly-colored, hairy beetle about 7 to 10 mm. long. The head, thorax, and base of the wing covers are dull red; the antennae and legs are red to pitch black; and the wing covers are mostly black with cross bands of whitish hairs. The larva is elongate, fusiform, and purplish with brown sclerotized areas.

Winter is spent in either the larval, pupal, or adult stages. In early spring, the adults emerge and fly to beetle-infested trees or logs and feed on bark beetles as they emerge from hibernation. Eggs are deposited in entrances to bark beetle galleries. Young larvae feed on bark beetle eggs; older ones feed on beetle larvae, pupae, and adults. Pupation occurs in cells in the outer bark *(367, 718)*.

F-519949
FIGURE 45.—Adult of *Chariessa pilosa*, a predator of wood-boring larvae.

Enoclerus nigripes (Say) larvae feed on bark beetles in conifers, and on wood borers in hardwoods. Adults are brightly colored and about 8 to 12 mm. long. The head, thorax, base of the wing covers, and the undersides are dull red; the remainder is black except for two yellowish cross bars on the wing covers. The larvae are similar to those of *Thanasimus dubius*. The **black-bellied clerid** *E. lecontei* Wolc., has many hosts including bark beetles and weevils in pine, spruce, and juniper. It also feeds on bark beetles, weevils, and small borers in hardwoods.

Monophylla terminata (Say) feeds on borers and bark beetles in hardwoods. There also are reports of its feeding on white pine weevil larvae in white pine. Adults are about 4 to 8.5 mm. long. The eyes are deeply notched in front, the last joint of the antenna is as large or larger than all of the others combined, the thorax is yellow with a black disk, and the sides of the wing covers are yellow. The larvae are white, soft-textured, and bear two well-separated hooks on the ninth abdominal segment.

Cymatodera bicolor (Say) is an important enemy of round-headed and flat-headed borers in hardwoods in Eastern United States. Adults are about 5 to 10 mm. long. The color is dull blackish except for the legs, thorax, and basal joints of the antennae which are reddish-yellow mixed with black. The larvae are purplish.

Tarsostenus univittatus (Rossi) is an important predator of powder-post beetles and other borers in dry, seasoned wood. The adult is small, slender, and shiny black except for a white mark across the middle of the elytra. The larva is very small and a

155

light violet, except for brown or yellow markings. There are two recurved hooks on the ninth abdominal segment.

Neichnea laticornis (Say) feeds on various species of bark beetles in the Middle Atlantic States. The adults are small, slender, and black except for a spot on the head and the sides of the thorax, which are golden yellow.

Many other clerids are also predaceous on various forest insects in the Eastern States. *Priocera castenae* Newm. feeds on bark beetles in conifers; *Phlogistosternus dislocatus* (Say) and *Orthopleura damicornis* (F.) feed on the larvae of borers and bark beetles in the twigs of hardwoods; *Cregya oculata* (Say) feeds on larvae of borers and bark beetles in both hardwoods and conifers. Knull (*432*) discussed the clerids occurring in Ohio.

FAMILY DERMISTIDAE

Dermestid Beetles

Dermestid beetles are compact, oval to convex, and usually extremely hairy. Some are spotted with gray, brown, or orange hairs which rub off easily. The larvae are cylindrical and covered with long hairs. Some larvae are soft; others are hard-shelled.

A few species are found under the bark of trees where they feed on dead insects. Some are troublesome pests in collections of insects or stuffed animals, on which they feed. The **hide beetle,** *Dermestes maculatus* DeGeer, and the **larder beetle,** *D. lardarius* L., have damaged cargoes of lumber in ship holds where hides were stored previously. In efforts to construct pupal chambers, *D. maculatus* has also been known to damage seriously the surface of lumber in warehouses. The majority of dermestids feed on skins, dried meats, furs, and carpets.

FAMILY BUPRESTIDAE

Flatheaded Borers

The flatheaded borers include several destructive pests of forest and shade trees. More than 150 species and varieties have been recorded east of the Mississippi River, many of which are discussed by Franklin and Lund (*264*). The larvae of all species are borers, and they feed in all parts of the tree. Some mine the leaves, and some construct tunnels in the inner bark and outer wood of the trunk, branches, and roots. The majority of species, however, excavate winding tunnels through sound and decaying sapwood. Many bark-boring species are capable of girdling and killing both healthy and injured trees. Wood-boring species are often highly destructive of recently felled sawlogs, often seriously reducing or destroying their uesfulness as lumber.

Buprestid beetles are usually somewhat flattened or oval-shaped, and are beautifully marked or metallic-colored. The head is strongly deflexed and is inserted into the prothorax to the eyes. The antennae are serrate, 11-jointed, and inserted on the front; the prosternum is prolonged behind and fits into the mesosternum; the elytra usually cover the abdomen; and the first two of the abdominal sternites are fused.

Buprestid larvae are distinguished primarily by well-developed ambulatory plates on the upper and lower surfaces of the first segment behind the head, by the presence of a central line, groove, or *V* on the upper plate, and by the absence of legs. The larvae of all bark and wood boring species are typically "flatheaded," a condition caused by the greatly enlarged first and sometimes second and third thoracic segments (fig. 46). Leaf-mining larvae are flattened, rather oval-shaped, deeply notched at the sides, and gradually taper toward the rear. The true head in all larvae is comparatively small, more or less retracted into the first thoracic segment, and scarcely visible.

FIGURE 46.—Typical larva of a flatheaded borer.

Bark- and wood-boring buprestids deposit their eggs singly or in masses either on the bark, in crevices in the bark or wood, or under the bark at the edges of wounds. Weakened, injured, dead, or dying trees and stumps are usually attacked. Occasionally, green trees are also infested. The larvae feed either under the bark, in the sapwood or heartwood, or in two or more of these places. Their mines are winding and usually oval in cross section. Eventually, they terminate in elongated pupal cells which are connected to the surface by short, oval exit holes. A characteristic of the mines is that they usually are packed tightly with layers of sawdust-like borings and pellets and their walls are scarred with fine, transverse lines. Many wood-boring species spend the winter as adults in pupal cells. A few overwinter in the larval stage. The life cycle usually requires 1 or 2 years, but in certain species it takes many years.

Key to the Adults of the Eastern Genera of Buprestidae

1. Hind coxal plates scarcely widened internally 2
   Hind coxal plates distinctly widened internally, front margin straight, hind margin oblique 10
2. Prothorax truncate at base 3
   Prothorax lobed at base 5
3. Mesosternum scarcely visible; breeds in small branches of oak ....*Mastogenius*
   Mesosternum emarginate 4
4. Scutellum indistinct ....*Acmaeodera*
   Scutellum plainly indicated ....*Ptosima*
5. Antennae not received in grooves on underside of prothorax 6
   Antennae received in grooves on underside of prothorax 7

6. First joint of hind tarsi scarcely elongate; gall formers on alder .... *Eupristocerus*
   First joint of hind tarsi as long as 3 following joints *Agrilus*
7. Tarsi over half as long as tibiae .... *Paragrilus*
   Tarsi much shorter than tibiae 8
8. Scutellum large; larvae leaf miners in certain leguminous plants .... *Pachyschelus*
   Scutellum small 9
9. Prosternum with posterior cavity; larvae leaf miners in various species of oak .... *Brachys*
   Prosternum without cavity; leaf miners in *Scirpius* and other allied plants .... *Taphrocerus*
10. Antennal pores scattered on both faces of serrate joints 11
    Antennal pores concentrated in pits on these joints 12
11. Apical ⅓ of elytral margin entire, or finely serrate; borers in pine stumps and logs .... *Chalcophora*
    Apical ⅓ of elytral margins strongly serrate; borers in hardwood trunks .... *Chalcophorella*
12. Front not narrowed at insertion of antennae; eyes scarcely approaching, often distant on vertex 13
    Front narrowed at insertion of antennae; eyes oblique, close together on vertex 21
13. Prosternal spine obtusely angulated behind prothracic coxae; epimera of metathorax not covered by abdomen 14
    Prosternal spine acutely angulated behind prothoracic coxae; epimera of metathorax partly concealed by abdomen 18
14. Prosternal spine obtusely rounded at apex 15
    Prosternal spine acute at apex; larvae heartwood borers in oak and ironwood .... *Cinyra*
15. Mentum entirely corneous 16
    Anterior edge of mentum coriaceous .... *Buprestis*
16. Elytra striate 17
    Elytra not striate .... *Trachykele*
17. Scutellum small, round, oval .... *Dicerca*
    Scutellum large, trapezoidal; pronotum with smooth median line .... *Poecilonota*
18. Anterior edge of mentum coriaceous .... *Melanophila*
    Mentum entirely corneous 19
19. Base of thorax trucate 20
    Base of thorax sinuate .... *Xenorhipis*
20. Last ventral segment of abdomen punctured like the segments preceding .... *Anthaxia*
    Last ventral segment of abdomen much more densely punctured than the preceding segments ...... *Agrillaxia*
21. Hind tarsi with 1st joint considerably longer than 2nd; 3rd joint not prolonged at sides; sapwood and bark borers .... *Chrysobothris*
    Hind tarsi with 1st joint only slightly longer than 2nd; 3rd joint prolonged at sides; heartwood borers in various hardwoods .... *Actenodes*

158

Key to the Larvae of the More Important Genera of Buprestidae

1. Leaf miners, larvae spindle- or wedge-shaped 13
   Twig or bark borers or occasionally gall makers; larval form elongate, parallel, last segment ending in a pair of spines 14
   Wood or bark borers; larvae hammer-headed or pestle-shaped; no spines 2

2. Dorsal plate of prothorax marked with an inverted Y, V, or U 3
   Dorsal plate of prothorax bearing only a single median impression or groove 12

3. Dorsal plate of prothorax bearing chinous rugosities 4
   Dorsal plate of prothorax smooth 8

4. Rugosities on prothoracic plates strongly developed forming ridges; margins of plates distinct 5
   Rugosities on plates not forming ridges, dispersed; plates indistinct on margins 6

5. Dorsal prothoracic plate marked with a distinct inverted Y; breeds in conifers .... *Chalcophora*
   Dorsal plate marked with an inverted V or U; breeds in hardwoods .... *Chalcophorella*

6. Asperate areas of dorsal plate longer than wide; ventral area completely bisected by median groove; first abdominal segment smaller than second; mandible usually tridentate .... *Melanophila*
   Asperate areas of dorsal plate wider than long or of approximately the same dimensions; ventral area not completely bisected 7

7. Dorsal plate marked by an inverted Y or U surrounded on the anterior half by the asperities suggesting a hood; ventral plate marked by a median groove extending from posterior margin forward but not completely bisecting plate; mandible usually tridentate, labrum usually tridentate .... *Buprestis*
   Dorsal and ventral asperate plates nearly circular; ventral bearing a median groove, which extends backward from the anterior margin about ⅔ of the distance; mandible usually bidentate; labrum entire .... *Chrysobothris*

8. Metathorax bearing a dorsal and ventral pair of ampullae, ventral groove not bisecting prothoracic plate .... *Anthaxia*
   Metathorax normal; ventral groove bisecting plate 9

9. Anterior end of dorsal inverted Y or V marking simple 10
   Anterior end of both dorsal and ventral markings with broad reticulated ends 11

10. Dorsal marking an inverted Y; breeds in oak .... *Cinyra*
    Dorsal marking an inverted V; breeds in willow and poplar .... *Poecilonota*

11. Dorsal marking an inverted V with a broad reticulated apex; mandible tridentate; breeds chiefly in hardwoods .... *Dicerca*

Dorsal marking an inverted *Y*, the apex surrounded by a depressed shiny diamond-shaped area; mandible tridentate; breeds in conifers ....*Trachykele*

12. First abdominal segment smaller than the rest; plates of prothorax whitish opaque; prothoracic grooves dark brown; breeds in redbud ....*Ptosima*

First abdominal segment broader than the second
Acmaeodera

13. First segment as broad or slightly broader than the others; body gradually tapering to the twelfth segment; slightly wedge-shaped ....*Brachys*

First segment narrower than the others; body tapering both ways from about the middle, more acute at the posterior end; spindle-shaped ....*Pachyschelus*

14. Dorsal plate marked by 2 moderately separated dark-brown lines which converge anteriorly; breeds in alder
Eupristocerus

Dorsal plate marked by a single median bisecting line; attacks various hardwoods ....*Agrilus*

Acmaeodera pulchella (Hbst.), the **flatheaded bald cypress sapwood borer**, breeds in bald cypress in the Eastern and Southern States. The adult is blue-black to blackish and about 6 to 10 mm. long (in some individuals the thorax is dull bronze and the wing covers and outer angles of the thorax are marked with spots and patches of waxy yellow). Full-grown larvae are about 13 mm. long and the prothoracic plates are marked by brownish median grooves or lines. The sapwood of dead and dying cypress trees and recently cut cypress logs is subject to severe attack and damage. The removal of unseasoned logs from the woods before the adults fly in the spring, or the girdling of trees in the fall that are to be felled in the spring, should aid in the reduction of damage.

The **two-lined chestnut borer**, *Agrilus bilineatus* (Web.), occurs in southern Canada and throughout Eastern United States. It breeds in various hardwoods, preferably chestnut and several of the oaks. Trees weakened by drought, defoliation, or other adverse factors are usually attacked. Adults are about 6 to 12 mm. long, subcylindrical, and black with a more or less greenish tinge. The sides of the thorax and elytra are clothed with light golden-yellow pubescence, and each elytron is marked with a stripe of the same color. The larva is slender, considerably flattened, about 25 mm. long, and has two spines at the posterior end.

Winter is spent in the prepupal stage in cells constructed in the outer layers of the sapwood and sometimes in the bark. In the spring, the adults emerge through characteristic *D*-shaped holes in the bark. Eggs are deposited on the bark in late spring or early summer. Young larvae bore directly through the bark to the phloem. There they excavate winding mines in the inner bark and outer wood of the main trunk and larger branches. These mines run back and forth in all directions (fig. 47), and in the event of heavy attack, they girdle and kill the trees. Attacks usually begin in the tops of trees and are extended downward as the trees continue to weaken. There is a 2-year life cycle in the North; in the South only one year is required.

Control under forested conditions is usually impracticable except for such management practices as are helpful in maintaining or promoting tree vigor. The watering or fertilizing of valuable shade trees should be helpful in protecting them from attack.

The **bronze birch borer,** *Agrilus anxius* Gory, apparently occurs throughout most of the range of birch in Canada and the United States. It breeds in various birches, paper and yellow being preferred. The adult is deep green-bronze and about the same size and shape as the adult of the two-lined chestnut borer. There are coppery reflections on the front of the pronotum; the front of the head is greenish in the male and copper-bronze in the female. Full-grown larvae are slender, flattened, about 25 mm. long, and have two spines at the posterior end.

Adults begin to emerge in late May or early June and continue until August, depending on locality, and they feed on leaves for about three weeks before egg laying begins. Eggs are deposited singly or in small groups beneath loose flakes of bark and in

FIGURE 47.—Galleries of the two-lined chestnut borer. *Agrilus bilineatus*, in the inner bark of black oak.

161

cracks and crevices in the bark, mostly on unshaded parts of the tree. Young larvae bore directly through the bark to the cambium area. There they excavate galleries between the bark and wood, with occasional side trips into the xylem to molt and then to spend the winter. The galleries wind back and forth, usually across the grain of the wood. Mature larvae construct oblong cells in the wood or thick bark in which they spend the winter and pupate in the spring. Larvae of all sizes and ages have been found in infested trees during the winter, but the only ones capable of developing to adults were those which became mature before winter set in and were later subjected to sub-freezing temperatures. In the North, 2 years are required to complete the life cycle; in the South there is one generation per year. Barter (*34*) reported on the biology of the bronze birch borer in New Brunswick.

The bronze birch borer prefers weakened or injured trees (471). Damage may be extremely severe in stands of such trees. Weakened residual trees following logging and individual shade and ornamental trees weakened by drought or other factors are often seriously injured. During the past several years, enormous volumes of birch suffering from "die back" were killed in the Northeastern States and Canada. In Canada, at least 1 million cords were killed during 1939 alone (*108*). The most effective control measures are those designed to promote and maintain host vigor.

The **bronze poplar borer,** *Agrilus liragus* B. & B., breeds in poplar in Canada and southward in the United States to Pennsylvania and Arizona. Adults are blackish with deep green reflections and are about 7 to 12 mm. long. Overmature or defective trees and young trees suddenly released by the removal of dominant trees are most often attacked; however, felled, topped, or girdled trees and trees damaged by *Saperda calcarata* and *Hypoxylon* canker are also attractive. Infestations in standing trees usually begin in the crown and move downward.

Adults are present during a period of several weeks during the summer and feed on the leaves of poplar. Eggs are deposited in bark crevices and the larvae feed in the cambial region, excavating long tunnels that zigzag back and forth in a compact manner. The larvae feed for two seasons in Ontario before becoming mature (*35*). Woodpeckers took heavy tolls of mature larvae, pupae, and, presumably, adults in standing trees in Ontario.

Agrilus horni Kerr occurs in Ontario and the northern tier of Eastern States, and breeds in young, apparently healthy aspen suckers, especially quaking aspen, some of which it girdles and kills. Adults are almost identical to those of the bronze birch borer except for shorter ovipositors in the females.

Eggs are deposited on the smooth bark at the base of aspen suckers. The larvae bore into the bark and tunnel downward and out along large roots, gradually working their way through the bark to the cambium region. Once here, they turn around and tunnel back toward the main stem, making spiral galleries which encircle the roots and which may be continued up the trunk for several inches. Pupation takes place in a cell in the center of the stem, and the life cycle requires two years. Damage appears to be most severe in sparsely stocked stands or in stands growing on poor sites. (568).

Agrilus arcuatus var. *torquatus* LeC., the **hickory spiral borer,** has been recorded from New York, Ohio, North Carollina, and Mississippi. It appears to favor hickory and pecan, but also infests many other hardwoods. It, or a closely related species, has been observed attacking young oaks and other hardwoods in the Piedmont section of the South (40). Adults are about 8 mm. long. Males have a greenish-bronze head and thorax, purplish-black elytra, and the brassy underparts. Females are completely bronze.

Adults appear from May to July and feed on the leaves of their host, eating large irregular holes. Eggs are deposited singly on the bark surface or on terminals or twigs, usually near the base of a small shoot of the current season's growth. The larvae feed downward beneath the bark during the summer, and, during the fall, they sever the wood by constructing a spiral burrow. The following spring, they continue to feed beneath the bark, constructing long, irregular tunnels that deeply engrave the wood. When they are full-grown, they make a second transverse spiral cut around the wood, working first toward the pith and then out again to the phloem, leaving the bark intact. Then, they mine upward in the phloem for an inch or two and construct pupal cells entirely within the pith. Two years are required to complete the life cycle (104). This species is often very destructive of hickory seedlings in the South.

Agrilus acutipennis Mann. has been observed attacking overcup oaks in Louisiana and Arkansas (539). Eggs are deposited on the bark. The larvae bore through the bark and then excavate patches of inner bark up to one-half inch in diameter. Later, they enter the wood and tunnel spirally upward in the outermost growth ring. Pupation occurs within the tunnel and the life cycle requires 2 years.

Damage by *Agrilus acutipennis* results in a defect known as "grease spot." This is caused by a fungus that spreads through the wood from the tunnels. In cross-section, grease spots are oval to diamond- or spindle-shaped and about 18 mm. wide. Their presence in lumber greatly reduces its value. Infestations have been found frequently in river bottoms where the trees were subject to backwater flooding during the winter and spring. In such situations, entire stands of trees over one-half inch in diamter are usually infested.

Many other species of *Agrilus* also occur in eastern forests Some of these and their more important hosts are as follows: *A. juglandis* Knull—butternut; *A. difficilis* Gory—honey locust; *A. lecontei* Saund. and *A. celti* Knull—hackberry; *A. betulae* Fisher —river birch; *A. cephalicus* LeC.—dogwood; *A. fuscipennis* Gory —persimmon; *A. egenus* Gory—black locust; and *A. otiosus* Say —hickory, oak, maple, dogwood, red bud, walnut, and persimmon.

The genus *Buprestis* L. is represented by a fairly large number of wood boring species. Many seem to prefer dead and decayed wood; others are found in either weakened or perfectly healthy trees. The larvae construct tunnels in the sapwood and often the heartwood and frequently cause serious damage. The adults come in many different colors: metallic green, blue, gold, red, yellow, or orange. Often, there are many color variations and patterns within a species.

The **turpentine borer**, *Buprestis apricans* Hbst., long considered the most important eastern member of the genus, occurs through-out the southern coastal regions from North Carolina to Texas, and breeds in longleaf, slash, loblolly, shortleaf, and pitch pines. The adult (fig. 48) is grayish-bronze with a greenish, metallic lustre and is about 25 mm. long. It is elliptical, somewhat flat-tened, and each elytron bears eight rows of large punctures. Full-grown larvae have the prothoracic plates roughened and marked above by a dark brown Y, and they are up to 40 mm. long.

Turpentine borer beetles emerge in February or March and feed for a short time on the needles in the tops of their hosts. Eggs are deposited in exposed wood containing season checks, especially at the edges of turpentine faces and on fire-scarred sur-faces. The larvae tunnel in the sapwood and heartwood, construct-ing long, narrowly oval, tortuous mines and filling them with solidly packed, fine, granular, pitchy frass. At maturity, they form cells in which to pupate near the surface. There the adult spends the winter. About 3 years are spent in the larval stage.

The turpentine borer used to be the most destructive insect in the turpentine orchards of the South (*38, 40*). Borer riddled trees were weakened so severely, they became subject to wind break-age. The lumber value of such trees was virtually destroyed, and gum production was seriously reduced. Attacks can be prevented or reduced through the exercise of care in preventing the ex-

FIGURE 48.—Adult of the turpentine borer, *Buprestis apricans.*

posure of dead, dry wood by fire, logging, or other forest operations. In recent years, acid treatment to increase gum flow in naval stores operations has virtually eliminated dry faces, thereby greatly reducing the damage caused by the species.

A number of other species of *Buprestis* are also encountered in eastern forests. A few of the more common ones and their hosts are as follows: *B. striata* (Fab.)—adult brown with greenish reflections (breeds in dead branches of pine, hemlock, and bald cypress) ; *B. lineata* (Fab.)—adult medium-sized and dark, usually with brick-red to yellow longitudinal markings on the elytra (attacks longleaf, loblolly, pitch, and scrub pines) ; *B. rufipes* (Oliv.)—adult slender and dark green, with a long yellow basal patch and two cross bars of yellow on the elytra (infestations occur around scars on elm, beech, hickory, oak, maple, yellow poplar, and sour gum) ; *B. salisburyensis* (Hbst.)—adult short, oval, and green with a tooth on the inner margin of each elytron (breeds in pitch pine) ; and *B. maculipennis* Gory—adult rather small and blackish, with a brassy tinge and scattered yellow spots or patches on the elytra (attacks pine and hemlock).

The genus *Chrysobothris* Esch. contains some of the most common and injurious members of the family. The larvae are all borers in the wood of both deciduous and coniferous trees. All parts of the tree are attacked, from the roots to the twigs in the crown, but the majority of attacks occur on the main trunk. The adults are small to medium-sized and are usually not conspicuously colored. The pronotum is usually wider than long and the scutellum is small and triangular. The elytra are rounded or angulate at the base and strongly converge posteriorly. The legs are robust, with the femora swollen at the middle. There usually is a large tooth on each front leg. Several species are very injurious, especially to young trees weakened by drought, defoliation, or other adverse factors. The genus has been revised by Fisher (*253*).

The **flatheaded apple tree borer**, *Chrysobothris femorata* (Oliv.), one of the commonest and best known of the flatheaded borers in America, occurs throughout most of Canada and the United States. It attacks a wide variety of deciduous trees such as sycamore, silver maple, boxelder, black walnut, willow, white and black oaks, yellow poplar, elm, beech, hickory, hackberry, apple, and pear. The adult is oval, flattened, dark green bronze above, bright brassy beneath, and about 7 to 16 mm. long. The elytra are marked with two wavy, depressed light bands. Full-grown larvae are about 25 mm. long.

Adults appear throughout the summer and feed on the foliage of their hosts, occasionally causing serious defoliation. Eggs are deposited under bark scales or in bark crevices on the main trunk or larger branches. The larvae bore into the bark and feed in the phloem and outer sapwood. Their tunnels are sometimes several inches long, especially in young trees. Tunnels in older trees are confined mostly to the thick inner bark. Mature larvae construct cells in the outer wood during late summer where they spend the winter and pupate the following spring. There is one generation per year (*242*).

The flatheaded apple tree borer is especially destructive of newly-planted trees and trees weakened by drought, defoliation, or other adverse factors. Young trees are often girdled and killed; larger trees are often seriously injured through the loss of large patches of bark over mined areas. Maintenance of tree vigor, wrapping the trunk with high grade wrapping paper or burlap when trees are planted or pruned, and shading the south side of newly-planted trees, are recommended control practices.

The **Australian-pine borer,** *Chrysobothris tranquebarica* (Gmelin), also commonly known as the mangrove borer, occurs in southern Florida and breeds in living mangrove and *Casuarina* trees. The adult is greenish-bronze in color and about 12 to 17 mm. long. Eggs are deposited in the spring under roughened areas of bark. The larvae feed beneath the bark until nearly full-grown, and then enter the wood to construct pupal cells. Damage to ornamental or windbreak trees is often severe. The removal and destruction of infested wood during fall and winter is helpful in control.

Chrysobothris orono Frost attacks living red and jack pines in the Lake States. Eggs are laid singly on the trunk. The larvae feed in the bark during the first three instars, excavating cells and causing flowing pitch to coagulate into large pitch masses (fig. 49). Older larvae feed in the wood. The winter is spent in the larval stage. In the spring of the third year, the larva constructs an *L*-shaped cell, plugged with frass and wood chips, where pupation occurs. This species is seldom injurious, although its injury may remain in the bole as a defect after the wounds have healed.

F-519916
FIGURE 49.—Pitch mass on red pine caused by feeding of the larva of *Chrysobothris orono.*

Several other species of *Chrysobothris* also occur fairly commonly in eastern forests. Some of these and some of their more important hosts are as follows: *C. pusilla* L. & G.—pitch, shortleaf, and white pines, white spruce, and hemlock; *C. dentipes* (Germ.)—white, shortleaf, longleaf, and scrub pines, and larch (this species is reported to be strongly attracted to sawmills) ; *C. floricola* Gory—probaly all species of pines; *C. scabripennis* L. & G.—pine, spruce, hemlock, and balsam fir; *C. trinveria* (Kby.)—white pine and spruce; *C. harrisi* (Hentz)—Virginia, white, and pitch pines; *C. azurea* LeC.—white oak, dogwood, maple, basswood, birch, and willow; *C. sexsignata* (Say)—ash, red maple, walnut, hickory, beech, yellow birch, white oak, hemlock, cypress, and pitch pine; *C. texana* LeC.—red cedar; *C. adelpha* G. & H.—hickory and pecan; *C. veridiceps* Melsh.—red maple, red oak, and cherry; *C. blanchardi* Horn—white, Virginia, and pitch pines, and larch; and *C. neopusilla* Fisher—balsam fir.

Chalcophora virginiensis (Drury), the **large flatheaded pine heartwood borer,** breeds in injured, dying, and dead pines and in pine stumps throughout eastern United States. Adults (fig. 50) are dull black or dark bronze beetles about 23 to 33 mm. long. The thorax is broader than long, and the elytra are marked with dark or shiny elevations and rough, grayish or brassy depressions. Full-grown larvae are up to 50 mm. long and the dorsal thoracic plate is marked with a *Y*. Eggs are deposited around scars on living areas and in bark crevices or holes in the bark of logs and stumps. Living trees may be severely damaged by larval tunnels in the wood. Pine logs left too long in the woods are also subject to severe damage. *C. liberta* (Germ.) and *C.*

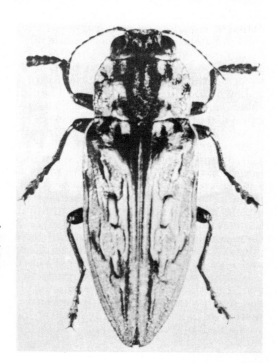

FIGURE 50.—Adult of *Chalcophora virginiensis*, the large flathead pine heartwood borer.

167

georgiana LeC. are often found in association with *C. virginiensis*. Adults of *C. liberta* are copper or brass-colored, while those of *C. georgiana* are golden-bronze.

The *Chalcophorella campestris* Kerr., **flatheaded sycamore-heartwood borer,** breeds in injured, dying, or dead sycamore, beech, oak, maple, yellow-poplar, and basswood, preferably in moist, rotting logs. The larvae resemble those of *Chalcophora virginiensis* except that they are longer, and the dorsal thoracic plate is marked with a *V* or *U* instead of a *Y*. This species often attacks at axe blazes and wounds and frequently riddles the wood beneath with its tunnels.

The genus *Dicerca* Esch. contains many species that breed in dead and dying trees and logs. The adults are dark-gray to brown, medium-sized, metallic beetles. The head is flat, the pronotum is wider than long and grooved or ridged down the middle, the scutellum is very small, the hind coxae are strongly dilated, and the elytra are extended into tail-like appendages. A few of the more common eastern species and some of their hosts are as follows: *D. divaricata* (Say)—various dead, dying, or injured hardwoods; *D. obscura* (Fab.)—various dead hardwoods; *D. punctulata* (Schon.)—various pines (often common around sawmills); *D. lurida* (Fab.)—hickory, blue beech, and basswood; *D. tenebrosa* (Kirby)—pines and spruce; and *D. tenebrica* (Kby.) poplar and willow.

The genus *Melanophila* Eschs. consists of small to medium-sized beetles, the larvae of which bore in the inner bark and outer wood of their hosts. The majority of species attack very slow-growing, dying, or recently felled trees and are of no economic importance. In the West, certain species are strongly attracted to fires and are known as "fire bugs." Sloop (*653*) published a revision of the North American members of the genus.

The **hemlock borer,** *Melanophila fulvoguttata* (Harris), occurs throughout eastern United States and eastern Canada. Hemlock appears to be the preferred host, but it also occasionally attacks several other conifers such as white pine, larch, balsam fir, and red, white, and black spruces. The adult is black with a metallic sheen and about 10 mm. long. Each elytron usually bears three equal-sized orange or yellow spots.

Adults appear from late spring to late summer and deposit their eggs in groups deep in bark crevices on weakened, dead, and dying trees or on logs and windthrown trees in which the cambium is still moist. The larvae bore into the inner phloem and, if conditions are not favorable for their development, they remain here until they die. Under more favorable growth conditions they penetrate to the cambium region and construct tortuous, frass-filled galleries (fig. 51). Before becoming full-grown, they construct cells in the outer bark in which they spend the winter. The life cycle may be completed in one year in dead trees and logs. In living trees, several years may be required.

Management practices designed to promote rapid growth and good health of hemlock trees should be helpful in preventing damage by the hemlock borer. Rapid salvage or cutting of heavily infested trees is helpful in preventing population build-up in stands weakened by windthrow or defoliation (*470*).

Several other species of *Melanophila* also occur in eastern forests. A few common ones and their hosts are as follows: The **flatheaded fir borer**, *M. drummondi* (Kirby)—fir, larch, spruce, and hemlock; *M. notata* (Lap.)—pines; *M. acuminata* (DeG.)— spruce, fir, pine, and eastern white cedar (adults are common around forest fires and scorched timber) ; and *M. aeneola* Melsh. —pines.

The genus *Brachys* Solier contains many species of leaf miners. The larvae differ from the larvae of wood- or bark-boring species in having the prothorax only slightly, if any, broader than the first abdominal segment. The adults are small and oval, and they feed on the leaves of hardwoods, sometimes riddling them with holes. The larvae mine the tissues of the leaves. *B. tesselatus* is very common on scrub oak in the sandhills of the southeastern Coastal Plain. Heavy annual defoliation is not unusual. *B. ovata* (Web.) also mines the leaves of oak. *B. aeruginosa* (Gory) mines the leaves of elms.

Numerous other species of bark- or wood-boring buprestids are also encountered in eastern trees. *Ptosima gibbicollis* (Say) breeds in living red buds. The adult is dark blue, about 6 mm. long, and has two yellow spots on each wing cover. Damage is sometimes severe. *Trachykele lecontei* (Gory) breeds in dead bald cypress in the Southern States. The adult is dark ashy-bronze, with black, velvety spots, and is about 9 mm. long. The larvae feed in both the sapwood and heartwood, often causing a serious degrade of lumber. *Actenodes acornis* (Say) breeds in the dry heartwood of red maple, birch, beech, oak, and hickory; *Poecilonta cyanipes* (Say) breeds beneath the bark at wounds

F-514869

FIGURE 51.—Mature larvae and galleries of the hemlock borer, *Melanophila fulveoguttata*, on the surface of the sapwood.

on living poplars; *P. thureura* (Say) breeds beneath the bark at wounds on willow; *Agrillaxia flavimana* (Gory) breeds in the small branches of white oak; and *Cinyra gracilipes* (Melsh) breeds in the dead branches of oak and ironwood.

FAMILY CERAMBYCIDAE

LONG-HORNED BEETLES OR ROUNDHEADED BORERS

The family Cerambycidae is one of the largest and most important of the families of wood-boring beetles. More than 1400 species have been recorded from the United States, about 450 of which occur east of the Mississippi River (*221*). Knull (*431, 432*) listed 262 species either known or believed to occur in Ohio alone. Fattig (*232*) discussed the species occuring in Georgia. The majority of species breed in the dead wood of trees and shrubs but many, including some of the most destructive ones, attack either slightly weakened or healthy trees and other plants.

Th larvae of all but a few members of the family live as borers in the tissues of trees and other woody plants. Almost no part of a tree of any age or size is immune to infestation by some species. The twigs, branches, and stems of sprouts and seedlings and the twigs of branches of mature trees are girdled and severed. The sapwood and heartwood of large limbs and trunks of living trees are often riddled and weakened, leading to windbreakage or death. Species that feed under the bark of living trees may weaken and kill their hosts, or cause defects and stains which seriously degrade lumber value. Species that attack recently felled trees, logs, or seasoned timber also cause heavy losses. Not all species are harmful, however, Many of those that attack slash, stumps, and dead and dying trees are actually beneficial, because they aid in the quick removal of such waste material from the forest floor and aid its incorporation into humus.

Cerambycid beetles are distinguished by their oblong, often cylindrical bodies, their long, usually 11-segmented antennae, and their long legs. The tarsi are five-segmented, with the fourth segment small and partly concealed by the bilobed third segment. The beetles move rapidly when disturbed and are strong fliers. Some species make squeaking noises when captured.

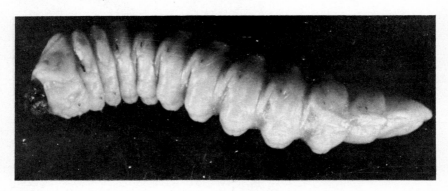

COURTESY OF DUKE UNIV. SCH. OF FOREST.

FIGURE 52.—Typical larva of a roundheaded borer.

Cerambycid larvae (fig. 52) are distinguished by a few prominent characters. They are always fleshy, thin-skinned, white or yellowish in color, and more or less cylindrical or depressed in form. In some species, the body tapers somewhat posteriorally, but the anterior segments are never suddenly and conspicuously larger than the following ones. The body is never curved and there are no prolegs or gripping processes on the last addominal segment. There are two overlapping, circular bands of skin between each pair of body segments, the ventral mouth parts are always about on a line with the base of the mandibles, and the tenth abdominal segment is modified into two or three small retractile lobes (*164, 165*).

Keys to Cerambycid Larvae

Cerambycid larvae can be conveniently grouped as follows:
I. Girdlers of twigs or stems.
II. Gall formers on living plants.
III. Borers in the bark of living plants.
IV. Borers under the bark or in the wood of living trees.
V. Borers in the roots of living plants.
VI. Borers under the bark or in the wood of recently dead, dying, or felled trees.
VII. Borers in older, moist wood in contact with the ground.
VIII. Borers in dry, seasoned wood or in cat faces and scars on living trees.

I. TWIG AND STEM GIRDLERS.

Many species of cerambycids sever small twigs or branches from living trees. These twigs may be seen hanging in the tree or lying on the ground in late summer, fall, or winter. They are cut either by the adult or the larva, the adult cutting from the outside inward and the larvae from the inside outward.

1. Twigs or stems girdled from the outside. Stem never hollowed out at point of severance 2
   Twigs girdled from within. Part of stem always hollow 3
2. Egg punctures and feeding scars on twigs or stems. Severed twigs containing larvae ....*Oncideres* spp.
   No evidence of egg punctures or feeding scars. Severed twigs never containing larvae ..... *Oberea* spp.
3. Larva found in girdled portion 4
   Larvae found in green portion of twig remaining on plant. Holes through bark of girdled portion 7
4. Twigs girdled by spiral cuts. Without holes in bark of twig 5
   Twigs severed by complete hollowing. Holes through bark in a straight line 6
5. Two ocelli on each side of head of larva; pronotum white and shining ..... *Elaphidionoides villosus*
   One ocellus on each side of head; pronotum brown and velvety ..... *Xylotrechus quadrimaculatus*
6. Head of larva shining; pronotum wider than long
   Aneflormorpha subpubescens

7. In twigs of poplars; mandible pointed ......*Oberea schaumi*
   In shrubby plants; larvae boring down into base 8
8. In sassafras ....*Oberea ruficollis*
   In sumac ....*Oberea ocellata*
   In shadbush and related plants ....*Oberea myops*

II. GALL MAKERS.

The larvae of several species of Cerambycidae cause galls or swellings on the twigs or branches, along the trunk, or at the base of trees or shrubs. They may be found either in the swelling proper or in a mine above or below the gall.

1. Galls on twigs and branches:
   On poplars and willows
      Pronotum with 4 impressed lines, the inner being darker and oblique ....*Oberea ferruginea*
      Pronotum with 2 impressed, parallel lines
         Saperda concolor; S. moesta
   On *Crataegus* ....*Saperda fayi*
   On oaks ....*Goes dibilis*
2. Galls on main stem or trunk:
   On willow ....*Oberea ferruginea*
   On red maple ....*Xylotrechus aceris*
3. Galls found at base:
   On alder ....*Saperda obliqua*
   On elder ....*Desmocerus* spp.

III. BORERS IN THE BARK OF LIVING TREES.

A few species of roundheaded borers are found in the bark proper of living trees.

1. Larvae found only in the corky bark
   Of elm ....*Physocnemum brevilneum*
   Of mulberry ....*Elaphidion incertum*
   Of white oak ....*Encyclops coerulea*
   Of thick-barked rock oak or chestnut oak
      Enaphalodes cortiphagus
2. Larvae bore into inner bark and often destroy the cambium
   In oaks and chestnut; at base or in crotches of branches in damp situations ......*Anoplodera nitens*
   In ash ....*Tylonotus bimaculatus*

IV. BORERS UNDER THE BARK OR IN THE WOOD OF LIVING TREES.

This group contains some of the most destructive roundheaded borers. Some feed mostly beneath the bark, destroying the cambium; the majority riddle the sapwood and heartwood, seriously weakening the tree.

1. Larvae feed gregariously; mines overlap and meander 2
   Larval mines essentially individual 3
2. In heartwood at base of large trees
   Pronotum shiny ....*Stenodontes* and *Archodontes*
   Pronotum asperate ....*Parandra*
   Beneath bark of firs, hemlocks, and larch ......*Tetropium*

In or beneath bark of ash; at base of privet

Tylonotus bimaculatus

At base of poplars .... *Xylotrechus obliteratus*

Beneath bark and in wood of elm

Eutetrapha tridentata

Beneath bark and in wood of linden .... *Saperda vestita*

3. Boring beneath the bark and then directly up through the
    wood; frass exuded through small hole in bark 4
    Boring in branches or main stems; long tunnel through
    center of branch or stem 7

4. In main trunks or branches 5
    At base 6

5. Head of larva longer than wide; fibrous frass exuded
    through holes in bark
    In fig trees and alder .... *Neoptychodes*
    In oak, beech, elm, and hickory .... *Goes*
    In poplar .... *Saperda calcarata*
    Head broader than long; granular frass exuded
    In oaks .... *Enaphalodes rufulus*
    In black locust .... *Megacyllene robiniae*
    In maple .... *Glycobius speciosus*

6. In small oaks, *Amelanchier*, chestnut .... *Goes tessellatus*
    In apple, *Amelanchier*, *Crataegus*, etc.

Saperda candida

    In poplar:
    Pronotum asperate .... *Saperda calcarata*
    Pronotum velvety pubescent and brownish

Plectrodera scalator

7. Last segment of body horny; in mesquite

Aneflus protensus

V. BORERS IN ROOTS.

The larvae of a few species of Cerambycidae are found in the
roots of living trees and shrubs. Some are true root feeders,
spending the entire larval stage in the roots; others spend only
the later instars in roots, having previously bored in the stems
above the ground.

1. Larvae feeding entirely in roots or directly at the base 2
    Larvae feeding in roots, but stem above ground always
    tunneled some distance; in shrubs 3

2. In elder; sometimes causing swelling at ground surface;
    basal portion of stem often hollowed .... *Desmocerus*
    In large hardwood trees or various shrubs .... *Prionus*

3. Mandible rounded at apex; pronotum smooth

Aneflormorpha subpubescens

    Mandible pointed at apex; pronotum roughened with fine
    points
    In sassafras .... *Oberea ruficollis*
    In sumac .... *Oberea ocellata*
    In rhododendron and related plants .... *Oberea myops*

VI. BORERS BENEATH THE BARK OR IN THE WOOD OF RECENTLY FELLED TREES

A number of species of cerambycids attack wood only when the
bark is present and still rather fresh and green. Trees dying

gradually are often subject to attack. After the wood has seasoned from 4 to 6 months it is nearly always immune to attack. This group of borers causes heavy losses in rustic work and log houses, and in lumbering operations when trees cut during the winter are left lying on the ground throughout late spring and early summer. Cordwood and pulpwood are also damaged.

The character of the frass, whether granular or fibrous or shredded, distinguishes certain species.

1. Larvae found in coniferous trees 2
   Larvae found in hardwood trees 9
2. Frass granular, closely packed behind larva 3
   Frass composed largely of fibrous or shredded material 8
3. Frass pushed out through small hole 4
   Frass tightly packed; filling entire mine behind larva 5
4. Underside of head having four small tubercles
        Callidium antennatum hesperum, C. texanum
   Underside of head without tubercles ....*Oeme*
5. In cypress ....*Physocnemum andreae*
   In cedars, junipers, and Douglas-fir 6
   In pines and spruces 7
6. Larvae without ocelli and without spines on last segment
        Semanotus ligneus
   Larvae with 1 ocellus and with 2 small spines on last
        segment above ....*Atimia confusa*
7. Head wider than long; form cylindrical
        Larvae with 2 small dorsal spines on last segment of
        body; mandible pointed at apex
                              Asemum, Arhopalus
        Larvae without spines; mandible rounded at apex
                                       Xylotrechus
   Head longer than wide; form depressed; ampullae velvety
        pubescent ....*Acanthocinus*
8. Head wider than long; 2 small dorsal spines on last body
        segment ....*Asemum, Arhopalus*
   Head wider than long and slightly keeled at sides; larvae
        very depressed ....*Stenocorus inquisitor lineatus*
   Head longer than broad; last body segment without dorsal
        spines ....*Monochamus*
9. Frass entirely granular 10
   Frass containing much fibrous material 11
10. Frass tightly packed behind larvae
        Larval pronotum smooth and white. Larval mines
        chiefly in the wood of ash, oak, and other hardwoods
                                       Neoclytus
        Larval pronotum covered with velvety, yellowish pubescence; larvae without legs; larval mines under
        the bark and in the wood ....*Xylotrechus*
   Frass exuded through small hole
        One ocellus on each side of the head; larvae yellowish
        and rather elongate; chiefly in hickory
                                       Knulliana cincta
        Two ocelli on each side of the head
                                       Elaphidion mucronatum

Three ocelli on each side of the head
    Found in hickory ....*Megacyllene caryae*
    Found in mesquite .... *Megacyllene antennata*
    Found in black locust ....*Megacyllene robiniae*

11. Pronotum brown, velvety pubescent; small irregular dorsal and ventral tubercles on body segments
    Leptostylus and related genera
    Dorsum of prothorax and dorsal and ventral surfaces of body segments armed with chitinous points
    In elms ....*Eutetrapha tridentata*
    In basswood or linden ....*Saperda vestita*
    In hickory ....*Saperda discoidea*

VII. BORERS IN OLDER WOOD IN MOIST CONDITION OR IN CONTACT WITH THE GROUND

This group is composed mostly of large borers which occur in large numbers in the same piece of wood until it is completely riddled. Some are found in wood that has been cut a year or more and that is in contact with the ground. They are rarely found in recently dead or dying trees. Several of the species included here are also considered in Group VI, as the larvae may continue to bore for several years in stumps and logs lying on the ground. Cross ties, mine props, fence posts, foundation timbers, and fire-killed timber are subject to serious injury. A few species which attack exposed heartwood at the bases of living trees cause serious damage to shade trees.

1. Pronotum armed with small recurved chitinous points
    Parandra
    Pronotum brown, covered with very fine hairs or points; two small dorsal spines on last body segments
    Asemum, Arhopalus
    Pronotum white, shiny, sometimes a little roughened or rugulose 2

2. Dorsal and ventral surfaces of body covered with small tubercles ....*Leptura*
    Dorsal and ventral surfaces of body smooth; 2 transverse impressions dorsally 3

3. Front of head just above the mandibles projecting in teeth or tubercles 4
    Front of head projecting in transverse dull carina (sometimes divided in middle) 5

4. Four rounded tubercles; body skin finely wrinkled
    Ergates (Western)
    Four flat, sharp-edged teeth; body skin finely wrinkled
    Tragosoma
    Two flat, projecting teeth; body skin smooth, shiny
    Orthosoma

5. Three ocelli on each side of head; body cylindrical
    Stenodontes and *Archodontes*
    One ocellus on each side of head; body wedge-shaped, tapering posteriorly ....*Prionus pocularis*

VIII. BORERS IN DRY, SEASONED WOOD.

The larvae of a number of species of the family Cerambycidae, belonging to several genera, are often referred to as "powder-post borers" because of their common habit of boring for year after year in the same wood, eventually leaving nothing but a thin outer shell filled with a mass of powder. Certain species attack only recently cut wood. Under normal conditions the life cycle of the progeny would be completed in a year or two. But if the wood, after being attacked, is placed in buildings or stored in drier conditions, the larval period may be prolonged for several years. Damage is often severe to stored lumber exposed to attack before storing, to structural timbers in houses such as rafters and beams, and to bridge timbers.

1. Three ocelli on each side of the head
   Hylotrupes bajulus
   One ocellus on each side of the head 2
2. Underside of mouth frame with 4 small projecting tubercles; in coniferous wood
   Callidium antennatum hesperum, C. texanum
   Underside of mouth frame without tubercles
   In bamboo .... *Chlorophorus annularis*
   In hardwoods 3
3. Legs smaller than palpi.
   A smooth white triangular arc on venter of prothorax
   Smodicum cucujiforme
   Underside of prothorax not so marked; legs very small; body dull, finely granulated above and below
   Neoclytus caprea; N. acuminatus
   Legs larger than palpi .... *Eburia*

The **locust borer,** *Megacyllene robiniae* (Forst.), one of the most important of the Cerambycids, occurs in eastern Canada and throughout most of the United States, wherever its host, black locust, grows. The adult is about 18 mm. long. The jet-black background is marked with bright yellow bands extending across the thorax and wing covers, the third band on the wings being *W*-shaped. The legs and antennae are moderately long and yellow. Full-grown larvae are robust and about 25 mm. long.

Adults are present in late summer or early fall, but are most abundant during September. They are commonly seen feeding on the pollen of goldenrod blossoms during morning hours. Later in the day, sometimes well after sunset, they are usually seen running up and down the trunks of black locust trees in search of oviposition sites. Eggs are usually deposited in rough bark crevices and around wounds on the trunks of living trees. Newly-hatched larvae bore into the inner bark and construct small hibernation cells in which they spend the winter. Activity is resumed in the spring when the leaf buds begin to swell. At this time, oozing sap may be seen around larval entry holes in the trunk. The larvae soon bore into the wood where they continue to feed until mature, around mid-July. During this period they construct extensive tunnels throughout the heartwood (fig. 53A). As the larva grows, it enlarges its tunnel to the exterior, through which it pushes its granular frass to the outside and through which the adult eventually emerges. There is one generation per year (*280*).

During the past several years, the locust borer has destroyed thousands of acres of natural regeneration and plantations of black locust. Enormous numbers of older trees, especially slowly growing overtopped trees, have also been badly damaged or killed. On the other hand, thrifty dominant trees over 10 years old have seldom been killed. Infested trees are physically weakened by the larval tunnels, the smaller ones often being restricted to shrub form by repeated attacks (fig. 53B). Trees growing on poor sites are especially susceptible to attack and suffer serious damage during periods of prolonged drought.

F-501514, 501515

FIGURE 53.—Damage caused by the locust borer, *Megacyllene robiniae:* A, larval damage in heartwood; B, damage to small trees.

A number of practices have been suggested for the prevention or reduction of damage by the locust borer. These include the planting of superior varieties of black locust, the use of mixed species in planting, the removal of old stag-headed brood trees, selection of good sites for planting, thinning and mulching of stands, and protection of young trees from fire or livestock grazing (*318, 511, 189*).

The **painted hickory borer,** *Megacyllene caryae* (Gahan), is widely distributed in the eastern United States. Freshly-cut, hickory logs are normally preferred for breeding, but dead trees of several other hardwoods such as black and honey locust, oak, hackberry, mulberry, walnut, butternut, and ash are also occasionally attacked. Hickory wood cut during the winter may be completely riddled by mid-summer. The adult closely resembles the adult of the locust borer, but is slightly larger on the average. The elytra also are more tapering, the prosternum is wider than long, and the antennae of the male are longer than the body.

Adults emerge in early spring and deposit their eggs beneath bark scales on logs cut the previous winter. The larvae feed for several weeks under the bark and then bore into the sapwood and later the heartwood. Pupation occurs in the fall at the end of the larval mine behind a wad of fibrous frass. The adult, like the adult of the locust borer, emerges through the larval gallery and entrance hole. Winter is spent in the pupal stage and there is one generation per year.

Megacyllene antennata (White), commonly known as the **mesquite borer,** breeds in mesquite and acacia in Texas and other Southwestern States. The adult is robust, brownish-black, and from 12 to 30 mm. long. It is marked with fine white or gray hairs and a dark spot in the center of the thorax. Eggs are deposited in crevices of the bark of recently cut wood. The larvae feed first beneath the bark and then in the wood, excavating extensive mines and pushing quantities of frass to the outside through a hole in the bark. This species is especially injurious to mesquite cordwood. Fence posts also are greatly weakened or destroyed. Craighead and Hofer (*168*) discussed methods of control.

The **banded hickory borer,** *Knulliana cincta* (Drury), occurs throughout much of eastern United States where it breeds in the dead branches and trunks of a wide variety of hardwoods, such as hickory, walnut, oak, American hornbeam, plum, and apple. Hickory appears to be preferred. The adult (fig. 54) is dark brown and about 22 mm. long. The body is clothed with grayish fine hairs, and there is a short sharp spine on each lateral margin of the thorax. Each elytron has an oblique yellow spot near the base and two slender spines at the tip.

Eggs are deposited during the summer beneath the bark or directly on the wood of recently felled, dying, or dead trees. The larvae feed beneath the bark during the remainder of the summer, deeply scarring the wood and pushing out huge quantities of granular frass through small openings in the bark. During the fall and following summer they bore into the wood and mine it extensively. Pupation occurs in the fall or spring between wads of fibrous frass at the end of the tunnel. The life cycle probably

FIGURE 54.—Adult of the banded hickory borer, *Knulliana cincta*.

F-480484

requires 2 years for completion. Cordwood, logs, posts and rustic work are frequently seriously damaged by the species. The prompt milling and seasoning of summer cut wood are recommended control practices.

The **cottonwood borer,** *Plectrodera scalator* (F.), breeds in the bases of living cottonwoods and willows in the Southern States. The adult is 25 to 35 mm. long and beautifully marked. The ground color is black, but this is obscured by patches and cross stripes of pure white, fine hairs that surround black, hairless areas (fig. 55, left).

Adults appear in late spring or early summer and feed on the tender shoots of young trees. These shoots often break, shrivel,

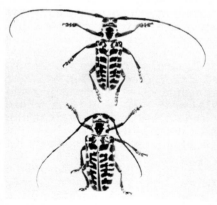

F-519918-9

FIGURE 55.—The cottonwood borer, *Plectrodera scalator:* Left, adults, right, larva.

179

and turn black. Eggs are deposited in pits chewed in the bark below the ground line at the base of the tree. Young saplings and nursery stock are subject to attack, but larger trees are usually selected. The larvae (fig. 55, right) feed in the phloem, mining downward and commonly entering a large root by fall. The second summer they continue feeding and excavating galleries and pushing out coarse frass through holes made near the egg slits. The base of infested trees may be practically riddled by their tunnels. Two years are required to complete the life cycle (533).

Cottonwoods planted on poor sites such as clay soils and sand flats in Mississippi may be killed, or they may be broken off at the ground by the wind. Damage may also be serious in natural stands growing on poor sites (538).

The **sugar maple borer,** *Glycobius speciosus* (Say), breeds in living sugar maples in southern Canada and throughout the Northeastern States, westward to the Lake States and southward through the Appalachians. The adult is robust, velvety black, and about 27 mm. long. The head is clothed with yellow fine hairs; the pronotum is much wider than long, constricted at the base, and marked with two parallel yellow bands on each side. Each elytron bears five yellow bands, with those at the front forming a *W*-shaped design. Full grown larvae reach a length of 50 mm.

Eggs are deposited in bark crevices, under bark scales, or around wounds, usually during July and August. The larvae feed beneath the bark. Their tunnels run more or less across the grain and cut deep channels in the wood. The winter is spent as a larva in a chamber formed in the sapwood. The following spring, feeding is resumed, with the larva cutting a larger gallery in the sapwood. The mature larva bores deep into the wood and constructs a pupal cell at the end of its tunnel. Prior to entering the cell, it cuts an exit hole through which the adult emerges. During this activity, they push considerable quantities of sawdust to the outside. Pupation occurs in the spring, and the life cycle requires 2 years (703).

The presence of transverse ridges or elevations on the large limbs or trunks of sugar maple, or of sawdust-like frass and moisture on the bark, are evidence of attack by the sugar maple borer. The bark over ridges is pushed outward at an angle or is broken up in the form of cracks, some of which may completely girdle the tree. These cracked, swollen areas often resemble cankers or galls. Damage is generally most severe to shade trees or to trees growing in open stands or along streams. Infestations in the forest appear to be heaviest in open second growth stands, or in heavily grazed, understocked stands. The growing of sugar maple in well-stocked groups, the avoidance of overgrazing, and the removal and burning of infested dead limbs and trees before adult emergence in the spring should be helpful in reducing losses (644). Borers in shade trees can be killed by the injection of a fumigant into their tunnels or by piercing their bodies with a wire pushed into their tunnels.

The **red oak borer,** *Enaphalodes rufulus* (Hald.) (=*Romaleum rufulum*), breeds in the trunks of living oaks in southern Canada and throughout eastern United States, west to Minnesota, Iowa, and Texas. In the Central States, red, scarlet, and black oaks are especially subject to attack. Adults are light brown with spots of lighter fine hairs, and are about 26 mm. long (fig. 56). There are two small tubercles on the disk of the thorax and one triangular spot at its rear. The elytra are notched at the apex, and the sutural angles are produced into spines.

F-520106
FIGURE 56.—Adult of *Enaphalodes rufulus*, the red oak borer.

Eggs are deposited singly on living trees over 2 inches in diamter in bark crevices or beneath lichen patches during the summer. Young larvae bore directly into the phloem, and they feed there during the remainder of the summer, excavating cave-type burrows about one-half inch square. The larvae spend the winter in these burrows and continue their phloem feeding in the spring. In early summer, they bore into the wood and direct their tunnels obliquely upward in the sapwood and straight upward in the heartwood for distances of 6 to 10 inches. The second winter is also spent in the larval stage, with pupation occurring in the spring. The life cycle requires 2 years. Granular frass pushed out from points of attack and wet spots caused by sap leakage are evidence of attack.

A large percentage of the large oaks in the Eastern, Southern, and Central States are attacked by this species, resulting in serious defects and serious degrade in the timber. Ants and fungi entering the wounds add to the injury. Occasionally, branches and entire trees are killed. Damage is severe in forest stands and to valuable shade trees in parks and cities. Damage to upland oaks in the Central States can be reduced by poisoning borer-infested trees with a herbicide after egg laying is completed in August. Larval mortality occurs in a short time if the tree is deadened while they are still feeding in the phloem. This can be accomplished during ordinary stand-improvement operations, because the trees selected for removal in this work are the very ones most likely to be heavily infested (*326*).

Enaphalodes cortiphagus (Craighead), the **oak-bark scarrer,** breeds in the bark of living, mature oaks throughout eastern United States and westward through the Ozark Mountains. Adults are dark brown with patches of short, gray, fine hairs on the head, pronotum, and elytra and are about 20 mm. long. Eggs are deposited in bark crevices in the spring, and the larvae feed in the bark for upwards of three years. At the end of this period they bore deeper into the bark and excavate a large pupal cell.

181

This excavation usually damages several layers of annual growth of the wood, causing a large black defect and the formation of scars on the outer surface of the bark. The presence of this defect results in considerable degrade of the lumber. The related species, *E. antomerius* (Drury), breeds under the bark at the bases of dead trees and on the stumps of oaks and chestnut in southern Canada and throughout eastern United States.

The genus *Goes* LeC. contains a few species which attack living hardwoods. Large tunnels constructed in the heartwood result in defects in lumber cut from infested wood. Eggs are deposited singly in oval pits chewed through the bark. Tunnels in the wood are excavated inward and upward and are kept open. Fibrous frass is expelled through openings maintained at the egg scar. Life cycles vary from 2 to 5 years, depending on species.

Goes tigrinus (DeG.), the **white oak borer,** the largest species in the genus, occurs throughout eastern United States. White oak is its preferred host throughout most of its range, but various other oaks, and hickory and walnut are attacked occasionally. In Mississippi, overcup oak is heavily infested. The adult is large, robust, dark brown, and from 25 to 30 mm. long. It is irregularly covered with a dense coat of white fine hair, giving it a white and brown mottled appearance (fig. 57). The basal part of the elytra is roughened with small, black, elevated points; and there is a strong spine on each side of the thorax. Full-grown larvae are up to 37 mm. long.

Adults emerge in May and June and feed for a week or two on the bark of tender twigs and leaves of oaks. Eggs are deposited in the trunks of young trees, usually from 1 to 12 inches in diameter, or in the branches of larger trees. The young larvae bore directly into the sapwood. Then they tunnel upward and penetrate deep into the heartwood, excavating tunnels up to one inch in diameter and to 10 inches in length. Each borer bores two

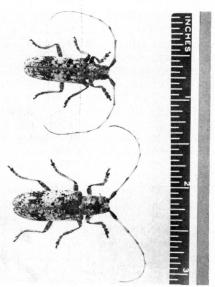

F-519921
FIGURE 57.—Adults of *Goes tigrinus,* the white oak borer.

separate holes in the tree—a small elongate entrance hole which it keeps open for the expulsion of frass and a round hole made for the emergence of the adult. The life cycle requires from 3 to 5 years, depending on locality.

The white oak borer is a major pest of overcup oak in the bottom lands of Mississippi (*679*). Small trees down to one inch in diameter are attacked and seriously damaged. Trees growing on heavy clay soil with poor drainage, or where flooding is prolonged into the growing season, are frequently infested.

Goes pulcher (Hald.) the **living-hickory borer,** occurs in southern Canada and throughout eastern United States and breeds in the sapwood and heartwood of the trunk and branches of hickory. The adult is dark brown and about 18 to 25 mm. long. Its body is dark brown, covered with yellowish fine hair. The elytra are clay-yellow with dark bands across the base and the middle. Eggs are laid in twig crotches and possibly at other places on the bark. The larvae feed for awhile beneath the bark and then bore into the wood where they continue to feed for 2 to 4 years. Hickories growing in the Piedmont area of North Carolina are particularly prone to attack by this species.

The **oak sapling borer,** *Goes tesselatus* (Hald.), occurs from Pennsylvania southward and in the Midwest where it usually breeds in the base and roots of small oak saplings, preferably white oak. Young chestnuts and shadbush are also attacked occasionally. The adult is dull brown, about 25 mm. long, and its body is covered with small patches of prostrate gray or yellowish fine hairs, occasionally arranged in rows. The larvae require 3 to 5 years to complete their development. During this period they may completely hollow out the base of the tree and cause its death. Less seriously damaged trees often produce bulb-like swellings around the wounds at the ground line. These trees are subject to wind breakage.

Goes pulverulentus (Hald.), the **living-beech borer,** breeds in the small trunks and branches of various hardwoods such as beech, oak, elm, and sycamore throughout eastern United States. The adult is brown, 18 to 25 mm. long, and its body is clothed with short, white hairs. The thorax has a sharp spine on each side, and the elytra are faintly barred at the middle and base with pale-brown fine hairs. The life cycle requires 3 to 4 years.

Goes dibilis LeC., the **oak branch borer,** breeds in small, living branches of oak, often causing gall-like swellings, in eastern United States. Adults are brownish and from 11 to 19 mm. long. The head, thorax, and apical half of the elytra are clothed with reddish-yellow fine hairs. The elytra are crossed by two irregular, brown bands, and each basal half is mottled with grayish hairs. The life cycle requires 2 to 3 years.

Many species of the genus *Neoclytus* Thom. occur in eastern forests and attack both coniferous and deciduous trees. The larvae feed first beneath the bark, then bore into the sapwood and heartwood, often completely riddling it with long mines tightly packed with frass. The adults are slender bodied beetles of medium size, with quite long legs and short and more or less clubbed antennae.

The pronotum bears transverse ridges and the body is marked with transverse yellow lines.

The **red-headed ash borer,** *Neoclytus acuminatus* (F.), one of our most common wood borers, occurs generally throughout the eastern United States and in southeastern Canada. Its hosts include nearly all dying and dead hardwoods, but chiefly ash, oak, hickory, persimmon, and hackberry. Unseasoned logs of ash, oak, and hickory with the bark intact are especially subject to heavy attack. The adult is about 15 mm. long. The head and thorax are reddish; the body is light brown with the apical part of the elytra sometimes much darker. The elytra are also marked with four transverse bands of fine yellow hairs and the middle and hind legs are long and reddish.

Adults become active by mid-February in the Deep South and progressively later until May or June in the North. Eggs are deposited beneath the bark of dead, unseasoned wood. The larvae feed first beneath the bark, then they tunnel into the sapwood and often reduce it to powder. In the South there are several generations per year; in the North, only one.

Neoclytus caprea (Say), the **banded ash borer,** occurs in eastern Canada and throughout much of the United States. Its hosts are recorded as ash, hickory, elm, mesquite, and, rarely, white oak. In eastern United States, it commonly breeds in ash logs. Adults are dark brown to almost black and from 12 to 25 mm. long. There is a line of fine, white or yellowish hairs on the thorax and four bands of the same material and color across the elytra. The first two bands meet, almost forming circles.

Adults emerge in early spring and fly to host material where they deposit their eggs in crevices in the bark. Ash logs cut during the winter are especially subject to attack. The larvae feed for awhile under the bark and then bore into the sapwood where they feed for the remainder of the summer. Pupation occurs in the fall, but the adult does not emerge from the wood until the following spring. There is usually one generation per year; however, if the infested material is sawed, stored, and dried out, the life cycle may require several years. Ash logs left in the woods or stored with the bark on may be literally honeycombed with tunnels tightly packed with frass (fig. 58).

Other species of *Neoclytus* likely to be encountered in eastern forests and some of their known hosts are as follows: *N. mucronatus* (F.) (fig. 59)—the dead branches and trunks of hickory; *N. jouteli* (Davis)—dead oak twigs; *N. fulguratus* Casey—dead branches of oak; *N. scutellaris* (Oliv.)—elm, oak, hickory; *N. muricatulus* Kirby—larch, spruce, pine (in southern Canada and from Maine to Ohio); and *N. muricatulus muricatulus* Kirby —small post oaks (in North Carolina).

The genus *Saperda* F. is represented in eastern forests by several important species. Depending on the species, the larvae either bore in (1) the large branches or trunks of living trees; (2) in small branches and produce galls; or (3) in living or dead wood of dying or recently killed trees. Adults are medium-sized and cylindrical in form. The head is quadrate in front and very flat; the antennae are about as long as the body; the first joint of the hind tarsus is elongated; and the body is rather densely

FIGURE 58.—Galleries of *Neoclytus caprea*, the banded ash borer. Note that tunnels are tightly packed with granular frass.

clothed with a hairy covering. Felt (*239*) published a monograph on the genus.

The **poplar borer,** *Saperda calcarata* Say, occurs throughout the United States and Canada, wherever poplar grows. Willows are also subject to attack. The adult is from 20 to 28 mm. long, grayish-black or reddish-brown, and densely clothed with gray and yellow fine hairs (fig. 60). There also are yellowish stripes on the thorax and orange-yellow markings on the wing covers. Full-grown larvae are creamy white and about 30 mm. long.

Adults appear during the summer, feed on the bark of young twigs, and deposit their eggs in small slits cut in the bark, usually in the middle third of the tree. The larvae bore into the inner bark and sapwood where they later spend the winter. In the spring, they bore into the sapwood and heartwood and feed there until they are mature. Attacked trees are characterized by the presence of swollen scars and holes in the trunk and larger branches. Each larva bores an opening out to and through the bark through which frass is expelled and sap exudes. Wet areas around these holes blacken and appear varnished. The life cycle requires 3 years in the North. In the Deep South it is shorter. In

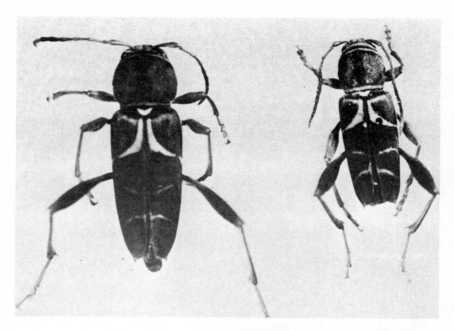

FIGURE 59.—Adults of *Neoclytus mucronatus.*

F-519920

FIGURE 60.—Adults of the poplar borer, *Saperda calcarata.*

the North, the second winter is spent as a mature larva in a cell at the end of its tunnel.

Small trees are occasionally killed by larvae girdling beneath the bark. Larger trees are seldom killed outright, but the large larval tunnels make them susceptible to windbreakage. They may be literally riddled with tunnels. Larval openings and tunnels serve as openings for various rots, decays, and other injurious insects which may kill the tree or degrade the lumber. Poplar plantations may be ruined and valuable shade trees severely damaged. Damage in forest stands also may be severe. In the Lake States, successful attacks appear to be concentrated in individual trees or small groups of trees unevenly distributed throughout the stand. These trees, commonly known as brood trees, are usually the larger, faster-growing trees in stands averaging between 3 and 7 inches d.b.h. Lakes States infestations also tend to increase with a decrease in stand density.

The best practice in the management of poplar in the Lake States apparently is to maintain well-shaded stands and then clear cut them at maturity. The removal of "brood trees" should also be helpful (*234*).

The **roundheaded apple tree borer**, *Saperda candida* F., occurs in Canada and throughout eastern United States. It is most serious as a pest of apple orchards, but it also breeds in mountain-ash, *Crataegus*, and shadbush. The adult is brilliantly white except for three broad, brown, longitudinal stripes extending the full length of the back, and is from 15 to 20 mm. long. Full-grown larvae are creamy-white and about 30 mm long (*344*).

Adults are present from June to September and deposit their eggs in slits cut in the bark at the base of living trees. They feed on the foliage and sometimes on tender bark. The larvae feed beneath the bark for one year and then bore into the wood, making large excavations and riddling it. The presence of tendrils of frass on the bark or at the base of the tree is evidence of attack. Heavily infested trees may be killed in a single season. Two or more years are required to complete the life cycle. Keeping trees healthy is an effective preventive measure. Borers in high value trees can be killed by injecting a fumigant into borer burrows.

The **linden borer**, *Saperda vestita* Say, occurs in the Northeastern States and Canada. Its preferred host is basswood but it also attacks poplars. The adult is reddish-brown, densely covered with prostrate fine olive-yellow hair, and from 12 to 21 mm. long. The tips of the antennae are brown, and there are three small black spots on each wing cover. Adults feed on leaf petioles, the larger veins of leaves, and the bark of growing shoots, often killing the tips of infested branches. The larvae feed beneath the bark and often bore deep into the wood. Unhealthy and weakened trees are most susceptible to attack.

Saperda discoidea F. breeds in dead and dying hickories and butternut from New York to Louisiana and Nebraska. Hickory trees infested with the hickory bark beetle are particularly subject to attack. Adults are 10 to 17 mm. long. The male is blackish with reddish legs and lines of grayish fine hair on the thorax. The female is reddish-brown or nearly black, clothed with yellowish fine hairs, and has two spots separated by a curved bar on the elytra. Eggs are deposited in bark crevices or in holes in the galleries of bark beetle during late spring and summer. The larvae feed gregariously beneath the bark, making extensive meandering mines. Most of the larvae mature in 1 year.

Saperda concolor LeC. breeds in the living branches and main stems of poplars and willows in the Northern and Central States. Adults are black with fine gray hairs and are about 12 mm. long. Eggs are laid in longitudinal slits in the bark. Callous tissue forming over these slits causes the formation of globose galls. The larvae mine around the stem and then bore into wood making galleries about 1 inch long that run parallel to the axis. Usually the infested twigs are not killed. Branches or small stems bearing numerous galls may stop growing, however, and become subject to wind breakage.

Saperda obliqua Say, the **alder borer,** breeds in the bases of living alders and sometimes birch in the Northern and Central States. The adult is reddish-brown and from 10 to 20 mm. long. There are two dark bands on the thorax and four oblique bands on the wing covers. Larvae feed first beneath the bark near the base, often girdling the stem. Later they bore into the stem and tunnel upward for several inches. Swollen areas appear at points of attack on stems that survive, and large amounts of frass are pushed out through the openings at the egg scars. Alders in ornamental plantings are frequently killed.

Saperda fayi Bland, the **thorn-limb borer,** occurs in the Northeast and Midwest and breeds in the twigs of hawthorn causing gall-like, gnarly swellings. Adults are reddish-brown and about 12 mm. long. There is a white stripe on each side of the thorax which extends upon the base of the elytra. The elytra bear two white spots at the base and tip, and a single large one in between. Infested twigs are subject to wind breakage. *S. moesta* LeC. causes the formation of globose galls on the stems and branches of poplar and willow in the northern parts of the United States. Adults are uniformly gray and about 10 mm. long. *S. lateralis* F. breeds in dead hickory, elm, basswood, oak, and Prunus and in hickory sprouts. Adults are black or brownish-black with the head, thorax, and elytra margined by broad, red lines, and are about 12 mm. long. The male has a tooth on each of its claws. *S. imitans* Felt and Joutel breeds in dead hickory, willow, and basswood; *S. cretata* Newm. in living apple and the limbs of living hawthorn; *S. mutica* Say in dead willow.

The **elm borer,** *Eutetrapha* (=*Saperda*) *tridentata* (Oliv.), occurs in southeastern Canada and throughout eastern United States and breeds in dead and dying American and slippery elms. The adult is grayish or fawn-colored and from 9 to 17 mm. long (fig. 61). An orange-yellow or yellowish band extends from the head to the tip of each wing cover, twin black spots occur below these bands on the thorax, and there is a cross band at the base of the wing covers followed by two oblique bands. Full-grown larvae are about 12 to 15 mm. long.

Adults are present from late spring to late summer, and feed on young leaves and young twigs. Eggs are deposited in small holes chewed in bark crevices, usually on freshly cut logs or

FIGURE 61.—Adult of the elm borer, *Eutetrapha* (= *Saperda*) *tridentata*.

weakened trees. The larvae bore beneath the bark, filling their mines with fibrous frass, and completely destroying the phloem and cambium (*587*). When they reach maturity they bore into the wood and construct cells in which to pupate. There is usually one generation per year; however, in rapidly dried wood 3 years may be needed to complete the life cycle.

Park and shade tree elms, especially the older ones and those in a weakened condition, are severely injured by this species. Affected trees tend to die very slowly, a branch at a time. The removal of infested branches is sometimes helpful in control.

Smodicum cucujiforme (Say), the **flat powder-post beetle,** occurs throughout eastern United States. The larvae excavate extensive meandering galleries in dry heartwood of oak and hickory. Stored lumber is frequently infested, the larvae continuing to feed in it until the wood is thoroughly riddled. The adult is small, elongate, very depressed, dull yellowish, shiny, and about 7 to 10 mm. long. Adults appear in July and August. Eggs are laid in crevices of exposed wood. The larvae excavate tunnels in the wood about 3 mm. in diameter, tightly packing them with frass. Pupation occurs in an enlarged portion of the mine near the surface of the wood. There is normally one generation per year. In dry wood, several years may be required to complete the life cycle.

The genus, *Oberea* Mulsant, is represented in the Eastern States by a number of slender, cylindrical beetles, the larvae of which bore in the twigs, branches, or stems of various forest, shade, and ornamental trees. These beetles are distinguished by the presence of a broad tooth on each tarsal claw.

The **dogwood twig borer,** *Oberea tripunctata* (Swed.) breeds in dogwood, elm, sourwood, laurel, azalea, *Viburnum,* and various fruit trees in eastern United States. The adult is yellowish and about 14 mm. long. The head is reddish or dark brown and there is a black spot on the scutellum. Adults appear in early spring and, after girdling the tip, the female deposits her eggs in living twigs of the host. The larva bores down the center of the twig, making a long series of holes for the expulsion of frass and cutting off portions of the twig as it bores on into the green wood. The winter is spent in the larval stage in the twig. Pupation occurs in the spring between two wads of fibrous frass. The portion

189

of the twig containing the cell may have been girdled previously. Occasionally dogwoods and elms are seriously damaged. The cutting off and burning of infested twigs might be helpful in control.

Oberea schaumi LeC. occurs in southern Canada and south in the Eastern States to the Gulf Coast. It breeds in poplar. Adults are about 14 mm. long; the thorax is yellowish to black and is marked by four round, smooth spots. The elytra are either yellowish or black. Eggs are laid in the stems and branches of suckers and seedlings; also in the twigs of saplings, poles, and large trees. The larvae feed near the pith, excavating tunnels up to 6 inches long, and boring holes to the outside for the expulsion of frass. Black, necrotic areas develop around these holes. Infested twigs die but are usually not sufficiently weakened to permit wind breakage.

Oberea myops Hald., the **rhododendron stem borer,** breeds in rhododendron, azalea, and laurel. The adult is pale yellow and about 12 to 15 mm. long. There are two black spots on the thorax and the elytral margins are dark. Eggs are deposited in the bark of twigs between two girdles about one-half inch apart. The larva bores down the twig, to and into the stem, and on down to the ground. Here, it cuts off the stem, and then bores into the roots. Frass is expelled through holes along the stem and at the ground line. This species is frequently a serious pest in ornamental plantings of rhododendron. Cutting off and burning of infested twigs as soon as they are noticed is recommended.

Oberea ocellata Hald., the **sumac stem borer,** occasionally causes serious injury in sumac plantings. Adults are about 13 to 15 mm. long. The head and underside of the body are red; the thorax is red with two black spots on the disk; and the elytra are black. The female girdles the tip of the plant and then lays an egg just below the girdle. The larva bores down the stem through the pith to the roots. Here, it proceeds to construct long tunnels and to feed for two seasons. During the fall of the second year, it cuts the plant off near the ground and plugs the stub with a wad of frass. Below this plug, pupation occurs the following spring.

Oberea ruficollis (F.) breeds in the stems and roots of sassafras. Adults are pale reddish-yellow and about 18 to 20 mm. long. The antennae, tibia, and tarsi are black and the elytra are densely clothed with fine gray hairs. The feeding habits of the larvae are similar to those of *O. ocellata* except that they seldom cut off stems near the ground. Infested plants usually survive but may be badly deformed.

Other species of *Oberea* sometimes encountered are: *O. pallida* Casey—in alder in Pennsylvania; *O. ulmicola* Chitt.—in the branches of oak, elm, hickory, dogwood, and black cherry in Ohio and Pennsylvania; and *O. ferruginea* Casey—in willow canes.

The genus *Oncideres* Serville contains several species, the females of which deposit their eggs in previously girdled terminals, twigs, or small branches of large trees, or in the stems of seedlings or sprouts. The girdled portions soon die and most of them fall to the ground. The larvae feed in the wood of this fallen material until the middle of the following summer, loosely filling their mines with frass. Pupation occurs in a cell formed by walling off a portion of the mine with fibrous frass. The adults appear in late summer or early fall and feed on the thin bark of twigs or stems. There is one generation per year in the South. In the North, many larvae do not pupate until the second year.

The **twig girdler,** *Oncideres cingulata cingulata* (Say), is the most important eastern member of the genus. Its hosts include hickory, persimmon, elm, oak, honey locust, hackberry, poplar, basswood, dogwood, sourwood, and various fruit trees. Adults (fig. 62A) are grayish-brown and about 15 mm. long. The front of the head is clothed with fine golden hairs; the elytra are clothed with gray, fine hairs and are marked with scattered yellow spots. Full-grown larvae are up to 18 mm. long.

FIGURE 62.—The twig girdler, *Oncideres cingulata cingulata:* A, adult; B, young hickory tree deformed by repeated attacks.

Adults emerge in late summer and feed on the tender bark and tips of twigs of their host. The egg laying and larval habits are as described earlier for the genus. On heavily infested large trees dozens of branches may be girdled and severed; often, many of them hang on for long periods before dropping to the ground. Such trees are not only damaged severely but are also ragged and unattractive. Hickory seedlings are especially prone to attack and damage, often becoming distorted following attack (fig. 62B). Honey locust seedlings in nurseries are also subject to serious injury. The collection and burning of infested twigs and branches during the fall or winter is an effective method of control, provided the trees to be protected are located at some distance from heavily infested stands.

Oncideres cingulata texanus Horn and *O. pustulatus* LeC. are common in parts of eastern or southwestern United States. The former is a pest of pecan in the South; the latter attacks huisache, acacia, and mesquite in the Rio Grande River Valley and other parts of the Southwest.

Eburia quadrigeminata (Say), the **ivory-marked beetle,** occurs in both eastern and western United States and breeds in the dry heartwood of various hardwoods. In the East, oak, hickory, ash, maple, honey locust, elm, chestnut, and cypress are attacked. Adults are light brown, with pairs of ivory spots at the base and middle of each elytron, and are about 24 mm. long. The larvae are wedge shaped, have tough, shiny skins, and are sparsely clothed with golden hairs. Mature oaks having "cat faces" or scars through which the larvae can gain access to the heartwood are often badly damaged. Seasoning lumber is also subject to occasional attack. The normal life cycle appears to be 2 years, but it may be considerably longer. There are records of adults emerging from flooring, door sills, and furniture 15 years after it was placed in use.

The **twig pruner,** *Elaphidionoides villosus* (F.) occurs throughout eastern United States. It breeds in the twigs and branches of living hardwoods such as the oaks, hickory, maple, locust, hackberry, walnut, elm, sweetgum, and pecan.Adults are slender, elongate, light brown and about 23 mm. long. The dorsal surface is clothed with irregular patches of fine gray hairs. There are spines on the first few joints of the antennae and the tips of the elytra are notched and bi-spinose.

Eggs are deposited in slits in the bark at leaf axils near the tips of twigs and small branches in late spring. Young larvae feed beneath the bark, often consuming much of the wood toward the base of the twig. Older larvae bore down the center of the stem toward the base until late in the summer. Then they sever the branch by making several concentric circular cuts from the center outward to, but not including, the thin bark (fig. 63). These branches, from 1/4-inch to 2 inches in diameter, break and fall to the ground with the larvae in them. The ground under heavily infested trees may be literally covered with these fallen twigs and branches. The larva returns up through the fallen branch and forms a cell between wads of fibrous frass where it pupates in the spring, or in the fall. There appears to be one generation per year. Heavily infested trees may be seriously damaged but are seldom killed. Shade and park trees may be so severely pruned they lose much of their esthetic value. The presence of numerous dead twigs and branches hanging in the crown also detracts from their appearance. The collection and burning of infested twigs and branches in the spring before the adults emerge should be helpful in control.

Elaphidion mucronatum (Say), the **spined bark borer,** also breeds in the dead branches of various hardwoods in eastern United States. Adults are dark brown, irregularly clothed with fine brown hair and are about 19 mm. long. Eggs are deposited be-

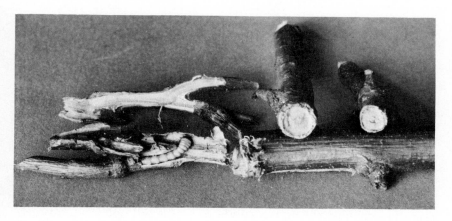

FIGURE 63.—Larva of the twig pruner, *Elaphidionoides villosus*, in an oak twig. Note ends of severed twigs.

neath bark scales, and the larvae feed beneath the bark during the first year of their lives. During the second year, they bore in the sapwood. Wood used in making rustic furniture is often damaged. *E. incertum* Newm., the **mulberry bark borer**, a species that closely resembles the spined bark borer, breeds in the outer bark of living mulberry trees in Eastern United States. Infestations have also been recorded in oak and hickory. It does not cause serious damage.

Desmocerus palliatus (Forst.), the **elder borer**, breeds in elder wherever it grows in eastern United States. Adults are bright, metallic blue with nearly all of the basal half of the elytra yellow, and are about 27 mm. long. The pronotum is much wider than long and is constricted at the apex; the wing surfaces are densely and coarsely punctured. Eggs are deposited in crevices of the bark at the base of the stem. The larvae feed in the roots and base of their host, eating out the pith and filling their mines with coarse, rather fibrous frass. The larval period lasts 2 to 3 years. Heavily infested plants may be seriously injured or killed.

Doraschema wildii Uhler, the **mulberry borer**, breeds in the living branches of mulberry and osage orange in the Southern and Central States. The adult is dark brown and from 16 to 22 mm. long (fig. 64). The body is covered with fine gray hairs except for small bare punctures scattered over the surface. Each wing cover has a light brown stripe along its outer margin.

In the Deep South, adults appear as early as mid-May. Eggs are deposited in niches chewed in the bark. Young larvae feed between the bark and wood, destroying irregular patches of cambium up to 2 square inches in area. After about 1 to 3 months they bore into the wood, constructing galleries that angle upward and inward for a couple of inches and then bend back towards the surface. These galleries are close together and often overlap. The winter is spent in the larval stage, and the life cycle varies from 1 to 2 years in length. Suppressed and fire-damaged trees are preferred, but vigorous, healthy trees are also attacked occasionally. Individual branches and even entire trees may be completely girdled and killed. Trees that recover usually have large scars

193

on the trunk (*678*). The smaller but related species, *D. alterna-tum* (Say) is commonly found in trees infested with the mulberry borer.

Aneflormorpha subpuescens (LeC.) the **oak-stem borer,** occurs in the Eastern, Southeastern and Central States. It breeds in small living oak and chestnut seedlings from ½-inch to 1 inch in diameter, and occasionally in the branches of larger trees. The adult is narrow, elongate, light brown, clothed with semi-erect fine brown hairs, and about 17 mm. long (fig. 65). There is a stout spine on each of the third and fourth segments of female an-tennae, and the tips of the elytra are notched and bi-spinose.

Eggs are deposited at leaf bases near the tops of seedlings and sprouts. The larvae bore into the center of the stem and tunnel downward, mining out the wood as they feed. Section after sec-tion of the stem is cut off as the larvae proceed toward the base. Frass is extruded through a single row of small holes cut through the bark to the outside. During late summer the full-grown larva burrows to the base of the main stem and often into a root. Here it constructs a pupal cell between two wads of fibrous frass. The stem is usually cut off at the ground line. There appears to be one generation per year. During certain years a high proportion of the oak seedlings in the Southeast are killed by this species.

The **black-horned pine borer,** *Callidium antennatum hesperum* Csy., occurs throughout the United States and breeds in dead or

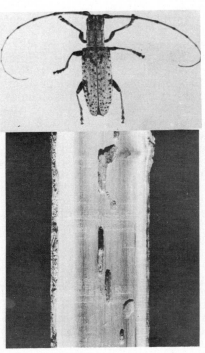

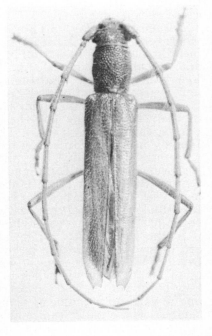

FIGURE 64.—*Doraschema wildii,* the mulberry borer: Top, adult; bot-tom, damage by larvae.

FIGURE 65.—Adult of *Aneflormor-pha subpubescens,* the oak-stem borer.

194

recently felled conifers, or in lumber with the bark on. It is especially common in dead pines in the South. The adult is flattened, bright metallic blue or bluish-black, and from 9 to 14 mm. long (fig. 66A). Male antennae are somewhat shorter than the body; the thorax is rounded, with depressions on each side of the middle; and the legs are black with large femora.

F-519946, (B, COURTESY DUKE UNIV. SCH. OF FORESJ.)

FIGURE 66.—The black-horned pine borer, *Callidium antennatum hesperum:* A, adult; B, larval galleries under the bark and in the wood.

Adults appear early in the spring and deposit their eggs be-beneath bark scales on dead trees or on cut wood that has seasoned over winter. The larvae feed in the phloem and outer sapwood making broad, wavy tunnels in the wood (fig. 66B) and pushing large quantities of frass through small holes in the bark. Pupation occurs in the wood in long cells plugged with wads of fibrous frass. There is usually one generation per year.

This species frequently causes serious losses to improperly edged lumber in lumber yards. Rustic work and houses built of pine logs are also subject to serious damage, the wood being badly riddled and weakened and the bark so loosened that it falls away. Prompt utilization of logs, the removal of wane on sawn lumber, and kiln drying are recommended methods of control.

Callidium texanum Schaeffer, the **black-horned juniper borer,** breeds in various conifers, preferably juniper and cedar, throughout the United States. Its habits are similar to those of the black-horned pine borer. Other eastern species include: *C. schotti,* Schffr. which breeds in the dead branches of cedar in the Midwest, and *C. violaceum* (L.) which occurs in red spruce in New York.

The genus *Acanthocinus* Stephens contains a number of species commonly known as pine-bark borers. The adults are elongate, rather flattened, and from 12 to 28 mm. long. They are also usually black and mottled or striped with grayish-white or brown pubescence. The basal joints of male antennae are fringed beneath with hairs, and the ovipositor of the female is characteristically extended.

195

Acanthocinus nodosus (F.) is a common species in the South where it breeds in the thick bark of pine logs and dying and recently killed pines. The adult (fig. 67) is gray with velvety black markings and is about 25 mm. long. Male antennae are sometimes at least three times the length of the body. Eggs are deposited in pits chewed in the bark or in the exit holes of bark beetles. The larvae feed in the bark where they often compete with and destroy bark beetle broods. Pupation occurs in nestlike chambers in the bark, near the surface. There is one generation per year. Other eastern species include: (1) *A. obsoletus* (Oliv.)—adults are about 10 mm. long. Hosts are recently killed pine and balsam fir. (2) *A. pusillus* (Kirby)—adults are about 10 mm. long. It has been reared from wind-thrown and fire-killed red and jack pines, balsam fir, and spruce.

The genus *Anoplodera* Muls. contains many species of rather robust and usually more or less triangular-shaped beetles that are nearly always beautifully colored and hairy about the head and thorax. They are also quick and active and are usually found on flowers. Eggs are laid in crevices of bark or wood in moist locations. The larvae feed in the wood for 2 to 3 years, excavating extensive galleries they then pack with fibrous frass. Infested wood may be reattacked repeatedly until it is completely disintegrated. Poles, cross ties, and other material in contact with the ground may be completely destroyed.

Anoplodera nitens (Forst.) the **chestnut-bark borer,** breeds in thick, moist bark in crotches and at the base of living chestnut and oak trees. The adult is velvety black and from 10 to 15 mm. long. There are golden-yellow bands on the margins of the thorax and on the elytra. Damage is seldom serious although large patches of bark are sometimes killed.

Anoplodera canadensis (Oliv.) breeds in dead pines, spruces, hemlock, and sometimes balsam fir in southern Canada and the Northern States. Living trees are also attacked occasionally at wounds, the larvae boring into the heartwood. The adult is dull black with the base of the elytra bright red. The upper surface

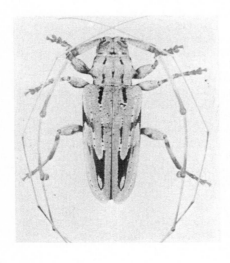

FIGURE 67.—Adult of *Acanthocinus nodosus,* a pine-bark borer.

is coarsely punctured, and the antennae are generally ringed with yellow.

Additional eastern species of *Anoplodera* and their hosts include the following: *A. minnesotana* (Casey)—hickory, elm, black cherry, sourgum, and red spruce; *A. vagans* (Oliv.)—butternut, hickory, birch and pine logs; *A. proxima* (Say)—maple, hickory, basswood, and sourgum; *A. nigrella* (Say)—pines and spruce; *A. mutabilis* (Newm.) and *A. vittata* Oliv.—red spruce; and *A. biforis* (Newm.)—white pine.

Phymatodes testaceus (L.), the **tanbark borer,** breeds in the bark of dead oak trees and occasionally in stored hemlock bark, in the Eastern and Central States. Adults are elongated, flattened and about 14 mm. long. Some are brownish-yellow or dark brown with lighter elytra and in some the thorax, abdomen, tibiae, and tarsi are reddish-yellow and the elytra, blue. The remainder are intermediate in color. The larvae feed within or beneath the bark and pupation occurs in the sapwood. Several years may be required to complete the life cycle. Bark stored for tanning purposes is subject to heavy damage. *P. dimidiatus* Kyb. breeds in fir and spruce in the Northern States. Adults are about 11 mm. long, and dark brown, with a light brown band across the base of the elytra. *P, varius* (Fab.) breeds in or beneath the dead bark of hickory and oak and possibly in various conifers. The adult is light brown or dark brown to black and shiny. There are white bands on the elytra, and the adult borer is about 10 mm. long.

Physocnemum andreae Hald., the **cypress bark borer,** breeds under the bark of girdled, felled, or dead cypress trees. The adult is reddish-brown and ranges in length from 11 to 21 mm. There is a curved white mark on each elytron, a small tubercle near the base of the thorax, and club-shaped femora. Eggs are deposited beneath bark scales, and the larvae feed beneath the bark, excavating large mines that deeply scar the wood. Winter is spent in the larval stage, and pupation occurs in the spring. The species often causes serious losses to cypress trees felled or girdled during lumbering operations. Rustic work constructed from this wood is also subject to serious damage. Rapid utilization of girdled or felled trees and the storage of logs in ponds are effective control practices.

Physocnemum brevilineum (Say), the **elm bark borer,** breeds in the corky bark of living elm trees in southern Canada and the Eastern and Central States (*317*). Adults are dark brown to black and about 17 mm. long. The elytra are frequently bluish with three longitudinal white marks. Eggs are deposited beneath bark scales. The larvae feed in the phloem, constructing meandering, frass-packed galleries. The bark over these galleries dies and falls off. *P. violareipenne* Hamilton breeds in the small branches of white oak in the Midwest. Adults are only about 9 mm. long; otherwise, they are very similar to those of the elm bark borer.

Parandra brunnea (F.), the **pole borer,** occurs throughout much of the United States, and attacks a wide variety of hardwoods and conifers. Logs, poles, and other wood products in contact with the ground, such as cross-ties and structural timbers, are also infested. The adult is flat, shiny, mahogany-brown, and about 18 mm. long. Full-grown larvae taper slightly toward the rear and are about 30 mm. long.

Adults appear during mid-summer and deposit their eggs singly but close together deep in either solid or decayed wood. Attacks on living trees are usually made at places where the wood is exposed such as at scars, wounds, or broken branches. The larvae feed in the wood for 3 or 4 years. Although the wood may be completely honeycombed, a covering shell of sapwood is always left intact. Pupation occurs in a cell in the wood. Many of the adults do not emerge from the wood but mate and lay eggs in the cavities in which they are working. In living wood, the wounds where the larvae gain entry will often heal over, leaving no external signs of attack. Shade trees, telephone and telegraph poles, and structural wood in moist locations or in contact with the ground are subject to severe damage. A considerable degree of protection of valuable shade trees can be provided by keeping them healthy, by the removal or treatment of exposed dead and decaying wood, and by covering pruning scars with paint.

The **cedar tree borer,** *Semanotus ligneus* (F.), occurs throughout the United States. Practically all species of conifers are subject to attack, but dying and recently felled cedars and junipers are preferred. Adults are dark brown to black and from 7 to 16 mm. long. The thorax is rounded and hairy, except for several bare spots on the disk. The elytra are sometimes black, but are usually dark blue with yellow or orange markings.

Eggs are deposited beneath bark scales in the spring. The larvae feed first beneath the bark, scarring the wood deeply. Then, they bore into the sapwood and occasionally the heartwood. There is one generation per year. The related species, *Semanotus litigiosa* (Casey), has been recorded from eastern United States but is primarily western in distribution. Its hosts include several species of true firs, Douglas-fir, larch, plus several spruces. Male adults are usually all black, whereas females are black marked with orange.

The genera *Asemum* Esch. and *Arhopalus* Serville contain a number of species that breed in the sapwood and heartwood of the stumps of felled trees and in the lower portions of dying trees. When abundant, the larvae may destroy large portions of the sapwood. *Asemum striatum* (L.) and *Arhopalus rusticus obsoletus* (Rand.) are common eastern species.

Tragosoma desparius (L.), the **hairy pine borer,** occurs from coast to coast in southern Canada and the Northern States. It also occurs southward through the Appalachians in the Eastern States where it breeds in various dead conifers. The adult is a heavy, shiny dark brown beetle from 20 to 40 mm. long. The underside of the body is very hairy, and the elytra are ridged. Larvae are tough-skinned and have four teeth on the front of the head. Occasionally crossties, poles, and timbers in contact with the ground are seriously damaged.

Atimia confusa (Say), the **small cedar-bark borer,** breeds in dying cedars, junipers, and related trees throughout the Eastern and Central States. The adult is small, stoutish, and about 9 mm. long. The head, pronotum, elytra, and venter are black. The dorsum is clothed with recumbent, fine gray hairs, and the elytra are notched at the apices. Adults appear in early spring and again in early fall and deposit their eggs beneath bark scales. The larvae feed entirely between the bark and wood, packing fibrous frass behind them. Pupation occurs in cells in the sapwood. The winter is spent as larvae or as adults. Rustic work constructed from improperly seasoned cedar and juniper is subject to attack and serious damage. The bark over damaged areas dries and peels off.

Aneflus protensus LeC. attacks living mesquite in Texas and other Southwestern States. The adult is light or dark brown, has spines on the basal joints of the antennae and the tips of the elytra, and is from 20 to 30 mm. long. Eggs are deposited in bark crevices at the forks of small branches. The larvae bore into the branch and hollow it out. Frass is extruded through small holes in the bark. Black, watery liquid drips from these holes and stains the foliage and ground beneath. The interior of the larval mine is always stained black. Two years are required to complete the life cycle. Infested branches and small trees are sometimes killed.

Tetropium cinnamopterum Kby., the **eastern larch borer,** breeds beneath the bark of living and dead coniferous trees, especially larch, and occurs from coast to coast in southern Canada and the Northern States. The adult is oblong, somewhat flattened, brown to blackish, and about 12 mm. long. The eyes are completely divided into upper and lower lobes. The larvae feed gregariously beneath the bark, packing frass behind them in the mines. There is one generation per year in the United States. This was the most common cerambycid borer attacking windthrown spruce in the Adirondacks following a severe windstorm in 1950.

Neoptychodes trilineatus (L.), the **fig tree borer,** breeds in the branches and trunks of living and dying fig trees in the Southern States. Alder is also attacked occasionally. The adult is gray except for small reddish-yellow spots on the body and white stripes on the elytra, and is about 18 to 25 mm. long. Eggs are deposited in small holes chewed through the bark. The larvae feed at first beneath the bark and then bore into the heartwood, where they construct long tunnels. The life cycle usually requires several years. Infested branches and small trees are often killed.

Tylonotus bimaculatus Hald., the **ash and privet borer,** breeds in a wide variety of deciduous trees and shrubs, preferably ash and privet, in the Eastern and Central States. Adults are dark brown and from 12 to 18 mm. long. There are light spots on the wing covers and a median line and two small, shiny spots on the thorax.

Eggs are deposited at the base of privet plants and beneath bark scales on living and dying ash trees during early summer. Young larvae feed in the phloem; later they penetrate deeper and scar the wood. Large branches of ash are usually attacked and killed before the trunk is attacked. Old, mature, and drought-ridden trees, especially those growing in parks and windbreaks, are killed gradually, branch by branch. Privet hedges are subject to severe damage. The larval stage extends over a period of 2 years.

Encyclops coerulea (Say), the **oak-bark scaler,** bores in the outer bark of living white oaks, yellow-poplar, maple, sourgum, black ash, and pignut hickory in the Eastern States. The adult is slender, metallic blue or green, has light brown legs, and is about 9 mm. long. Dry scales over damaged areas of bark peel off.

Oeme rigida (Say) breeds in dead and dying cypress and juniper throughout eastern United States. The adult is light to dark brown and between 12 and 22 mm. in length. Eggs are deposited beneath bark scales and the larva feeds beneath the bark and in the wood, exuding large quantities of granular frass. Deadened cypress and rustic work constructed from improperly seasoned wood are often severely damaged, causing the bark to peel off and sometimes causing destruction of pieces of wood up to 3 inches in diameter.

The genus *Prionus* Geoff. consists of a number of species of robust, black or brownish-black, shiny beetles from 25 to 45 mm. long. The antennae have from 12 to 27 segments and are heavy and imbricated in the male. There are three spines, or teeth, on each side of the prothorax. Several species are known to feed in the roots of a wide variety of living fruit, forest, and shade trees in eastern United States. Root rots, such as *Armillaria,* and various species of secondary boring insects often attack the damaged roots and kill the trees. Mature trees growing in open stands, in well-drained gravelly soil and hillsides, in pastures, and in heavily used recreation areas are especially subject to attack. Small trees and shrubbery are occasionally killed by borers that cut off their roots at the ground line.

The **broad-necked root borer,** *Prionus laticollis* (Drury), breeds in the roots of a wide variety of trees and shrubs in eastern United States, mostly hardwoods. Oak, poplar, chestnut, and basswood are especially favored. Infestations have also been recorded in the logs and stumps of all the above species. The adult is dark-brown, shining, and up to 45 mm. long. The head is depressed between the eyes; the antennae of the male are shorter than the body; and the base of the pronotum is as wide as the elytra. Full-grown larvae may reach a length of 75 mm. Eggs are deposited in groups on the ground and the young larvae crawl to the roots to feed. At first, they feed in the bark, but soon enter the root which is completely hollowed out and occasionally severed. They move from root to root through the soil, feeding on the surfaces of smaller roots as they go and causing many injuries or wounds. Mature larvae come to within 3 to 5 inches of the soil surface in the spring and form oval, compact cells in which to pupate. The life cycle is believed to require 3 years. This species seldom causes substantial damage in the forest.

The **tile-horned prionus,** *Prionus imbricornis* (L.), occurs throughout much of eastern United States and breeds in the living roots of oak, chestnut, pear, and various herbaceous plants. Adults (fig. 68) are dark brown, shiny and up to 37 mm. long. Male antennae are 18- to 22-jointed, and the segments overlap. Eggs are deposited in groups in the soil around the base of the tree. Larval habits are similar to those of the broad-necked root borer. The life cycle requires at least 3 years.

Prionus pocularis Dalm. breeds in decaying coniferous logs and stumps in the Central, Middle Atlantic and Southern States. Adults are light brown, shiny, and about 42 mm. long. The elytra are densely punctured.

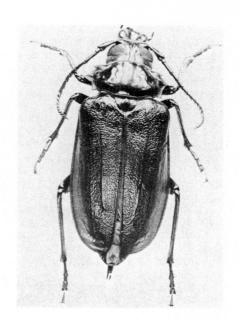

FIGURE 68.—Adult of the tile-horned prionus, *Prionus imbricornis.*

Several species of *Xylotrechus* Chev. occur in eastern forests. Adults are characterized by their moderate size, their short, filiform antennae, and a *V*-shaped callosity on the front of the head.

Xylotrechus quadrimaculatus (Hald.), the **birch and beech girdler,** breeds in the branches of birch, beech, blue beech, maple, and alder in the Eastern States. Adults are about 12 mm. long. The thorax is black with four yellow spots; the wing covers pale brown with faint white marks. Eggs are deposited in the axils of twigs, in bark crevices, and in healed over injuries on branches. Young larvae feed beneath the bark, often girdling and killing the branch quickly. Later they bore toward the pith in concentric circles until the branch is almost severed. At this point, they turn and bore toward the tip, packing their tunnels with granular frass. Before reaching the tip they construct pupal cells in which they spend the winter and in which they pupate in the spring. Damaged branches up to 2 inches in diameter frequently fall to the ground, with the larvae in them, during mid-summer. There is one generation per year.

The **gall-making maple borer,** *Xylotrechus aceris* Fisher, breeds in the trunks and branches of various maples, causing the formation of galls. The adults resemble those of the birch and beech girdler, although they are somewhat smaller and have fainter spots on the thorax and stronger markings on the elytra. Eggs are deposited during mid-summer in wounds or at the bases of small dead twigs along the trunk. The larvae bore directly into the sapwood. Later they construct tunnels in the heartwood, often completely destroying the center of the trees and causing the formation of galls or swellings about the wounds. During the second summer of their lives, they bore either directly upward or downward and pupate in cells at the end of their tunnels. Infested trees are never killed outright but are seriously weakened, becoming subject to breakage by the wind.

Xylotrechus obliteratus LeC., the **poplar-butt borer,** a serious pest of aspen and other poplars in the Rocky Mountain region, also occurs in many parts of eastern United States. The adult is dark-colored and about 10 to 18 mm. long. The thorax is crossed by yellow bands at the front and rear margins; the elytra are crossed by three yellow bands—the first one oblique, the middle one curved, and the last one transverse.

Adults are present during late summer. Eggs are deposited in irregularities of the bark or exposed wood, and the larvae feed beneath the bark until fall. The following year they bore into the wood where they feed for several years, much of the time in parts of the tree below the ground line. Females continue to deposit eggs in the butts of infested trees until the wood is completely honeycombed and the tree dies or is broken by wind or ice.

Xylotrechus sagittatus (Germ.) breeds in dead conifers in eastern Canada and the Northern States. In areas where pines predominate, it is especially common. Logs, slash and trees killed by fire or bark beetles are particularly attractive. Adults (fig. 69) are dark brown and about 18 mm. long. Each elytron is marked with variable stripes of fine gray hairs—one stripe along the sutural margin, one along the outer margin, and one at the apex. The larvae feed first beneath the bark, then they tunnel deep into the wood.

The **rustic borer,** *Xylotrechus colonus* (F.), one of the commonest of all cerambycids in eastern United States, feeds under the bark of almost all dead hardwoods. It occurs also in southern

FIGURE 69.— Adult of *Xylotrechus sagittatus.*

FIGURE 70.—Adult of the rustic borer, *Xylotrechus colonus.*

Canada. The adult (fig. 70) is light to dark brown and about 14 mm. long. Each elytron is marked with an irregular line of fine yellow hairs back of the base and three transverse bands of gray hairs—one band just behind the yellow line at the base, one back of the middle, and one at the apex. The larvae feed almost exclusively in the bark without scarring the wood (*279*). Recently killed trees are preferred.

Xylotrechus annosus (Say) and *X. undulatus* (Say) both occur in eastern United States. *X. annosus,* a western species, breeds in poplar in the Lake States; *X. undulatus* breeds in recently cut balsam fir, larch, hemlock, and spruce in the northern tier of States.

The genus *Monochamus* Serville is represented by several important wood-boring species in eastern forests, all of which breed in various conifers. The larvae are commonly known as 'sawyers' because of the loud noise they make while feeding. Freshly cut, felled, dying or recently dead trees are preferred. Young larvae feed on the inner bark, cambium, and outer sapwood, forming shallow excavations called surface galleries and filling them with coarse fibrous borings and frass. As they grow older, they bore deep into the heartwood, and then turn around and bore back toward the surface, thereby forming a characteristic **U**-shaped tunnel. A pupal cell is formed at the outer end of the tunnel, from which the adult emerges by chewing a hole out through the remaining wood and bark. Full-grown larvae are often more than 50 mm. long. Members of this genus often cause heavy losses in windthrown or fire-killed timber, in sawlogs left too long in the woods before milling, and in improperly handled pulpwood. Hopping (*378*) published a key to the adult of the genus.

The **southern pine sawyer,** *Monochamus titillator* (F.), occurs throughout the Eastern and Southern States and breeds in recently-cut, windthrown, fire-killed, insect-killed, and dying pines. The adult is mottled gray and brown and from 18 to 30 mm. long (fig. 71). Male antennae are often 2 to 3 times as long as the body; there is a strong spine on each side of the thorax; and the elytral sutures are prolonged into sharp spines. Full-grown larvae are up to 60 mm. long.

In the Piedmont area of the South, adult emergence reaches a peak in April and May. However, adult activity continues until late fall and probably to some extent throughout the winter. Larval habits are as described above for the genus. There are at least two generations per year in the South, with overlapping broods (*750*). Prompt salvage and utilization of windthrown and dead and dying trees, debarking recently dead trees, and water storage of logs will prevent attacks by this species.

The **white-spotted sawyer,** *Monochamus scutellatus* (Say), occurs from Newfoundland to North Carolina, Minnesota, and Alaska. White pine appears to be its favorite host but it also attacks many other conifers such as red and jack pines, balsam fir, white, black, and red spruces, and larch. The adult (fig. 72) is about 18 to 25 mm. long. The male is completely shiny black except for a small rounded white spot at the base of the elytra; females are of the same color or have the elytra mottled with white spots.

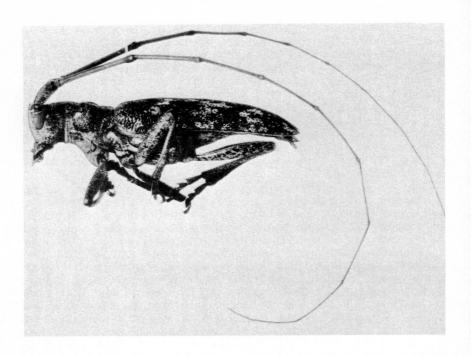

F-480483

FIGURE 71.—Adult of the southern pine sawyer, *Monochamus titillator.*

Two years are required to complete the life cycle in the Lake States and Canada. Farther south there is one generation per year. Adults emerge through circular holes cut in the bark and feed for short periods on needles and tender bark of various conifers. Eggs are then deposited in slits or niches chewed in the bark, preferably near old branch scars or in wrinkled areas on logs, pulpwood, and recently killed trees (*773, 618*).

The white-spotted sawyer causes heavy losses to sawlogs and pulpwood in the Northern States and southern Canada. Damage to sawlogs can be prevented by cutting the trees between September and early June and removing them from the woods before

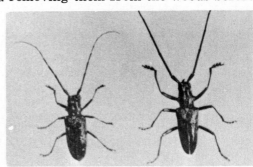

F-496927

FIGURE 72.—Adults of the white-spotted sawyer, *Monochamus scultellatus.*

204

late June. Damage to pulpwood can be reduced by piling it in the shade of standing trees or covering the piles with layers of slash 1 to 2 feet thick.

The **Northeastern sawyer,** *Monochamus notatus* (Drury), occurs in eastern Canada and in the Northeastern States, westward to the Great Lakes region, and breeds in dead and dying white pine and balsam fir and in windthrown red spruce. Adults are dark brown and up to 30 mm. long. The head and pronotum are irregularly clothed with fine white hairs; the elytra are covered with fine gray and white hairs arranged in the form of interrupted stripes. The female head is greatly flattened and elongated.

The **balsam fir sawyer,** *Monochamus marmorator* Kby., breeds in balsam fir in eastern Canada and the Northeastern States, west to the Great Lakes region and south to North Carolina. Adults are dark brown, marbled with irregular bands of white and yellow, and from 18 to 25 mm. long. Recently felled trees are particularly attractive to them. *M. carolinensis* (Oliv.) breeds in dead and dying pines in the Southeastern States. Adults are only about 17 mm. long, otherwise they are very similar in appearance to those of the southern pine sawyer. The **spotted pine sawyer,** *M. maculosus* Hald., a common species in the far West, also occurs in eastern forests. It breeds in dead and dying pines. Adults are dark reddish to blackish with patches of fine yellowish hair, and are about 16 mm. long. The tip of each elytron is prolonged into a tooth.

Orthosoma brunneum (Forst.), the **brown prionid,** breeds in decaying coniferous and hardwood logs in southeastern Canada and throughout much of eastern United States. The adult is light brown, flattened, and from 25 to 50 mm. long. The pronotum is narrower than the elytra and has three sharp spines on each side. There are three fine, raised longitudinal lines on each elytron. The body of the larva is slightly tapering and shines with a lemon or yellowish tinge.

Eggs are deposited from June to late summer in wood that has been dead for several years, especially in wood with very high moisture content and containing decay fungi. The larvae feed for 2 to 3 years, packing their tunnels with coarse, fibrous frass. Cross-ties, structural timbers, poles, or other wood in contact with the ground may be severely damaged or destroyed. Damage can be prevented by keeping the wood dry or by treating it with a preservative before placing it in contact with the ground.

Stenodontes dasytomus (Say), the **hardwood stump borer,** occurs from Virginia southward and westward and breeds in the heartwood of living hardwood trees such as various oaks, sycamore, willow, and boxelder. Wood in contact with the ground is also attacked. The adult is a large, somewhat flattened, reddish-brown beetle from 30 to 45 mm. long. The head is large and the sides of the prothorax are armed with small, fine teeth. Eggs are deposited around wounds, particularly near the base of the tree, and the larvae bore into the heartwood. They feed there gregariously for 3 or 4 years, completely honeycombing the wood. Shade trees are sometimes weakened so badly that they break and fall during storms. Cross-ties and other wood products in contact with the ground are also subject to serious damage.

Archodontes melanopus (L.) breeds in the roots of live oaks and possibly hackberry and pecan from Virginia to Florida and westward along the Gulf Coast. The adult is broad, rather flat, dark brown, and from about 43 to 56 mm. long. The head is distinct and rather large, and the edges of the prothorax are finely toothed. Full-grown larvae are almost 90 mm. long and are about as thick as one's finger.

Eggs are deposited at the base of young trees, just below the ground line. The larvae bore into the roots and excavate large, flattened galleries in the wood. Huge galls form on infested roots and interfere with the growth of the tree. Heavily infested trees may die and be replaced by clumps of bush-like suckers. It has been suggested that this species was largely responsible for the creation of large areas of comparatively barren areas of scrub oak in parts of southern Georgia and Florida.

Stenocorus inquisitor lineatus (Oliv.), the **ribbed pine borer**, occurs throughout the United States and in southern Canada, and it breeds in the inner bark of various species of dying conifers. The adult is black except for mottlings of reddish-brown or gray and is about 12 to 16 mm. long. The thorax is slender and bears a spine on each side. The larvae are distinguished by their very thin, flat heads. Eggs are deposited in early spring in crevices of the bark of trees that died or were cut during the preceding winter. Trees dead for only a short time and containing considerable amounts of moisture are preferred by the larvae. They feed entirely beneath the bark, excavating irregular galleries and packing them with fibrous frass. When they become full-grown they construct oval, fibrous-edged cells in which they pupate and spend the winter as adults.

The **old-house borer**, *Hylotrupes bajulus* (L.), a European species introduced into North America more than a century ago, is now known to occur in the Atlantic Coastal States from Massachusetts to Florida. Adults have also been collected in the Gulf Coast States of Mississippi, Louisiana, and Texas. It breeds in dry, seasoned, coniferous sapwood. Pine and spruce wood appear to be preferred, but hemlock, true fir, and Douglas-fir wood are also attacked. The adult (fig. 73 A) is a slightly flattened, brownish-black beetle from 12 to 18 mm. long. The head and forward part of the body are clothed with gray hairs; the thorax has several small tubercles at the side and a black line and two black spots on the disk; and each wing cover bears patches of gray which fuse to form two cross bands or two whitish spots. Full-grown larvae are wedge-shaped, deeply segmented, and up to 30 mm. long.

Eggs are deposited in fan-shaped clusters, or in rows and layers in holes or tight crevices. Stacked lumber and cracks and natural checks in the wood of houses are especially subject to attack. Young larvae feed near the surface of the wood; older ones bore into the sapwood and seriously damage it with their frass-packed tunnels. The larvae seldom break through the surface of the wood. Thus, timbers so severely damaged as to be near collapse may appear from the outside to be perfectly sound. The length of the life cycle is not exactly known. In the Southern States, from 3 to 5 years may be required. In the northern parts of its range, an additional 2 to 3 years may be necessary. The length of the cycle may also vary considerably in a given building. In attics, where generally warmer temperatures prevail, adults may emerge up to 2 years earlier than those in wood in the basement.

The old-house borer causes severe damage in houses and other buildings. Structural timbers (fig. 73 B), framing members, and other wood parts are seriously weakened by its mining and tunneling. Air-dried pine floor joists, plates or sills, and sub-flooring are apt to be damaged most severely. Other framing such as studs, stair carriages, furring strips, and roof rafters are sometimes attacked.

When an old-house borer infestation is discovered, two types of remedial action are necessary: (1) the repair or correction of serious structural defects and (2) controlling the remaining insects present in wood left in place (*486*).

Chlorophorus annularis (F.), has been recovered from infested imported bamboo at several locations in this country, and it may be established here. The adult is blackish, with green markings on the thorax and a yellow, *X*-shaped mark on the elytra, and are about 10 mm. long. The first two pairs of legs and the inner parts of the antennae are red. Well-seasoned bamboo is mined extensively, and the mines are tightly packed with fine, powdery frass. This species is a serious pest of bamboo in India and Japan.

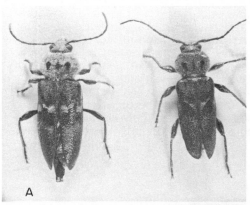

F, 494430, 494432
FIGURE 73.—The old house borer, *Hylotrupes bajulus:* A, adults; B, damage.

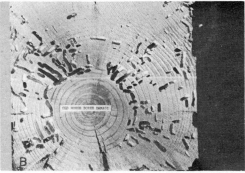

Rhyncophora

(Snout Beetles)

Snout beetles differ from other Coleoptera in having the head of the adult more or less prolonged to form a beak or snout, the gular sutures united in a median line, and the joints of the palpi usually rigid. The larvae are whitish, C-shaped, more or less cylindrical, and legless. A great many species occur in eastern North America, nearly all of which feed on trees and other types of vegetation. The larvae usually are burrowing in habit, infesting fruits, nuts, twigs, roots, and terminals. Trees of all ages are attacked, and damage is often severe. Forest nurseries and plantations are especially susceptible to serious injury (84).

FAMILY BRENTIDAE

BRENTID BEETLES

Only one tree-infesting species of this family occurs in eastern United States. The remainder are confined almost entirely to the tropics.

The **oak timberworm**, *Arrhenodes minutus* Drury, breeds in hardwoods, chiefly oak, beech, and poplar in the Eastern States. Adults are dark reddish-brown to black and up to 35 mm. long. The snout of the female is straight, narrow, and much longer than the head. In the male, it is broader and flatter and armed with powerful mandibles (fig. 74). The larvae are elongate, cylindrical, and soft-skinned.

In Missouri, adults are active from early May to late August and the female deposits her eggs in deep holes chewed into the wood, often at fresh wounds. Living trees and trees dead up to 3 years are subject to attack. The larvae bore through the wood, constructing pinhole galleries across the grain in all directions. The life cycle usually requires 3 years (117).

F-519917
FIGURE 74.—Adults of the oak timberworm, *Arrhenodes minutus*. Male on left; female on right.

208

The oak timberworm is capable of causing serious injury. Occasionally, much of the timber in infested stands is so badly damaged it is unfit for many uses. Control is difficult, but the removal of dead and dying snags and fire-scarred trees and the prevention of wounds in living trees should be helpful.

FAMILY ANTHRIBIDAE

FUNGUS WEEVILS

Fungus weevils are of little or no economic importance but are frequently encountered in the wood of dead hickory, beech, and maple trees. The adult is brown to whitish mottled and has a broad, flat, and very short beak. The larvae feed by boring into decaying wood directly beneath fungus sporophores and up into the woody part of the sporophore itself.

FAMILY BELIDAE

BELID BEETLES

The **New York weevil,** *Ithycerus noveboracensis* (Forst.), is the only known member of this family. It is rather widely distributed in the Eastern and Central States, but seems to be most abundant in the Mississippi River Valley (*193*). Adults have been collected from oak, hickory, beech, and various fruit trees, and the larvae, from within twigs of oak and hickory. The adult is robust, shiny black, and from 12 to 18 mm. long. A covering of ash-gray and pale-brown prostrate hairs gives it a mottled appearance.

FAMILY CURCULIONIDAE

WEEVILS

This family is reported to contain more species than any other in the animal kingdom (*391*). Many species are extremely destructive pests of agricultural crops. Many others are serious pests of forest, shade, and ornamental trees, also of seedlings and young trees in nurseries and plantations. The adults of many species drill holes in fruits, nuts, and other plant tissues to feed. The larvae generally feed inside fruits, nuts, seeds, buds, and the stems of their host. The adults of most species are typical snout beetles, the head bending downward and forming a well-defined and usually curved beak. The antennae are clavate and elbowed, and are located at about the middle of the beak.

The **white-pine weevil,** *Pissodes strobi* (Peck), occurs throughout the range of its most common host, eastern white pine, in eastern North America. In descending order of preference, its most commonly attacked hosts are: eastern white pine, Norway spruce, jack pine, Scotch pine, pitch pine, and red pine. Most other conifers, both native and introduced, occurring within its geographic range also may be attacked. The adult (fig. 75 A) is a small, brownish weevil, about 4 to 6 mm. long. The snout is curved and about as long as the prothorax, and the elytra are marked irregularly with brown and white scales. Mature larvae are yellowish-white, legless, and slightly longer than the adults. The pupae are creamy-white and about as long as the adults.

Winter is spent in the adult stage in the litter. Adults emerge from March to May, depending on locality, and feed on the succulent growth of the terminal leaders of their host, usually on the bark about 7 to 10 inches below the dormant buds. Eggs are deposited in small punctures in the bark of the leader and hatch in a week or 10 days. The young larvae bore downward side by side in a ring, feeding on the inner bark and outer wood. By late July

FIGURE 75.—White-pine weevil, *Pissodes strobi:* A, adult; B, infested terminal of a young white pine; C, white pines deformed by weevil attack,

or late summer, they become full-grown and pupate in chambers formed in the wood or pith. Adults appear in 10 to 15 days and feed until late fall on both old and mature new growth. Sometimes, this feeding alone is severe enough to kill entire shoots.

The white-pine weevil is the most serious insect pest of eastern white pine in North America. Its damage results in two types of loss: (1) reduction in recoverable volume; (2) lumber degrade in the remaining volume. Studies in New Hampshire showed an estimated volume loss of 40 percent in the sawlog portion of saw-timber trees and 70 percent loss in the portion above sawlog limits of merchantability. The average volume loss in pole-size trees was 13 percent (*744*).

The first evidence of attack in the spring is excessive pitch flow from feeding punctures on the preceding year's terminal shoots (*468*). Later, the new growth appears stunted, and finally, the needles wilt (fig. 75 B). Trees up to 3 feet tall may be killed. Killed terminals on taller trees are replaced by one or more branches of the topmost living whorl assuming vertical growth, resulting in crooked or forked stems (fig. 75 C). Trees suffering this type of damage for several years become multiple-stemmed, cabbage-shaped, and worthless.

The white-pine weevil has been studied intensively during the past several years, and much has been learned about its biology, ecology, and control. As a result of these investigations, the following management practices have been recommended for reducing losses to white pine: (1) the planting of white pines with hardwoods or under a hardwood cover; (2) the planting of white pine on medium soils only where soil matting or hard pan does not occur within 3 feet of the surface and where the trees will not suffer from competition with hardwoods or jack or red pines; (3) the selection and improvement by pruning of the least injured pines for a final crop in heavily infested stands; and (4) the removal of less desirable trees from white pine stands (*467, 705, 706, 303, 56, 796, 507, 159, 598*). Other types of indirect control, such as that exerted by insect parasites and predators and birds, are helpful in preventing excessive high weevil populations, but are incapable of preventing intolerable levels of loss. Harman & Kulman (*321*) published an annotated list of the parasites and predators of the species.

The **northern pine weevil**, *Pissodes approximatus* Hopk., a close relative of the white-pine weevil, occurs from the Atlantic Coast to Manitoba in Canada and southward to Minnesota and North Carolina in the United States. Its preferred hosts appear to be red and Scotch pines, but it also attacks eastern white, pitch, jack, shortleaf, Virginia, Table-mountain and Austrian pines, and red, black, and white spruce. The adult is very similar to the adult of the white pine weevil but is somewhat larger, being about 5 to 8 mm. long. The beak is also somewhat larger, and the spots on the elytra are uniformly smaller, the posterior ones rarely connected (*244*).

Winter is spent mostly in the adult stage in the duff and top soil beneath infested trees and under scales and crevices of the rough outer bark of these trees. The remainder overwinter in the larval and pupal stages in the tree. Overwintering adults emerge in the spring and feed for several weeks on the inner bark of pine branches and on the stems of seedlings and small trees. Adults developing from the overwintering larval and pupal stages appear in July and August. The life cycle may be completed in 1 or 2 years.

The insect breeds beneath the surface of the bark on recently cut stumps and logs, and on the main stems or branches of dead or dying trees. Attacks occur on the tree from the roots up to branches as small as one-half inch in diameter. Attacks also occur at the root collar and on the lower stems of apparently healthy young trees. Eggs are deposited in pockets chewed through the bark by the female. Normally, a pocket contains only one egg, but frequently as many as four or five are found in one. The larvae feed either upward or downward or right or left from the site of the egg, usually following the grain of the wood. In large, infested material, they pupate in "chip cocoons" in the outer surface of the wood; in smaller diameter material, they pupate at the center of the stem.

Damage is often severe in regions where there are large quantities of breeding material, such as fresh stumps in Christmas tree plantations and in stands under intensive management. Because of the scarcity of breeding material in natural pine stands, damage there is of little consequence. Damage in nurseries and plantations can be reduced by destroying breeding sites or rendering them unsuitable for egg laying (*250*).

The **deodar weevil**, *Pissodies nemorensis* Germ., occurs in the Southern States north to Pennsylvania and breeds in deodar cedar, imported Atlas cedar, cedar of Lebanon, and various species of pines. The adult is rusty-red to grayish-brown, has a long snout, and is about 6 mm . long (fig. 76).

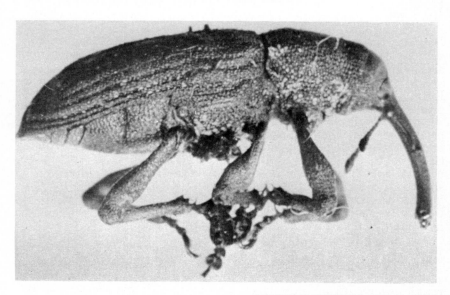

FIGURE 76.—Adult of the deodar weevil, *Pissodes nemorensis*.

Eggs are deposited in the inner bark of laterals and terminals through holes chewed in the bark. The larvae feed beneath the bark in a manner somewhat similar to that of white pine weevil larvae, girdling and often killing the stem. Evidence of their presence is the swelling of the bark over feeding areas. Pupation occurs in chip cocoons in the wood during March. Adults appearing in April disappear immediately and aestivate until fall when they again appear. Then they feed on the twigs and leading shoots, puncturing the bark and eating large areas of the inner bark and wood around the holes. Weakened deodar cedars are often seriously injured or killed by the species. Damage to healthy trees is less serious, consisting of the killing of leaders only. Small pines may be girdled and killed.

Several other species of *Pissodes* also attack various coniferous species in eastern forests. *P. affinis* Rand. breeds in the stumps and logs of eastern white, red, jack, and Scotch pines from New England to the Lake States. The adults feed on the inner bark of branches of living trees up to 50 feet tall. They are dark brown or black, from 5 to 8 mm. long, and are marked with white spots. *P. dubius* Rand. breeds in windthrown, dying, or recently dead balsam fir and red spruce. It is probably the most important insect attacking dead and dying balsam fir following spruce budworm defoliation (*700*). It also commonly attacks balsam fir weakened or killed by the balsam woolly aphid. *P. rotundatus* LeC. and *P. fiskei* Hopk. breed in windthrown red spruce.

The genus *Hylobius* is represented in North America by six species, several of which are important pests. Millers et al. (*532*) published a key to five of the species.

The **pales weevil**, *Hylobius pales* (Herbst.), a very destructive pest of young pines, occurs in southeastern Canada from Nova Scotia to southern Ontario, and throughout eastern and southern United States west to the Great Plains. It breeds in all species of pines within its range, and occasionally in spruce, fir, hemlock, juniper, larch, cedar, and cypress. The adult is an oblong, robust, black to reddish brown weevil, about 6 to 10 mm. long. The elytra are covered with small, scattered patches of yellowish hairs (fig. 77 A).

In the north, winter is spent either as adults beneath the litter or as larvae in the roots; in the South, it is spent as adults in the soil. Overwintering adults emerge from April to June, depending on location, and feed for a brief period on the tender bark of the twigs of saplings and at the bases of seedlings. This feeding occurs at night, the weevils hiding in the soil about the bases of the seedlings during the day. After a few days of feeding, they fly to recently cut over or damaged pine land. Here they feed, mate, and lay eggs in the roots of pine stumps or weakened trees. Occasionally, they burrow through the soil for distances of a foot or more to reach a root. The larvae feed beneath the bark until early fall. Then they form cells in the sapwood where they pupate. Adults appearing during late September and October feed for awhile on pine bark, twigs, and needles and then enter the soil to hibernate. In the North, the life cycle usually requires 2 years; in the South there are 1 and usually a partial second generations per year.

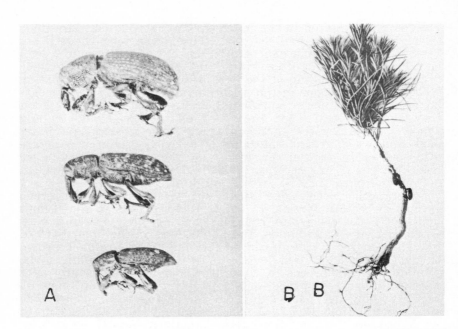

F-514141, 514140

FIGURE 77.—The pine reproduction weevils: A, top, pitch-eating weevil (p. 217), middle, pales weevil (p. 213), and bottom, deodar weevil (p. 212); B, adult pales weevil feeding on bark of pine seedling.

Prior to 1940 when it was first observed damaging pine reproduction in North Carolina (42), the pales weevil was a pest of importance only in the Northeast. Since then, it has developed into one of the most destructive insects in cutover pine lands in the South. The first evidence of its attack is a series of small holes or pits made in the bark by feeding adults. On lightly infested trees these holes fill with oleoresin and heal over. Continued feeding causes the damaged areas to merge (fig. 76 B). Heavy feeding results in the girdling and death of seedlings up to one-half inch in diameter. During fall feeding, the adults may feed on the terminals and twigs. On large trees, damage is not serious, although the ends of damaged branches may be killed. In contrast, small trees in nurseries and plantations, as well as natural reproduction, are severely damaged or killed. Damage in Christmas tree plantations is also severe. The girdling and killing of the lower branches of residual trees makes them unfit for the Christmas tree trade.

Damage to young pines planted in cut-over or disturbed pine lands in the South can be reduced by planting only in areas cut over or disturbed before July. In the North, the waiting period should be 2 years. Where stands are to be established by direct seeding in the South, seeding should be delayed for one year. Before seedlings are planted on recently cut-over pine lands, on areas adjacent to recent cutting or site preparation, or in places where trees have been killed by fires or other disturbances, they should first be chemically treated (683).

The pales weevil has been the subject of considerable interest for many years, and several publications on its biology, ecology, and control have been issued (*245, 589, 682*).

The **pine root collar weevil**, *Hylobius radicis* Buch., breeds in the root collars of healthy pines in southern Canada from Newfoundland to Manitoba and in all of the Northeastern States south to Virginia and west to Minnesota. Of its hosts, Scotch pine seems to be the most severely damaged; but jack, red, Austrian, eastern white, pitch, and mugho pines are also attacked. The adult (fig. 78) is dark reddish-brown to black and about 10 to 12 mm. long. It is marked with irregular patches of white-to-yellow hairlike scales, and the elytra have longitudinal rows of elongated indentations.

In most localities, eggs are deposited from early May to late September in cavities in the inner bark at the base of the tree, or in the soil nearby (*640*). The larvae feed downward in the inner bark of the base of the trunk and in the bases of large roots below the ground line, widening their galleries as they develop. Galleries are also formed in the soil around the base. The following winter is spent in the larval stage in the Lake States. In Southern Ontario, it is spent in the larval and adult stages and occasionally in the pupal stage (*246*). Pupation occurs from June to September in cells constructed in the soil. Adults appear from August to October but do very little egg laying before entering the soil or bark crevices where they spend the winter. When they emerge in the spring, they feed during the day on the bark of duff-covered branches, mate, and lay eggs. During warm evenings, they feed on the bark of the upper branches and fly to other trees. Most of these adults overwinter a second time and then are active for part of the following season (*785*).

Heavily infested trees may be severely injured (fig. 79). Small trees, from 1 to 4 inches in diameter are most severely damaged—smaller ones are seldom attacked. The presence of pitch flows at

F-488105

FIGURE 78.—Adult of the pine root collar weevil, *Hylobius radicis*.

215

F-488104
FIGURE 79.—Damage by the pine root collar weevil, *Hylobius radicis*, at the base of a pine tree.

the root collar and layers of pitch-infiltrated soil near damaged areas are evidences of infestation. A number of silvicultural practices have been suggested for reducing populations (*780*). Finnegan and Stewart discussed methods of direct control (*251*).

Hylobius rhizophagus M. B. & W. is a newly-described species recently discovered attacking jack pine in the Lake States (*532*). The adult is black and about 14.5 mm. long. Dense patches of coarse scales occur on the dorsum and the elytra bear longitudinal rows of pits containing fine setae. The larvae feed in roots less than one-half inch in diameter, tunneling from the smaller end toward the base. Pupation occurs in cells in the roots. Pole-sized pines in closed plantations on formerly cultivated land are most frequently infested; reproduction in well-established infestations and red pines growing in mixture with jack pine are also attacked occasionally.

Hylobius warreni Wood attacks most species of conifers growing on moist to wet sites in southern Canada and south to North Carolina in eastern United States. The adult is a large, robust, reddish-brown to black weevil, from 12 to 15 mm. long. The wing covers are thick, tough, and veinless and each bears 10 rows of longitudinal punctures. The hindwings are vestigial. Eggs are deposited around the root collars of healthy trees, and the larvae feed in the inner bark and cambium of roots and root collars for 1 to 2 years. Infested trees bleed heavily at the ground line and severely injured ones may be completely girdled and killed. Up to 40 percent of the trees in a 40-year-old Scotch pine stand in Quebec are reported to have been killed by the species. *H. pinicola* (Couper) occurs throughout the same range as *H. warreni* and apparently breeds in the same species of trees. The adults of the two species are similar in appearance, but differ in that the hindwings of this species are fully developed. Warren (*741*) described *H. warreni* in detail.

Hylobius congener Dalla Torre, Schenkling and Marshall occurs from the Northeastern Coast to Alaska and breeds in the inner bark on logs and stumps of red, Scotch, and white pines. Adults resemble the adults of the pales weevil but are slightly smaller.

Hylobius aliradicis Warner is a newly-described species (*740*) recently discovered attacking the roots of healthy young slash pine seedlings in south Georgia (*219*). The larvae hollow out the smaller roots and bore extensively in the root collar area. Heavily infested seedlings are killed. Infestations in plantations up to 4 years old on disturbed sites appear to be the most serious.

Pachylobius picivorus (Germ.), the **pitch-eating weevil,** occurs throughout eastern United States, but is most common in the South. It attacks various species of pines, the adults chewing on the bark of the twigs and the larvae boring in the roots. Damage is often serious in recently cut pine areas, especially where plans call for the establishment of a new crop of seedlings during the first year after the cutting of the old stand. Adults are dark brown, robust, and clothed with patches of short, flattened, yellowish or reddish-brown hairs. The tibiae are thick with the outer part enlarged; the tarsi are densely hairy underneath with the third segment bilobed.

Adults are attracted to and breed beneath the bark of dying pine stumps or roots. To lay eggs, the female bores directly down through the soil to green roots, sometimes to a depth of 3 feet. Eggs are deposited in the cambial region of roots as small as 5 mm. in diameter. Burrowing may occur as far as 25 feet from the stump. Small piles of large soil particles surround the entrance holes into the soil. The newly-hatched larvae feed beneath the bark, packing their mines with fine, red, boring dust and frass. The surface of the sapwood may be etched, depending upon the number and size of the larvae and the size of the root. Mature larvae excavate cells and construct "chip cocoons" in which to pupate. Where populations are heavy, these cells are formed in the wood. Adults emerge when stump root systems are 6 to 11 months old, depending on the season in which the tree was cut, and they fly to fresh cutting areas where they feed and repeat the cycle. Adult feeding occurs mainly at night and on cloudy days, mostly on seedlings near fresh stumps (*708*).

Damage varies with the season, and with the size and vigor of the host. It is severe early in the spring following planting. All of the buds, bark, and foliage is frequently removed all the way down to the ground line. Portions of root bark also may be removed to depths of 8 inches. Newly established seedlings, if attacked at all, are usually severed. Later in the season, damage consists mainly of the removal of patches of bark and puncture wounds. Very little feeding occurs in July and August and only a limited amount during the fall. Heavy mortality has been incurred among seedlings planted within 3 months after overstory pines were cut. Heaviest attack and seedling mortality occurred in east Texas between March and June.

Pine seedlings may be planted safely during the winter in east Texas on areas cut earlier than the previous July. Farther north, a longer wait may be necessary. Before seedlings are planted on areas cut within 6 months, they should be chemically treated.

Stands may be cut during seed years without danger of excessive losses to regeneration.

The **poplar-and-willow borer,** *Cryptorhynchus lapathi* (L.), an introduced species first recorded in North America in New York City in 1882, now occurs from coast to coast in southern Canada, in Washington and Oregon, and south to Virginia in eastern United States. Its principal hosts are poplars and willows, but it also attacks alder and birch. The adult (fig. 80) is brown to black and about 8 to 10 mm. long. The snout is as long as the head and thorax combined, and the sides of the thorax, parts of the legs, and the posterior half of the elytra are clothed with pale, pinkish scales intermixed with large, erect black bristles. Full-grown larvae are thick, whitish, and about 12 mm. long; the pupae are whitish to yellowish and armed with a pair of strong brown hooks at the tip of the abdomen (*509*).

Adults appear in late July and August and feed on the inner bark of young shoots. Eggs are deposited singly or in groups of two to four in slits cut in corky bark, often in lenticels and scar tissue. Young larvae feed in the cambial region and outer layers of sapwood, tunneling in all directions and pushing out their borings through small holes. In late fall, they hollow out small chambers in the inner bark in which they spend the winter. Feeding is resumed in the spring, with the larvae usually boring around the branch or stem and often causing girdling. When ready to pupate, the larvae bore upward and inward and construct cells in the center of the stem. There is one generation per year.

The first evidence of attack is the occurrence of dead patches or cracks in the bark on the trunks of small trees or on the branches of larger ones, and the presence of small holes chewed in the bark. The wood under these patches eventually becomes honeycombed with larval tunnels. Branches or entire small trees may be completely girdled or so badly weakened by tunnels that they break. All poplars and willows over 1 inch in diameter are subject to attack, recently planted trees and nursery stock especially. The most serious damage usually occurs near the base.

The **pine gall weevil,** *Podapion gallicola* Riley, occurs throughout eastern United States and southeastern Canada. It breeds in red, pitch, Virginia and scrub pines. The adult is black and about 5 mm. long. During June, eggs are laid in niches chewed into the bark of 1-year-old twigs. Young larvae feed first on the sides and floor of the egg niche and then bore into the cambium. Here they separate and tunnel outward from the niche. They continue to feed through three seasons. Pupation occurs in funnel-shaped cells in the bark during May of the fourth season. Galls are formed by hypertrophy of the xylem tissue surrounding each larva. They first appear as slight swellings on one side of the stem. By the time the adults emerge, these swellings are larger, generally ovoid, and taper gradually toward the distal end (fig. 81). Old galls continue to enlarge, even after the insects leave them, some reaching a length of 37 mm. When several galls are formed on a small branch, the branch may be killed (*776*).

The **arborvitae weevil,** *Phyllobius intrusus* Kono, an introduced species first recorded on nursery stock in Rhode Island in 1947, is

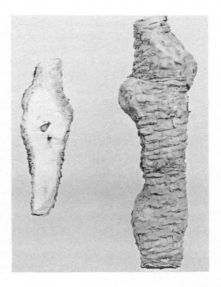

F-519950

FIGURE 80.—Adult of the poplar-and-willow borer, *Cryptorhynchus lapathi.*

F-501808

FIGURE 81.—Galls in pine produced by the pine gall weevil, *Podapion gallicola.*

now known to occur also in Massachusetts, Maine, Connecticut, Vermont, New York, and Pennsylvania. It feeds on a wide variety of species in the genera *Thuja, Chamaecyparis,* and *Juniperus.* Certain varieties of *T. occidentalis* and *C. obtusa* appear to be particularly favored. The adult is light brown with grayish wings and is about 6 mm. long. The beak is short, not quite as long as broad, and there are light, metallic green hairs on the legs and antennae.

Eggs are deposited in the soil during May and June, and the larvae feed on the roots of the host plant for the remainder of the season. Winter is spent in the late larval or pupal stage, and the adults appear from early May to July (*415*).

The arborvitae weevil is destructive in both the larval and adult stages, primarily in the larval stage. Damage in nurseries may be severe where infestations occur over a period of many years. In severely infested areas, well over 200 larvae may be found feeding on the roots of a single plant. This results in severe root pruning.

Phyllobius oblongus (L.), the **European snout beetle,** an introduced species first recorded in the United States at Rochester, N. Y. in 1923, is now known to occur at least as far west as Ohio. It feeds on a fairly wide variety of hardwoods including elm, maple, willow, cottonwood, pear, apple, and plum. Adults feed on the leaves and young shoots of their hosts; the larvae feed on the roots of various plants.

The **Japanese weevil,** *Pseudocneorhinus bifasciatus* Roelofs, an introduced species first recorded in the United States at Westville, Conn., in 1920, is now rather widely distributed in the Northeastern States. It feeds on a wide variety of trees and shrubs such as flowering dogwood, hemlock, red bud, azalea, rhododendron,

219

and the sprouts of oak, sycamore, and walnut. The adult is stout, sluggish, brownish-gray with two black bands across the elytra, and about 4.5 to 7 mm. long. The snout is almost as wide as long, and the elytra are apparently fused. Eggs are deposited in folds at the margins of dead leaves or leaf fragments. The female then seals the free edge of the fold to the basal portions of the leaf, forming a pod in which the eggs are enclosed. When the eggs hatch, the larvae enter the soil and feed on the roots of their hosts. Adults feed at leaf margins, cutting out notches and causing a ragged appearance. Infested plants are occasionally heavily defoliated by fall.

Polydrusus impressifrons Gyll., an introduced species first recorded in New York State in 1906, feeds on various hardwoods, chiefly willow, poplar, birch, and plum in New York and Connecticut, and possibly adjoining States. The adult is rather slender, uniformly light metallic green, and from 4 to 5.5 mm. long. Birch, poplar, apple, and pear appear to be preferred hosts. Adults occur on a much wider variety of trees, however, and probably feed on them to some extent. Eggs are deposited around scars and beneath loose flakes of bark in roughened areas. The cut ends of pruned branches and twigs of seedlings and young trees are especially attractive as oviposition sites. Young larvae drop to the soil, enter it and feed on the roots of their hosts or other plants. Pupation occurs in the soil, and the adults appear from mid-May to early June. They feed on developing buds, foliage, and succulent shoots. In heavy infestations, defoliation may be severe, and large numbers of succulent stems may be girdled and killed. Damage is usually most serious in nurseries (*581*).

Thylacites incanus (L.), an introduced species, has been recorded from Massachusetts and Long Island. Its hosts are various species of pine where the adults feed on the needles and the larvae, on the roots. Adults are brownish, with metallic reflections, and are from 8 to 11 mm. long. This species is often a serious pest of pine and spruce in Europe. So far, it has not been very injurious in this country.

The **black vine weevil**, *Brachyrhinus sulcatus* (Fab.), a probable introduction from Europe, is widely distributed in the Northern States. It feeds on a wide variety of plants, yew, arborvitae, and rhododendron, in particular. The adult is a brownish-black, flightless weevil, from 9 to 12 mm. long. The thorax is densely covered with rounded tubercles, each bearing a short hair, and the elytra are often speckled with white. The hindwings are reduced to mere pads.

Winter is spent mostly in the larval stage, but also, to some extent, as pupae and adults at depths of 6 to 18 inches in the soil. Adults emerge from early May to late July and are present during the remainder of the season. Generally, they hide during the day beneath pieces of earth, stones, sticks, dried grass, or leaves on the ground, or beneath loose flakes of bark of their host. They feed at night by climbing up the stems and eating notches or holes in the margins of the leaves. Eggs are deposited on the ground in trash or among soil particles, under loose bark, or among the leaves of their hosts. The larvae enter the soil and feed on the roots of various plants. On woody plants, they feed first on the young rootlets; later, on the cortex of larger roots. Infested roots may be stripped entirely of their bark for several inches, or they may be gouged out on one side only. Pupation occurs in cells formed near the surface of the ground. There is one generation per year (656).

Damage may be severe in nurseries, especially to yews, azaleas, and rhododendrons. Clean cultivation and the rotation of seedbeds and transplant beds, and allowing infested areas to lie fallow and be thoroughly cultivated in alternate years, are helpful in preventing damage.

The **strawberry root weevil**, *Brachyrhinus ovatus* (L.), a close relative of the black vine weevil, occurs throughout the Northern States. Seedlings of hemlock, arborvitae, yew, juniper, and spruce are especially favored as hosts. The adult is similar to the adult of the black vine weevil except for its smaller size and the absence of white specks on its wing covers. The life histories of the two species are also similar. This species also frequently causes heavy losses in nurseries and to ornamental plants. Hemlock and blue spruce seedlings have been seriously damaged in nurseries in the Northeast.

The **Asiatic oak weevil**, *Crytepistomus castaneus* (Roelofs), an introduced species first recorded in North America at Montclair, N. J. in 1933, is now known to occur from New Jersey to Georgia and Missouri. Oaks and Asiatic chestnut appear to be its preferred hosts but it also attacks hickory, beech, dogwood, hazelnut, and azalea (720). Adults are black to reddish-brown, irregularly clothed with minute, green scales, and about 6 mm. long.

The Asiatic oak weevil is parthenogenetic and has a 1 year life cycle. Apparently, eggs are laid in the soil from early July to mid-September. Larvae have been found around the roots of oak seedlings at depths of 6 inches in the soil. Winter is spent mostly in the larval stage. Adults appear in the spring and feed on the leaves of sapling oaks and chestnut. They chew in from the margins toward the midribs and devour everything but the larger veins. Later, they fly to larger trees to feed. During the fall, they sometimes invade houses in large numbers, presumably in search of hibernation quarters.

Odontopus calceatus Say occurs from New England to Florida and Louisiana and west to Michigan, Iowa, and Missouri. It feeds on the foliage of yellow poplar, magnolia, and sassafras. Adults are mostly black and about 2.5 to 4 mm. long. The front legs are strongly incurved, and the antennae, mouth parts, and tarsi are usually dark brown.

Adults spend the winter in leaf litter. They emerge and begin feeding on swelling buds and stipules on warm days in late April and early May in the latitudes in Ohio and Pennsylvania. In Florida and along the Gulf Coast they may emerge as early as February. Later, as the leaves unfold, they also are attacked. Feeding damage consists of rice-shaped holes in the leaves about 3 mm. in diameter. Eggs are deposited in the midrib on the underside of the leaves during May and early June. The midrib usually breaks at the oviposition site. The larvae bore into the leaf and mine the interior, commonly side by side in one or two groups. Occasionally, there are two mines per leaf. As the larvae

221

increase in size they extend their mines and extrude filaments of dark fecal material from them. Pupation occurs in spherical silken cocoons in inflated portions of the mine. Newly-emerged adults feed on the foliage, sometimes chewing through the leaves, but more often leaving the upper surface intact (fig. 82). This results in chlorotic spots and produces a "burned" appearance on severely attacked trees. Adults stop their feeding by mid-July, aestivate, then hibernate until the following spring. There is one generation per year (*126*).

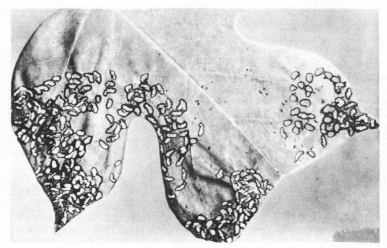

F-519311
FIGURE 82.—Adult feeding damage to yellow-poplar leaf by
Odontopus calceatus.

This species has been particularly abundant on yellow-poplar in eastern Kentucky since 1960. Heavy infestations have also occurred in Ohio, West Virginia, Virginia, and Tennessee. Prior to 1960, it seems to have occurred most commonly on sassafras and magnolia. Parasites have destroyed up to 50 percent of the pupae in certain areas of Kentucky. Late spring frosts have contributed importantly to the control of the species in the northern portions of its range.

The **willow flea weevil**, *Rhynchaenus rufipes* (LeC.), occurs in eastern Canada and south and west through the Eastern States to New Mexico. Willow is its preferred host, but it also feeds on many other hardwoods such as elm, red maple, aspen, red oak, gray and white birch, cherry, shadbush, and apple. The adult is black, broadly elliptical, and about 2 mm. long. The eyes are large and almost meet in front; the antennae are reddish-yellow and elbowed; the scutellum is white; the legs are reddish-yellow; the hind femora are thick and fitted for jumping; and there is a small white spot at the base of the wing covers.

In Maine, winter is spent in the adult stage beneath loose bark, under stone walls, in debris, or in the soil. Overwintering adults emerge in early spring, fly to their hosts, and feed by eating circular holes in opening buds and new leaves. Eggs are laid in pits on the underside of leaves, and the larvae feed almost entirely within the tissues of the leaf, forming large blotch mines. Pupation occurs within the mine and new adults appear in August. In heavily infested areas, they may crawl over buildings in such large numbers as to be a nuisance (*553*). The **apple flea weevil,** *Rhynchaenus pallicornis* (Say), feeds on apple, hawthorn, winged elm, hazelnut, and quince from New York to Illinois and Missouri. Adults are black and about 2.5 mm. long.

Rhynchophorus cruentatus (F.), the **palmetto pill bug,** occurs from North Carolina to Florida and Louisiana and breeds in the trunks of weakened palm trees and cabbage palmettos. The adult has a red thorax with black margins, shiny black wing covers, fringes of long yellowish hairs on the legs, and is 29 to 30 mm. long. It feeds on bruised terminal buds or on sap exuding from wounded or recently felled trees.

Several species of *Attelabus* L. feed as leaf-rollers on the foliage of various trees and shrubs in eastern United States. Adults are robust and from 3 to 6 mm. long. The beak is flat and about as long as the thorax; the color is usually dull red to black; and the elytra have rounded tips, leaving the last abdominal segment exposed from above. The female cuts a slit from each edge to the midrib of a leaf and then rolls the portion beyond the slit into a solid roll. One or more eggs are deposited in the roll. The female then gnaws the petiole partly in two, and the leaf eventually falls to the ground. The larvae feed on the inner parts of the roll and eventually pupate in the ground. *A. analis* Ill. and *A. bipustulatus* F. commonly occur on oaks, hickories, and walnut; *A. nigripes* LeC., on sumac and hickory; and *A. rhois* Boh., on alder and hazelnut.

Adults of the genera *Cimberis* and *Diodyrhynchus* feed on the staminate flowers of various pines and other conifers from Canada to Florida. They are usually dull red, have flat snouts which are about as long as the thorax, and are usually less than 5 mm. long. Several species of the genus *Eugnamptus* feed on the leaves of various hardwods. *Dryophthorus americanus* Bedel occurs very commonly in hickory killed by the hickory bark beetle. *Stenoscelis brevis* (Boh.) is common in dead, dying, and rotting hardwoods.

The subfamily Cossoninae, the broad-nosed bark weevils, contains several genera and many species. A number of species breed in the sapwood of hardwoods and conifers killed by bark beetles; others, some of which are important pests, breed in the woodwork of buildings. The larvae of all species cut meandering galleries across the grain of the wood and pack them tightly with granular frass except for that portion immediately behind their bodies. Adults may be found in the wood, but they usually occur under the bark about a year after the tree is killed. Anderson (*10*) described the larvae of a number of species.

Several species in the genus *Cossonus* Clairville breed in the sapwood of bark-beetle killed trees. *C. corticola* Say, a shiny black species—under the bark of dying pines; *C. platalea* Say, a flat, shiny black species—under the bark of hardwoods; *C. impressus* Boh., a dull black species,—in the sapwood of both conifers and hardwoods (reported from Florida); and *C. cossonus* Boh. and *C. impressifrons* Boh.—under the bark of hardwoods.

Species of Cossoninae that attack and damage wood in buildings deposit their eggs in crevices in the wood. Adults of certain species reattack the wood from which they emerge, thus intensifying the damage they've already caused. The more important eastern species are as follows: *Hexarthrum ulkei* Horn—damages woodwork in old buildings, often reducing the wood to powder; *Tomolips quericola* (Boh.)—damages seasoned coniferous wood such as pine flooring and pecky cypress paneling; and *Pselactus spadix* (Hbst.)—occasionally damages damp wood beneath buildings and salt water piling above the high water mark.

A number of species of the genus *Graphognathus,* better known as **white-fringed beetles,** have been introduced into the Southern States in recent years. The adults feed on the foliage of hundreds of species of plants, including such tree species as pecan, hackberry, black gum, poplar, black jack oak, hawthorn, and sassafras, but their damage is of minor importance. Most of the injury caused by this group results from larval feeding on the roots of plants. There are records of damage to tree seedlings in nurseries and fields.

The female adult (no males have been found) is dark gray and about 21 mm. long. The body is densely covered with short pale hairs, with those on the elytra being somewhat the longest. The forewings are fused together on the inner margins, and the hindwings are rudimentary, thus the beetle can't fly. Eggs are deposited in masses covered and held together by a sticky, gelatinous substance which hardens upon drying. They may be attached to plants or other objects at the ground line or in the soil, just below the surface. Winter is usually spent in the larval stage, and there is one generation per year (*800*).

The **black elm bark weevil,** *Magdalis barbita* (Say), breeds in the trunks and branches of unhealthy, weakened elms from North Carolina to southern Canada. Adults are jet black, have long slender beaks, and are about 6 mm. long. They emerge in May or June and deposit their eggs in the bark. The larvae feed in the inner bark and sapwood, constructing galleries up to 1½ inches long. Pupation occurs in oval cells just beneath the bark. There appears to be one generation per year. The bark of heavily infested trees may be literally peppered with small, circular, emergence holes.

The **red elm bark weevil,** *Magdalis armicollis* (Say), occurs in the Eastern States and southern Canada and breeds in dying or recently dead elms or occasionally in dead branches of living, suppressed elms. The adult (fig. 83) is reddish and somewhat smaller than the adult of the black elm bark beetle. Eggs are deposited in punctures in the bark, often in groups around knots or at the bases of twigs. Larval tunnels usually radiate away from the egg laying site and follow the grain of the wood, scarring both the inner bark and the wood. Pupation occurs in cells at the end of the tunnels. There is one generation per year.

Magdalis perforatus Horn. breeds in the dead and dying branches of pines from Canada to Florida. The adult is bluish-black, wedge-shaped, shiny, and from 4 to 6 mm. long. Eggs are deposited at or near the tips of branches. The larvae bore to the center of the stem and then tunnel through the pith toward its

224

FIGURE 83.—Adult of the red elm bark weevil, *Magdalis armicollis.*

base. Trees under 12 feet tall killed by insects or disease appear to be preferred; however, slash left during thinning or pruning operations and the dead, lower branches of old trees in closed stands are also attacked. Adults feed on the new shoots of pines, usually on trees growing in young, open stands. Deep pits are chewed at the bases of needle fascicles.

Several other species of *Magdalis* are also encountered in eastern forests. *M. austera* Fall. and *M. hispoides* LeC.—on the needles of white pine in the Northeast (*596*). The adults bore through the scales of succulent, young needles, causing the distal portions of the injured needles to turn yellow and break off. *M. austera substiga* Fall.—on young Scotch pines; *M. olyra* (Hbst.) —on weakened hickories; *M. salicis* Horn.—on willow and chestnut; and *M. barbicornis* (Latr.) and *M. pandura* (Say)—on elms.

The genus *Curculio* L. is represented in eastern United States and eastern Canada by 15 species, many of which are important pests of acorns, hickory nuts, chestnuts, and pecans, and the seeds of several other nut-bearing trees. Damage is often severe. The entire seed crop of certain tree species is destroyed in some years. Injury is caused by the larvae which feed on the contents of the acorns or nuts and destroy them.

Gibson (*290*) revised the species of *Curculio* occurring in North America, north of Mexico. Many of the old names found in current literature were changed and many species described by previous workers were placed in synonymy. Up-to-date information on the distribution and hosts of valid species was presented. The taxonomy, biology, and ecology of several eastern species were discussed by Brezner (*98*).

The life history and habits of all species of *Curculio* are basically similar: Adults are found from early April to late November in southern United States and from early June to late October in the northernmost parts of the species' range. They usually appear 2 to 3 weeks before acorns and nuts begin to ripen. The female drills a hole through the shell of an acorn or nut and excavates one or more small chambers near or in its inner surface, then

225

deposits one egg in each chamber. The larvae feed on the nut meat until full grown, then they cut exit holes through the shell. Most of the larvae vacate the nuts in the fall in northern areas, but some may remain in them until the following spring. Full-grown larvae enter the soil, usually within 2 or 3 inches of the vacated nut, and burrow down to depths ranging from ½ inch to 1 foot, where they form cells in which to pupate. Here they usually remain in diapause for 1 to 2 years, depending upon the species, before pupation begins. Newly-emerged adults fly immediately to acorn-or nut-bearing trees.

Curculio adults are light tan to brown, or red and reddish-brown to black; they are densely clothed with hairs, and range in length from 4.2 to 13 mm. The beak is long and slender, sometimes longer than the body in the female, but always shorter than the body in the male. The antennae are 11-segmented, elbowed, long, and slender; they are inserted into the beak near its middle in the male; in the female, they are inserted near the middle or near the base.

The **pecan weevil**, *Curculio caryae* Horn., ranges from New York to Iowa and south to Georgia, Oklahoma, and Texas. The adult is dark reddish-brown and is from 7.5 to 12 mm. long. The female beak is slightly recurved and longer than the body; the male's is only slightly more than one-half as long as the body. Adults appear in late summer, and the female deposits several eggs in a single nut. The larvae, only two or three of which survive, devour the entire contents of the nut within a month Mature larvae vacate the nuts, enter the soil, and remain there until the second summer after entry before they pupate. Heavy tree losses are often incurred in commercial pecan and hickory nut orchards. In some pecan orchards, up to 65 percent of the crop has been destroyed.

The **large chestnut weevil**, *Curculio caryatrypes* Boheman [=*proboscideus* (Fab.)], and the **small chestnut weevil**, *C. sayi* (Gyll.) [=*auriger* (Casey)], were important pests of American chestnut before the latter disappeared from the American scene. Now, they are troublesome only in plantations of Asiatic chestnuts (*106, 732*). *C. neocarylus* Gibson feeds exclusively in hazelnut. Several other species feed in the nuts of various hickories and pecan.

Several other species of *Curculio* breed in the acorns of a large number of oaks: *C. sulcatulus* (Casey) in nearly all species within its range; *C. pardalis* (Chittenden) in 19; *C. orthorhynchus* (Chitt.) in 13; *C. longidens* Chitt. in 11; and *C. humeralis* (Casey) in 10.

The genus *Conotrachelus* Dejean also contains a number of species important as pests of acorns, nuts, and fruit. The adults resemble adults of the genus *Curculio*. They differ, however, in having shorter and less curved beaks, in having the body scaled on the upper surface, and in having the breast grooved for reception of the beak. Life histories are also similar to those of the *Curculios*, except that *Conotrachelus* adults appear in the fall and spend the winter in the ground litter (*288*). Gibson (*289*) published keys to the larvae, pupae and adults of acorn-infesting species. Schoof (*642*) discussed the species occurring in the North Central States.

The most destructive species is the **plum curculio,** *Conotrachelus nenuphar* (Herbst.), which breeds in plum, cherries, peaches, apples, and other fruits. Adults are dark colored, have two prominent tubercles on the back, and are about 8 mm. long.

Three acorn-infesting species occur in the United States: *Conotrachelus naso* LeC., *C. posticatus* Bohemian, and *C. carinifer* Casey.

Conotrachelus naso LeC. occurs from Maine to Florida and west to Minnesota in eastern United States. It has been bred from acorns of 16 species of oaks. The adult is shiny black to light reddish-brown, and from 4.8 to 6.6 mm. long. The beak is moderately stout and curved, and slightly longer and less stout in the female than in the male. Adults emerge from April to August, depending on locality. Eggs apparently are deposited in damaged, cracked, sprouted, or previously infested acorns. The larvae become full-grown in 2 to 3 weeks. Then they vacate the nuts and enter the soil to pupate. New adults emerge about 1½ to 3 months later.

Conotrachelus posticatus Boheman occurs throughout much the same range as *C. naso*. It is known to breed in acorns from nine species of oaks. The adults have dark, reddish-brown wings with black splotches, the black sometimes predominating, and their bodies are 4¼ to 5 mm. long. The beak is feebly curved, longer than the prothorax, and of the same length in both sexes. Adults emerge from June to August. The eggs, like those of *C. naso,* are deposited in damaged, cracked, sprouted, or previously infested acorns. The larval stage lasts 10 to 30 days. The first winter is spent as a larva in the soil; the second, as an adult beneath leaves on the ground.

Conotrachelus carinifer Casey occurs in the Coastal States from New Jersey to Texas and west to Arizona. It has been reared from the acorns of eight species of oaks. The wing covers are dark reddish-brown with a few black areas, and the prothorax is black. The beak is curved in both sexes. Adults emerge in late summer or early fall and begin laying eggs within 4 days. The larvae become mature and vacate the acorns within 12 to 18 days.

Other common eastern species of *Conotrachelus* include (1) *C. juglandis* Le.C.—breeds in butternuts; (2) *C. retentus* (Say) —breeds in walnuts; (3) *C. hicoriae* Schoof and *C. affinis* Boh.— breed in hickory nuts; (4) the **quince curculio,** *C. crataegi* Walsh— breeds in the fruit of hawthorn; (5) *C. aratus* (Germ)—feeds on the young shoots and leaf petioles of hickory; and (6) *C. anaglypticus* (Say—breeds in the tissues around fresh wounds on various deciduous trees such as hickory, birch, beech, maple, chestnut, and oak (*105*).

FAMILY SCOLYTIDAE

BARK BEETLES

The family Scolytidae comprises three groups: (a) the true bark beetles which mine between the bark and wood, usually engraving both, of the twigs, branches, trunk, and roots of various trees; (b) wood-boring bark beetles which mine directly into the wood and feed on the woody material in both the larval and adult stages; and (c) ambrosia beetles which bore directly and deeply into the sapwood, and in some cases into the heartwood, and feed entirely on fungi which grow on the tunnel walls. Several publications dealing with eastern members of the family are available (*41, 197, 70, 698*).

Bark beetles are typically soft and yellowish when first formed but soon harden and turn reddish to dark brown or black. They are small, cylindrical beetles, from about 0.9 to 9.5 mm. long. The larvae are small, white, curved, legless grubs with enlarged thoracic segments. The heads and mandibles are usually strongly sclerotized and darker in color than the remainder of the body. As a group, the larvae are so similar in appearance to larvae of the family Curculionidae that it is next to impossible to separate the two groups in the larval stages.

When they attack a tree, twig, branch, or log, the adults construct entrance tunnels directly through the bark to the phloem or into the wood, depending on the species. The entrance tunnel is only long enough to reach a nuptial chamber or directly into an egg gallery. Pitch and sap exuding from these holes harden at the surface in various forms of pitch or resin tubes on conifers. In the case of ambrosia beetles, boring dust is pushed out through the holes. Egg tunnels of true bark beetles are constructed from the entrance tunnels along the surface of the wood, cutting through the inner bark and often scarring the wood. Egg tunnels of wood-feeding species are completely within the wood, while those of ambrosia beetles are deep in the sapwood. The latter may be simple, branched, or compound. The females of many species deposit their eggs in niches cut into the sides of the tunnel, cover them with frass, and plug the opening toward the tunnel. Others deposit their eggs in larger niches or in grooves or layers and cover them with boring dust. Still others, particularly some of the ambrosia beetles, place their eggs free in the tunnels.

When bark beetle larvae hatch they feed away from the egg tunnel, more or less at right angles to it. The larvae of many species construct galleries with a specific, recognizable pattern. Ambrosia beetle larvae, in contrast, remain in the egg tunnel and feed on fungi growing on its walls. A large number of species pupate in cells at the ends of larval galleries, either in the wood, in the outer bark, or between the wood and bark. The adults remain in those cells until their exoskeletons harden, sometimes even longer. When first formed, they are soft and yellowish; later, after hardening, they become reddish to dark brown or black. While there, they feed on the phloem, often consuming all that remains after the larvae finish feeding. When ready to emerge, the beetles gnaw holes through the bark to escape. The majority leave a given tree within a few days. The Ambrosia beetle adults emerge through their parent's entrance tunnels.

Bark beetles either fly to and attack new host trees as soon as they emerge or congregate under the bark of the host tree and hibernate or wait until sexually mature before flying. A few species feed on the twigs, buds, or bark of other trees before attacking a tree for breeding purposes. Generally speaking, the adults spend only enough time in flight, or outside the bark, to find new host material.

Winter is usually spent in the tree in the egg, larval, or adult stage. Activity is resumed with the advent of warm weather in the spring. Old adults continue their egg laying in the extended portion of galleries started the year before or in newly constructed tunnels in freshly attacked trees. In the South, there usually are several generations per year. In the north and at high elevations there may be only one or a partial generation per year.

The true bark beetles comprise one of the most destructive of all the groups of forest insects in the country. During an average year, they are credited with killing 4½ billion board feet of sawtimber, an amount equal to at least 90 percent of all of the insect-caused mortality and 63 percent of the total growth impact in the forests of the country (729). Losses caused by these insects are not confined to damage resulting from their feeding activities alone; they are intensified and often greatly increased by disease-causing organisms which the beetles introduce into the affected trees.

Many environmental conditions operate to control the abundance of bark beetles. When favorable conditions prevail, many species increase rapidly to epidemic proportions. At other times, their numbers may be low enough to escape notice. Some of the better known factors affecting abundance are: food supply, weather conditions, prevalence of natural enemies, and associated fungi (41). Many species increase most rapidly when there is an abundance of overmature or decadent trees, windfalls, slash, lightning-struck trees, or trees weakened by crowding, fire, drought, excessive moisture conditions, disease, or other causes. Factors tending to hold populations in check include natural enemies, low winter temperatures, and stands of healthy, vigorous trees. The most important natural enemies are insect parasites and predators and other closely related arthropods. Thatcher (707) presented a list of the parasites and predators of southern bark beetles, and Bushing (128) published a synoptic list of the parasites of Scolytidae in the United States and Canada.

Key to Injuries by Scolytidae and Platypodidae

1. Entrance gallery leading directly through the bark to the surface of the wood, where it is elaborated into one of various types of bark burrows 2
   Entrance gallery extending through bark into the wood or even into the pith 23
2. In the inner bark of coniferous trees 3
   In the inner bark of deciduous trees 20
3. In exposed roots or basal part of trunk 4
   In main trunk or thick barked, primary branches 6
   In medium to small branches 11
   In twigs 16
   In cones 19
4. In fresh stumps or the bases of living pines and spruces; the entrance hole often marked by large pitch tubes;

the egg gallery of irregular elongate type, extending
downward from entrance 5
In older stumps or the bases and roots of dying trees;
preferring fermenting bark
Hylastes spp., *Hylurgops pinifex*
5. Beetles reddish brown, 5 to 9 mm. long; common in all
parts of the United States .... *Dendroctonus valens*
Beetles nearly black, slightly smaller; Southern States,
rarer in Northeast .... *Dendroctonus terebrans*
6. In thicker bark of pines 7
In thicker bark of spruces 8
In thicker bark of standing and felled balsam fir; burrows
radiate; beetle reddish brown, 2.5 mm. long
Pityokteines sparsus
In thicker bark of decadent and felled juniper, arborvitae,
cypress, etc.; also causing injury by feeding on the
twigs:
Arborvitae, Northeastern States
Phloeosinus canadensis
Juniper, Eastern and Southern States
Phloeosinus dentatus
Cypress, Southern States .... *Phloeosinus taxodii*
7. Brown to black beetles about 3.6 mm. long. In healthy
southern pines; S-shaped egg galleries in the inner bark
Dendroctonus frontalis
Reddish brown to black beetles, 3.5 to 6.5 mm. long; some-
times in smaller trees or the tops of larger trees, but
usually in dying or cut trees; burrows radiate
Ips calligraphus
Ips grandicollis, Ips pini
Beetles 3 to 6.5 mm. long, reddish brown to black; in
radiate burrows in the inner bark of trunks of dying or
cut pines .... *Ips longidens, Orthotomicus caelatus*
8. Brown to black beetles, 5 to 6 mm. long; longitudinal egg
galleries in mature, living spruce .... *Dendroctonus obesus*
Reddish brown to black beetles, 2 to 4 mm. long; in radiate or forked burrows in the bark of the trunk or
larger limbs of dying or cut spruce 9
9. Beetles shining black, 3 mm. long; forked burrows
Scolytus piceae
Beetles dull black or brown, 2.4 mm. long; burrows
radiate .... *Polygraphus rufipennis*
Beetles reddish brown, 3 mm. long; 3 teeth each side at
rear end; radiate burrows .... Orthotomicus caelatus
10. Dark reddish-brown beetles, 3.5 to 5 mm. long; straight
or wavy egg galleries in the bark of living, felled, or
decadent larch trees .... *Dendroctonus simplex*
Small bark beetles in decadent or felled larch
Scolytus piceae, Polygraphus rufipennis
Orthotomicus caelatus
11. In medium to small branches of pine 12
In branches of spruce 16
In branches of larch
Scolytus piceae, Polygraphus rufipennis

In branches of balsam fir
       Pityokteines sparsus, Taenioglyptes fraseri
12. In slash usually but also in decadent and weakened
    branches and tops 13
    Usually in slowly dying, shaded-out limbs, less commonly
    in slash 15
13. In smooth, thin bark of white pine, less common in other
    pines ....*Pityogenes hopkinsi, P. plagiatus*
                 Ips pini, Pityophthorus cariniceps
    In rougher bark of pine slash 14
14. In southern pines ....*Ips grandicollis, Ips avulsus*
       Pityogenes plagiatus, Pityophthorus pulchellus
                      Pityophthorus pullus
    In northern pines ....*Ips grandicollis, Ips pini*
15. In southern pines only
       Pityogenes meridianus, Pityoborus comatus
    Most commonly in eastern white pine but also in other
    pines
       Pityophthorus consimilis, Pityophthorus nudus
16. In medium-sized branches of spruce:
    In longitudinal forked burrows ....*Scolytus piceae*
    In radiate burrows ....*Polygraphus rufipennis*
    In transverse forked burrows ....*Phloeotribus piceae*
    In the smaller branches of spruce
       Taenioglyptes ruficollis, Pityophthorus
           cascoensis, P. shepardi, P. tonsus
              P. pulchellus, P. consimilis
                     P. nudus
17. In twigs of pines 18
    In twigs of spruce
    Various species of *Pityophthorus, Taenioglyptes* spp.
    In twigs of larch ....*Pityophthorus* spp.
    In twigs of balsam fir
       Pityophthorus spp., *Taenioglyptes* spp.
    In twigs of juniper, arborvitae, cypress, etc.; young
    adults eat out the bases of twigs causing them to wilt
    or to break off ....*Phloeosinus* spp.
18. In living pine twigs, boring through the bark and wood
    to the pith:
    In red pine ....*Myeloborus fivazi*
    In white pine ....*Myeloborus ramiperda*
    In various pines ....*Pityophthorus pulicarius*
    In twigs of decadent or severed branches; principally
    in the inner bark but often affecting the wood
       Carphoborus bifurcus, Pityophthorus spp.
19. In the cones of various pines:
    White pine cones ....*Conophthorus coniperda*
    Red pine cones ....*Conophthorus resinosae*
    Loblolly pine cones ....*Conophthorus taedae*
    Virginia pine cones ....*Conophthorus virginianae*
20. Under the bark of the main trunk and larger branches
    of hardwood trees 21
    In the inner bark of the smaller limbs and twigs of
    hardwood trees 22

21. Larvae forming centipedelike engravings on the inner
    bark, killing the trees. Young adults feeding on the
    small twigs of living hickory
                                Scolytus quadrispinosus
    In the inner bark of decadent or felled elms:
        Making short, simple, longitudinal egg galleries;
        young adults injuring small twigs in feeding
                                Scolytus multistriatus, S. mali
        Making branched, transverse galleries; young adults
        often hibernating in bark of healthy elms
                                Hylurgopinus rufipes
    Breeding in the inner bark of decadent and felled ash;
        making regular, transverse, branched engravings
                                Leperisinus aculeatus, L. fasciatus
    Breeding in the trunk and larger branches of decadent or
        felled birch, beech, sweet gum, and wild cherry; ir-
        regular radiate galleries in the inner bark
                                Dryocoetes betulae
    Engraving the inner bark and sapwood of decadent and
        felled mulberry; adults hibernating in inner bark of
        living trees ....*Phloeotribus frontalis*
    Breeding in the inner bark of injured wild plum and wild
        cherry:
        In short, unbranched, longitudinal galleries
                                Scolytus rugulosus
        In forked, transverse galleries
                                Phloeotribus liminaris, P. mississippiensis
        In the thin bark of sumac trunks
                                Pityophthorus rhois, P. crinalis, P. scriptor
22. Breeding in the smaller limbs and twigs of hickory:
        Short, unbranched burrows in the smaller limbs
                                Chramesus hicoriae
        Very slender, branched, longitudinal burrows in twigs
                                Cryptulocleptus dislocatus
    Breeding in the small branches of hackberry:
        Unbranched, longitudinal galleries
                                Scolytus muticus, Chramesus chapuisii
        Transverse branched galleries
                                Phloeotribus dentifrons
    Breeding in the small branches of oaks and chestnut
                Pseudothysanoes lecontei, Pseudopityophthorus spp.
    Breeding in the small branches of basswood
                                Pseudothysanoes rigidus
    Breeding in the small branches of redbud
                                Pityophthorus natalis
    Breeding in the small branches of sweet gum
                                Pityophthorus liquidambarus
    In the bark, wood, or pith of small branches and twigs
        of various hardwoods ....*Hypothenemus* spp.
23. Unstained pinhole burrows in the wood   24
    Stained pinhole burrows extending into the wood   28
24. Very small pinholes in the living twigs of pines, extend-
    ing through the wood to the pith and continued there
    as egg galleries; entrance covered by pitch tube:

232

In red pine ....*Myeloborus fivazi*
In white pine ....*Myeloborus ramiperda*
In various eastern and southern pines
                          Pityophthorus pulicarius
Pinhole burrows in the wood or pith of dying or dead
    hardwoods, branching into several egg galleries in the
    sapwood or pith 25
25. Small beetles with the posterior tapering to a point 26
    Small beetles with the posterior rounded 27
26. Small beetles with the basal joint of the antenna
    flattened, expanded, and ornamented with long hairs:
    In the wood of willow, redbud, and poplar
                         Micracis swainei
    In redbud and other hardwoods ....*Micracis suturalis*
    In willow and redbud ....*Micracis meridianus*
    In pith of oaks, maple, etc.
                        Micracisella opacicollis
    In pith of oaks, etc. ....*Micracisella nanula*
    Small beetles with the first joint of antenna normal:
    In honeylocust, hackberry, and other hardwoods
                        Hylocurus langstoni
    In hickory, maple, etc. ....*Hylocurus rudis*
    In hickory:
        New York to North Carolina ....*Hylocurus biorbis*
        Mississippi ....*Hylocurus bicornus, H. harnedi*
        Pennsylvania to North Carolina
                        Hylocurus spadix
27. Small, dull, yellowish-brown to black beetles; the basal
    joint of the antenna club-shaped with long hairs:
    Yellowish-brown; in oaks, hickory, and other hard-
        woods, from Pennsylvania to Florida and Texas
                        Thysanoes fimbricornis
    Dark brown; in oaks and maples in Mississippi and
        Georgia ....*Thysanoes lobdelli*
    Dark brown; in elm and rattan vine from Virginia to
        Texas ....*Thysanoes berschemiae*
    Small, shining, reddish-brown beetles; wing covers
    coarsely, irregularly punctured; in maple and hickory
                        Lymantor decipiens
28. In stained ambrosial burrows usually confined entirely to
    the sapwood; in both coniferous and broadleaved trees   29
    In stained ambrosial burrows, in both sapwood and
    heartwood; in both conifers and hardwoods 36
29. In hardwoods; burrows of various types 30
    In decadent or felled conifers; burrows compound 35
30. In living hardwoods; compound burrows in yellow-
    poplar, maple, oak, etc. ....*Corthylus columbianus*
    In dying or dead hardwoods, especially in recently cut
    timber 31
31. Constructing simple, unbranched, burrows in sapwood
    of various hardwoods:
    Beetles 2 mm. or less in length; eastern part of the
        United States ....*Xyleborus saxeseni*
    Constructing branched burrows in various hardwoods   32

Constructing compound burrows in various hardwoods ... 33
32. In the sapwood of dying and recently dead hickories; cylindrical beetles 4 mm. or more in length
Xyleborus celsus
In the sapwood of various species of dying and dead hardwoods; beetles from 1 to 4 mm. long:
In beech, birch, maple, oak, etc.; Northeastern States
Anisandrus obesus
In branches of apple, maple, etc.; Eastern States
Anisandrus pyri
In small branches and twigs of maples and beech; Northeastern States ....*Anisandrus minor*
In stumps and logs of hardwoods in New Jersey, New York, Connecticut, and the upper Ohio Valley
Xylosandrus germanus
33. In narrow, black-stained burrows in various hardwoods; beetles small and slender 34
In notably coarser, black-stained burrows in hardwoods; beetles larger and much stouter:
In birch, beech, maple, etc.; beetles brown to black
Xyloterinus politus
In poplars; Northeastern States; beetle with smoky yellow stripe on each wing cover
Trypodendron retusum
In various birches; Northeastern States; stripe of yellow on each wing cover
Trypodendron betulae
34. Beetles very slender, more than 3 times as long as wide; antennal funicle 2-jointed:
Beetle reddish brown, wing covers all one color; in many hardwoods ....*Monarthrum mali*
Beetle dark brown, wing covers with cross band of yellow; in many southern hardwoods
Monarthrum fasciatum
Beetles less than 3 times as long as wide; antennal funicle 5-jointed; in various hardwoods
Xyleborus affinis, X. xylographus, X. fuscatus
35. In rather narrow, compound, ambrosial burrows in the wood of decadent or felled conifers:
In pine; Pennsylvania and New York
Xyleborus howardi
In pine; South Dakota ....*Gnathotrichus aciculatus*
In pine, spruce, larch, balsam, etc.; in Eastern and Southeastern States ....*Gnathotrichus materiarius*
In notably coarser, compound, ambrosial burrows in decadent and felled conifers; beetles stout, dark brown to black, marked with lighter brown or yellow;
In pine; wing covers often with indistinct stripe of smoky brown or black
Trypodendron scabricollis
36. Flatheaded beetles making compound ambrosial burrows in southern hardwoods; beetles less than 5 mm. long:
In hickories, oaks, gums, cypress, etc.
Platypus compositus

In southern oaks and chestnut

Platypus quadridentatus

Flatheaded beetles making compound, ambrosial burrows in southern conifers, especially in pines; more than 5.5 mm. long ....*Platypus flavicornis*

The genus *Scolytus* Geoff. is represented in eastern North America by a number of species of true bark beetles, several of which are of economic importance, all except one that breeds in deciduous trees. The adults differ from other bark beetles in having short, thick, brown or black bodies, in having the outer angle of the fore tibia produced into a curved hook, and in having the ventral surface of the abdomen ascend abruptly to the rear. In some cases declivity is concave or excavated and ornamented by spines, tubercles, etc. Blackman (*74*) revised the genus.

The **smaller European elm bark beetle**, *Scolytus multistriatus* (Marsh.), the principal vector of the Dutch elm disease fungus, *Ceratocystis ulmi* (Buisman) C. Moreau, in the United States, is an introduced species, having been first observed in North America at Boston, Mass., in 1909 (*132*). Since then, it has spread over most of the United States and into southern Canada. Its hosts include all native and introduced species of elms and the related species, *Zelkova serata*. Adults are small, dark reddish-brown, shiny beetles about 3 mm. long. The under-side of the posterior is concave and armed with a noticeable projection or spine on the undersurface of the abdomen (fig. 84 A). The larvae are typical, legless grubs, and about 3 mm. long.

Winter is spent in the larval stage under the bark, and pupation and transformation to adults occurs in the spring. The adults begin to appear about mid-May through holes made in the bark. On heavily infested trees or cut material the bark may be literally peppered with these small "shot-holes." Soon after emergence and before entering other dead, dying, or recently cut elms for breeding purposes, they ordinarily fly to the smaller twigs of nearby living, healthy elm trees to feed. Feeding occurs in the crotches of twigs, usually in the outer perimeter of the crown, but also occasionally in its center. It is while the beetles are feeding in these twig crotches that healthy trees are inoculated with the Dutch elm disease fungus. Beetles emerging from trees killed by the disease or from fungus-infected logs carry the spores of the fungus on their bodies. When some of these spores rub off and become lodged in the feeding wounds, infection can occur. Chances of innoculation of a healthy elm are greatest in the spring and early summer when the long vessels of the tree are open and functioning and are near enough to the surface for the beetles to cut them while feeding.

After having fed on healthy elms, the beetles seek out suitable places for breeding purposes. Preferred breeding material consists of living elms severely weakened by drought, trees rapidly dying from disease or injury, broken limbs, firewood, or any recently cut elm wood. None of this material is ever attacked, however, if the bark has been removed or if it has dried to the point of cracking. The beetles bore through the bark and construct egg galleries 1 or 2 inches or more in length in the inner

A

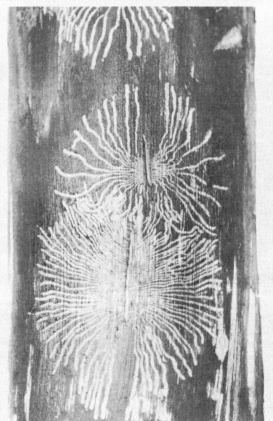

B

F-519943-4

FIGURE 84.—The smaller European elm bark beetle, *Scolytus multistriatus:* A, adult; B, gallery pattern.

236

bark, grooving the surface of the wood, parallel with the grain (fig. 84 B). Eggs are deposited in niches along the sides of the gallery. The maternal gallery is typically unbranched and runs parallel to the grain. This distinguishes it from the maternal gallery of the native elm bark beetle which is Y-shaped or biramous. The larvae feed in the inner bark and the surface of the wood, angling away from the gallery. When they become full grown, they form cells in which to pupate in the bark. During the spring and summer, the life cycle may be completed in 35 or 40 days. In the United States there usually are two generations per year. Farther north in Canada, there are one and a partial second generations per year.

Because of its role in the transmission of Dutch elm disease, the smaller European elm bark beetle has been the subject of considerable research, and huge expenditures have been made in efforts to eradicate or control it. Efforts to eradicate it proved futile, but much progress has been made in research on its control. So far, the most effective known method of reducing losses is the destruction of beetle breeding places (*763*).

Scolytus mali (Bechst.) (=*sulcatus* Say) occurs in Connecticut, New York and New Jersey, and probably in surrounding states. It breeds in apple, cherry, and elm. The adult is from 3.4 to 4.4 mm. long, and is about one-half as wide as long. The elytra have the punctures arranged in regular strial and interstrial rows of nearly equal size. The abdomen is weakly concave on the ventral side. The fifth sternite is longer than the third and fourth combined and the posterior margin of the abdomen is lacking in the male. The adult occasionally feeds in the twig crotches of elm and is capable of transmitting the Dutch elm disease fungus. Dying and weakened limbs and freshly cut wood are preferred for breeding purposes. Winter is spent in the larval stage in the bark, and there is one generation per year.

The **hickory bark beetle**, *Scolytus quadrispinosus* Say, a serious pest of hickories, occurs from Quebec to Georgia, Alabama, and Mississippi and west to Minnesota, Kansas, Oklahoma, and Texas. It has also been recorded feeding on butternut and pecan. The adult is short, stout, black, almost hairless, and 4 to 5 mm. long. There is a short curved spine or hook on the front tibia. The venter of the male is deeply excavated. The third abdominal segment is armed with three spines, the fourth, with one large median spine. The venter of the female is without spines.

Adults appear in early summer and feed for a short time at the bases of leaf petioles and on the twigs of hickory before flying to the trunks and branches of living trees, and boring into the bark. Here they construct rather short, longitudinal egg galleries between the bark and wood (fig. 85). In thick-barked trees, the gallery may scarcely touch the wood; in thin-barked limbs it may occur almost entirely in the wood. Eggs are deposited in pockets at each side of the gallery. The larvae feed in the phloem until nearly full grown, and gradually angle away from the gallery. Before reaching maturity they leave the phloem and bore into the bark where they construct cells in which to pupate. The winter is spent in the larval stage and pupation occurs in the

FIGURE 85.—Galeries of the hickory bark beetle, *Scolytus quadrispinosus*, in phloem of hickory. Note short vertical egg galleries and fan-shaped larval galleries.

spring. There is one generation per year in northern areas. In the south, there are normally two broods per year.

The hickory bark beetle is not only the most important insect enemy of hickory, but also one of the most important insect pests of hardwoods in eastern United States (*41*). During drought periods, outbreaks often develop in the Southeast, and large tracts of timber are killed. At other times, damage may be confined to the killing of single trees or to portions of the tops of trees. The foliage of heavily infested trees turns red within a few weeks after attack, and the trees soon die. Control practices include the felling of infested trees and destroying the bark during the winter months or the storing of infested logs in ponds. To be effective, this type of control should be conducted over large, natural units.

The **shot-hole borer**, *Scolytus rugulosus* (Ratz.), an introduced species, known to have been in the United States since 1878, now occurs throughout most of the Eastern States and in several Western States. It breeds in most of the common fruit trees and, to a lesser extent, in mountain-ash, wild cherry, wild plum, hawthorn, and elm. The adult is grayish-black, and from 1.7 to 2.9 mm. long. The elytra are covered with short hairs and are reddish-brown at the apex. The venter is shallowly excavated at the rear and unarmed. Because of its preference for broken, cut, or dying material, this species is of minor economic importance as a forest pest. There are one to three generations per year, depending on locality.

Scolytus fagi Walsh breeds in beech and hackberry from Illinois to Texas. Adults are 4.5 to 5 mm. long. The elytral striae are distinctly impressed, and the strial punctures are much coarser than those of the interspaces. The species is of slight economic importance.

The **hackberry engraver,** *Scolytus muticus* Say, occurs from New Jersey to Florida, Texas, Kansas, and Minnesota, and breeds in dying and dead limbs of hackberry. The adult is reddish-brown to black, and from 4.5 to 7.5 mm. long. There are long, ashen hairs on the elytra and sides of the pronotum. Egg galleries are similar to those of the hickory bark beetle. The larvae feed first between the bark and wood; later they burrow into the wood. Pupation occurs just beneath the surface of the wood. There are two generations per year in the Deep South and one per year in the Lake States.

Scolytus piceae (Swaine), the **spruce scolytus,** occurs from Quebec to Manitoba, and from Maine to Colorado and Montana: Its hosts are recorded as white, red, and Engelman spruces and larch, and balsam fir. Adults are readily distinguished from other eastern members of the genus by the presence of a tubercle or spine extending backward from the center of the second ventral abdominal segment. The burrows of the species also differ from those of other eastern species in consisting typically of two and sometimes three egg galleries extending longitudinally from a central nuptial chamber. Broken limbs and tops are preferred for breeding purposes.

The genus *Crypturgus* Erichson is represented in eastern forests by three common species. The adults are very small, brown or black, about 1 mm. long, and are found in the inner bark of dead or dying conifers. Their burrows usually originate from the burrows of larger bark beetles, but sometimes from ventilation holes made by *Monochamus* spp., and are very short. *C. alutaceus* Schw., the smallest of all North American bark beetles, occurs from New Jersey to Florida. It breeds in species of pine, and in black and Norway spruces. *C. borealis* Swaine breeds in various conifers from Maine to Pennsylvania. *C. atomus* LeC. attacks pine, spruce, balsam fir, and larch in eastern Canada and from Maine and New York to West Virginia and the Lake States.

The genus *Carphoborus* Eichoff is represented in eastern forests by at least two species. The adults are dark-brown to black, more or less covered with short scalelike hairs, and are less than 2 mm. in length. *C. bifurcus* Eichhoff is a fairly common species in the South. It breeds in dying, broken, and cut limbs of pines.

The genus *Chramesus* LeC. is represented in the East by two species of stout, strongly convex, 'humpbacked' beetles, less than 2 mm. long. They are further distinguished by their large, long-oval, unsegmented antennal clubs and the five-segmented antennal funicle attached to the side of the club. Both species breed in broken or dying twigs and small limbs. The adults construct longitudinal, unbranched egg galleries, partly in the bark and partly in the sapwood. *C. hicoriae* LeC. attacks various species of hickory throughout the Eastern States and in eastern Canada. *C. chapuisi* LeC. attacks hackberry from Pennsylvania to Florida and Texas (75).

The genus *Phloeotribus* (=*Phthorophloeus*) is represented by a number of eastern species, all but one of which breed in deciduous trees. The adults are distinguished from other bark beetles by the loosely jointed antennal club, all three parts of which are extended on the inner side into a leaf-like process. They breed in dead or cut material or in weakened or dying trees. Young adults burrow into the bark of living trees during the fall where they spend the winter. Their burrows often extend into the outer part of the living bark, causing irritations which result in abnormal growths. These may show up as swellings on the trunks of a badly infested tree. Infested trees are not killed, but they may be seriously weakened.

Phloetribus frontalis Zimm. breeds in mulberry and is believed to occur wherever its host grows in eastern United States. Adults are brown and about 2 mm. long. The branches and trunks of living trees or the trunks and stumps of killed trees are preferred for breeding. The female constructs a short transverse egg gallery between the bark and wood, usually consisting of two short-branched tunnels extending in either direction from the entrance hole and deeply engraving the wood. The adults often cause serious damage when they bore into the bark and feed on the phloem of living healthy trees. They tend to congregate in groups, and several groups may occur in a single tree. When patches of bark are killed they slough off.

Phloetribus dentifrons (Blackman) occurs in the South and commonly in the Midwest. It breeds in hackberry. Adults are dark brown to black and 1.5 mm. long. Injured or dying limbs are preferred as breeding material. Girdled or weakened trees or green logs are also attacked if the bark is fairly smooth and not too thick. Many of the adults of the fall generation spend the winter in their burrows. Others may emerge, then bore into the bark of living trees to hibernate. Adults over-wintering in their burrows often destroy the gallery patterns during their prolonged periods of feeding under the bark.

The **peach bark beetle,** *Phloeotribus liminaris* (Harris), occurs in southern Canada and from New Hampshire to Michigan, Tennessee, and North Carolina in eastern United States. It is primarily a pest in peach orchards, but it also attacks elm, mulberry, wild cherry, wild plum, and mountain-ash. Breeding is usually confined to weakened trees but the adults feed in the bark of living trees. Adults are light brown to nearly black, feebly shiny, sparsely clothed with long, whitish, fine hairs, and from 1.5 to 2.2 mm. in length. The galleries and habits of the species are similar to those of *P. frontalis,* except that the galleries tend to be somewhat more irregular. Damage in peach orchards may be severe. In the forest, it is of minor importance.

The genus *Dendroctonus* Erichson contains many of the most destructive insects affecting conifers in North America. The adults are reddish-brown to black and from 2 to 9 mm. in length. The body is cylindrical and rather stout; the head is broadly rounded and visible from above; the antennal funicle is five-segmented; and the short antennal club is sutured toward the tip. Hopkins (*368*) and Wood (*793*) published important papers on the biology and taxonomy of the genus.

The **southern pine beetle,** *Dendroctonus frontalis* (Zimm.), the most destructive of the eastern species of bark beetles, occurs throughout the Southeastern and Southern States. From 1948 to 1966 over a billion board feet of pine timber was killed during a series of outbreaks in the Southern States (fig. 86). It also occurs as far west as Arizona and south to Honduras. During a catastrophic outbreak in Honduras in the early 1960's, about 10 billion board feet of pine was killed. It breeds in all species of yellow pines in its range; also in white, red, and spruce pines, and red and Norway spruce. Shortleaf, loblolly, Virginia, and pitch pines appear to be most highly favored among the yellow pines. Infestations in white pine are usually unsuccessful because of heavy exudations of pitch. Attacks on red spruce are also unsuccessful, the beetles dying in them after constructing short tunnels (438).

F-519566

FIGURE 86.—Stand of pines killed by the southern pine beetle, *Dendroctonus frontalis.*

The southern pine beetle adult (fig. 87A) is chocolate brown to black and from 2.2 to 4.2 mm. long. There is a prominent tubercle on each side of a vertical median groove on the front of the head; the pronotum is slightly narrowed at front, broadest at the middle, and about as long as wide; the elytra are as wide as and over twice as long as the pronotum; and the declivity is convex. The full-grown larva is a legless grub with a glossy reddish-brown head, and it is about 5 mm. long.

241

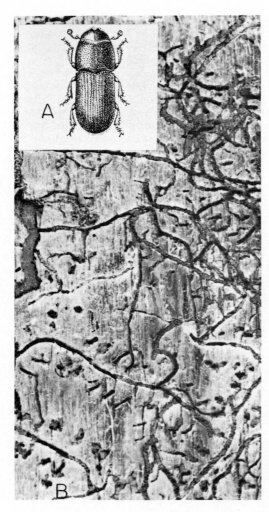

F-486343
FIGURE 87.—The southern pine beetle, *Dendroctonus frontalis:* A, adult; B, gallery pattern. S-shaped adult galleries are characteristic of this species.

Winter is spent in the bark in all life stages—eggs, larvae, pupae, and adults. Dates of adult appearance in the spring vary with the overwintering stage and climatic conditions. In the Southern Appalachians, the overwintering adults emerge about mid-April, while those that develop from overwintering eggs may not appear until late June. The bark of trees through which the adults emerge is peppered with small, round holes (fig. 87B). Hibernating beetles do not attack healthy, living trees after they emerge. Instead, they seek out and invade trees attacked but not killed the previous fall (*367*). Generally, they attack the middle and upper trunk first, especially in the Middle Atlantic States. Later they continue their attacks down the trunk to within 5 feet or less of the ground. In the Deep South they emerge in March and may attack the lower trunk first.

The female bores directly into the cambium and constructs a nuptial chamber. Points of attack are characterized by the presence of distinct pitch tubes, fine reddish boring dust, or white resinous boring particles on the bark. The female is joined in the chamber by a male and after mating she begins construction of a gallery diagonally across the grain of the wood, etching the surface of the wood faintly. The direction of the gallery eventually is reversed thus creating a typical S-shaped or serpentine pattern (fig. 87B). Eggs are deposited at intervals of one-eighth to one or more inches in niches in each side of the gallery, one egg per niche. Hatching occurs in 3 to 9 days, and the larvae tunnel away at right angles to the gallery. Young larvae produce thread-like mines. They are visible when the inner bark is exposed. As the larvae develop, their mines become larger and are usually concealed in the inner bark. As the larva approaches maturity, it constructs a cell in the middle bark in which to pupate. Each adult bores its own emergence hole. All of the adults in a given brood may emerge during a period of 10 to 32 days. Three to five generations per year have been recorded in western North Carolina. In Virginia and West Virginia four and a partial fifth generations occur. In the Deep South there probably are five per year.

Newly-emerged beetles may attack immediately adjacent trees or they may fly to stands some distances away. Trees under 15 years of age and less than 2 inches in diameter are rarely attacked. When outbreaks are developing, scattered groups of pines in young dense stands are attacked. Once an epidemic is underway, stands of all age classes and densities are vulnerable. Spot infestations, which may be anywhere from one-eighth to several hundred acres in size, are characterized by a central zone of defoliated trees, a surrounding zone of red-topped trees, and a periphery of infested trees with green or fading crowns. The needles of pines infested during mid-summer turn yellow in 2 or 3 weeks and reddish-brown in 4 to 6 weeks. Death results either from the girdling of the main stem or from the effects of the blue stain fungus, *Ceratocystis minor*, which the beetles introduce into the tree.

Southern pine beetle outbreaks appear to be caused by conditions that favor an increase in the vigor and size of beetle populations but which, at the same time, reduce the vigor of host trees. Drought, overstocked stands, stand disturbances, and a reduction in the abundance and effectiveness of natural enemies are probably responsible at times. In some parts of the region, especially at high elevations and in the northern parts of the insect's range, low winter temperatures are often highly effective in terminating outbreaks (*39*). A return to normal in conditions affecting the size and vigor of populations as well as the vigor of trees also appear to be helpful in the control of outbreaks.

Management practices designed to improve and maintain the vigor of stands, and the removal of high-risk trees, such as those struck by lightning or those attacked and weakened by other insects, are helpful in preventing outbreaks. Once an outbreak is underway, the salvage or chemical treatment of infested trees is also helpful in suppressing populations. To be effective, these practices must be applied before the beetles emerge from the trees.

Several publications on the biology and control of the southern pine beetle have been issued. This material is reviewed by Dixon and Osgood (*194*) and Thatcher (*707*).

The **black turpentine beetle,** *Dendroctonus terebrans* (Oliv). occurs from New Hampshire to Florida, Missouri, and Texas. All species of southern pines and red spruce are attacked, but loblolly and slash pines apparently are the most seriously injured. The adult (fig. 88) is dark reddish-brown to black, and from 5 to 10 mm. long. The head is densely granulate, roughly punctate, and convex in front. The pronotum and elytra are coarsely and shallowly punctate. Full-grown larvae are about 12 mm. long and are marked with brown tubercles along each side of the body.

Winter is spent in the adult stage in the northern parts of the insect's range. In the Deep South all life stages are present throughout the year. Eggs are laid in the basal parts and large roots of weakened and dying trees and in freshly cut stumps. Green logs are also attacked occasionally. The female bores a hole through the bark of the cambium. Here, she is joined by a male and, working together, they excavate an egg gallery as large as one inch wide and 20 inches long on the face of the sapwood, usually in a downward direction. Eggs are deposited in a linear group on one side of the gallery. The larvae feed away from the gallery in the phloem. They feed together in groups and excavate large cave-like galleries, usually somewhat fan-shaped, and occasionally up to one foot across. Before they become full grown they construct pupal cells either in corky bark or between the bark and wood. The adults emerge through holes chewed through the bark and fly to trees or stumps to start a new generation. Several may emerge through a single hole. There are two to three generations per year in the Deep South.

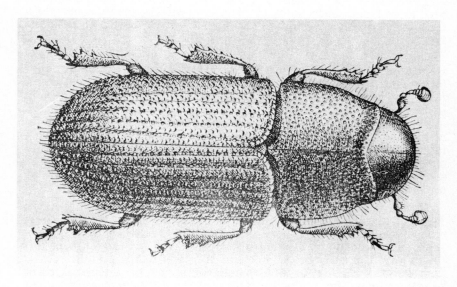

FIGURE 88.—Adult of the black turpentine beetle, *Dendroctonus terebrans.*

Freshly cut stumps are usually preferred for breeding; large trees weakened by fire or other insects, or during naval stores operations, are also highly susceptible. Occasionally, perfectly healthy trees are infested. Attacks are usually confined to the lower 6 feet of the trunks of standing trees. Sometimes, though, they occur to a height of 12 feet. Infested trees are characterized by large, reddish to whitish pitch tubes on the bark surface (fig. 89). They are also almost always invaded by ambrosia beetles. The presence of the ambrosia beetles is signified by piles of white sawdust around the base of the tree.

Prior to about 1949, black turpentine beetle damage was confined largely to the killing of patches of bark on healthy pines. The first evidence of its widespread killing of trees occurred during an outbreak from 1949 to 1951 in Louisiana when several million board feet and several thousand cords of pulpwood were killed. Since then, severe infestations of slash, longleaf, and loblolly pine have been reported from Florida, Georgia, Alabama, Mississippi, and east Texas. Losses in turpentine orchards have been severe. Heavily infested trees yield little resin and usually die within a few months. Losses of unprotected seed trees and in seed orchards also may be severe.

Some degree of natural control, but usually not very much, is provided by other insects such as engraver beetles, borers, weevils, and termites which compete with the larvae for food. In lowlying areas, considerable brood mortality also occurs during periods of flooding. Losses may be prevented or reduced by the avoidance of stand disturbance during logging operations or by the rapid salvage of infested trees. Where the salvage of infested

F-519568
FIGURE 89.—Pine tree attacked by the black turpentine beetle, *Dendroctonus terebrans*. Pitch tubes are reddish to white at first but soon assume a grayish hue.

trees is not practicable, they may be sprayed to kill the broods (*668*).

The **red turpentine beetle**, *Dendroctonus valens* LeC,, the largest species of the genus, occurs in southern Canada and Mexico, and in all the coniferous forests of continental United States except in the Southern Atlantic and Gulf Coast States. It attacks all species of pine within its range and, occasionally, spruce, true fir, Douglas-fir, and larch. The adult is light reddish-brown to dark brown and from 5.5 to 9 mm. long (fig. 90A). Full-grown larvae are marked with brown tubercles on each side of the body and are from 10 to 12 mm. long. The adult is frequently confused with lighter specimens of the black turpentine beetle, especially where the ranges of the two species overlap.

The habits of the red turpentine beetle are very similar to those of the black turpentine beetle. It, too, usually attacks trees of reduced vigor, but can attack apparently healthy trees. Individual trees or groups of trees and fresh stumps are attacked most frequently. However, destructive populations may also develop in trees disturbed by logging, fire, or land clearing. Injured trees around construction sites or adjacent to piles of fresh lumber are infested frequently. Trees of pole size or larger are most susceptible (*664*).

In the colder parts of the insect's range, the winter is spent chiefly in the adult stage, but also, to some extent, in the larval stage. In the warmer parts of its range, adults fly intermittently during the warmer, winter months. Attacks in standing trees are initiated by females boring through the bark to the wood, usually in the basal 6 feet of the tree, but sometimes to a height above 12 feet. Like those of the black turpentine beetle, these attacks are characterized by the presence of pitch tubes on

F-494425, 494422, 494420
FIGURE 90.—Red turpentine beetle, *Dendroctonus valens:* A, adult; B, gallery with mass of eggs along the side; C, pitch tubes at base of pine.

246

the bark (fig. 90C). The gallery first runs horizontally or slightly upward; then it turns downward. When the attack is made just above the ground line the gallery may be continued below ground line along a large root. Eggs are laid in elongate masses along the sides of the gallery (fig. 90B). The larvae feed gregariously away from the gallery in the phloem. A fully-developed gallery may be be from a few inches to more than a foot wide. Pupation occurs in cells located between the bark and wood, either in the gallery or a short distance forward in fresh phloem. Adults emerge through holes chewed through the bark; sometimes several use the same hole. In southern latitudes and at lower elevations, there may be two or three generations per year. Farther north and at higher elevations, there may be only one generation per year or every two years.

In areas where lumbering is continued for several years, the red turpentine beetle often becomes very abundant. The sudden discontinuance of these operations, therefore, may lead to attacks on healthy trees causing catfaces and the killing of decadent trees in the stand. Shade tree pines in areas of new construction are also attacked and may be weakened or killed. Damage can be reduced or prevented by not chopping into trees, digging up or damaging roots, pushing deep earth fills over roots, or piling lumber or green logs near trees. It is also helpful to debark or spray freshly cut stumps and to cut and remove pines dying from other causes. Watering or fertilizing of individual trees also increases their resistance.

The **eastern spruce beetle,** *Dendroctonus obesus* (Mann). (= *piceaperda* Hopk.), occurs throughout the spruce forests of eastern America, and breeds in native, red, white, and black spruces. The adult is dark brown to uniformly black and from 4.5 to 6.2 mm. long. Normally windfalls, prostrate dying green trees, and overmature or weakened standing trees over 8 inches d.b.h. are attacked. During epidemics, however, almost all trees are attacked regardless of size or vigor. Attacks usually begin on the lower third of the bole except for the first two or three feet above the ground. Later in the season, they are continued upward and downward, exclusive of limbs and parts of the trunk less than 8 inches in diameter.

Females construct vertical, almost straight egg galleries in the phloem, engraving the wood. Eggs are deposited in groups along the side of the gallery. After the eggs are laid, the adults may vacate their galleries and construct new ones in the same tree or in nearby ones. They lay more eggs then die. The younger larvae feed gregariously; older ones singly, in individual mines. Pupation occurs in cells at the end of larval tunnels and the winter is spent in the bark in either the larval or adult stages. Signs of attack are red boring dust and pitch tubes on the bark, the fading and dropping of needles, and the reddish appearance of the twigs after the needles drop.

Several outbreaks have occurred in eastern forests during past years. One, from 1897 to 1901, killed more than a billion board feet of valuable spruce in Northern New England and eastern Canada (*368*). The underlying causes of outbreaks are not well understood, but piles of slash in mature stands are believed to

247

produce heavy populations and trigger off outbreaks (*699*). Some degree of control is possible by cutting infested trees in the fall and removing them from the woods before spring, or by storing the logs in water.

The **eastern larch beetle,** *Dendroctonus simplex* LeC., occurs in the Northeastern States south to West Virginia and west to Minnesota. It also occurs from coast to coast in Canada and north-westward to Alaska. Its preferred host is eastern larch, *Larix laricina,* but it has also been recorded from red spruce. Adults are dark brown, the elytra often having a reddish cast, and are from 3.4 to 5 mm. long.

Winter is spent mostly as young adults in the brood gallery; otherwise as larvae. Adults are active from May until late August. Eggs are deposited in niches arranged in alternate groups of three to six eggs each along the sides of longitudinal, more or less winding galleries. The larval mines are in the inner bark and are quite short. Adults responsible for this brood may re-emerge and construct several additional galleries during the season. Up to three broods may be produced. The first of these reaches maturity by mid-summer and the second, by mid-September. The third brood spends the winter as larvae or young adults.

The eastern larch beetle is not generally considered to be important economically, because of its preference for dying or injured trees. Living trees may be attacked and killed at times, however, but are usually only after being weakened by other causes, such as larch sawfly defoliation.

The genus *Phloeosinus* Chapuis is represented in North America by at least 40 species, five of which occur in eastern forests (*77*). They breed preferably in cut, broken, or decadent conifers; in short, longitudinal egg galleries constructed between the bark and wood. Newly-emerged adults feed briefly before attacking a new host. Sometimes they clip off and eat young leaflets on healthy trees. Generally, however, they bore into the twigs, gouging out much sapwood. This occasionally causes the twigs to wilt, die, break, and drop to the ground.

Phloeosinus dentatus (Say), the **eastern juniper bark beetle,** occurs from New Hampshire to Georgia and westward to Texas and Nebraska. Its most common host is eastern red cedar, but it also attacks arborvitae and Atlantic white-cedar. The adult is piceous-brown to black, is clothed with rather abundant short, gray hairs, and is 2.25 to 2.8 mm. long. Eggs are laid in short galleries that extend upward from the entrance hole. The larvae mine for short distances across the grain, then upward with the grain (fig. 91). Infestations are usually found in cut, broken, or fire-damaged trees. Attacks have been reported on living over-topped red cedars infested with the root rot fungus, *Fomes annosus,* in North Carolina. Neither the insect nor the fungus working alone usually killed the trees. Working together, however, they killed trees of all sizes (*41*). Cutting and burning of infested twigs and keeping the trees in a healthy condition should be helpful in control.

Phloeosinus taxodii Blackman, the **southern cypress beetle,** breeds in bald cypress and probably occurs wherever its host grows in the South. The adult is brownish-black to black, has

248

reddish-brown elytra, and is from 2.1 to 3 mm. long. Logging slash and the larger limbs and trunks are especially attractive for breeding purposes. The galleries, larval, and adult feeding habits are similar to those of the eastern juniper bark beetle. Because it apparently does not attack and kill living trees, the species is of minor importance.

The other three species of *Phloeosinus* occurring in eastern America are: (1) *P, canadensis* Swaine—on eastern red cedar, arborvitae, and Atlantic-white cedar (in eastern Canada and from Maine to the Lake States); (2) *P. pini* Swaine—on various pines (in the Lake States and southern Canada); and (3) *P. texanus* Blackman—on Mexican juniper (in Texas).

The genus *Leperisinus* Reitter contains a number of species which breed by preference in various species of ash and are commonly known as ash bark beetles. The adults differ from most other bark beetles in having variegated coloration, the markings being produced by bands or spots of light colored scales alternating with areas of dark scales. The body is rather stout, and the elytra gradually descend behind; the antenna has a seven-jointed funicle, with the club elongate, fusiform, and compressed. Favorite breeding material consists of recently cut or broken trees; however, living trees weakened by mechanical injury, disease, or fire may be attacked also. Parasites and predators, especially the braconid, *Coeloides scolytivorus* (Cresson), and the clerid, *Enoclerus quadriguttatus*, provide a considerable degree of control at times.

Leperisinus aculeatus (Say), the **eastern ash bark beetle,** is the most common eastern species. It occurs throughout the eastern

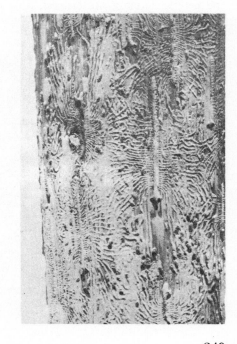

FIGURE 91.—Egg galleries and larval mines of *Phloeosinus dentatus*, the eastern juniper bark beetle, on trunk of red cedar.

part of the United States and southeastern Canada and breeds in various species of ash. The adult is grayish-brown with nearly black markings and is about 2 to 3 mm. long. Winter is spent in the adult stage in tunnels in the bark of living or felled trees. The adults emerge in the spring and fly to the trunks or limbs of recently felled, dying, or seriously weakened trees to breed. Egg galleries are constructed between the bark and wood, both of which are deeply engraved. The galleries are biramous and transverse, the two arms being connected by a short tunnel or nuptial chamber just below the entrance hole (fig. 92). Eggs are laid in niches along the sides of the gallery. The larvae feed away from the gallery, following the grain of the wood and deeply engraving it. Pupation occurs in deep oval cells between the bark and wood. There are one to three generations per year, depending on location. As the adults bore into the bark to hibernate, they sometimes cause slight injury; otherwise, the species causes little or no damage.

The genus *Hylurgopinus* Swaine is monotypic, only one species occurring in North America. It is distinguished by its seven-segmented antennal funicles, the strongly chitinized first two sutures of the antennal club, and the widely separated fore coxae.

The **native elm bark beetle,** *Hylurgopinus rufipes* (Eighh.), occurs in southern Canada and throughout eastern United States north of Alabama and Mississippi. It breeds in various species of elm; also, reportedly, in basswood, ash, and wild cherry. The adult is brownish-black, thinly clothed with short, stiff yellow hairs, and from 2 to 3.5 mm. long (fig. 93). The head is convex, thickly punctured, and nearly invisible from above; the antennal club is almost twice as long as wide; the pronotum is narrow in the front, densely punctured, and reddish at the rear; the elytral striae are composed of deep punctures; and the legs and abdominal sternites are red.

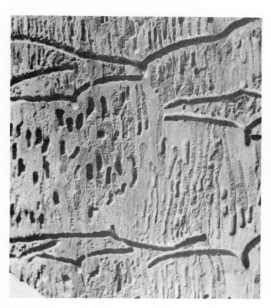

COURTESY OF
DUKE UNIV. SCH. OF FOREST.
FIGURE 92.—Transverse egg galleries and vertical larval tunnels of *Leperisinus aculeatus,* the eastern ash bark beetle, in white ash.

250

FIGURE 93.—The native elm bark beetle, *Hylurgopinus rufipes:* top, adult; bottom, gallery pattern.

Winter is spent in the bark of elm trees in either the larval or adult stages. Overwintering adults emerge during May and fly to living trees and feed in the bark. Later they fly to dead and dying trees, broken limbs, or recently cut logs or limbs to breed. Usually, dying or fairly moist dead limbs at least 2 inches in diameter are selected. Entrance holes are made in bark crevices or under overhanging bark flakes and they penetrate directly to the surface of the wood. A biramous egg gallery is constructed with the arms extending away from the entrance hole at various angles (fig. 93). The gallery may be constructed horizontally, but is most often inclined from the horizontal. Galleries may be constructed entirely in the bark, or they may scar the wood slightly. Eggs are laid on both sides of the gallery, sometimes very close together. Young larvae feed away from the gallery, usually following the grain. Pupation occurs in cells at the end of the larval tunnels in the bark. There appears to be two generations per year in the southern portions of the insect's range. In the northern portions there may be only one or one and a partial second (*410*).

When the adults emerge from elms dying from Dutch elm disease, they often carry spores of the disease-causing fungus on their bodies. When they bore into the bark of healthy elms to feed or hibernate, some of the spores rub off onto the walls of their tunnels, inoculating the tree with the disease. In most parts of the United States, the spread of the disease by the native elm bark beetle is secondary to its spread by the much more abundant smaller European elm bark beetle. Farther north in Canada, where the latter species is either rare or absent, this species is the primary vector of Dutch elm disease.

The genus *Hylastes* Erichson is represented by 21 species in North America, several of which occur commonly in eastern United States (76). They usually breed in the bases or roots of dying pines and spruces or in stumps or the bottom sides of logs in contact with the ground. The adults occasionally kill pine transplants or young plantation trees by chewing the bases of the stems; otherwise, members of the genus are of minor economic importance.

Hylastes porculus Erichson occurs from Maine to the Carolinas and west to the Lake States. It breeds in stumps and the roots of stumps and in dying pines. The adult is dark reddish-brown to black and from 4 to 5.3 mm. long. Adults are strongly attracted to freshly cut lumber or to current building operations. In the Southeast, they fly from April to November.

Hylastes salebrosus Eichh. occurs commonly in the South Atlantic States. It has been recorded breeding in loblolly, longleaf, and shortleaf pines and spruces. It is also strongly attracted to freshly sawn lumber. The adult is dark reddish-brown and about 4.5 mm. long.

Hylastes tenuis Eichh. occurs over most of eastern United States from New York to Florida and Texas. Its hosts are listed as shortleaf, longleaf, and loblolly pines; spruce; and fir. The adult is dark reddish-brown to black and from 2 to 3.5 mm. long.

Hylastes exilis Chapuis occurs in the Southern States from the District of Columbia to Florida and Texas. The adult is dark reddish-brown and about 2.9 mm. long. Its hosts are not known, but it has been collected while flying to downed pines.

The genus *Hylurgops* LeC. is represented in eastern forests by only one species, *H. pinifex* (Fitch). It is widely distributed in eastern United States and Canada and breeds in logs, stumps, and basal portions of dead and dying pines, spruces, and larch. The adult is reddish-brown to nearly black and from 4.5 to 5 mm. long. The undersurface is black and the declivity is covered with small, ash-gray scales and a few long, erect hairs.

The genus *Hylocurus* Eichh. contains a number of species that rear their brood in the wood of their hosts. In attacking the host, the adults bore directly into the sapwood or pith. Here they construct slightly enlarged nuptial chambers. From each chamber, one or several egg galleries are then extended obliquely through the wood or in several directions through the pith. The majority of species are of minor importance since they normally breed in recently cut, dying, or dead limbs of their hosts. Adults are quite small, 3 mm. or less in length. The head is concealed from above by the pronotum, which is strongly roughened in front; the first joint of the antennae is club-shaped; and the elytra are elongated and pointed at the apex.

Hylocurus rudis (LeC.) breeds in the twigs and branches of hickory, walnut, maple, and hackberry throughout much of eastern United States. The adult is dark brown to black and 2.2 to 3.0 mm. long. *H. spadix* Blackman, *H. biorbis* (Blackman), *H. bicornus* (Blackman), and *H. harnedi* (Blackman) breed in hickory.

Hylocurus langstoni (Blackman) occurs in the South from the East Coast to Texas. It breeds in the limbs and trunks of dying or recently killed honey locust, hackberry, mulberry, and slippery elm. Green poles and posts are also frequently attacked and damaged. The damage resembles that caused by powder-post beetles.

The genus *Micracis* LeC. contains a number of species that breed in the wood or pith of their hosts. Adults are similar to those of the genus *Hylocurus* but differ in having the first joint of the antennae flattened and ornamented with long hairs.

Micracis swainei Blackman, a widely distributed species in the South and Southwest, breeds in poplar shoots and in dead and dying twigs of red bud and willow. The adult is brown, and about 2.7 mm. long. The terminal hook of the anterior tibia is strongly curved. *M. suturalis* LeC. breeds in the twigs and small branches of red bud and walnut, and *M. meridianus* Blackman breeds in the twigs and small branches of redbud and willow.

The genus *Micracisella* Blackman was described by Blackman (*78*) to include certain species formerly included in the genus *Micracis*. Female adults have the antennal scape flattened and somewhat extended laterally and clothed with long hairs.

Micracisella opacicollis (LeC.) is widely distributed in the Eastern and Southern States. It breeds in the pith of dead twigs, sprouts, and shoots of oaks, maple, redbud, and cypress. The adult is dark-brown to black and from 1.7 to 1.9 mm. long. *M. nanula* (LeC.) breeds in oaks and redbud from South Carolina to Florida and Texas.

The genus *Thysanoes* LeC. is closely allied to the genera *Hylocurus, Micracis,* and *Micracisella,* but differs in having the apex of the elytra broadly rounded. *T. fimbricornis* LeC. breeds in the twigs of red and black oaks, redbud, hornbeam, hackberry, hickory, and acacia from Pennsylvania to Texas. The adult is yellowish-brown and from 1.6 to 1.9 mm. long. Egg galleries are constructed almost entirely in the sapwood, nearly encircling the twig in a diagonal direction just beneath the bark. Larval galleries run parallel with the grain. The related species, *T. lobdelli* Blackman has been observed breeding in oaks and maple in Mississippi and Georgia and *T. berschemiae* Blackman, in elm and rattan vine from Virginia to Florida and Texas.

Members of the genus *Pseudothysanoes* Blackman are closely related to those of the genus *Thysanoes.* They differ, however, by breeding in the bark instead of the wood of their hosts. *P. lecontei* Blackman attacks various oaks, hackberry, hop hornbeam, chestnut, and walnut from Maryland and West Virginia to North Carolina. The adult is dark brown, shiny, and about 1.2 mm. long. *P. rigidus* (LeC.) breeds in basswood from Canada to Michigan, Ohio and West Virginia.

The genus *Cryptulocleptus* Blackman is represented by a single species, *C. dislocatus* (Blackman), in eastern forests. The adult is brown and about 1.3 mm. long. The head is slightly concave at the middle, with a row of long hairs at the lower margin of the concavity. The antennal funicle is six-segmented, the club unsegmented, and the scape armed with long hairs. It constructs its galleries just beneath the bark of twigs of its hosts. It has been recorded from hickory in West Virginia, the Carolinas, and Mississippi, and from acacia in Texas.

The genus *Lymantor* Lovendal is also represented by a single species, *L. decipiens* (LeC.), in the United States. The adult is reddish-brown and about 17 mm. long. The antennal funicle is four-segmented; the club sutured on both sides and slightly longer than wide. It breeds in dead dry limbs, sprouts, and seedlings of hickory, maple, and apple. Its burrows are constructed in the wood, usually just beneath the bark but sometimes deeper. The adults and larvae reportedly feed on certain black wood fungi which are always present in the dead wood (*698*).

The genus *Hypothenemus* Westw. contains numerous species that breed in dying and dead twigs, dead bark, seeds, and hulls. Included in the genus are species formerly assigned to the genus *Stephanoderes* Eichh. The latter is now recognized as a subgenus by most American specialists in the family Scolytidae. Very few species are economically important. However, a few of the seed-infesting ones may be injurious at times.

Hypothenemus (*Stephanoderes*) *dissimilis* (Zimm.) is widely distributed in eastern America from Quebec to Florida and west to Michigan. It breeds in dying branches and dead twigs of various hardwoods such as the hickories, oaks, honey locust, hornbeam, and redbud. The adult is dark brown to black and from 1.2 to 1.8 mm. long. Deep entrance holes are bored and one or more elongate tunnels are constructed more or less parallel to the grain. They may be found in the sapwood just beneath the bark, deep in the sapwood, or in the pith. Where numerous, they may honeycomb the wood.

Hypothenemus (*Stephanoderes*) *rotundicollis* (Eichh.) occurs in the Southeastern States and breeds in the limbs of oaks and hickories. The adult is dark brown to black and about 1.6 to 1.8 mm. long. *H.* (*S.*) *quercus* (Hopk.) attacks various oaks, hop hornbeam, honey locust, and hickories in the Southeastern States. The adult is dark brown and from 1.5 to 1.9 mm. long. *H.* (*S.*) *chapuisi* (Eichh.) breeds in sassafras and redbud. It has been recorded from Texas, Mississippi, Georgia, and North Carolina. The adult is dark brown to black and about 1.9 mm. long. *H.* (*S.*) *salicis* (Hopk.) has been observed breeding in willow in North Carolina, West Virginia and Pennsylvania. The adult is brown to black and about 1.6 mm. long. *H.* (*S.*) *interstitialis* (Hopk.) attacks oaks, hickory, and walnut. It has been recorded from Texas, Mississippi, and North Carolina. The adult is dark brown to black and from 0.9 to 1.6 mm. long. There is a slightly reddish rugose area on the pronotum. *H.* (*S.*) *georgiae* (Hopk.) has been collected from the seeds of wild cherry, from pecan nuts, and from the twigs of pine and several hardwoods in the Southeast. The adult is dark brown and from 1.1 to 1.6 mm. long. *H.* (*S*) *obscurus* (F.), an introduced species, has been recorded from a wide variety of hosts, including black locust. *H. eruditus* Westw. attacks dogwood, redbud, hickory, and black cherry from West Virginia to Mississippi. The adult is dark brown to black and from 1.1 to 1.3 mm. long.

The genus *Pityophthorus* Eichh., the largest of all the genera of bark beetles, is represented by numerous species in eastern forests. The majority of species breed in the inner bark of twigs or small branches, but a few may be found in larger material. Some species breed in the pith. Conifers, especially pines, are usually preferred, but a few species confine their attacks to deciduous trees. Attacks are usually confined to broken, cut, decadent, or dying material, but perfectly healthy material may be attacked. The adults are quite small, mostly from 1.3 to 1.75 mm. long, and range in color from light brown to black. Females are distinguished by the presence of long, yellowish hairs on the front of the head (*69, 70, 71, 698*). A few common species of *Pityophthorus* Eichh. are discussed here.

Pityophthorus natalis Blackman breeds in redbud from Maryland and West Virginia to Mississippi. The adult is reddish-brown and about 1.5 mm. long. *P. liquidambarus* Blackman breeds in sweetgum, probably wherever it grows. The adult is reddish-brown and 1.3 mm. long. *P. rhois* Swaine, *P. crinalis* Blackman, and *P. scriptor* Blackman breed in sumac.

Pityophthorus pulicarius (Zimm.) occurs throughout eastern United States and in eastern Canada. It attacks all species of pines in its range and has also been recorded from deodar cedar. Infestations occur in the wood and pith of twigs of dead and dying trees, in small trees killed by fire, in slash, and in one-year old cones of felled pines. Scions of grafted slash pines being prepared for seed orchard establishment in Florida have been seriously injured. The adult is reddish-brown and 1.3 to 2.0 mm. long.

Additional eastern species of *Pityophthorus* and their hosts are as follows: *P. opaculus* LeC.—white pine, larch, balsam fir, and various spruces from Maine to West Virginia and South Dakota; *P. patchi* Blackman—red spruce and balsam fir in New York; *P. biovalis* Blackman—red spruce and red pine in New York and Michigan; *P. balsameus* Blackman—balsam fir, red spruce, and red pine in Maine and West Virginia; *P. dentifrons* Blackman— red spruce from Maine to North Carolina; *P. cariniceps* LeC.— white and red pines in the northern tier of states and southern Canada; *P. annectens* LeC.—living trees and slash of various pines from West Virginia to Florida and Texas; *P. shepardi* Blackman—white and red spruce in Maine and New York; *P. pulchellus* Eichh.—probably all species of pines from Maine to North Carolina and Texas; also red spruce and balsam fir; and *P. puberlus* (LeC.)—all species of conifers from southern Canada to North Carolina and westward to the Lake States and Kansas.

The genus *Pseudopityophthorus* Swaine is closely allied to the genus *Pityophthorus*. It differs in that the adults have a longer and more acute prosternal process. The first segment of the antennal club also is longer than those in *Pityophthorus*, and the males rather than the females have long, yellowish hairs on the front of the head. The majority of species prefer to breed in the inner bark of recently cut or dying limbs of various species of oaks. A few species attack other tree species, and some attack and kill perfectly healthy limbs. The genus was revised by Blackman (*72*).

Pesudopityophthorus minutissimum (Zimm.), the **oak bark beetle,** a common and widely distributed species from Quebec and Massachusetts to Georgia and westward to Mississippi and Colorado, breeds in various species of oaks and occasionally in many other hardwoods. The adult is dark reddish-brown and from 1.5 to 1.9 mm. long. In the southern portions of its range, it is active throughout the year, and there are at least two generations per year as far north as the Lake States. Eggs are laid in circumferential galleries in branches from ½ to 4 inches in diameter and the larvae tunnel away from the gallery, following the grain of the wood. When the adults emerge, they fly to the tops of the trees and feed on the buds, in twig crotches, in the axils of leaves, and in immature acorns. Because of these habits and because of the abundance of the species in oak-wilted stands, this species is strongly suspected of playing a primary role in the transmission of oak wilt disease (116).

Other common eastern species of *Pseudopityophthorus* are as follows: (1) *P. pruinosus* (Eichh.)—breeds primarily in dead and dying oaks; also in beech, blue beech, hickory, maple, and hop hornbeam. Smooth-barked branches in the upper parts of standing trees are preferred, but slash and other recently felled material also are attacked. The adult is dark brown and about 1.8 to 2 mm. long. This species is also under suspicion as a possible vector of the oak wilt fungus (615). (2) *P. pubescens* Blackman—breeds in various oaks, American hornbeam, and chestnut in the Southeast. The adult is dark brown and about 1.8 mm. long. (3) *P. asperulus* (LeC.)—breeds in various species of oaks, chestnut, and gray birch from Maine to Florida and Texas. The adult is dark reddish-brown and from 1 to 1.5 mm. long.

The genus *Conophthorus* Hopk. contains a number of species which have the unique habit of breeding in the cones of conifers. The adults are small, stout, dark brown to black, and about 1.25 to 4 mm. long. The female adult bores into a cone at the base and then up through the axis, constructing a small tunnel and depositing eggs at intervals in small niches along its sides. The larvae feed on the scales, seeds, and tissues of the cone, often completely honeycombing the interior. Infested cones wither and die before reaching maturity.

The **white-pine cone beetle,** *Conophthorus coniperda* (Schwarz), occurs throughout most of the natural range of its host, white pine, in eastern America. The adult is shiny-black, from 2.8 to 4.2 mm. long, and covered with moderately long, erect hairs.

Winter is spent in the adult stage in infested cones on the ground. These adults begin to emerge in late April and fly to the tops of nearby pines. When a female finds a suitable cone, she bores into it and across the axis. Then she turns and bores along the axis. Males join her at this time and the tunnel is extended the full length of the cone (fig. 94). The larvae feed on the seed and tissues until full-grown and then pupate in cells at the ends of the tunnels. Infested cones die and fall to the ground in a few weeks. Some adults emerge during the fall but the majority do not emerge until the following spring. Some of the fall-emerging individuals fly to the tops of pines and attack first-year conelets; the remainder stay on the ground where they attack other infested cones. There is one generation per year.

This is one of the most destructive insect pests of white pine seed. During certain years entire seed crops in many stands in New England are completely destroyed (572). Most of the damage results from the killing of second-year cones; however, con-

F-505549
FIGURE 94.—Cone damage by
the white-pine cone beetle,
Conophthorus coniperda.

siderable damage also results from attacks on first-year conelets,
shoots, and occasionally buds and male flowers.

The **red-pine cone beetle,** *Conophthorus resinosae* Hopk., occurs
in southeastern Canada and the northern tier of states from
Maine to Minnesota. It breeds by preference in second-year red
pine cones, but also attacks current-year red pine shoots and
occasionally second-year jack pine cones. The adult is shiny black,
with sparse short fine hairs and is about 3 to 3.5 mm. long (*463*).

Seasonal activity begins in May when the overwintering adults
emerge and attack current-year's shoots and second-year cones of
red pine. The adults feed for a few weeks and then attack cones
for oviposition purposes. Cones are entered by females near the
petiole on the underside, the entrance tunnel often forming an
open groove at the cone base. The tunnel is extended to the pith
and is then continued in the pith to the end of the cone. Eggs are
deposited singly in niches along the sides of the tunnel. After
oviposition is completed, the female returns to the base, fills the
base of the tunnel with a plug of resin and debris, then vacates
the cone. Infested cones soon wither, harden, turn brown, and
occasionally drop from the tree. The larvae feed on seeds and
scales in the cone and pupate in frass-lined cells, often near the
base. New adults remain inside the dead cones at least until they
become hard and black. During late summer, they emerge either
through the plugs in the bases of the tunnels, or through the top
or sides of the cones. Soon after emergence they bore into short,
current-year's red pine shoots and then tunnel forward through
the pith into vegetative buds where they spend the winter.
Weakened at points of beetle entry, these shoots soon break off

and fall to the ground. There is one generation per year. Damage by this species is often severe enough to make the commercial collection of red pine seed impractical or impossible.

Conophthorus sp., a species closely related to *C. resinosae*, also occurs in the Lake States and southern Canada. It breeds principally in the shoots of jack pine but also in Scotch pine. The adults bore into the shoots about one inch below the bud then tunnel toward the bud, either to feed or to deposit their eggs. The oviposition period lasts from late May into mid-July. Infested terminals are often killed, leading to multiple branching and the flat-topping of infested trees. Damage to natural jack pine reproduction and in jack pine plantations is often severe. Winter is spent in infested buds, and there are two generations per year.

Conophthorus taedae Hopk. has been recorded damaging cones of loblolly pine and Virginia pine in Virginia and *C. virginianae* Hopk. in West Virginia.

The genus *Pityogenes* Bedel contains a number of species, all of which breed in the twigs and thin-barked limbs of pines. Some species prefer to breed in slash, whereas others most commonly attack decadent lower limbs of living trees. Vigorous trees are usually not attacked, except in heavily infested areas. Occasionally, young, healthy pines are attacked. Trees weakened by drought or transplanting, or by ground fires or mechanical means, are frequently attacked and killed. Adults are usually stout and sparsely pubescent. The antennal funicle is five-segmented, and the antennal club is flat and sutured on both sides. The elytra are marked with rows of punctures, excavated, and ornamented with teeth at the posterior end.

Pityogenes hopkinsi Swaine occurs commonly in eastern Canada and eastern United States. White pine appears to be the preferred host, but other pines such as jack and red, and red spruce are also subject to attack. The adult is black with reddish-brown elytra and is about 2 mm. long. The limbs and smooth bark of recently killed trees may be heavily attacked. Shaded-out limbs on large trees and weakened small trees in plantations may be attacked and killed also. Destruction of infested slash or infested trees by burning should be helpful in control.

Pityogenes meridianus Blackman is known to occur in North Carolina and Mississippi. It breeds in slash and the dead and dying lower branches of pines weakened by shading or injured by ground fires. The adult is dark reddish-brown and from 2.7 to 3 mm. long. Its burrows consist of two to five galleries originating at and radiating away from a central nuptial chamber. The related species, *P. plagiatus* (LeC.), breeds in pines in the Atlantic States. It is especially common in Pennsylvania and West Virginia. The adult of this species is somewhat similar to the adult of *P. hopkinsi*. The male differs in having the dorsal tooth of the declivity enlarged and hooked at the end.

The genus *Pityoborus* Blackman contains only one eastern species, *P. comatus* (Zimm.). It is widely distributed in the Southeastern States, but appears to be most common in the Mississippi area. Its known hosts are shortleaf, loblolly, longleaf, and slash pines. It breeds beneath the bark on the undersides of living but weakened branches of its host and is of little or no importance.

Egg galleries radiate in any direction, deeply engraving the wood. The larvae construct wide, short, connecting galleries. The adult is distinguished by the presence of a patch of fine, dense, silky hair on each side of the pronotum of the female. The female is also brown to black with yellowish appendages and is about 1.8 mm. long.

The genus *Myeloborus* Blackman is represented by only two species in eastern forests. The adults are very similar in appearance to those of *Pityophthorus,* but differ in not having the antennal club septate. They breed in the pith of living twigs of pines. Entrance holes are bored directly through the bark and sapwood to the pith. Here they are enlarged to form nuptial chambers. Two egg galleries are then excavated away from the chamber in opposite directions. The larvae feed on the wood, pith, and bark, killing the twigs. Entrance holes are marked by small but conspicuous white or cream-colored pitch tubes. These are most frequently seen on the lower branches of the sides of trees exposed to sunlight. Attacks on small trees may cause some damage, but large trees are not seriously injured. *M. ramiperda* Swaine breeds in white pine in eastern Canada and from Maine to the Lake States. *M. fivazi* Blackman breeds in red pine in New York.

The genus *Taenioglyptes* (=*Cryphalus*) consist of small, dull, dark brown to black beetles about 2 mm. or less in length. They usually breed in the decadent bark of twigs or small limbs. *T. fraseri* (Hopk.) attacks Fraser fir in the Southern Appalachians and balsam fir throughout the Northeastern States and in eastern Canada. *T. ruficollis* (Hopk.) is found commonly in red and white spruce in Maine and New York. *T. rubentis* (Hopk.) has been collected from red spruce in West Virginia.

The genus *Ips* DeGeer ranks next in importance to the genus *Dendroctonus* among the bark beetles in its destructiveness to forest trees, particularly the pines and spruces. Infestations normally occur in recently felled trees such as windfalls, snowbreak, logging, and road slash. However, when heavy populations develop in this material, the adults emerge and attack and kill adjacent groups of young healthy pines and the tops of older trees. Infestations in green timber are usually of short duration unless the trees have been weakened by drought, fire, or other disturbances. Spot or group killing in pulpwood- or pole-size trees or, less often, in mature stands are characteristic of outbreaks. Widespread outbreaks occur frequently during which losses may be extremely severe. More than 500 million board feet of commercial timber and more than 700 thousand cords of pulpwood were killed in the South Atlantic and Coastal States during the period of 1952–55 (*707*). It is estimated that annual losses of 300 thousand cords of pulpwood are incurred in Florida alone. Hopping (*369, 370, 371, 372, 373, 374, 375, 376, 377*) arranged the North American species of *Ips* into a number of natural groups.

The male initiates the attack by boring through the bark to the wood and constructing a nuptial chamber. Here, he is joined by three or more females, each of which excavates an egg gallery in the phloem. These galleries radiate away in all directions from the chamber through the phloem, but eventually tend to run parallel with the grain of the wood. The total pattern tends to form a rough *H* or *I* shape. Eggs are deposited in small niches at irregular intervals along the sides of the gallery, and the larvae tunnel in the phloem until full grown. Pupation occurs in cells hollowed out in the inner bark. Young adults feed for a short time beneath the bark and then emerge, several often using the same exit hole. In northern areas, the winter is spent either in the adult stage under the bark of trees killed the previous year, or under bark scales around the base of the tree. In the south, it may be spent in the bark in all life stages.

Ips calligraphus (Germ.) occurs throughout eastern America and breeds in practically all species of pines within its range. The trunks, stumps, and large limbs of recently felled trees appear to be favored for breeding purposes, but the trunks of apparently healthy pines are also attacked at times. Attacks on living trees usually occur on the lower portions of trunks with diameters of 6 inches or more. In the south, this is one of the first species of *Ips* to attack drought-ridden trees. It is also the first species to attack thick-barked loblolly pines.

The adult is dark reddish-brown to black and from 3.5 to 6.5 mm. long. The declivity is deeply excavated and coarsely punctured. Each side is armed with six teeth, and the apical margin is strongly produced. The egg galleries, usually three to five, radiate from a central nuptial chamber and run longitudinally, grooving both the bark and wood (fig. 95). The larval mines are broad, tortuous, often long, and transverse. In the south, the life cycle may be completed in 25 days, and there may be six or more generations per year.

Ips grandicollis (Eichh.), the **southern pine engraver,** occurs in eastern Canada and in eastern United States from Massachusetts to Minnesota, Nebraska and Texas and south to Florida and Mississippi. Its hosts are shortleaf, loblolly, Scotch, Virginia, longleaf, pitch, jack, eastern white, and Caribbean pines. Recently felled trees and slash are preferred, but the trunks and limbs of apparently healthy trees are also subject to attack. Heaviest infestations in large living trees are found on limbs and the upper portions of trunks. Spot- or group-killing of pines is characteristic of the species. During periods of extreme drought, these groups increase in size and abundance. Populations normally develop in areas of recent logging operations.

The adult is dark reddish-brown to black and from 2.8 to 4.7 mm. long. The declivity is deeply excavated, coarsely punctured, armed with five teeth at each side, and the apical margin is strongly produced. The egg galleries, three to five, radiate from a central nuptial chamber and run longitudinally, grooving both the bark and wood (fig. 96). The larval mines are more or less transverse. In the south, the life cycle requires from 20 to 25 days and there are six or more generations per year.

Ips avulsus Eichh., the smallest of the eastern species of *Ips,* breeds in all species of pines from Pennsylvania to Florida and Texas. Thin-barked slash, such as the limbs and tops of pines, is preferred, but groups of young, vigorous trees and the tops of large living trees are also attacked frequently and killed. Attacks on large trees are usually associated with attacks on the lower

260

FIGURE 95.—Gallery of *Ips calli-graphus* on limb of a shortleaf pine.

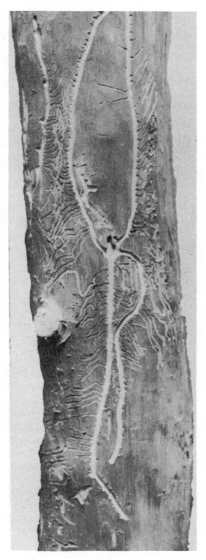

FIGURE 96.—Gallery of *Ips grandi-collis*, the southern pine engraver, on limb of loblolly pine. Note egg niches and incompleted larval mines.

portions of the trunks by other species of *Ips*. Adults are attracted to freshly-cut and injured trees. Any disturbance that causes pitch flow may induce attack. Apparently healthy trees are also attacked occasionally. Spot-killing occurs at times among pines showing no evidence of previous injury or decreased vitality.

261

The adult is reddish-brown to black and about 2.3 to 2.8 mm. long. The declivity is shallowly excavated and deeply punctured. Each side is armed with four small teeth and the apical margin is slightly produced. One to several long, winding egg galleries originate from a central nuptial chamber (fig. 97). Larval galleries are short, transverse, and each ends in a pupal cell in the phloem. In the south, the life cycle may be completed in 18 to 25 days, and there may be 10 or more generations per year.

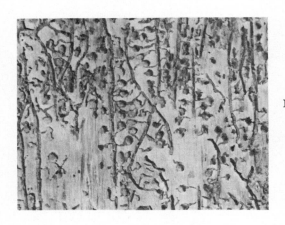

FIGURE 97.—Galleries of *Ips avulsus* in bark of short-leaf pine. Note radiate tunnels of adults, short larval mines, and pupal chambers.

The **pine engraver,** *Ips pini* (Say), occurs throughout the boreal forests of North America and south to Tennessee in the Eastern States. It breeds in several species of spruce and probably all species of pine within its range. Infestations usually develop in slash and windfalls or in trees dying of other causes. When heavy populations build up in this type of material, nearby healthy trees may be attacked and killed. Heavy infestations have occurred in cut-over and burned-over areas in Canada.

The adult is brown to black, is from 3.5 to 4.5 mm. long, and has four teeth on each side of the declivity. Egg galleries, from three to six, radiate away from a central nuptial chamber in the phloem, deeply scarring the sapwood. Larval tunnels extend a short distance in the inner bark and end in pupal cells. Adults remain under the bark for a short period before emerging. While there, they eat irregular, meandering food tunnels, deeply engraving the wood. Winter is spent in the adult stage on the ground. There appears to be three generations per year as far north as Wisconsin (*641*).

Other less common eastern species of *Ips* include: (1) *I. perturbatus* (Eichh.)—breeds in white spruce in the Lake States and Canada. (2) *I. perroti* Swaine.—breeds in red and jack pines in Minnesota. (3) *I. borealis* Swaine.—breeds in spruce in the Lake States. (4) *I. latidens* (LeC.).—breeds in white, red, jack, and Scotch pines, white spruce, and hemlock in the Lake States.

The genus *Orthotomicus* Ferrari is represented by two species in eastern forests. It is closely related to the genus *Ips,* but the adults differ in having obliquely truncate antennae and feeble teeth on the margin of a shallow concave declivity.

Orthotomicus caelatus (Eichh.) occurs throughout eastern United States and eastern Canada. It commonly breeds in thick bark on stumps and logs or at the bases of weakened or dying pines, spruce, larch, and balsam fir. The adult is dark reddish-brown to nearly black and from 2 to 2.3 mm. long. Short, radiating egg galleries originate at central nuptial chambers, and from one to six eggs are laid in large niches or pockets along their sides. Specimens of a morphologically closely related species, possibly a biological variety, have been collected from the twigs of fire-killed young loblolly pines in North Carolina, where they were apparently breeding as well as mining out the pith and wood. Adults were also reared from dry twigs and the tips of longleaf pine logging slash (*41*). The western species, *O. vicinus* LeC., breeds in black spruce in the Lake States.

The genus *Pityokteines* Fuchs is represented in the United States by several species, only one of which occurs in eastern forests. The beetles breed primarily in dying or felled trees, particularly firs and spruces. The eastern species, *P. sparsus* (LeC.), is frequently injurious to balsam fir, killing large groups of trees. Pines, spruce, and larch are also attacked. Infestations are found in slash, in the limbs and tops of trees dying suddenly, in windthrows, and in weakened and perfectly healthy trees. The adult is about 2 to 3 mm. long and is distinguished by long, yellow hairs arising from the front of the head and from the apical margin of the pronotum. Eggs are deposited in large niches along the sides of several galleries which radiate away from a central nuptial chamber and scar the wood deeply. Larval tunnels are longitudinal and follow the grain of the wood.

The genus *Dryocoetes* Eichh. is represented in North America by seven species, five of which occur in eastern forests (*99*). They usually breed in the upper portions of trunks, in the roots of injured or dying trees, or in windfalls. Both coniferous and deciduous trees are attacked.

Dryocoetes affaber (Mann.), the most common North American species, occurs throughout the spruce forests of the continent north of North Carolina and New Mexico. Spruces are preferred hosts, but pines and larch are also attacked. Infestations occur in felled trees, stumps, and the trunks of standing trees. The female adult is reddish-brown to black, has the frons pubescent, and is from 2.5 to 3.3 mm. long.

Dryocoetes autographus (Ratz.) is widely distributed in the coniferous forests of North America. Infestations are usually found at the base and in the roots of dying or injured standing trees, or in stumps or felled trees. A wide variety of trees are attacked including spruce, hemlock, Fraser fir and pines. There have also been reports of infestations in yellow poplar. The adult is from 3.5 to 5 mm. long. It differs from the adults of all other species in the genus in having a distinctly punctured pronotal disk, a convex declivity with the sutural interspace only slightly raised, and in the absence of a dense mat of hair on the female frons.

The **birch bark beetle**, *Dryocoetes betulae* Hopk., occurs from coast to coast in Canada and south to Florida and Mississippi in the Eastern States. Its hosts are recorded as birch, beech, sweet-gum, wild cherry, and pear. Attacks are generally confined to dead and dying trees, logs, and stumps. The adult female is reddish-brown, has a dense mat of hairs on the frons, and is from 2.8 to 4.5 mm. long.

Dryocoetes caryi Hopk. occurs throughout the northern conif-erous forests and south to North Carolina in the Eastern States. Its hosts are white, red, and Engelmann spruces. Infestations are usually confined to the trunks of small, weakened, shaded out, suppressed trees. The female adult is reddish-brown and from 2.1 to 2.7 mm. long.

Dryocoetes granicollis (LeC.), a rather rare species, breeds in spruce from Quebec to North Carolina. The female adult is reddish-brown and from 2.3 to 3 mm. long. *D. piceae* Hopk. is often very abundant in windthrown spruce.

Polygraphus rufipennis (Kirby), the **four-eyed spruce bark beetle**, occurs in the spruce forests of the United States south in the Eastern States through the Appalachians. Its hosts, in addi-tion to the spruces, are larch, pine, and balsam fir. Infestations are usually found in slash and in dead and dying trees. However, when heavy populations develop in such material, nearby living trees are also subject to attack. The adult is dark brown to black and about 2.3 mm. long. Eggs are laid in the sides of three to five irregular short galleries which radiate away from a central nuptial chamber. The bark, but not the wood, is slightly engraved.

The Ambrosia Beetles

(Pin-hole Borers)

Numerous species of beetles in the families Scolytidae and Platypodidae are known as ambrosia beetles because, in all cases, both the adults and larvae feed on a mold type of fungus, known as 'ambrosia.' The beetles introduce this fungus into tunnels bored into the sapwood and sometimes heartwood of trees and logs, where it grows on the walls and is propagated. It was dis-covered recently that female ambrosia beetles possess specialized structures called mycetangia (*291*). They are variously located in and on the body of the insect. In a few species these organs are found in the male and, in at least one species, *Xyloterinus politus* (Say), it is found in both sexes (*1*). Since the discovery that these specialized organs are possessed by ambrosia beetles, much important knowledge regarding the relationship of beetles to their specific microsymbiotic complexes has been gained (*19, 37, 263*).

About 36 genera of ambrosia beetles, some of which include up to 200 species, have been recorded throughout the world. A number of species breed in living trees, but decadent, dying, or recently cut trees, logs, pulpwood or stumps are usually preferred. All species require a considerable amount of moisture for de-velopment. In the Southern States, timber is not attacked unless the moisture content of the wood is at least 48 percent. Seasoned timber is never infested (*138*).

Ambrosia beetles are important chiefly because of the degrade of sawn timber that results from their invasion of trees or logs.

264

This degrade is caused both by holes bored into the wood and by the presence of black stains caused by the fungus inhabiting the tunnels. Trees cut during the summer in the South and left for more than 2 weeks in the woods are often severely damaged. This is especially true of gum, cypress, and oak logs.

There are three types of ambrosia beetle tunnels; simple, branched, and compound. Simple tunnels are unbranched, often penetrating deeply into the wood. Branched tunnels penetrate deeply into the wood and then break up into several branches, which extend in various directions in the same plane. Compound tunnels also branch off from a single entrance gallery but have egg niches extending from the sides of the tunnel. As these tunnels are excavated the beetles push the sawdust to the outside. The larvae of certain species live and feed in so-called cradles which branch off from the main galleries. Others live in the main galleries. Ambrosia beetle galleries differ from those of other wood-boring insects in that they are of uniform diameter throughout, are free of borings or other refuse, and have their walls stained black or brown.

Ambrosia beetles are discussed at greater length in several publications (*388, 698, 252, 734, 41*).

FAMILY SCOLYTIDAE

This large family of bark beetles contains several species of ambrosia beetles.

The **Columbian timber beetle,** *Corthylus columbianus* Hopk., occurs from Michigan to Massachusetts south to Georgia and Arkansas. It breeds in various living deciduous trees such as sugar, silver, and red maple, sycamore, yellow poplar, boxelder, basswood, beech, elm, yellow birch, and several species of oaks. Adults are stoutish, black, and about 4 mm. long (fig. 98 A). The front of the head of the female is convex and covered with short, stiff hairs. The pronotum is broadly rounded and asperate in front. The elytra are shiny, striate, and coarsely and shallowly punctured. The declivity is armed with small tubercles.

Adults become active during May and June in Indiana and West Virginia (*407*). They tend to reattack the tree in which they develop, but some dispersal occurs. The wood is entered through bark crevices, usually on the main trunk near the base. Holes are bored straight into the sapwood until the tunnel nears the heartwood, then it turns right or left (fig. 97 B). Entrance holes are clean-cut and from 1/32 to 1/16 inch in diameter. Short tunnels or chambers leading from the upper and lower surfaces of the main tunnel are excavated at intervals. Eggs are laid in the chambers and the larvae live and develop in them. The larval food is a yeast of the species *Pichia* (*408*). It is stored and transmitted by prothoracic mycetangia possessed by the male beetle (*292*). Winter is spent in both the pupal and adult stages in the galleries of last attacks. There are two to three generations per year.

The Columbian timber beetle seems to prefer vigorous trees, and it attacks trees of practically all sizes. Damage is conspicuous in cross-sections of the trunk of infested trees. Streaks of stain

FIGURE 98.—The Columbian timber beetle, *Corthylus columbianus:* A, adult; B, tunnels in the wood of a living white oak. Note that the entrance hole had healed over several years before the tree was cut.

originating from the tunnels extend, often for considerable distances, above and below them. These and the black-stained tunnels cause defects known variously as "grease spots," "steamboats," "spot worm," "flag-worms," and "black holes." Damaged wood is rendered unfit for such uses as veneer, cooperage, or furniture. In southern Indiana, red and silver maple wood, which is highly valued in the furniture industry, is reduced in value by 38 percent (*499*).

Corthylus punctatissimus (Zimm.), the **pitted ambrosia beetle,** occurs from southern Canada to Georgia and westward to the Great Plains. It breeds in a variety of trees and shrubs, such as maple, dogwood, American hornbeam, hop hornbeam, sassafras, rhododendron, and azalea. Young sugar maples are especially subject to damage, destructive infestations in them having been reported both in North Carolina and southern Canada. Cultivated rhododendrons and azaleas are also frequently attacked and killed. The adult is rather stout, cylindrical, dark brown or black, and about 4 mm. long. The antennae and legs are rusty red-brown. The prothorax is longer than wide, roughly tuberculate in front, finely and sparsely punctured, shiny behind, and extends hood-like over the head. The elytra are strongly punctured but not in rows, are rounded behind, and are without furrows or teeth.

The adult bores into its host near the ground line, then excavates a tunnel which may encircle the stem one or more times, girdling it. Small stems, from 3 to 10 mm. in diameter, are usually attacked. Severe mortality of young sugar maples from 1 to 5 feet tall has occurred in dense, mature stands in Canada. In some areas, almost all of these young trees have been killed. Finnegan discussed the biology of the species in Canada (249); also its method of transfer of fungus spores (247).

Two species of the genus *Monarthum*, *M. fasciatum* (Say) and *M. mali* (Fitch), occur in eastern North America. Adults of *M. fasciatum* are marked with pale yellow bands across the elytra and are about 2.5 to 3 mm. long. In this species, mycetangia are possessed by the female (461). This species is most common in the South. It breeds in most species of hardwoods, and has also been observed in pine and hemlock. Adults of *M. mali* resemble those of *M. fasciatum* except for their slightly smaller size and their uniformly brown color. This species breeds in dying, injured, or recently cut logs and stumps of practically all species of hardwoods throughout the Eastern States. Both species are highly destructive of green lumber and fresh logs of gum in the Gulf States.

Xyloterinus politus (Say), a widely distributed species in eastern North America, breeds in injured, dying, and recently cut trees and limbs of a variety of trees such as beech, birch, hard and soft maples, hickory, ash, magnolia, black cherry, red spruce, pine, and hemlock. The adult is dark brown to black and about 2.3 to 3.5 mm. long. The pronotum is almost square, rugose in front, and has the anterior margin armed with two to four teeth. The elytra are reddish-brown and covered with short, yellow hairs. The galleries of this species differ from those of other ambrosia beetles in that not only do they often fork and branch secondarily, but they also possess four rows of larval cradles, two above and two below the gallery (492, 493). Lumber cut from infested wood may be severely degraded by adult entrance holes and by associated stains.

Five species of the genus *Trypodendron* Stephens occur in eastern America. Adults are distinguished by having divided eyes and by the absence of distinct surtures in the antennal club. The antennal funicle is four-segmented; the front of the male is broadly excavated; the oral region of the head is visible from above; and the corneous basal segment of the antennal club is strongly angulate in front and produced toward the middle.

The **striped ambrosia beetle**, *Trypodendron lineatum* (Oliv.), occurs throughout Canada and the Northern States and breeds in a wide variety of conifers. It also occurs in the mountains of western North Carolina. The adult is brown to black and from 3 to 3.5 mm. long. The elytra are dark brown to black, and are usually marked with lighter colored stripes along the suture. The main gallery of the species extends straight into the wood for 1 to 2 inches and then divides into two or more branches. Larval cradles are situated at the upper and lower surfaces of these branches. Damage to felled timber, and to damaged, injured, dying, or fire-scorched trees is often severe.

Trypodendron scabricollis (LeC.) occurs from New York to North Carolina and Mississippi and breeds in various species of pine and hemlock. The trunks (fig. 99) and larger limbs of weakened and dying pines are preferred, but freshly cut lumber is also subject to attack and serious damage. Adults are reddish-brown and from 3 to 3.5 mm. long. The elytra are smooth and finely striate.

FIGURE 99.—Tunnels of the ambrosia beetle, *Trypodendron scabricollis*, in wood of the lower bole of a loblolly pine.

Trypodendron retusum (LeC.), the largest of the eastern species, attacks poplars and paper birch throughout the Northern States and southern Canada. It has also been recorded from West Virginia and several Western States. Adults are from 3.8 to 4.6 mm. long; the pronotum is broadly emarginate in front; and there is a broad, smoky yellow stripe on each elytron. *T. betulae* Swaine occurs throughout the Northern States and eastern Canada and breeds in birch. Adults are black and from 3 to 3.5 mm. long. There is a faint yellow band toward the rear of the pronotum and a broad yellow stripe on each elytron. *T. bivittatum* Kirby, the **spruce timber beetle,** occurs in eastern United States and eastern Canada and breeds in pines, spruces, fir, arborvitae, larch, and hemlock. Its color is similar to that of *T. betulae,* and it is about 3 mm. long.

The genus *Gnathotrichus* Eichh. contains several species of true ambrosia beetles. The adults are small, cylindrical, and dark brown or black. The head is invisible from above, and the body surface is finely punctured, smooth, and sparsely covered with hairs near the elytral declivity. Blackman (*73*) revised the genus.

Gnathotrichus materiarius (Fitch) occurs from eastern Canada south to Florida and westward to Nebraska and Texas. It breeds in the lower portions of the trunks of dead and dying pines, spruce, balsam fir, larch, arborvitae, and other conifers. Adults are dark brown to black and about 2.7 to 3.1 mm. long. The prothorax is asperate in front; the disc is much longer than broad; the elytra taper slightly at the rear end, and the declivity is slightly grooved at the suture and covered with short, sparse hairs.

Adults bore directly into the wood and their main galleries may have several branches (fig. 100). Larval cradles are extended both upward and downward from these galleries, and run parallel to the grain of the wood. Pines killed by *Ips* bark beetles in the South are often attacked by the species. The western species, *G. aciculatus* Blkm., has been observed attacking ponderosa pine in South Dakota.

FIGURE 100.—Tunnels of the ambrosia beetle, *Gnathotrichus materiarius*, in the wood of a shortleaf pine.

Ambrosiodmus lecontei Hopk. has been recorded from Florida and North Carolina and has been collected from Asiatic Chestnut, red maple, and walnut (*41*). The male adult is yellowish-brown and 1.7 mm. long. The entrance galleries run straight into the wood for a short distance and the egg galleries branch perpendicularly and run generally parallel to the grain of the wood. *A. linderae* Hopk. and *A. tachygraphus* (Zimm.) have been recorded from several eastern and southern States. *A. linderae* has been collected from Asiatic Chestnut; *A. tachygraphus* from yellow poplar, sugar maple, boxelder, beech, and birch.

Anisandrus pyri (Peck), the **pear blight beetle,** is widely distributed in southern Canada and the United States. It attacks all of the common fruit trees as well as a great many other deciduous trees. In North Carolina, it has been collected from yellow poplar, chestnut, holly, honey locust, and hackberry (*41*). Dead, dying, or weakened trees are preferred, but apparently healthy trees may also be attacked. Female adults are black with yellow appendages and are about 3 mm. long.

The genus *Xyleborus* Eichhoff is represented by 17 species in the United States and Canada, 16 of which occur in eastern United States. All species are ambrosia beetles. Many breed in both coniferous and deciduous trees and shrubs of all sizes. Dying, unhealthy, felled, or weakened trees or wounds and dead areas in living trees are preferred for attack. Distinguishing characteristics of the adults are: a five-segmented antennal funicle with the fifth joint short and broad; the outer face of the antennal club obliquely truncate; and the eyes emarginate. The pronotum is longer than broad and without serrations on the anterior margin. Beal and Massey (*41*) published keys to many of the species commonly found in the eastern United States. Bright (*100*) published keys to all species occurring in the United States and Canada.

Xyleborus saxesensi (Ratz.) occurs commonly throughout southern Canada and the United States and breeds in a wide variety of trees. Some of its more important eastern hosts are pecan, hickory, honey locust, walnut, sweetgum, yellow poplar, dogwood, persimmon, holly, hemlock, cypress, and shortleaf and loblolly pines. The adult is light brown to black and from 1.5 to 2.2 mm. long. The female scutellum is conical; the elytral declivity steep and armed with rows of acute granules. There is also a tooth-like tubercle on each side of the suture. The slope of the declivity of the male begins so high on the elytra that the beetle is humpbacked in appearance. The gallery of the species consists of a single tunnel bored directly into the wood. Once inside it is widened into a chamber in which eggs are laid and in which the larvae live and feed. The life cycle is short and can be completed in 2 months.

Xyleborus celsus Eichh., the largest member of the genus occurring in the United States, breeds in dead, dying, and recently felled trees and stumps of hickory in eastern United States west to Kansas. Adults are light reddish to reddish-brown and about 2.3 to 4.5 mm. long. The declivity of the female is steep and abrupt, the sides and upper margin are armed with several acute granules, and there are four large teeth opposite the second interspace. The galleries of the species extend directly into the wood to a depth of 12 to 18 mm., then branch one or several times. Hickories killed by the hickory bark beetle are especially subject to attack in the Southeast.

Xyleborus ferrugineus (F.) occurs from New York and Michigan south to Florida and Texas. It breeds in dead, dying, or felled trees of a wide range of species including oak, hickory, ash, cypress, walnut, pine, beech, and sweetgum. Adults are light reddish to reddish-brown and from 2 to 3 mm. long. The elytral declivity of the female is flat. The third interspace is armed with three acute granules; the fourth and fifth interspaces are armed with two to four granules each. Galleries resemble those formed by *X. celsus* except that they are smaller; they also may be longer and more winding and branch less frequently in the same plane. Side branches are formed which lead to other sets of galleries at different levels.

Xyleborus affinis Eichh. occurs in eastern United States east of a line from Michigan to Texas and south of New York. It breeds in dying trees and in green logs and lumber of various hardwood trees such as oak, hickory, sweetgum, river birch, hackberry, mimosa, persimmon, cypress, and black locust. Adults are light reddish to reddish-brown and are from 1.8 to 2.8 mm. long. The elytral declivity of the female is dull, opaque, and broadly sloping, and the interspaces are armed with a few minute granules. Galleries consist of short, transverse entrance holes and elongate tunnels from which many transverse galleries often branch. This species is very destructive of sweetgum in the Gulf Coast States.

Xyleborus xylographus (Say) occurs in eastern Canada and in the United States west to Kansas. It reportedly attacks the lower portions of dying trees and the stumps, roots, and slash of its hosts. Oak appears to be favored, but hickory, chestnut, walnut, and pine also are attacked. Favorite points of entry appear to be the edges of wounds, deep crevices, or burrows made by other insects. Adults are yellowish or reddish-brown to black and from

270

2.2 to 2.8 mm. long. The elytral declivity of the female is steep, opaque, finely granulate, and marked by rather large striae punctures. Galleries run obliquely across the grain of the wood at depths of an inch or more (fig. 101). Eventually they branch and the arms follow the grain.

Other eastern members of the genus and their hosts are as follows: *Xyleborus pini* Eichh.—probably occurs in various hardwoods and conifers; *X. howardi* Hopk.—pines; *X. cavipennis* (Eichh.)—recorded from *Rhizophora* in southern Florida; *X. obliquus* (LeC.)—birch, hickory, and chestnut; *X. rubricollis* Eichh.—oak; *X. lecontei* (Hopkins)—hickory and palm in Florida; *X. tachygraphus* Zimm.—wide variety of deciduous trees; *X. obesus* LeC.—wide variety of deciduous trees; *X. sayi* (Hopkins)—wide variety of deciduous trees; *X. dispar* (Fab.)—wide variety deciduous trees and certain conifers; *X. volvulus* (Fab.) —probably various deciduous trees and shrubs in southern Florida; and *X. pecanis* Hopk.—various hardwoods in Southern States.

Xylosandrus zimmermani (Hopk.), an introduced species, has been recorded in southern Florida. Its hosts are listed as *Ardisia* sp., *Ocotea catesbyana*, and probably *Chrysobalanus*. *X. germanus* (Blandford), also an introduced species, breeds in the branches, logs, and stumps of elms in areas surrounding New York City and in the Ohio River Valley. It also attacks many other species of hardwoods. Heavy infestations have been found in elms killed

FIGURE 101.—Tunnels of the ambrosia beetle, *Xyleborus xylographus*, in the wood of a shortleaf pine.

by the Dutch elm disease. Buchanan (*115*) demonstrated its ability to transmit the Dutch elm disease fungus to healthy trees.

FAMILY PLATYPODIDAE

All members of this family are ambrosia beetles and they occur principally in the tropics and subtropics. Only one genus has been recorded from the United States. The adults differ from those of other ambrosia beetles in having longer and more slender bodies and wide heads flattened in front. The first segment of the tarsus is as long as all the other tarsal segments combined, and there are spine-like projections at the seam of the elytra of the males.

Members of the family are usually more destructive than other ambrosia beetles. Their tunnels are more extensive, and they extend deeper into the sapwood and heartwood. Dying, weakened, or recently felled trees are usually preferred; however, vigorous, healthy trees are also attacked if dead areas of bark are present. Eggs are laid in small loose clusters in the tunnels. Larvae and adults are also found in these tunnels.

Platypus flavicornis (Fab.) breeds commonly in various species of pines and occasionally in several hardwoods. Dead and dying trees, stumps, and logs cut or left in the woods during the summer are preferred. Adults are reddish-brown and about 5 mm. long. The front of the head is flat and clothed with moderately long hairs; the pronotum is longer than broad and densely but shallowly punctured; and the elytra are elongate and striate, with the third, fifth, seventh, and ninth interspaces produced into tooth-like processes on the declivity of the male. The adult bores a horizontal gallery in the sapwood (fig. 102). Here, it may branch extensively and extend deep into the heartwood. The lower portions of infested trees are sometimes literally riddled. In the south, this species is so abundant that very few dying pines,

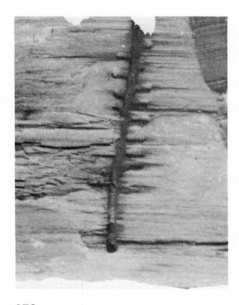

COURTESY OF DUKE UNIV. SCH. OF FOREST.
FIGURE 102.—Tunnel of the ambrosia beetle, *Platypus flavicornis*, in a chip from a recently felled shortleaf pine.

stumps, or logs escape attack. Large amounts of white downy-frass is evidence of attack.

Platypus quadridentatus (Oliv.) occurs throughout the South and north to West Virginia and North Carolina. Various species of hardwoods, especially the oaks, are most commonly attacked. Magnolia seedlings have also been severely damaged in a nursery in Florida. Adults are dark reddish-brown and about 4.5 mm. long. The front of the head is shallowly and densely punctured and sparsely clothed with moderately long hairs. The pronotum is longer than broad, and, in the female, it bears two large pits just behind the middle. The third, fifth, and seventh interspaces of the elytra are produced into toothlike processes on the elytral declivity of the male. Two large tuberosities also occur on the lower edge of the declivity, and two hook-like spines are on the fourth abdominal segment.

Platypus compositus (Say) occurs throughout the Southern States northward to southern New York and southern Illinois. It breeds in a wide variety of deciduous trees such as hickory, pecan, birch, poplar, oak, chestnut, basswood, elm, beech, sweetgum, sourgum, magnolia, persimmon, and cypress. Recently felled or girdled cypress is often seriously damaged (fig. 103). Adults are light reddish-brown and about 4.5 mm. long. The front of the head is densely punctured above, and there are two centrally located pits just behind the middle of the pronotum. The first, third, and seventh interspaces of the elytra of the male are produced into small tubercles on the declivity. The declivity also bears two large tridentate teeth at the outer apical angle.

Control of Ambrosia Beetles.—Ambrosia beetle control is largely a matter of prevention of damage to recently cut logs through the regulation of woods practice, and in the proper handling of milled products (*41*). Control for several months has also been obtained by spraying with an approved insecticide (*404, 405*).

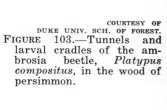

FIGURE 103.—Tunnels and larval cradles of the ambrosia beetle, *Platypus compositus*, in the wood of persimmon.

Order LEPIDOPTERA

Butterflies, moths, skippers

This is the second largest order of insects and one of the most important economically. More than 5,000 species occur in eastern United States alone, and many are serious pests of forest, shade, and ornamental trees. The adults differ considerably in appearance from those in all other orders and are not difficult to recognize. The wings and practically all other parts of the body are typically covered by a layer of short, flattened hairs, or scales, which rub off like dust when the insects are handled. The mouth parts, when present, are in the form of a long, slender, flexible tube which is carried coiled up like a watch spring beneath the head. The wings are usually very broad, sub-triangular in form, and the front pair is larger.

Moth, butterfly, and skipper adults usually differ in habits and appearance as follows: (1) Moths usually fly at night and are frequently attracted to lights; butterflies and skippers fly in the day time. (2) Moths usually have the wings wrapped around the body, folded roof-like on the abdomen, or spread horizontally while at rest; butterflies usually fold their wings above the back in a vertical position; skippers usually hold the front and hindwings at a different angle. (3) Moth antennae are usually thread-like or feather-like; butterfly antennae are thread-like and clubbed at the tip; the antennae of the skippers are usually recurved or hooked.

Lepidopterous larvae are all very similar in structure. They are usually cylindrical in shape, and, besides the head, the body is composed of 13 segments, three thoracic and 10 abdominal. Each thoracic segment bears a pair of jointed legs, terminating in a single claw, whereas the abdominal segments bear unjointed fleshy projections of the body called prolegs, typically one pair each on segments three to six and 10. Occasionally, some or all of the prolegs are missing. A distinctive feature of the prolegs of Microlepidoptera is the presence of fine hooks, known as crochets, usually in a circle at the apex. The crochets usually form bands or rows. Another important characteristic of the Lepidoptera is the ability of the larvae to produce silk. Many larvae use this material in making cocoons, and some use it for making shelters. The first instar larvae of certain species also frequently drop down from the crowns of trees in large numbers when disturbed, hanging suspended at the ends of long strands of silk. Many of these are often borne aloft by the wind and transported for considerable distances. Many nearly full grown larvae descend the tree in search of better food or pupation sites.

True silk moth larvae typically spin silken cocoons in which to pupate. Some miscellaneous groups form tough silk or parchment-like cocoons, often with debris. The pupae of many others are naked or are enclosed in slight cocoons of attached leaves. Depending on the species, these cocoons may be found in the soil, in tunnels in wood, or in other larval habitats. The caterpillars of butterflies usually do not make cocoons. Their pupae are naked and are commonly known as chrysalids. They are often attached to leaves or twigs from which they hang head down. Some, such as those of the families Papilionidae and Pieridae, are girdlers and do not hang head down. Skippers pupate in cocoons made of leaves fastened together with silk.

The order Lepidoptera contains several destructive forest and shade tree insects. Several species such as the spruce budworm, the forest tent caterpillar, and the gypsy moth often occur in outbreaks covering tens of thousands of acres of woodlands, and losses are very great. Large volumes of timber may be killed, and larger volumes are lost through reduced growth of surviving trees. Many other species cause serious losses by boring into and destroying the buds and shoots of seedlings and young trees in forest nurseries and plantations, or by mining the tissues between the upper and lower surfaces of leaves. The attractiveness of shade trees, parks, and other recreational areas is often reduced or destroyed by these insects, fire danger is increased, and wildlife habitats are impaired.

For a more extensive treatment of the order Lepidoptera the reader is referred to the following publications: Borror and De-Long (*90*), Dyar (*213*), Edwards (*222*), Forbes (*258*), Fracker (*262*), Holland (*364, 365*), Klotz (*422*), McGugan (*482*), Prentice (*607, 608, 609*), McDunnough (*478*), and Freeman (*267*).

Field Key to Some Common Lepidopterous Larvae Attacking
Eastern Forest and Shade Trees

1. Defoliators 2
   Borers 15
2. Miners, casebearers, bagworms 3
   Skeletonizers (leaves not webbed together) 9
   Leaf rollers and leaf tiers 10
   Webworms and tent makers 11
   Free feeders 12
3. Non-casebearing leaf miners 4
   Casebearing leaf miners, other casebearers, webworms 7
4. In the foliage of deciduous plants 5
   In the needles of Pinaceae 6
5. (1) **Oak**—
       a. Very small, flat, and reddish brown or black.
          Solitary. ....*Lithocolletis hamadryadella.*
       b. Very small, flat, and reddish brown or black.
          Gregarious. ....*Lithocolletis cincinnatiella.*
   (2) **Tupelo**—Head and cervical shield dark-brown; body
       pale green and about 8 mm. long
                              Antispila nyssaefoliella.
6. (1) **Arborvitae**—
       a. Head, cervical shield, and anal plate blackish;
          body reddish ....*Coleotechnites thuiaella.*
       b. Head brown; body yellowish-white with shield-
          shaped areas behind the head
                              Argyresthia thuiella.
       c. Head greenish or brownish; body yellowish-green
          to green (also on red cedar)
                              Argyresthia freyella.

(2) **Redcedar, juniper**—Head, cervical shield and true legs light brown; remainder of body pale green with a pinkish tinge

Coleotechnites juniperella.

(3) **Baldcypress, hemlock**—Head, cervical shield, and true legs pale brown; body greenish with brownish tinge ....*Coleotechnites apictripunctella.*

(4) **Pines** (jack, pitch, etc.)—Head, anal plate, and true legs dark brown; body pinkish. About 6 mm. long

Exoteleia pinifoliella.

(5) **Spruce** (Norway, white, Colorado blue)—

  a. Head, cervical shield, thoracic legs, and anal plate blackish; body dirty white to reddish. About 8 mm. long ....*Epinotia nanana.*

  b. Head and cervical shield light brown; body reddish to light cinnamon brown

Coleotechnites piceaella.

  c. Head flattened and yellowish-brown; shields pale greenish; body light greenish brown, semitransparent, and sparsely clothed with hairs

Taniva albolineana.

7. Case composed of part or parts of a leaf 8
  Case tough, oval, silken ....*Acrobasis* spp.
  Case baglike, silken, covered with bits of host plant

Family Psychidae.

8. (1) **Sugar maple**—Head amber brown; body dull white, with a broad longitudinal stripe; about 6 mm. long (case flat and circular)

Paraclemensia acerifoliella.

(2) **Oak**—Case ellipsoidal, portable, composed of bits of leaves and silk; open at each end

Cincinnus melsheimeri.

(3) Cases cigar- or pistol-shaped
  a. Elm ....*Coleophora limosipinella.*
  b. Alder, birch ....*Coleophora fuscedinella.*
  c. Hickory, pecan ....*Coleophora caryaefoliella.*
  d. Apple, hawthorn ....*Coleophora serratella.*
  e. Larch ....*Coleophora laricella.*

9. Skeletonizers (leaves not webbed together)
  (1) **Oak** ....*Bucculatrix ainsliella.*
  (2) **Birch** ....*Bucculatrix canadensisella.*
  (3) **Apple, Hawthorn** ....*Bucculatrix pomifoliella.*
  (4) **Paper** and **river birches** ....*Acleris logiana.*

10. Leaf rollers and leaf tiers (some are skeletonizers)
  (1) **Basswood**—Head black; body green. A leaf roller

Pantographa limata.

  (2) **Beech**—Head brown; body pinkish. A leaf tier

Psilocorsis faginella.

  (3) **Elm**—Body green; margins of segments tinged with yellow. In silken web between 2 leaves

Canarsia ulmiarrosorella.

  (4) **Hickory**—
    a. Head, shield, tubercles black; body dull green with black, prominent tubercles

Archips infumatanus

b. Head pale green, tinged with brown; body pale, translucent ....*Argyrotaenia juglandana.*

(5) **Black locust—**
   a. Head and cervical shield blackish; body green with yellowish lines ....*Nephopteryx subcaesiella.*
   b. Head light brown; body light green
      Nephopteryx virgatella.
   c. Head dull yellow; 2 yellow spots on lower part of face; neck and sides of first thoracic segment red; cervical shield black; body light green, marked with fine black rings
      Epargyreus clarus.

(6) **Maple—**
   a. Head yellowish; body light green (In a trumpet-like tube) ....*Epinotia aceriella.*
   b. Head and cervical shield reddish brown; body dull, yellowish-green ....*Sparganothis pettitana.*
   c. Head tan; body yellowish-green
      Sparganothis acerivorana.

(7) **Oak—**
   a. Head and cervical shield dark brown to black; body light green ....*Archips argyrospilus.*
   b. Head amber yellow; body light green
      Argyrotaenia quericifoliana.
   c. Body greenish (between two leaves tied together with silk) ....*Psilocorsis* spp.
   d. Head pale; thoracic legs brown to black; body dirty white to light green. About 12 mm. long
      Croesia albicomana.

(8) **Pine—**Head greenish-brown, with dark patches on the sides; body greenish-brown
      Argyrotaenia pinatubana.

(9) **Poplar—**
   a. Head and cervical shield brown; body translucent; legs and tubercles black
      Anacampsis innocuella.
   b. Head blackish; shields mostly black; body dull olive green ....*Choristoneura conflictana.*
   c. Head large, dull brownish or reddish-brown; body pale green ....*Erynnis icelus.*
   d. Head brown; body light green
      Amorbia humerosana.

(10) **Redbud—**Body white with black markings
      Fascista cercerisella.

(11) **Sassafras—**Body largest at 3rd thoracic segment; dorsum pea green and sides yellowish; black line across prothorax; eyelike spots with blackish centers on enlarged segment; pair of spots on 1st abdominal segment ....*Papilio troilus.*

(12) **Spruce, fir—**
   a. Head black; body brown, with conspicuous pale tubercles ....*Choristoneura fumiferana.*
   b. Head brownish or black; body bright green
      Acleris variana.

c. Head brownish yellow; body yellowish to grayish-green (Opening buds and terminal needles webbed together in the spring)
Zeiraphera ratzeburgiana.

(13) **Sumac—**
a. Body green, more or less tinged with red
Episimus argutanus.
b. Head yellow and brown; body yellow green, with brick red lines ....*Nephopteryx sugfuscella.*

(14) **Sycamore**—Body light green; tapers toward each end
Adoxophyes furcatana.

(15) **Tupelo**—Head yellowish; body black
Actrix nyssaecolella.

(16) **Willow—**
a. Head large, dull brownish or reddish brown; body dull, pale green ....*Erynnis icelus.*
b. Head light brown; body light green
Amorbia humerosana.

(17) **Various hosts—**
a. Head brownish; body pale green
Choristoneura rosaceana.
b. Head light to dark brown; body dull green
Archips rosanus.
c. Head dark brown or black; body light green
Archips argyrospilus.
d. Head black; body dark brown
Spilonota ocellana.
e. Head yellow brown; body translucent, greenish with 4 whitish, longitudinal lines
Dichomeris ligulellus.
f. Head large; body green and tapering
Machimia tentoriferella.

11. Webworms and tent makers
(1) **Ailanthus**—Body dark olive brown, marked with white lines ....*Atteva aurea.*
(2) **Wild cherry, apple**—Body dark colored with a white stripe on the dorsum ....*Malacosoma americanum.*
(3) **Apple, wild plum, cherry**—Head light brown; body dark brown to almost black, with a broken white line on each side and 2 conspicuous reddish spots on the back near the rear end
Nygmia phaeorrhoea.
(4) **Cherry, elm, apple, persimmon, and many other species**—Body generally pale yellowish or greenish, with a broad, dusky longitudinal stripe on the back and a yellowish stripe on the sides; clothed with whitish to reddish hairs arising from black and orange warts ....*Hyphantria cunea.*
(5) **Beech**—Body yellowish green with faint stripes
Tetralopha spp.
(6) **Birch, Willow**—Body dark brown to black, with black dots on the sides below which are spots that vary from white to red ....*Eulype hastata.*

(7) **Cherry—**
   a. Looper; body black and yellow (In nest of leaves near end of the branch ....*Calocalpe undulata.*
   b. Head black; body yellow (in a dense web)
   Archips cerasivoranus.
(8) **Juniper—**
   a. Body brown and black
   Dichomeris marginellus.
   b. Head dark; body brownish yellow
   Phalonia ruitilana.
(9) **Maple**—Body brown with yellow and black stripes (In small nest) ....*Tetralopha* sp.
(10) **Oak—**
   a. Head black; body gray green
   Archips fervidanus.
   b. Body brown with yellow stripes; legs and spiracles black ....*Tetralopha asperatella.*
(11) **Pine**—Body yellowish brown with darker stripes (In silken tubes in globular masses of frass and silk) ....*Tetralopha robustella.*
(12) **Poplar—**
   a. Head black; body dark brown, with yellowish lines (nest of leaves drawn together and lined with silk) ....*Ichthyura inclusa.*
   b. Body brown and yellow striped; spiracles and legs black ....*Tetralopha* spp.
(13) **Mimosa, honey locust**—Body pale green to dark brown with 5 longitudinal white lines. About 12 mm. long ....*Homadula anisocentra*
12. Larvae sluglike 13
    Typical caterpillars (not sluglike) 14
13. Densely hairy larvae
   (1) **Oak, elm, hackberry, maple, sycamore, etc.**—Densely clothed with long, yellowish and reddish brown or mouse gray hairs, with those at the rear end forming a sort of tail ....*Megalopyge opercularis.*
   (2) **Oak and many other hardwoods**—Body almost oval and covered with long silky hairs, with those on the back raised to a ridge and sloping off rooflike on each side ....*Lagoa crispata.*
   Larvae smooth or armed with spines
   (1) **Oak, apple, dogwood, and many other hardwoods—** Body brownish in color, with a green patch on middle of the back resembling a saddlecloth; in middle of patch an oval purplish-brown saddle-like spot; sides armed with fascicles of spines, and a pair of spiny tubercles at each end
   Sibine stimulea.
   (2) **Norway and sycamore maples plus a wide variety of other hardwoods**—Body marked with yellow, blue, green, and purple; upper surface marked with a dumbell-shaped purple area; long, shiny tubercles

arise from each end and shorter ones along the sides .... *Cnidocampa flavescens.*

(3) **Various hardwoods and shrubs**—Body with 9 pairs of lateral brown processes, the 3rd, 5th, and 7th pairs curved, twisted, and longest. These processes clothed with stinging hairs

Phobetron pithecium.

17. (1) **Apple, birch, basswood, elm, oak, etc.**—Head black; neck with yellow ring; cervical shield waxy yellow; body black with narrow, yellow stripe

Datana ministra.

(2) **Oak, beech, gray birch, hickory, butternut**—Similar to *ministra* except for an entirely black cervical shield .... *Datana angusi.*

(3) **Oak and sycamore**—Head and neck black; cervical shield waxy orange-yellow; body black, with white or yellow stripes; clothed with longish hairs

Datana contracta.

(4) **Walnut, butternut, hickory**—Head and body black; clothed with long, dirty white hairs

Datana integerrima.

(5) **Apple, azalea**—Head, cervical shield, legs mahogany red; body black with a broken white line

Datana major.

(6) **Sumac**—Head dark red or black; shield reddish-brown; anal plate blackish; body yellow with reddish to blackish stripe .... *Datana perspicua.*

18. (1) **Oak, birch, poplar, etc.**—Head yellow and black; body dusky with 5 pairs of blue spots followed by 6 pairs of red spots on the back
Porthetria dispar.

(2) **Poplar and willow**—Head black with bluish tinge; body blackish, with a row of white blotches on top and a narrow, broken, subdorsal line; sides mottled with black and white ....*Stilpnotia salicis.*

(3) **Poplar, sugar maple, tupelo, etc.**—Head and body pale bluish; a row of keyhole-shaped white spots on the dorsum ....*Malacosoma disstria.*

(4) **Persimmon, palmetto, ground oak**—Head orange brown; front of prothorax, legs, anal segment, and undersurface of body yellowish green to orange; tops of other body segments crossed by 2 yellowish stripes and a row of orange-colored warts
Seirarctia echo.

(5) **Ash, basswood, elm, maple, oak**—Body flattened, gray, and with faint longitudinal lines; lateral lappets with long hairs, forming a fringe around the body; a pair of warts bordered by a black band on the thorax ....*Tolype velleda.*

19. (1) **Elm, maple, poplar, sycamore, willow, etc.**—Head red; a pair of long, black hair pencils on prothorax and another pair on the 8th abdominal segment; reddish dots on top of 6th and 7th abdominal segments; tufts whitish
Hemerocampa leucostigma.

(2) **Various hardwoods**—Head black; body dark gray; tufts whitish; a pair of black hair pencils on top of prothorax and one on each side of the 2nd abdominal segment ....*Orgyia antiqua.*

(3) **Sycamore**—Head yellowish brown; body yellowish, clothed in whitish to yellowish hairs; long orange-colored, hair pencils ....*Halisidota harrisii.*

(4) **Various hardwoods**—Head black; body blackish, clothed in gray to yellowish hairs with an olive tinge; hair pencils brownish to black with some white ....*Halisidota tessellaris.*

(5) **Butternut, hickory, walnut**—Head black; body grayish-white with white markings, clothed in grayish-white hairs; a row of black tufts on the dorsum, and 2 long black hair pencils on 2nd thru 6th abdominal segments ....*Halisidota caryae.*

(6) **Apple, birch, maple, oak, aspen, etc.**—Head black; body blackish; row of mostly black tufts on dorsum; yellow tufts on sides of abdominal segments 2 to 6; others black; tufts on thoracic and 8th abdominal segments longest and containing some yellow or white hairs ....*Halisidota maculata.*

(7) **Apple, maple, etc.**—Head shiny black; body greenish white above and blackish below; clothed with fine yellowish hairs; 2 long black hair pencils on each

281

of 1st and 3rd abdominal segments and a single 1
on the 8th ....*Acronicta americana.*
(8) **Poplar and willow**—Head, shield, and true legs black;
body dull, whitish, clothed in long, yellow hairs; a
single, long hair pencil on each of 1st, 3rd, 4th, 5th
and 8th abdominal segments
Acronicta lepusculina.
(9) **Poplar, birch, willow**—Head greenish-white or marked
with black; body clothed with long, fine, curved,
white or yellow hairs; a few bristly black hairs at
ends of the body ....*Acronicta leporina vulpina.*
(10) **Maple, cherry**—Head rounded and yellowish; body
whitish or yellowish on the back, except for a row
of black spots; blackish beneath; densely clothed
with long, fine white or yellow hairs; long hair
pencils on 2nd and 3rd thoracic segments and
8th abdominal segment ....*Apatelodes torrefacta.*
20. Caterpillars with transverse rows of prominent, branched
spines on the dorsum.
(1) **Elm**—Head dark red; body brownish, mottled with
yellow; spines light colored, some tipped with
black ....*Polygonia interrogationis.*
(2) **Birch**—Head black; body reddish to blackish on top,
dotted with green; spines above spiracles black
Nymphalis j-album.
(3) **Elm, poplar, willow**—Head black, bilobed; body black,
sprinkled with whitish dots; black dorsal line
broken by row of 7 or 8 reddish dots; spines black;
abdominal legs reddish ....*Nymphalis antiopa.*
(4) **Various hardwoods**—Head pea green and glossy; body
pea green with a broad, reddish spiracular stripe
below which is a white stripe and another reddish
line; spiracles yellowish ringed with black
Automeris io.
(5) **Oak**—Head reddish brown; body dull brown to blackish, covered with small, pale yellowish dots; spiracles pale; clothed with rusty, brown-tipped bristles and black or white, branched compound spines
Hemileuca maia.
21. Thorax with long, prominent spines 22
Thorax with short, blunt spines or only enlarged tu-
bercles 25
22. Thorax with 1 pair of spines 23
Thorax with 2 or more pairs of spines 24
23. (1) Head bilobed and covered with small, sharp tubercles; a pair of large, barbed, club-shaped spines
on 2nd thoracic segment ....*Limenitis* spp.
(2) A pair of slender, stiff spines, about as long as body
is thick, on 2nd thoracic segment; other spines
short ....*Anisota* spp.
24. (1) **Elm, poplar, cherry, willow, etc.**—Head and hump on
back of 1st abdominal segment red, body black,
with black and yellow lines; a double row of short,

black, sometimes uniformly green or yellow, or
mottled brown, tan, or rose
Ennomos subsignarius.

(7) **Hemlock, balsam fir, arborvitae, spruce, larch, etc.**—Yellowish green to grayish or even darker; head and
body flecked with black ....*Lambdina fiscellaria.*

(8) **Hemlock**—Head yellowish, with brownish or blackish spots; body yellowish with the top lighter than
the sides; sides marked with wavy, dark reddish
brown lines, interrupted with dashes of white
Lambdina athasaria athasaria.

(9) **Pitch, red, and shortleaf pines**—Straw to greenish yellow in color; head freckled; body with blackish
dots and wavy lines
Lambdina athasaria pellucidaria.

(10) **Oak, red maple**—Head flat, quadrangular, mottled
with black; body flesh colored with many wavy
blackish lines; thoracic segments thick; hairy tubercles on all body segments ....*Phigalia titea.*

(11) **Basswood, elm, hickory, maple, oak, etc.**—Head rusty
brown; body bright yellow with 10 wavy black
lines on top; legs yellow ....*Erannis tiliaria.*

(12) **Oak**—Head angular, bilobed; first 2 thoracic segments mottled with reddish brown and black;
body stout and "armed" with brownish tubercles
Phaeoura quernaria.

(13) **Sassafras, tulip poplar**—Head small and reddish
brown; body stout, yellowish to dark brown with
many fine, irregular, wavy lines
Epimecis virginaria.

(14) **Pine, fir, spruce, hemlock, larch**—Head and legs
flecked with brown; body pale yellow, marked
with a wide, orange-red dorsal stripe and thin,
longitudinal, black and white lines
Nepytia semiclusaria.

(15) **Hemlock, spruce, fir, larch**—Head pale whitish or
reddish brown, with 5 or 6 large and a few small,
black dots; body whitish tinged with yellow or
red, marked with black dots, yellowish lateral
stripe and subdorsal rows of white spots
Nepytia canosaria.

Measuring worms more than 50 mm. long.

(1) **Hickory, basswood, ash, maple, etc.**—Yellowish green,
tinged with red; head bilobed; body smooth with
swollen areas on top of abdominal segments 2 to
5 and conical tubercles on top of the 8th
Deuteronomos magnarius.

(2) **Willow, poplar, wild cherry, etc.**—Head deeply cleft
and flat in front; body greenish to reddish brown;
anal claspers large ....*Biston cognataria.*

28. Body naked; 1 or more dorsal humps on abdomen

(1) **Elm**—Head pale green with 4 broad white bands in
front and on sides; body polished, bluish green;

thoracic segments unarmed; first 8 abdominal segments each have a large forward projecting prominence ending in a bifid ridge; a pair of small, dorsal tubercles on 9th abdominal segment

Nerice bidentata.

(2) **Oak, beech, elm, maple**—Head orange red; body smooth, naked, shining and increasing in diameter to orange-red enlargement on 8th abdominal segment; a yellow, subdorsal and a yellow, stigmatal stripe and several fine blackish lines

Symmerista spp.

(3) **Oak and beech**—Head bilobed and pale, with dark brownish, branched band on each side outlining whitish patches on the face; large, slightly cleft dorsal tubercle on 1st abdominal segment; smaller brownish tubercle on 8th abdominal segment; body color pea green with shades of brown

Dicentria lignicolor.

(4) **Poplar and willow**—Head oval, flattened in front, and vertex slightly lobed; body pearl gray, somewhat marbled with brown and marked with a reddish brown, dorsal line from head to 2nd tubercle; conical tubercles directed posteriorly on 2nd and 3rd segments; prominent hump on 8th abdominal segment ....*Hyperaeschra stragula.*

29. Body naked, with two anal projections
(1) **Poplar, willow, wild cherry**—Prothorax with lateral tubercles wider than the head; body green and brown, tinged reddish or purplish, and tapering gradually to the rear; anal legs filamental and about 18 mm. long ....*Cerura* spp.

(2) **Beech, maple, poplar, oak, etc.**—Head conical, pinkish on sides; thickest in middle, a yellowish dorsal stripe; filamentous and legs not quite as long as body is thick ....*Fentonia marthesia.*

(3) **Hackberry**—Head broad and armed with branched antlers; body greenish often marked with yellow stripes and spots, widest in middle and tapering toward each end. Two anal projections

Asterocampa spp.

30. Measuring worms—not over 1 inch long
(1) **Birch** (gray and paper)—Body green to yellowish brown, with fine yellowish lines and a broad subspiracular stripe ....*Brephos infans.*

(2) **Elm, apple, etc.**—Light green to dark brownish green; darker dorsal stripe; rudimentary prolegs on 5th abdominal segment ....*Alsophila pometaria.*

(3) **Elm, apple, etc.**—Reddish or yellowish brown to greenish; body lines numerous and irregular, sometimes almost invisible; prolegs on 6th and anal segments only ....*Paleacrita vernata.*

(4) **Hemlock**—Head broader than thorax, brown, and bilobed; body greenish tinged with redish brown;

286

swelling usually on each side of 2nd abdominal segment ....*Anacamptodes ephyraria.*

(5) **Hemlock, fir, larch, spruce**—Head pale whitish, sometimes reddish brown, with 5 or 6 large and some small dots; body whitish with yellow or reddish tinge; dotted with black and with 4 dark, wavy, hair lines below a yellowish, lateral stripe

Neptyia canosaria.

(6) **Sugar maple, poplar, beech, etc.**—Body light green with 3 narrow yellowish-white stripes on each side of the body; 2 pairs of prolegs

Operophtera bruceata.

(7) **Red maple, etc.**—Head pale green, slightly bilobed; body green, skin much wrinkled, a double, whitish, dorsal line bordered by yellowish white lines; spaces between segments yellowish

lobed; body greenish tinged with reddish brown; swelling usually on each side of 2nd abdominal seg-

Physostegania pustularia.

(8) **White pine**—Head slightly brownish; body deep green with greenish-white line on the dorsum and a narrow subdorsal and stigmatal white stripe

Eufidonia notataria.

(9) **White pine, spruce, fir, larch**—Head brownish; body light green, sometimes brownish above; 2 longitudinal, light stripes on dorsum between which are 2 lighter stripes ....*Semiothisa granitata.*

(10) **Black locust**—Body green with many obscure, wavy lines giving a reddish tinge

Semiothisa ocellinata.

(11) **Black and choke cherry**—Head and thoracic shield dark amber; body blackish above, with 4 longitudinal lines, and straw yellow beneath; about 20 mm. long ....*Calocalpe undulata.*

Measuring worms—25 to 50 mm. long

(1) **Alder, beech, yellow birch**—Head rather small and rather flattened in front; body green to brownish with whitish spots on dorsum; spiracles black

Hyperetis amicaria.

(2) **Birch, maple, oak, walnut, etc.**—Head brownish, somewhat mottled; body reddish to chocolate brown, with pair of blunt tubercles on top of 8th abdominal segment ....*Ectropis crepuscularia.*

(3) **Yellow birch, maple**—Head bilobed; body dull brown, with lighter and darker blotches; prominent swollen area on top of 6th abdominal segment

Plagodis serinaria.

31. Naked, without prominent tubercles, and with 5 pairs abdominal legs.

(1) **Beech, sugar maple, etc.**—Head large with broad reddish, lateral band; body yellow green, or light green with bluish cast; usually a reddish-brown or purplish saddle-shaped patch on the back

Heterocampa guttivitta.

(2) **Beech, oak, basswood, elm, etc.**—Head large, blackish with whitish band on each side; body smooth yellowish green with a pale median line on each side *Heterocampa manteo.*

(3) **Hemlock, larch, spruce**—Head yellowish; body light green; pale median stripe, and a subdorsal and stigmatal stripe on each side; the stigmatal stripe bordered in red _____*Feralia jocosa.*

(4) **Maple, ash, etc.**—Pale green; head with yellowish tint, body with broad stripe on top; skin dotted with white; a narrow subdorsal and broad stigmatal stripe on each side ____*Lithophane antennata.*

(5) **Oaks mostly**—Pale pea green; head large and rounded; body with yellowish, subdorsal stripes; spiracles red _____*Nadata gibbosa.*

(6) **White, pitch, and jack pines**—Head triangular, conical, with a pale, yellow stripe on each side; body grass green, with 3 longitudinal white stripes on each side; broad, brick-red, median dorsal stripe on dorsum of abdomen _____*Lapara bombycoides.*

(7) **Spruce**—Head somewhat mottled; body dull brown with a dark dorsal stripe; spiracles and tubercles black _____*Epizeuxis aemula.*

(8) **Willow, elm, maple, poplar, etc.**—Body wine-colored, with four large whitish spots on the front of the prothorax and marked with many irregular, wavy, longitudinal lines and creamy-white spots *Lycia ursaria.*

32. Borers in buds, stems, shoots, twigs.

(1) **Pines (red, Scotch, Austrian, etc.)**—Head and thoracic shield black; body brownish; almost 12 mm. long. In buds and expanding shoots *Rhyacionia buoliana.*

(2) **Pines (Pitch and other hard pines)**—Head and cervical shield blackish; body yellowish to pale brown; about 9 mm. long. In buds and succulent growth at tips of twigs ___*Rhyacionia frustrana frustrana.*

(3) **Pines (Red, Scotch, jack)**—Head dark brown to black; prothoracic shield black; anal plate dark brown; remainder of body yellowish-brown to reddish-brown; about 8 mm. long. In buds and new shoots *Rhyacionia adana.*

(4) **Pines (Red, Scotch, Austrian, longleaf, etc.)**—Head, cervical shield, anal plate brown to dark brown; body yellowish; about 6 mm. long. In buds *Battaristis vittella.*

(5) **Pines White, red, Scotch, jack, etc.)**—Head yellowish-brown, with a round, blackish spot at the hind margin; most of remainder of the body a dirty white. In laterals _____*Eucosma gloriola.*

(6) **Jack pine**—Larva brownish gray and about 12 mm. long. In new shoots _____*Eucosma sonomana.*

(7) **Pines (pitch, etc.)**—Head and cervical shield dark brown; body pale brown; about 12 mm. long. In twigs _____*Petrova comstockiana.*

(8) **Pines (Jack, etc.)**—Head and cervical shield light brown; body reddish with small, shiny tubercles. In young branches ....*Petrova albicapitana.*

(9) **Pines, fir, spruce**—Head dark reddish brown with dark brown maculations; body moderately slender, somewhat fusiform, the dorsum usually reddish purple, the venter pale reddish purple, tinged with green; about 20 mm. long. In shoots, branches, and the trunk ....*Dioryctria abietella.*

(10) **Pines (Longleaf, loblolly)**—Head shiny red-brown; thoracic legs and thoracic and anal shields brown; body greenish-white with brownish markings above; about 25 mm. long. In terminals and trunk galls ....*Dioryctria amatella.*

(11) **Pines (red, Scotch, white, jack, shortleaf, loblolly, etc.)** —*In the North*: head brown, body pink to greenish and covered with small, black dots; about 19 mm. long. *In the South*: uniformly bluish-black above, excepting the top of the thorax, and greenish-blue with a violaceous tint, below: 18 to 25 mm. long ....*Dioryctria zimmermani.*

(12) **Pines (Scotch, red, jack, longleaf, loblolly, scrub)**—*In the North*: slender, olive-green to buff and from 14 to 18 mm. long. *In the South*: moderately slender, grayish-buff, and 20 to 25 mm. long. In staminate flowers and cones

Dioryctria disclusa.

(13) **Spruces, firs, larch, and jack pine**—Head and cervical shield reddish-brown; body brown to amber and ornamented with piliferous warts; about 18 mm. long. In needles, buds, staminate flowers, and cones ....*Dioryctria reniculella.*

(14) **Black locust**—Head brownish-black; body greenish with broken stripes of dark brown; about 16 mm. long. Girdling near ground line

Elasmopalpus lignosellus.

(15) **Spruce**—Head brownish-yellow; cervical shield paler; body yellowish or grayish-green; about 18 mm. long. In buds ....*Zeiraphera ratzeburgiana.*

(16) **Gray birch, black cherry, maple, oak, etc.**—Head slightly bilobed and rusty red; body greenish-brown; pair of prominent tubercles on 1st abdominal segment; a pair of long, fleshy brownish filaments on each of 2nd and 3rd segments; broad white stripe on back from prothorax to 1st pair of filaments; about 18 mm. long

Nematocampa limbata.

33. Borers in fruit, nuts, seeds, and cones.

(1) **Oaks, beech, hazel**—Full-grown larvae pink or whitish; 18 mm. long. In acorns, hazelnuts, and beechnuts ....*Melissopus latiferreanus.*

(2) **Oak, hickory**—Body grayish white or yellowish with black spots on top; cervical and anal shields brownish. In acorns and hickory nuts

Valentinia glandulella.

(3) **Hickory and pecan**—Head light brown; body creamy white and about 9 mm. long. In hickory nuts and pecans ....*Laspeyresia caryana.*

(4) **Pines (Red, Scotch, Austrian, longleaf, etc.)**—See 32(4) for description. In cones and buds
Battaristis vittella.

(5) **Pines (Various species, particularly Southern pines)**—See 32(11) for description. In seeds and cones
Dioryctria zimmermani.

(6) **Pines and spruce**—See 32(9) for description. In cones and seeds ....*Dioryctria abietella.*

(7) **Pines (Scotch, red, jack, longleaf, loblolly, scrub)**—See 32(12) for description. In cones and flowers
Dioryctria disclusa

(8) **Pines (longleaf, loblolly)**—See 32(10) for description. In cones ....*Dioryctria amatella.*

(9) **Spruce, fir, etc.**—See 32(13) for description. In flowers and cones ....*Dioryctria reniculella.*

(10) **Red pine**—Head and pronotum brown; remainder of body grayish-white; about 12 mm. long. In cones ....*Eucosma monitorana.*

(11) **Pines (Slash, loblolly, longleaf, shortleaf)**—Head reddish-brown or nearly black, with dark markings; thoracic shield brownish; anal shield brownish-yellow; about 18 mm. long. In conelets and cones
Dioryctria clariorellia.

34. Borers in branches, trunk, or roots.

(1) **Ash, lilac, privet**—Whitish or yellowish. In main stem
Podosesia syringae syringae.

(2) **Flowering dogwood**—Whitish with brown heads. Under the bark ....*Synanthedon scitula*

(3) **Elm, locust,oaks, green ash, etc.**—Greenish-white; head shiny brown, with powerful, nearly black mandibles; thoracic legs yellowish, with pointed, curved tarsal claw; 50 to 75 mm. long
Prionoxystus robinae.

(4) **Elm, maple, etc.**—Head and thoracic and anal plates brownish-black; body pale yellow, frequently with a pinkish tinge, sparsely hairy and spotted with brown or black tubercles; about 50 mm. long. In twigs, limbs, and trunk. Twigs and branches frequently girdled ....*Zeuzera pyrina.*

(5) **Hickory, oak, pecan**—Head, cervical shield, and anal plate shiny dark-brown; body pinkish, and sparsely clothed in fine hairs; about 37 mm. long. In the pith of twigs at first; later in large galleries several inches long in larger limbs and the trunk
Cossula magnifica.

(6) **Linden (European)**—Head brown; body whitish with contents of alimentary tract visible through the integument. About 6 mm. long. In the bark of limbs and trunk ....*Chrysoclista lineella.*

(7) **Maples**—Head brownish; body white; about 12 mm.

long. In bark and sapwood. usually around wounds
Sylvora acerni.

(8) **Maples (red and silver)**—In small branches causing gall-like swellings ....*Carmento corni.*

(9) **Persimmon**—In solid wood of main stem or taproot, sometimes to a depth of 18 inches in the ground
Sannia uroceriformis.

(10) **Poplar and willow**—Head brownish; body white and about 12 mm. long. In roots, trunks, or large limbs. Extensive burrows and swellings
Aegeria apiformis.

(11) **Rhododendron, laurel, azalea**—Yellow-white and about 12 mm. long. Under the bark of twigs, branches, and stems ....*Synanthedon rhododendri.*

(12) **Pines (various species)**—See 32 (11) for description. In branches and stems ....*Dioryctria zimmermani.*

(13) **Pines (White, pitch) and spruce**—White to pink and about 62 mm. long when full-grown. In the inner bark or sapwood. Pitch masses 75 to 100 mm. in diameter at entrance hole................*Vespamima pini.*

FAMILY PAPILIONIDAE

SWALLOWTAIL BUTTERFLIES

Swallowtail butterflies are of considerable interest to many people because of their large size and striking appearance; otherwise, they are of minor importance. The adults are distinguished by the wavy margins and tail-like prolongations of the hindwings; the larvae, by the protrusive, bright-colored forked processes rising from the first thoracic segment. They also emit a disagreeable odor when disturbed.

The **tiger swallowtail**, *Papilio glaucus* L., occurs commonly in eastern North America. The caterpillars feed on various deciduous trees such as ash, birch, basswood, cherry, and poplar. Full-grown larvae are dark green and about 37 mm. long. The third thoracic segment is enlarged and marked on each side by a large, yellow spot. This spot is edged with black and encloses a small, purple spot which is also edged with black. The posterior part of the first abdominal segment bears a transverse, yellowish ridge, edged posteriorally with black. The caterpillar spins a silken mat upon the surface of the leaf which usually causes the leaf to fold lengthwise. Resting caterpillars are found inside this fold. Transformation to the chrysalis usually takes place on some object above the ground.

The **spice-bush swallowtail**, *Papilio troilus* L., occurs throughout the eastern part of the United States and its principal food plants are spicebush and sassafras. Full-grown larvae are about 37 mm. long. The body is widest in diameter at the third thoracic segment. The head and venter are pink, the dorsum pea-green, the sides yellowish, and there is a transverse black line on the prothorax. The third thoracic and first abdominal segments each bear two orange spots. Those on the thorax have black centers. Six small spots are on abdominal segments two to seven and four on the eighth. *P. cresphontes* Cramer feeds on prickly ash in the Northern States.

Graphium marcellus Cramer, the **zebra swallowtail**, feeds on pawpaw.

FAMILY NYMPHALIDAE

Brush-Footed Butterflies

This family contains some of our most common butterflies. The adults are medium to large and are distinguished by having the forelegs much reduced and without claws. Only the middle and hind pairs are used for walking. The head of the caterpillar is usually bilobed, the tips of the lobes often supporting branched spines, and the body is spiny or bears fleshy, hair-covered warts. The chrysalids are naked and are usually suspended by the cremaster.

Polygonia interrogationis (F.), the **question-sign** feeds on elm, oak, and hackberry in eastern America, especially on sprout growth along roadsides. Full-grown caterpillars (fig. 104) are brownish with yellow mottlings and are about 37 mm. long. Each body segment bears a transverse row of light-colored branched spines. There are two generations per year. *P. comma* (Harr.), the **comma butterfly,** occurs on elm, nettle, and hop from Canada to the Carolinas and Texas. Full-grown caterpillars are yellowish white, and each body segment bears a transverse row of branched spines.

Nymphalis j-album Bdv. and LeC. feeds principally on gray and paper birches, but also on poplar and willow in Canada and south to Pennsylvania in the Eastern States. Caterpillars have black heads, the body is reddish to blackish on the dorsum with

F-519524

FIGURE 104.—Larvae and chrysalis of the butterfly, *Polygonia interrogationis*, the question-sign.

dots of light green, and each segment bears a transverse row of branched spines.

The **mourning-cloak butterfly,** *Nymphalis antiopa* (L.), is a widespread species, occuring throughout the subarctic regions of North America. The larvae, commonly known as **spiny-elm cater-pillars,** feed on elm, willow, poplar, and hackberry, and are some-times abundant locally, especially on shade and ornamental trees and along fence rows. Adults are black-bodied and have wing-spreads of 60 to 80 mm. The upper wing surface is dark red-dish-brown except for a broad, creamy-yellow border, which contains a row of blue spots. Full-grown caterpillars (fig. 105) are black, with a scattering of white dots and a red dot on the dorsum of abdominal segments one to seven. The head is covered with tubercles; the body with many large, branched spines.

FIGURE 105.—Larvae of the mourning-cloak butterfly. *Nymphalis antiopa.*

Winter is spent in the adult stage, and the adults appear in early spring. Eggs are deposited in clusters around small twigs. The larvae feed gregariously until almost full grown and usually defoliate one branch before moving to another. Chrysalids are formed in June or early July. Adults soon appear and lay the eggs for a second brood. Larvae of this generation are present until September. Then they pupate and the adults emerge to hi-bernate. There are one or two generations per year, depending on location.

The mourning-cloak butterfly is of minor importance in the forest, but is sometimes injurious to shade and ornamental trees. Infestations can be controlled by cutting and burning infested twigs and small branches.

The **viceroy,** *Limenitis* (=*Basilarchia*) *archippus* (Cramer), occurs over most of the United States and feeds on poplar, willow, and plum. The adult resembles the well-known monarch butterfly, *Danaus plexippus* (L.), but differs by being slightly smaller, hav-ing a narrow black line across the hindwings and only a single row of black spots in the black marginal band of the wings. The full-grown caterpillar is about 37 mm. long. The head is large, pale green, and bilobed. Body segments one and two are pinkish to brownish; segments three to six and the sides of seven are brownish or greenish; the tops of segments seven and nine and nearly all of eight are pale-pinkish or whitish; and the top of nine and nearly all of the last three are brownish or greenish. There are two barbed, club-shaped, brown tubercles on top of the second thoracic segment and two smaller ones armed with spines on the top of the others. There are two generations per year. The two related species, *L. arthemis* (Drury) and *L. astyanax* (F.), are found on poplar, willow, birch, black cherry, apple, and basswood. The caterpillars are similar in appearance to those of *L. archippus*.

Asterocampa clyton (Bdv. & LeC.) occasionally seriously defoliates hackberry in the Lake States. Full-grown caterpillars are 25 to 37 mm. long. The body is greenish except for a yellow stripe down the back and a deep blue, yellow-bordered stripe on each side. The head is armed with branched, antler-like spines, and there are two projections at the posterior end of the body. *A. celtis* (Bdv. & LeC.) is also abundant occasionally on hackberry in the Lake States. The caterpillar is greenish with a row of yellow dots down the back and three yellow lines along each side. Otherwise, it resembles the caterpillar of *A. clyton*. Langlois & Langlois (*449*) discussed its life history.

FAMILY HESPERIIDAE

SKIPPERS

Members of this family are commonly known as skippers because of the way they flit or dart from place to place. They are distinguished by the head which is nearly as wide or wider than the thorax, and the antennal club which usually has two pairs of spurs. The larvae usually have large heads and strongly constricted necks. They are also usually solitary, each one concealing itself under part of a leaf which it cuts and folds over.

The **silver-spotted skipper**, *Epargyreus clarus* (Cramer), one of the largest species in the family, is widely distributed throughout the United States and southern Canada, and the larvae feed on black locust, ground nut, and wisteria. Adults are brown except for yellow and white triangular spots on the forewings. The forewings are elongate, and the hindwings have rounded tips. Full-grown larvae are nearly 50 mm. long. The body is leaf-green; the head dull red except for two yellow spots on the lower part of the face; the neck and sides of the first thoracic segment are red; and the cervical shield is black. The body is also marked with five black rings.

The larvae feed from within nests made by tying several leaves together with silk. Sometimes they cause heavy defoliation locally. Pupation takes place in loose cocoons spun among the leaves, usually on the ground. In the South there are two generations per year. Farther north there may be only one or one and a partial second.

FAMILY SPHINGIDAE

SPHINX MOTHS

The adults of this family are distinctive in appearance and are known by such common names as sphinx moths, hawk moths, and hummingbird moths. They have stout, spindle-shaped bodies and long, narrow, very strong wings. The antennae are more or less thickened at the middle or toward the tip and are usually pointed or curved back in the form of a hook. The mouth parts are usually very long, and when not in use are held coiled beneath the head like a watch spring. Mature larvae are long, usually naked, and each bears either a horn, an eyelike spot, or a low tubercle on top of the eighth abdominal segment. The pose of the larva while at rest is distinctive—it clings to its support with its abdominal legs, holds the front part of the body aloft, and bends its head downward.

Sphinx moths are strong fliers. Some fly only at night, others, at twilight or during the day. They are usually seen hovering like hummingbirds over flowers and feeding on nectar while in flight.

The **elm sphinx**, *Ceratomia amyntor* (Hbn.), feeds on basswood, birch, and elm throughout eastern United States. Full-grown larvae are pale green to reddish-brown, are marked on each side with seven oblique, whitish stripes; bear pairs of horns on the tops of the second and third abdominal segments; and have one caudal horn. They are about 75 mm. long. *C. undulosa* (Wlkr.) feeds on white ash and lilac from eastern Canada and Maine to the Carolinas and westward to the Mississippi River Valley. Full-grown larvae are about 62 mm. long. The head is bluish-green marked by a broad, pale band. The pea green body tapers toward the head and is marked by seven oblique, yellow stripes on each side; the spiracles are orange-colored; and the caudal horn is reddish and curved towards the tip.

The **catalpa sphinx**, *Ceratomia catalpae* (Bdv.), occurs from New Jersey to Florida and westward to Michigan, Kansas, Iowa, and Texas, but appears to be most abundant in the Southeastern States. It feeds exclusively on catalpa trees, often completely defoliating them. The adult is heavy-bodied and has a wingspan of about 75 mm. The front wings and body are gray with irregular dark and light bands and markings; the hindwings are almost uniformly brownish-gray. Full-grown larvae are about 75 mm. long and armed with a stout, black horn near the posterior (fig. 106). There are two color forms of large larvae—dark and light (*385*). The dark form is black on top and pale yellow underneath;

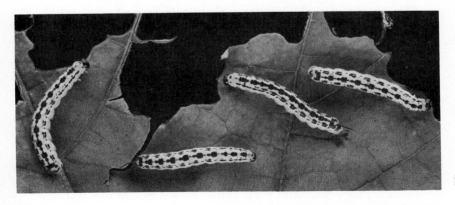

FIGURE 106.—Larvae of the catalpa sphinx, *Ceratomia catalpae*.

295

the light form is pale yellow with markings and patches of black on top.

Winter is spent as a pupa in the soil. Adults begin to appear as early as March in the South, but much later farther north. Eggs are deposited in large masses on the undersides of leaves or in smaller masses on twigs and branches. Young larvae feed gregariously; older ones, singly. In the Deep South, all life history stages may be present during the summer, and there may be three or four generations per year. In the North there is only one generation per year. Larvae are often heavily parasitized by the hymenopteron, *Apanteles congregatus* (Say) (fig. 107).

F-519572
FIGURE 107.—Larvae of the catalpa sphinx bearing cocoons of *Apanteles congregatus*.

The **great ash sphinx**, *Sphinx chersis* (Hbn.), feeds on lilac and white ash throughout the United States. Full-grown larvae are usually light green with bluish heads and are about 75 mm. long. There are seven light yellowish stripes, edged above with bluish-green, on each side of the body, and the caudal horn is pale blue and curved downward. The larvae are found most commonly on young trees and sprout growth in the open or along roadsides. Populations are sometimes heavy enough to cause noticeable defoliation in such areas.

Sphinx kalmiae J. E. Smith feeds on white ash, fringe tree, mountain laurel, rhododendron, and lilac from southern Canada through the Atlantic States to Georgia. Full-grown larvae are yellowish-green and about 75 mm. long. The body is marked by seven oblique, black stripes edged below with yellow; the caudal horn is arcuate and blue with black, raised markings. *S. luscitiosa* Clem. feeds on poplar and willow in the Atlantic Coast States.

S. drupiferarum J. E. Smith, a widely distributed species, feeds on apple, beach plum, wild cherry, hackberry, plum, and peach.

White, pitch, red, and jack pines are fed on by the larvae of *Lapara bombycoides* Wlk. in eastern Canada and from the Atlantic Coast to the Mississippi River Valley. The larvae are present from July to September. Full-grown specimens are green except for a broad, brick-red, median, dorsal stripe; a reddish ventral stripe; and three longitudinal white stripes on each side. They are about 50 mm. long. Brick-red patches sometimes enclose the spiracles, and there is no caudal horn. *L. coniferarum* (J. E. Smith) feeds on pine in the same general territory.

Aspen, willow, and sometimes apple and birch are fed on in the Atlantic States by *Paonias excaecatus* (J. E. Smith). Full-grown larvae are light green, studded with pointed granulations, and about 62 mm. long. There are seven oblique yellowish stripes running backward on each side of the body; the head is conical, granulated, and has a white or pale yellow stripe on each side, meeting at the apex. The spiracles are deep lilac or black; the caudal horn is usually green and nearly straight, and the thoracic legs are lilac or reddish. *P. myops* (J. E. Smith) larvae feed on black cherry in eastern United States. They have rose-colored spiracles; otherwise, they closely resemble the larvae of *P. excaecatus*. The larvae of *Smerinthus jamaicensis* (Drury) (=*geminatus* Say), feed on aspen and willow. They also resemble the larvae of *P. excaecatus*. They differ mainly in having a bluish-purple caudal horn, violet thoracic legs, and sometimes sub-dorsal rows of reddish spots on each side of the body.

The **walnut sphinx**, *Cressonia juglandis* (J. E. Smith), occurs from eastern Canada to Florida and westward to the eastern boundary of the Great Plains. The larvae feed on black walnut, butternut, the hickories, beech, and hop hornbeam. Full-grown larvae are light green to reddish, coarsely granulated with white, and about 50 mm. long. The head bears a yellowish stripe on each side and two rough, brownish projections on the apex. There are seven light-yellowish oblique stripes, sometimes bordered above with reddish, on each side of the body. The caudal horn is brownish and very granulated. There are two generations per year in the South.

FAMILY SATURNIIDAE

Giant Silkworm Moths

This family contains some of the largest and most colorful moths in eastern United States. The larvae, also large and conspicuous, are more or less armed with tubercles and spines. Because of their habit of spinning large, dense silken cocoons in which to pupate, they are known as giant silkworms. The larvae feed on a wide variety of trees and shrubs; however, because they usually occur singly and in low numbers, they are seldom injurious. Some of the most common species are discussed briefly below.

The **cynthia moth**, *Samia* (=*Philosamia*) *cynthia* (Drury), was introduced into this country from Asia about 100 years ago and now occurs from Connecticut to Virginia. Its preferred host is ailanthus, but wild cherry and plum are also infested. The adult is brown with rows of tufts of white hairs on the abdomen and has a wingspread of 150 to 200 mm. Full-grown larvae are about 75 mm. long and have yellowish-green heads and lemon-yellow prothoracic segments. The rest of the body is light bluish-green to yellowish, dotted with black, and there are long, bluish tubercles with short bristles on each body segment. Moths are present from June to September; larvae from July to October. Winter is spent as pupae in cocoons on the tree or on the ground.

The **cecropia moth**, *Hyalophora* (=*sami*) cecropia L., occurs throughout eastern United States and in southern Canada. The larvae feed on a wide variety of hardwoods such as ash, birch, cherry, hawthorn, walnut, maple, sassafras, pussy willow, elm, poplar, and basswood. Feeding damage is often rather severe in shelterbelt plantings in the Northern Great Plains. The moth has a wing expanse of 125 to 150 mm. There is a white, crescent-shaped spot near the center of each wing, a red-bordered crossband on each wing, and a dark spot near the end of each forewing. Full-grown larvae are 75 to 100 mm. long. The head is green with two black spots on each side, and the body is pea green. There are four, large, coral-red tubercles on the top of the second and third thoracic segments, 15 yellow tubercles on top of the first to eighth abdominal segments, and blue tubercles on each side. All tubercles bear stiff, black bristles. Winter is spent in large, thick, tough, gray-brown silken cocoons firmly fastened lengthwise to bare branches. Larvae may be found from June to October depending on location. The tachinid, *Lespesia ciliata* (Mac.), is a common parasite in the Northeast.

The **promethea moth**, *Callosamia promethea* (Drury), occurs throughout most of eastern United States and southern Canada, and feeds on a variety of hosts such as ash, wild cherry, lilac, sassafras, spicebush, yellow-poplar, maple, and birch. The adult has a wing expanse of about 75 mm. The wings of the female are reddish-purple to brown with light brown borders, are crossed near the middle with a wavy white line; each bears an angular white spot near the middle. Each forewing also bears an eyelike spot near the apex. A full-grown larva is about 50 to 62 mm. long. The head is small and yellow; the body bluish or greenish white. The second and third thoracic segments bear four large, coral-red tubercles or horns; the eighth abdominal segment, bears a large yellow one. Each segment is also ornamented by a deep blue wart or button. Winter is spent in a tough, light, colored cocoon enclosed in a leaf. The petiole of the leaf is attached to the twig by a very strong band of silken threads.

The **luna moth**, *Actias* (=*Tropaea*) *luna* (L.), occurs from southern Canada to Florida and Texas and has many hosts such as beech, birch, persimmon, sweetgum, willow, oak, hickory, black walnut, ironwood, and butternut. The adult moth, a very beautiful insect, has delicate green wings which expand up to 100 mm. Each forewing bears a conspicuous eyelike spot, and is edged with a purplish-brown band. The hindwings extend into long, curved swallow-tails. The full-grown larva is about 75 mm. long. The head is bluish-green with brown on the sides; the body pale green with six pinkish or greenish tubercles armed with bristles

298

arising from each segment. A pale, yellow line runs along each side of the body. The tips of the dorsal tubercles on the second and third segments are red; the remainder, yellow. Winter is passed in a cocoon, usually on the ground. Moths are present from April to September, depending on location. There may be two generations per year in the South.

The **polyphemus moth,** *Antheraea* (=*Telea*) *polyphemus* (Cram.), is widely distributed throughout the United States and Canada and feeds on many species of trees including basswood, beech, birch, elm, hawthorn, hickory, maple, oak, yellow-poplar, willow, ash, butternut, walnut, sassafras, and sycamore. The moth is brownish-yellow and has a wing expanse of 100 to 150 mm. There is an eyelike transparent spot on each wing and a sooty, transverse stripe outwardly edged with light pink near the outer margin of the wings. Full-grown larvae are apple green in color and about 75 mm. long. The head is reddish-brown, and the thoracic shield is sometimes margined along the front with yellowish-green. Body segments are angular on the back, and each bears six orange or golden tubercles from each of which arise one to three bristles. The last segment bears a purplish-brown *V*-shaped design. Winter is spent in a tough, thick cocoon usually enclosed in a leaf on the ground. Larvae may be found from June to October. The tachinid, *Lespesia frenchii* (Williston), is a common parasite in the northeast.

The **io moth,** *Automeris io* (F.), occurs throughout eastern United States and attacks a wide variety of trees including paper birch, wild cherry, black locust, aspen, willow, beech, apple, maple, oak, hickory, elm, mulberry, dogwood, and sycamore. Female moths are purplish-red and have a wing expanse of about 75 mm.; males are yellowish and slightly smaller. There is a large, circular, black eyespot with a tiny white center on the upper surface of each hindwing and a smaller but similar one on the lower surface of each forewing. Full-grown larvae are about 75 mm. long. The body is pale green with a broad, reddish-brown stripe on each side, margined with white and reddish-lilac. Whorls of branched, black-tipped, green, poisonous spines rising from small conical tubercles on each body segment, cause a severe nettling effect when they come into contact with the skin. Moths are present from June to July; larvae from July to September. Winter is spent in the pupal stage, in a tough, brown, oval cocoon often covered with bits of dead leaves and other debris, usually on the ground.

The **buck moth,** *Hemileuca maia* (Drury), occurs from New Hampshire to Georgia, Louisiana, and Oklahoma, and it apparently feeds almost exclusively on various species of oak. Adults have black, thin-scaled, sometimes semi-transparent wings. A common white band crosses both the forewing and hindwing near the middle. Full-grown larvae are about 62 mm. long. The head is deep reddish-brown; the body, dull brownish to black and covered with small, yellowish dots. Each body segment has tufts of bristles or compound spines arising from tubercles. The spines cause a nettling effect when in contact with the skin. Winter is passed in the egg stage, and larvae are present from May to August. A common parasite in the Northeast is the tachinid,

Leschenaultia fulvipes (Bigot). *H. lucina* Hy. Edw. feeds principally on *Spiraea latifolia,* but also on wild black cherry, gray birch, and oak in the Northeast. *H. nevadensis* Stretch, the **Nevada buck moth,** has been reported feeding on poplar and willow in Nebraska and Oklahoma.

FAMILY CITHERONIIDAE

Royal Moths

Royal moths are medium-sized to large, with stout bodies and large, strong wings. The head is generally sunken in the prothorax, and the male antennae are feathery for only a little more than half their length. The larvae are armed with horns or spines, and some are thinly hairy. The horns or spines on the second and sometimes third segments are long and usually curved. The larvae feed on the foliage of various trees, and they pupate in the ground without forming cocoons.

The **spiny oakworm,** *Anisota stigma* (F.), feeds on oak and hazelnut from southern Canada and New England to Georgia and Kansas. The adult has a wing expanse of about 50 mm. Its forewings resemble those of the orange-striped oakworm, but differ in being darker, more speckled, and having the outer portion often tinged with lilac. Full-grown larvae are about 37 to 50 mm. long. The body is tawny, often tinged with rose or pink. It is covered with tiny ivory-white specks, denticles, or granules, and is marked with single dorsal and lateral stripes. There are two long, curved spines on the second thoracic segment. The remaining segments bear backward-pointing spines.

Adults are present in June and July and the larvae from July to September. The winter is passed as a pupa in the ground, and there is one generation per year. This species is normally not very abundant, but outbreaks have been recorded, some of which covered hundreds of acres.

The **orange-striped oakworm,** *Anisota senatoria* (J. E. Smith), feeds on various oaks from eastern Canada to Georgia and westward to Minnesota, Iowa, and Texas. The adult has a wingspread of 37 to 62 mm., and its thick body is covered with yellowish-red hairs. The forewings are orange-purple and are marked with an oblique band, a white spot, and numerous black dots. The hindwings of the male are distinctly triangular and only about two-thirds as long as the body. Full-grown catrpillars are black, with eight longitudinal orange-yellow stripes on the dorsum and sides, and the caterpillars are about 50 mm. long. There is a pair of black, slender, stiff, erect, blunt, recurved spines on the second thoracic segment. Each succeeding segment bears a number of small, sharp, black spines (fig. 108).

Adults appear during June or July and deposit their eggs in clusters of several hundred eggs each on the undersides of leaves. Young larvae feed in groups on each side of the leaf, consuming everything but the veins. Older larvae are less gregarious and are often seen crawling around on lawns or the sides of houses, or feeding singly on the foliage of their host. During September

FIGURE 108.—Adult, eggs, and larva of the orange-striped
oakworm, *Anisota senatoria.*

or October, they crawl to the ground and often do considerable
wandering in search of suitable places to pupate. Pupation takes
place in the soil at a depth of 3 to 4 inches. There is one and
possibly two generations per year, depending on location. During
recent years this species has been responsible for a considerable
amount of defoliation in oak stands in Connecticut, New Jersey,
and Pennsylvania.

The **pink-striped oakworm,** *Anisota virginiensis* (Drury), occurs in southern Canada and throughout the eastern half of the
United States. The larvae feed principally on various oaks, but
also on many other hardwoods such as chestnut, hazel, maple,
and birch. There are two generations per year in the southern
parts of its range. Adults (fig. 109) are brownish-red, often with
a purplish cast. Females have a wingspread of about 37 mm.
Males are considerably smaller. The forewings are thinner, less
speckled, and more transparent beyond the discal dot than those
of the orange-striped oakworm or the spiny oakworm. Full-
grown larvae are about 50 mm. long. The body is greenish to
brownish-yellow with two dorsolateral, rose-colored stripes and
a similarly colored stripe along each side. Two spines on the
second thoracic segment are slightly curved and are conspicuously longer than the others.

The **green-striped mapleworm,** *Anisota rubicunda* (F.), is found
throughout most of eastern United States and in adjacent areas
of Canada. Its preferred hosts are maples, but it also feeds on
various oaks and boxelder, especially where they are growing in
mixture with maple. Populations may become heavy enough to
cause serious defoliation anywhere within its range, but this is

COURTESY OF DUKE UNIV. SCH. OF FOREST.
FIGURE 109.—Adult of the pink-striped oakworm, *Anisota virginiensis*.

most likely to occur in the South. The moth (fig. 110A) has a woolly body and a wingspan of 37 to 50 mm. The body is yellow on top and rose-pink beneath. The forewing is rose-pink on the inner and outer borders with a yellow band between. The hindwings are either pure yellow, or yellow with rose-pink streaks. Full-grown larvae (fig. 110B), have cherry-red heads, pale yellow-green bodies and are about 37 mm. long. The body also has seven dark green or nearly black lines running its entire length, two prominent, slender horns on the second thoracic segment, two rows of short spines on each side of the body, and four larger spines on the terminal abdominal segments.

There are one and two generations per year in the North and South, respectively. Eggs are laid on the undersides of leaves

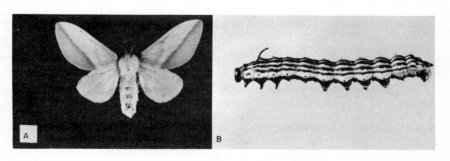

F-500801, 500799

FIGURE 110.—The green-striped mapleworm,
Anisota rubicunda: A, adult; B, larva.

during May and June and hatch in about 10 days. Larvae feed singly, devouring entire leaves, and become full-grown in about a month. In the South, where two generations per year occur, trees may be defoliated twice in the same season. Full-grown larvae crawl to the ground and form cells in the soil or duff where they pupate and spend the winter.

Several species of parasites of the green-striped mapleworm have been recorded, but never in any great abundance. Birds devour some of the larvae but are probably not very effective in control (774).

The **regal moth**, *Citheronia regalis* (F.), occurs throughout the Southern States, northward to Illinois and Massachusetts. The larva, known as the **hickory horned devil** feeds on a wide variety of plants, including many species of trees such as hickory, walnut, butternut, persimmon, sweet gum, sycamore, ash, and sourwood. Adults are quite large, males having wingspreads of 100 to 125 mm., and females 125 to 150 mm. The head and body are orange-colored with pale yellow markings; the forewings are olive-gray with reddish-brown veins and yellow spots and the hindwings are orange-red with somewhat redder veins. Full-grown larvae are 100 to 125 mm. long and are startling to behold (fig. 111).

Adults appear in June and larvae are present from July to September. Winter is spent in the pupal stage in the ground. In most of its range there is only one generation per year, but in the Deep South there may be a partial second. This species is of little or no economic importance. It is of interest mostly because of the frightening appearance of the larvae.

Citheronia sepulchralis G. & R. is occasionaly found feeding on the needles of pines from Maine to Florida. Moths are dark brownish-gray with a lilac tinge. There is a dusky discal spot on each forewing, and the wingspread is about 75 to 100 mm. Full-grown larvae are dull brown, armed with short, orange colored horns, and about 100 mm. long.

The **imperial moth**, *Eacles imperialis* (Drury), occurs in eastern United States and southern Canada. The larvae feed on the foliage of a wide variety of trees including pines, red cedar, oaks, sweetgum, elm, persimmon, hickory, maple, beech, honey locust, and cypress. The moth is sulfur yellow with lilac mark-

FIGURE 111.—The **hickory horned devil**, larva of *Citheronia regalis*.

ings and has a wingspread of 100 to 150 mm. Full-grown larvae are heavy-bodied and about 100 mm. long. The head is orange yellow with green sides; the body, pale green to dark green or reddish purple and covered with long, whitish hairs. Adults appear during June and July and larvae are present from July to October. Winter is spent in the pupal stage in the ground, and there is one generation per year.

Eacles imperialis pini Michener feeds on white and jack pines in New York, Michigan, and southern Canada. The adults are smaller than those of the imperial moth and have dark markings of pink to pinkish-brown. Markings on the surfaces of the wing are also heavier than those of the imperial moth. Adults are present from mid-June to mid-July.

FAMILY CTENUCHIDAE

Lymire edwardsii (Grote) has been recorded feeding as larvae on the foliage of banyan and *Ficus* trees in Florida. The adult is a sluggish, bluish gray to purplish gray moth, with blue and plumose antennae. The thorax is orange-red beneath, the abdomen white beneath and blue above. Larvae are somewhat whitish with a dark tuft of hairs on the thorax. When touched, they usually flip from the leaf to drop to the ground on silken threads. This species is occasionally destructive of shade or ornamental trees (*283*).

FAMILY ARCTIIDAE

TIGER MOTHS AND ALLIES

This is a large family of stout-bodied moths with moderately broad wings. In general they are moderate in size and have broad heads and pectinate or ciliate antennae. Many species are marked with brightly colored spots and stripes. All are night fliers and are attracted to lights. They usually fold their wings roof-like upon the abdomen while at rest. The larvae of most species are clothed with dense clusters of hairs. In some species, certain of these clusters are larger and longer than others, causing the larvae to resemble those of the tussock moths in the family Lymantriidae. The hairs of certain species are irritating. The majority of species prefer the foliage of low growing plants. A few feed on the foliage of trees and shrubs.

The **hickory tussock moth**, *Halisidota caryae* (Harr.), occurs in southern Canada and south in the Eastern States to North Carolina. The larvae feed on the foliage of a wide variety of deciduous trees and shrubs including walnut, butternut, hickory, birch, elm, black locust, basswood, and aspen. Walnut, butternut, and hickory appear to be preferred. Adults are light brown or buff in color, with numerous silvery white spots on the forewings, and they have wingspreads of about 50 mm. Full-grown larvae are grayish-white and about 37 mm. long. The body is clothed with short, spreading tufts of grayish-white hairs. There is a row of black tufts on the first eight abdominal segments and pairs of long black hair pencils on the first and seventh abdominal segments (fig. 112).

Adults appear from late May to early July. The female deposits her eggs in batches of 50 to 400 eggs each in a single layer on the undersides of the leaves. The larvae feed gregariously until nearly mature. Winter is spent in the pupal stage in gray, hairy cocoons under rubbish and stones on the ground. There is one generation per year. This species is often abundant locally, but it seldom, if ever, causes serious defoliation.

The **spotted tussock moth**, *Halisidota maculata* (Harr.), occurs from coast to coast in the Northern States and southern Canada. The larvae feed on the foliage of various deciduous trees such as oak, poplar, birch, beech, black locust, boxelder, wild black cherry, maple, and willow. The oaks, willow, and poplar are particularly attractive. The adult is pale yellow, with long, somewhat pointed, brown-spotted forewings and has a wingspread of 37 to 50 mm. Full-grown larvae are about 30 mm. long, dull black above, are thickly clothed with tufts of black and bright yellow to whitish hairs, and have a row of short tufts down the middle of the dorsum. The tufts on the third thoracic and eighth abdominal segments are longest and bear an intermixture of white, yellowish, and black hairs, with those on the thorax overhanging the head. The larvae are solitary feeders except during outbreaks and are found from July to October. Winter is spent as a pupa in a hairy cocoon and there is one generation per year. This species is occasionally abundant enough to damage shade trees.

The **pale tussock moth**, *Halisidota tesselaris* (J. E. Smith), occurs in southern Canada and throughout the eastern part of the United States. The larvae feed on practically all common, deciduous trees and shrubs. The adult is pale yellow and has a wingspread of about 50 mm. The forewings are translucent and crossed by five broad, darkish bands. Full-grown larvae are darkish and densely clothed with compact tufts of light yellow or dirty white fine hairs. Black pencils rise in pairs from the second and third thoracic and eighth abdominal segments (fig. 113). Adults appear in June and July and the larvae, which usually feed singly, are present from August to October. The winter is spent as a pupa in a brownish, hairy cocoon, and there is one generation per year. This species is frequently abundant in the forest and along roadsides in the South Central States, but is usually of minor importance.

FIGURE 112.—Larvae of the hickory tussock moth, *Halisidota caryae*.

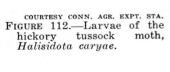

FIGURE 113.—Larva of the pale
moth, *Halisidota tessellaris.*

The **sycamore tussock moth,** *Halisidota harrisii* (Walsh), feeds
on sycamore and London plane trees, and it probably occurs
wherever sycamore grows in this country. Adults are indistinguishable from those of the pale tussock moth, and the larvae
of the two species differ only in color. Those of this species have
yellowish bodies clothed in whitish to yellow hairs and their long
hair pencils are orange-colored. Infestations are often heavy on
shade and ornamental sycamore in the Northeast.

The **fall webworm,** *Hyphantria cunea* (Drury), occurs throughout the United States and southern Canada. Its hosts include
more than 100 species of forest and shade trees. The adult has a
wingspread of 30 to 42 mm., and the bases of the front legs are
orange or bright red. In the southern part of its range, the moth
is white, usually with dark spots on the wings. In the North,
particularly in eastern Canada, it is nearly always pure white
and is often referred to as *H. textor* Harris. Full-grown larvae
are usually pale yellowish or greenish, with a broad dusky stripe
down the back and a yellowish stripe down each side. They are
about 25 mm. long. The larvae of the *textor* form are dark. Their
bodies are covered with long silky, gray hairs arising in tufts
from orange-yellow or black tubercles.

Adults appear mostly from May to July and deposit their eggs
in hair-covered masses of several hundred eggs each, usually on
the undersides of leaves. Newly-hatched larvae immediately begin
to spin a silken web over the foliage on which they feed; and,
as they grow, they enlarge the web to enclose more and more
foliage (fig. 114). On heavily infested trees several branches may
be enclosed in webs. Small trees are often enclosed entirely. The

F-519570

FIGURE 114.—Defoliation and webbing caused by the fall webworm, *Hyphantria cunea*.

larvae are gregarious until the last instar. During the early instars they feed on the upper surface of the leaves; later they devour entire leaves excepting the larger veins and midribs. As they approach maturity, some of them leave the web and feed individually. Pupation occurs in thin cocoons usually spun in the duff or just beneath the surface of the soil. There are one or two generations per year, depending on location.

The fall webworm is ordinarily of no great importance as a forest pest since it usually attacks understory, weed species of no economic value. Outbreaks may occur, however, sometimes encompassing tracts several miles in extent. It is often a serious pest of shade trees and ornamentals. These trees may not only be heavily or completely defoliated, but the presence of numerous, unsightly webs detracts greatly from their esthetic value. Oliver[11] discussed the ecology of the species in the Deep South, and (*575*) its natural and biological control in Louisiana. Tothill (*715*) discussed its natural and biological control in Canada.

Seirarctica echo (J. E. Smith) larvae feed on the foliage of persimmon, ground oak, and sabal palmettos from Florida to Mississippi. The adult is white and has a wingspread of about 55 mm. The wing veins are edged with dark brown or black. Full-grown larvae are clothed with coarse, black-tipped hairs and are about 50 mm. long. The body is black on top except for a pair of yellowish stripes and a row of orange-colored warts that cross each segment.

Other species of arctiids likely to be encountered in eastern forests include: *Haploa clymene* (Brown)—on maple, hickory, and apple; *H. lecontei* (Guer.)—on maple, birch, oak, and cherry; *Apantesis radians* (Wlk.)—on slash pine seedlings in Georgia; and *Lexis bicolor* Grt—on balsam fir and spruce.

[11] Oliver, A.D. 1963. An ecological study of the fall webworm, *Hyphantria cunea* (Drury), in Louisiana. PhD Thesis, Louisiana state Univ.

FAMILY NOCTUIDAE

UNDERWING MOTHS

This is the largest of all the families of Lepidoptera in North America. The adults are mostly nocturnal in habit. The majority of the moths attracted to lights at night belong to this group. The larvae are usually dull-colored and naked. Many are foliage feeders, some are borers, and others gnaw in fruits. Many are found on the foliage of forest and shade trees and shrubs, but they usually do not cause serious damage. Other species attack seedlings in nurseries and young trees in plantations and occasionally cause serious injury. This family has received extensive treatment by Smith and Dyar (658), Crumb (176), and Knutson (433).

The genus *Acronicta* contains upwards of 100 species, many of which feed on the foliage of forest and shade trees. Some are known as "dagger moths" because of the presence of a dagger-like mark near the anal angle of the forewing.

The **American dagger moth,** *Acronicta americana* (Harr.), occurs throughout eastern United States and from Newfoundland to Alberta, Canada. Its hosts include a wide variety of hardwoods such as boxelder, basswood, red and sugar maples, white and yellow birch, elm, ash, oak, willow, hickory, and sycamore. Full-grown larvae are about 50 mm. long. They are clothed with fine, yellowish hairs and there are long, black hair pencils on the backs of abdominal segments one, three, and eight. Larvae are present from June to October, and winter is spent in the pupal stage in dense silken cocoons. During an outbreak in Maine in 1945, larvae were so abundant that they literally swarmed all over buildings and gardens.

The **cottonwood dagger moth,** *Acronicta lepusculina* Guen., occurs from coast to coast in southern Canada and the Northern States. Its favorite hosts appear to be trembling aspen and willow, but it also occasionally infests other species of poplar. Full-grown larvae are clothed with long, soft, yellowish hairs and are about 37 mm. long. There are single, long, black hair pencils on the backs of abdominal segments one, three, four, five and eight. Larvae are present from July to October. Winter is spent in a cocoon composed of silk and bits of wood.

Many other species of *Acronicta* are also found on trees in eastern forests. Some of these with some of their more common tree hosts are as follows: *A. innotata* Guen.—hickory and birch; *A. morula* Grote & Rob.—elm and basswood; *A. interrupta* Guen. elm, cherry, birch, and apple; *A. lithospila* Grote—hickory and oak; *A. funeralis* Grote & Rob.—hickory, elm, and birch; *A. modica* Wlk.—oak; *A. retardata* (Wlk.)—maple; *A. leporina vulpina* (Grote)—poplar, willow, and birch; *A. distans* (Grote) — birch, cherry, poplar, willow, apple, and alder; and the **smeared dagger moth,** *A. oblinita* (J. E. Smith)—usually hebaceous vegetation but also occasionally poplar, willow, boxelder, wild cherry, alder, and apple.

The genus *Catocala* contains many large, conspicuous species, the larvae of which feed on the foliage of various forest trees and shrubs. As a group, they are of little economic importance. The forewings are usually grayish and mottled with lighter and darker spots. This makes them very inconspicuous when they are resting with their wings folded on the trunks of trees. The hindwings, in contrast, are beautifully marked with bright red, yellow, white, or brown. This has given rise to the common name "underwing moths." More than 50 species have been recorded from New York State alone, mostly on oak and hickory. Barnes and McDunnough (*33*) discussed the life histories of many species.

Many other species of noctuids' are commonly known as **cutworms**. The larvae are usually stout, naked, and dull grayish or brownish in color. They are seldom seen, however, because of their habit of feeding at night and hiding on the ground or under bark during the daytime. A number of species feed on the roots, or on portions of stems or foliage near the ground; many others climb the stems or trunks of their hosts and feed on buds, flowers, fruit, and other succulent parts.

The more important species of cutworms in nurseries and forests in eastern America and some of their hosts are as follows: *Feralia jocosa* (Guen.)—hemlock, spruce, larch; *Epizeuxis semula* (Hbn.)—spruce (particularly in ornamental plantings, the larvae commonly being found in webbed masses of dried needles and frass on the branches) ; *Panthea furcilla* (Pack.)—pines; *P. acronyctoides* (Wlk.)—spruce; *Papaipema furcata* (Sm.)—ash seedlings in nurseries in the Lake States; *Colocasia propinquilinea* (Grote)—birch, beech, maple, walnut; *C. flavicornis* (Sm.)—hickory; *Charadra deridens* (Guen.)—oak, maple, elm, birch; *Raphia frater* Grote—poplar, willow; *Euxoa scandens* (Riley)—young white and overcup oaks (serious defoliation reported in Minnesota) ; the **zebra caterpillar,** *Ceramica picta* (Harr.)—usually most abundant on herbacious vegetation, but occasionally damages pine seedlings in nurseries in the Northern Great Plains; *Orthosia hibisci* (Guen.)—the opening buds and fruit of many deciduous trees and shrubs and a few conifers; *Lithophane latincerea* Grt.—many species of deciduous trees (severe defoliation of red maples on islands in Penobscot River, Maine, since 1935) ; the **green fruitworm,** *L.* (=*Grapholitha*) *antennata* (Wlk.) —ash, boxelder (has occurred in large numbers locally in New York and Vermont) ; *Anomogyna eliminata* Gn—various conifers, especially balsam fir and jack pine (one of the most common of the cutworm larvae on conifers in the Northeast) ; and *Palthis angulalis* Hbn.—a wide variety of conifers, especially balsam fir and white spruce,also occasionally on various deciduous trees.

Clean cultivation is recommended for preventing the development of damaging populations of cutworms in forest nurseries.

FAMILY NOTODONTIDAE

NOTODONTID MOTHS

More than 100 species of notodontid moths occur in the United States and Canada, and many of the larvae feed on the foliage of a wide variety of deciduous trees and shrubs. The family name refers to the fact that in some species there are backward-projecting tufts on the hind margin of the wings which protrude when the wings are folded. The larvae are usually solitary, but some are nest builders. When disturbed, they often elevate each end of the body and remain attached by the four pairs of prolegs at the middle of the body, Many feed exposed on the foliage; others feed from within folded leaves or tents.

The **poplar tent maker,** *Ichthyura inclusa* Hbn., occurs in southern Canada and from New England to Georgia and Colorado and feeds on various species of poplar and willow. The adult is brownish-gray, with three whitish lines crossing each forewing, and it has a wingspread of about 25 mm. There is a crest of dark brown hairs on the front of the thorax, and the hindwing is crossed by a wavy band. Full-grown larvae are brownish to nearly black and up to 42 mm. in length. There are four lines of light yellow on top, and one bright and several indistinct lines and yellow marks are on the sides. Also, there are black tubercles on the tops of the first and eighth abdominal segments.

Adults appear from March to July and from July to August, depending on location. Eggs are laid in clusters on the undersides of leaves. The larvae are gregarious and live in tents or webs which they construct by pulling together the edges of one or more leaves and lining them with silk (fig. 115). They feed from May to October, then crawl to the ground and pupate in loose cocoons to spend the winter. Old, abandoned nests often remain on trees throughout the winter. There are one and a partial second or two generations per year. This species often seriously defoliates

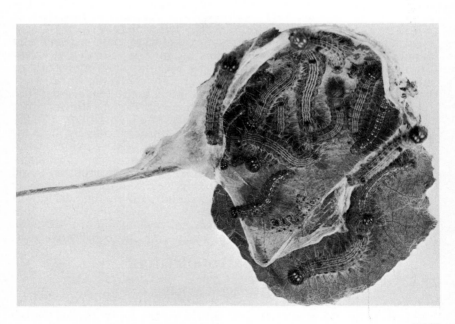

F-519526

FIGURE 115.—Nest of the poplar tent maker, *Ichthyura inclusa*, torn open to show the larvae.

small groups of trees, especially trees growing more or less in the open. Twigs supporting large webs sag badly.

Other species of *Ichthyura* frequently encountered are *I. albosigma* Fitch on aspen; and *I. apicalis* Wlkr., *I. brucei* Hy. Edw., and *I. strigosa* Grote on aspen and willow. None are very important.

The **yellow-necked caterpillar**, *Datana ministra* (Drury), occurs in southern Canada and throughout most of eastern United States. Its food plants include many species of fruit, shade, and forest trees. Important forest and shade tree hosts include white and yellow birch, basswood, elm, oak, maple, butternut, walnut, mountain ash, hop hornbeam, and honey locust. The adult has a wingspread of about 50 mm., and its forewings are cinnamon-brown, marked with irregular dark lines. Full-grown larvae are about 50 mm. long and are moderately clothed with long, soft, white hairs. The head is jet black; the prothorax, bright orange-yellow; and the body is marked longitudinally with alternate yellow or whitish and black stripes.

Adults appear during June and July. Eggs are laid in masses of 100 or more each on the undersides of the leaves. The larvae feed in colonies (fig. 116.) near the ends of twigs and branches. When disturbed, they elevate both ends of the body. At maturity, they drop to and enter the soil to depths of 2 to 4 inches where they pupate and spend the winter. There is one generation per year.

Damage is seldom serious in the forest, although heavily infested trees may be completely defoliated. Fruit, shade, and ornamental trees are injured most severely. Two species of tachinid parasites, *Compsilura concinnata* Meig. and *Winthemia datanae* Town. are important natural enemies.

Datana angusi G. & R. feeds on hickories, oaks, beech, gray birch, and butternut and occurs throughout eastern United States, west to Illinois, and along the north shore of Lake Erie in Ontario, Canada. Full-grown larvae resemble those of *D. ministra*, but differ in having an entirely black cervical shield.

FIGURE 116.—Cluster of larvae of the yellow-necked caterpillar, *Datana ministra*.

311

Datana perspicua G. & R., **the sumac datana,** feeds on sumac throughout most of eastern United States and in southern Canada. Full-grown larvae are moderately hairy and about 50 mm. long. The head is dark reddish to black, the cervical shield reddish brown, and the anal plate, blackish. The body is deep straw or lemon yellow, with 11 longitudinal, dark reddish-brown to blackish stripes.

Datana contracta Wlkr. feeds on oak and sycamore in eastern United States west to the Lake States and Arkansas. Full-grown larvae are about 50 mm. long and clothed with long, white hairs. The body is black with 11 longitudinal, yellowish-white stripes.

Datana drexeli Hy. Edw. feeds on basswood, walnut, sassafras, and witch-hazel from the Atlantic Coast to Ohio. Full-grown larvae are moderately hairy and about 50 mm. long. The head and body are black; the cervical shield and front of the thorax honey yellow; and the body bears 11 longitudinal stripes.

The **walnut caterpillar,** *Datana integerrima* G. & R., occurs commonly in southern Ontario and throughout eastern United States where it feeds on a wide variety of deciduous trees, preferably walnut, butternut, pecan, and hickory. Adults are stout-bodied, have wingspreads of about 50 mm., and are clothed with dull brown to chestnut brown scales. The forewings are brownish and crossed by dark, irregular lines. Full-grown larvae are up to 50 mm. long. The body is black with longitudinal, yellowish stripes and is covered with long white, or dirty gray hairs.

Adults are present during the spring and summer. Egg laying begins in early June, the eggs being deposited in masses on the undersides of leaves. The larvae feed in colonies until almost full grown (fig. 117). They are often found in masses on the trunk

FIGURE 117.—Colony of larvae of the walnut caterpillar, *Datan integerrima.*

and larger limbs where they congregate to molt. Later, they return to the foliage to continue their feeding. Full-grown larvae drop to the ground and wander about searching for pupation sites. At this time they are often found in large numbers along the foundation walls of houses. Pupation occurs in the soil and there are one or two generations per year, depending on locality (*323*).

The walnut caterpillar is frequently a serious pest of walnut. Trees heavily defoliated 2 or more years in succession are seriously injured or killed. Isolated trees or trees growing in small groups are especially subject to heavy attack. Losses have been particularly severe in the Central States.

Datana major G. & R. feeds on azalea and apple and various shrubs from the East Coast to Illinois. Full-grown larvae have mahogany red heads, cervical shields, and legs. Their bodies are marked with longitudinal, yellow lines broken with black, giving them a finely spotted appearance.

Hyperaeschra stragula (Grote) has been recorded from southern Canada and the Northern States, where it feeds on willow and aspen. Full-grown larvae are about 37 mm. long. The head is flattened in front and slightly bilobed. The body is mostly pearly gray with a reddish-brown dorsal line between the head and second tubercle. The second and third abdominal segments each bears a conical tubercle directed backward, and there is a prominent, pale rust hump on the eighth abdominal segment. Larvae are found from June to October and the winter is spent as a pupa in the ground. There are one and sometimes a second generation per year.

Pheosia rimosa Pack. Occurs rarely in eastern Canada and from Coast to Coast in northern United States. Its hosts are recorded as poplars, especially trembling aspen, and willow. Full-grown larvae are lead-colored with a purplish tinge and about 43 mm. long. The body segments are slightly smaller at the middle, and the eighth segment bears a well-developed horn. Larvae are present from July to October, depending on locality, and the winter is spent as a pupa in the ground. There may be one or two generations per year.

Lophodonta angulosa (J. E. Smith) occurs from southeastern Canada to Florida and Texas and feeds on various species of oaks. Full-grown larvae are pea green and about 37 mm. long. The body is marked with a faint, double, whitish line down the middle of the back, and a distinct reddish stripe down each side. Larvae may be found from May to October, and winter is spent in silken cocoons on the ground. There are two generations per year in the South, but only one in the North. *L. ferruginea* Pack. occurs on paper birch in the Northeastern States and southeastern Canada.

Nadata gibbosa (J. E. Smith) occurs from Coast to Coast in southern Canada and throughout the United States. The larvae feed on the foliage of a wide variety of deciduous trees such as various species of oaks, red and sugar maples, beech, paper birch, and willow. Full-grown larvae are pale pea green, have large, rounded heads and tapering bodies, and are about 43 mm. long. The spiracles are deep red, and there is a yellowish stripe along each side. Larvae may be found from May to October, and winter is spent as a pupa in the ground. There may be two generations per year as far north as New England.

Nerice bidentata Wlkr. feeds on elm in southern Ontario and from New England to the Lake States and Kansas. Full-grown larvae are bluish-green and about 30 mm. long. There are four white bands on the front and sides of the head, and there is a large forward-pointing tubercle on each of the first eight abdominal segments, and a pair of small ones, on the ninth. Larvae are present from June to September, and the winter is spent in silken cocoons on the ground. There are one or one and a partial second generations per year.

Symmerista canicosta Franclemont [=*albicosta* (Hbn.)], the **red-humped oakworm,** occurs in southeastern Canada and throughout much of northeastern United States. Its hosts are various oaks, preferably white and bur, and several other deciduous trees such as basswood, sugar maple, paper birch, beech, and elm. An outbreak covering several thousands of acres of oak type occurred in Michigan in 1957 and 1958. The adult is ash gray, with a long, white area near the outer two-thirds of the costal margin of each forewing, and it has a wingspread of 37 to 50 mm. The full-grown larva has a rounded, orange-red head and a yellowish body that increases in width back to an orange-red enlargement on the eighth abdominal segment. The body is also marked with fine black dorsal lines (fig. 118).

Adults appear from May to July and the female deposits her eggs in masses on the undersides of leaves. The larva feed gregariously at first and skeletonize the foliage. Later, they scatter out and feed singly, devouring entire leaves except the larger veins. Mature larvae move to the ground and spin cocoons in rolled leaves where they pupate and spend the winter. There appears to be one generation per year.

Populations are usually too light to cause serious injury. Sometimes though, they are heavy enough to cause severe defoliation in isolated spots.

Symmerista albifrons (J. E. Smith) occurs in southern United States. Its hosts are much the same as those of the red-humped oakworm, a species with which it is easily confused both in appearance and habits. At least 12,000 acres of northern hardwoods were defoliated in Upper Michigan and Wisconsin during an outbreak in 1961. There are two generations per year. The **orange-humped mapleworm,** *S. leucitys* Franclemont, occurs in the

F-519531
FIGURE 118.—Larvae of *Symmerista canicosta,* the red-humped oakworm.

314

Northern States and southern Canada where it feeds principally on sugar maple. Its life history and habits are similar to those of the red-humped oakworm.

The **variable oak leaf caterpillar,** *Heterocampa manteo* (Dbldy.), occurs in nearly all of the States and Canadian Provinces east of a line drawn from western Ontario through eastern Texas. Its hosts include a wide variety of deciduous trees. All species of oaks are attacked, but white oak is preferred. Other important species attacked include beech, basswood, paper birch, American elm, walnut, boxelder, persimmon, and apple (*771*). The adult is ashy gray and has a wingspread of about 37 to 42 mm. (fig. 119 A). Full-grown larvae are yellowish green and about 37 mm. long. The body is variously marked, usually with a broad band down the back (fig. 119 B).

Pupation occurs in early spring, and the adults appear from early in May in the South to late May or early June in the North. Eggs are deposited singly on the leaves, each female laying up to 500 eggs. Young larvae skeletonize the lower surfaces of the leaves and older ones eat entire leaves, excepting the larger veins. Mature larvae move to the ground and spin cocoons in the litter or top soil. Winter is spent in the prepupal stage. There are two generations per year in the South and one in the North.

Trees of all sizes are attacked, and heavy defoliation may occur anywhere in the insect's range, especially in the South. Some outbreaks have been extensive, covering millions of acres and extending for hundreds of miles. Tree mortality has usually not been serious, however, since most trees of sapling size or larger are able to withstand several years of extensive defoliation.

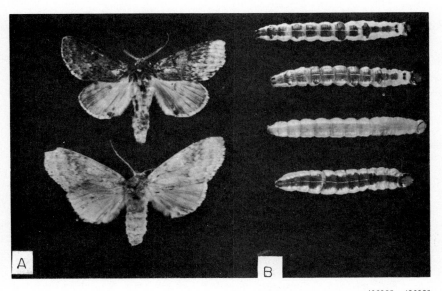

F-496932, 496931

FIGURE 119.—The variable oak leaf caterpillar, *Heterocampa manteo*: A, adults; B, larvae.

The **saddled prominent,** *Heterocampa guttivitta* (Wlkr.), occurs in southeastern Canada and throughout eastern United States. Beech, paper birch, and sugar maple are its preferred hosts, but practically all other species of deciduous trees are fed upon in heavily infested stands, particularly the oaks and poplar. The adult is greenish gray or brownish gray with splotches of creamy-white, and has a wingspread of about 50 mm. Full-grown larvae are usually green with purple, gold, and brown markings on the back, and they are about 30 mm. long (fig. 120).

Adults emerge in late May or early June and the female deposits up to 500 eggs singly on the leaves. Young larvae skeletonize the upper surface of leaves; older ones eat the entire leaf except the principal veins. They often migrate from tree to tree and where abundant may collect in large numbers about the bases of defoliated trees. Pupation occurs in the leafmold from mid-July until late August. Winter is spent in the pupal stage. There is one generation per year in the northern parts of the insect's range.

Many outbreaks have been recorded since the turn of the century (*148, 582*), during which heavy defoliation occurred over large forested areas. In areas suffering two consecutive years of defoliation, considerable tree mortality occurred. Many of the trees that survived lost some of their large branches as well as large portions of their tops.

Other species of *Heterocampa* likely to be encountered in eastern forests include: *H. umbrata* Wlkr.—oak and maple; *H. biundata* Wlkr.—beech, paper birch, wild black cherry, and maple; and *H. bilineata* (Pack.)—elm and birch.

Fentonia marthesia (Cram.) occurs from Maine to Florida and Texas and feeds on the leaves of beech, maple, aspen, oak, and sycamore. Full-grown larvae are pale green and up to 50 mm. long. The head is flat in front, there is a small, double reddish tubercle on the prothorax, and the body is marked with a longitudinal, yellowish white stripe and occasional pink spots on the back. Larvae feed from July to October then spin cocoons between leaves on the ground in which to pupate and spend the winter.

Dicentria lignicolor (Wlkr.) feeds on various species of oaks and beech throughout eastern United States. The larva is about 37 mm. long and resembles larvae of the genus *Schizura*. Its prominent characters include a pale, bilobed head, with dark branched bands on each side of the face meeting on the vertex. There is also a large, slightly cleft tubercle on the first abdominal segment and a smaller brownish one on the eighth abdominal segment. The sides of the thorax are pea green. Adults appear in July and August in the Northeastern States; the larvae, from August to October. Winter is spent in a tough, parchment-like cocoon on the ground.

The **red-humped caterpillar,** *Schizura concinna* (J. E. Smith), occurs throughout the United States and in most of the Canadian Provinces. Its hosts include fruit trees and a long list of forest and shade trees, such as elm, trembling aspen, willow, hickory, black locust, dogwood, sweetgum, persimmon, and paper birch. The adult is grayish brown and has a wingspread of about 30 mm. Full-grown larvae are about 25 mm. long. The head and a hump on the eighth abdominal segment are red; the body is marked with black and yellowish lines and bears a double row of short, stout, black lines on top (fig. 121). When at rest, the larva holds the rear end in an elevated position, and, when handled, it gives off a pungent, disagreeable odor.

Adults appear from late May to August depending on locality. Eggs are laid in masses containing up to 100 eggs each on the undersides of leaves. The larvae are gregarious. At first, they skeletonize the undersurfaces of the leaves. Later, they devour entire leaves, except the midrib. During their feeding, they completely defoliate one branch before moving on to another. Mature larvae move to the ground and construct parchment-like cocoons in the duff in which to spend the winter. There is one generation per year.

Populations are often heavy in unsprayed apple orchards, along roadsides and fence rows, and on ornamentals. In light infestations or on ornamentals, it is often practicable to collect and destroy the colonies as soon as they are discovered.

Three other eastern species of *Schizura* are sometimes common locally: the **unicorn caterpillar**, *S. unicornis* (J. E. Smith), *S. leptinoides* (Grote), and *S. ipomaeae* Dbldy. Each species feeds on a wide variety of hosts, such as apple, wild cherry, elm, aspen, hickory, beech, paper birch, and willow.

Gluphisia septentrionis Wlkr. occurs in southeastern Canada and the northern portions of eastern United States. It feeds on various poplars, especially trembling aspen. Full-grown larvae are pale green and about 37 mm. long. The head has blackish stripes on each side; the body is largest in the middle, and is marked with pinkish to reddish blotches on the back and a yellow line along each side. Larvae are found from June to September, and winter is spent in the pupal stage in cocoons on the ground. As a rule, there is one generation per year, but in some localities there may be two.

F-519533
FIGURE 120.—Dorsal and lateral views of larvae of the saddled prominent, *Heterocampa guttivitta*.

COURTESY CONN. AGR. EXPT. STA.
FIGURE 121.—Larva of the redhumped caterpillar, *Schizura concinna*.

The genus *Cerura* is represented in eastern forests by *C. borealis* (Bdv.), *C. occidentalis* Lint., *C. cinerea* Wlkr., and *C. multiscripta* Riley. The first feeds on aspen, willow, and black cherry; the last three on aspen and willow. *Notodonta simplaria* Graef. also feeds on aspen and willow. *Misogada unicolor* (Pack.) occurs on sycamore, and *Hyparpax aurora* (J. E. Smith) and *H. perophoroides* (Stecker) are found on oak.

FAMILY LYMANTRIIDAE

TUSSOCK MOTHS

This family includes some of the most serious tree defoliators in the United States. The female moths of certain species are wingless; others, though winged, are so heavy bodied that they are either unable to fly, or can fly for only short distances. The remainder are strong fliers. The females of some species pack and cover their eggs with their abdominal hairs; others coat their eggs with a viscid secretion which hardens and forms a protective covering. The hairs of certain species are poisonous in all stages to man when they come into contact with skin. The larvae of our native species also bear conspicuous tufts of hairs on top of certain body segments.

The **rusty tussock moth**, *Orgyia* (=*Notolophus*) *antiqua* (Linn.), an introduced species, occurs throughout southern Canada and in the northern part of the United States. Its hosts include scores of species of both deciduous and coniferous trees. The male adult is rusty colored. The forewings are crossed by two darker bands and each bears a conspicuous white spot near the border. Females are gray and wingless. Full-grown larvae are about 28 mm. long and have black heads and dark-gray bodies. The second abdominal segment bears a black hair pencil on each side, and there are reddish-orange tubercles bearing hairs. The tufts on the prothorax and abdomen are similar to those on the larvae of the white-marked tussock moth. The female deposits her eggs in a single-layered, naked mass on the cocoon from which she emerges. There are one and possibly two generations per year north to New England. This species is sometimes abundant locally. Conspicuous defoliation has been recorded in Canada.

The **white-marked tussock moth**, *Hemerocampa leucostigma* (J. E. Smith), occurs commonly throughout eastern United States and eastern Canada and feeds on a wide variety of deciduous and coniferous trees. Preferred species appear to include the following: apple, basswood, elm, and poplar; Norway, silver, and sycamore maples; sycamore, paper, and yellow birches; larch; and balsam fir. The female adult is wingless, grayish to light-brown, hairy, and about 12 mm. long. Males are ashy-gray and have fully-developed wings, spanning about 30 mm. The forewing has a conspicuous, white spot near the anal angle, and is marked with dark wavy bands. Full-grown larvae (fig. 122) have coral-red heads and thoracic shields, yellow to cream-colored bodies, and are about 25 to 37 mm. long. There is a pair of upright pencils of black hairs on the prothorax and another black tuft on the eighth abdominal segment. There are also brush-like tufts of white or

318

FIGURE 122.—Larvae of the white-marked tussock moth, *Hemerocampa leucostigma*.

yellowish hairs on each of the first four abdominal segments and reddish dots on the sixth and seventh segments. The sides of the body are clothed in white and blackish hairs radiating from rows of small yellow tubercles.

Winter is spent in the egg stage and hatching occurs between April and June. Young larvae feed on the surface of the leaves, skeletonizing them. Later, they chew holes in other leaves and finally consume all but the larger veins. Young larvae often spin down on silken threads and are sometimes transported considerable distances by the wind. The larvae become full-grown in 5 or 6 weeks, then, under branches or in bark crevices, they spin grayish cocoons consisting of silk and hairs from the body. The pupal stage lasts about 2 weeks, and the number of generations per year varies from one in the northern parts of the insect's range to three in the South.

The white-marked tussock moth is a pest of shade trees, particularly American elm, in cities and towns. It also occurs in forested areas but usually causes minor damage there. Howard (*382, 383*) discussed the life history, habits, and parasites of the species.

Hemerocampa definita (Pack.), the **definite-marked tussock moth,** occurs in southern Ontario and several of the Eastern States and feeds on quite a wide variety of deciduous trees such as willow, apple, wild cherry, elm, paper birch, red oak, red maple, and ash. The adults and larvae closely resemble those of the white-marked tussock moth in form and size, and in the arrangement of the tufts of hairs on the larvae. Wingless females are clothed in golden-brown hairs. They lay their eggs in masses on the cocoons from which they emerge, covering them with hairs from their bodies. In the Northeastern States these egg masses are often mistaken for those of the gypsy moth. In addition to the conspicuous pencils and tufts of hair, the larva is yellow, with a faint dorsal stripe and a black spot behind each of the second and third tufts of hair on the abdomen. This species is seldom of economic importance.

The genus *Dasychira* is represented in eastern forests by a number of species, a few of which are economically important. Adults of the different species are very similar in appearance and are difficult to distinguish. In both sexes, they are winged, and

319

the females are heavy bodied. The larvae have tufts of hairs characteristic of the tussock moth group and their bodies are densely clothed with hairs. In some species there is a feathery black hair in each lateral tuft.

Dasychira basiflava (Pack.), the **dark tussock moth,** is sometimes locally common in the Eastern States, where it feeds on various deciduous trees such as slippery elm, white oak, beech, flowering dogwood, and hickory. The head of the larva is hidden by yellowish clusters of barbed spines, and there are tufts of hairs on the first and fourth abdominal segments. Heavy infestations on valuable shade and ornamental trees may cause serious damage.

The **pine tussock moth,** *Dasychira* (=*Olene*) *plagiata* (Walker), occurs in the Northeastern States west to the Lake States and in southeastern Canada. The larvae feed on various conifers such as jack pine, red pine, eastern white pine, spruce, and fir. Jack pine is especially favored. The moth is gray-brown with lighter and darker stripes across the forewings and has a wing expanse of 25 to 37 mm. Full grown larvae are gray-brown and about 37 mm. long. There are four tufts of grayish or brownish hairs on the dorsum. The first tuft has two black hair pencils on the front and three similar ones on the rear.

Adults are present from early July to early August in the Lake States. Eggs are usually deposited in small, irregular clusters on or near the female pupal case, mostly on the needles near midcrown but also on the trunk, dead twigs, and similar vegetation. Young larvae feed on the flat surfaces of needles. During August, second or third instar larvae spin a few silken threads about themselves and go into hibernation. They may be found beneath rough bark on large trees or between the bases of needles on young, smooth-bark trees. Feeding is resumed in the spring on staminate flowers and young needles. Later, old needles are also attacked, with everything being consumed down to the needle sheath. In heavy infestations the entire tree may be completely defoliated. Full-grown larvae spin silken cocoons on twigs or among needles. There is one generation per year (*736*).

Several extensive outbreaks have occurred in the Lake States since the turn of the century, and losses, especially of jack pine, have been serious. During 1961-62, outbreaks covering tens of thousands of acres of jack pine, red pine, and white spruce were recorded in the region.

Other eastern species of *Dasychira* are as follows: *D. atomaria* (Wlkr.), and *D. vagans* (B. & McD.)—sometimes fairly abundant on oaks in the Northeast; *D. meridionalis* (B. & McD.)—on oak in the Southeast; *D. cinnamomea* (G. & R.)—on elm from New England to the Lake States; and *D. tephra* Hbn.—on oak in Maine and southern Canada.

The **gypsy moth,** *Porthetria dispar* (L.), was introduced into the United States in 1869 when a French scientist brought a number of egg clusters from France for the purpose of crossing the species with the silk worm. During the course of his work, some of the eggs were spilled or lost or some of the larvae escaped, and the species became established. About 20 years later, it had spread over an area of about 350 square miles around Boston, and shade and fruit trees were being completely defoliated. During the next 5 years, it spread rapidly, and populations increased enormously. Since that time, it has continued to spread, but at a far less rapid rate. It now occurs throughout the New England States, except northern New Hampshire, Maine, and northeastern Vermont. It also occurs in eastern New York, northern New Jersey, northeastern Pennsylvania, southeastern Quebec, and in the vicinity of Lansing, Michigan. Its hosts include most species of hardwoods, the oaks, gray birch, and poplar being most highly favored. Several conifers are also attacked, usually when growing in mixture with the more highly favored hardwoods. Mosher (548) published a list of host plants, dividing them into groups of favorability.

The male of the gypsy moth (fig. 123 A) is dark brown, with blackish bands across the forewings and has a wingspread of about 37 mm. Females (fig. 123 B) are almost white and have

F-489191-5

FIGURE 123.—Life stages of the gypsy moth, *Porthetria dispar:* A, adult male moth; B, adult female moth; C, female pupa and cast larval skin; D, full-grown larva; E, egg mass laid on bark of a white oak tree.

wingspreads of about 50 mm. The female abdomen is clothed in yellowish hairs and is too large and heavy for her to fly. Full-grown larvae (fig. 123 D) are about 37 to 60 mm. long. The head has yellow markings; the body is dusky or sooty-colored and hairy; and there is a double row of 5 pairs of blue spots, followed by a double row of 6 pairs of red spots, on the dorsum. The pupa (fig. 123 C) is reddish brown with a sprinkling of reddish hairs.

Adults appear and mate in late July and August. The males fly vigorously in a zig-zag manner, often within a few feet of the ground on warm days. The females, being unable to fly, crawl a short distance from the empty pupal case and mate. Immediately after mating, they lay their eggs in oval masses, (fig. 123 E) about 100 to 1,000 eggs each then cover them with buff-colored hairs from their abdomens. While the majority of the masses are deposited on the trunks and limbs of trees, many are also laid in various other places such as under stones, inside hollow stumps and trees, on leaves, and even on buildings. The winter is spent in the egg stage, and hatching occurs about the first of May, usually about the time oak leaves unfold.

Young larvae crawl from the egg mass and move towards the tops of trees in search of foliage. During this period they often spin down on silken threads, especially when disturbed, and some may be transported considerable distances by the wind (147). Newly-hatched larvae feed first on leaf bases, then on the leaf surfaces, chewing small holes in the leaves. Older larvae feed almost entirely from the edge of the leaf. During this part of their lives, they feed mostly at night and tend to congregate in sheltered places during the day (259). Large larvae consume entire leaves, except the larger veins and midribs. In heavily infested stands the entire crop of foliage may be consumed before the larvae reach maturity. When this happens, the larvae usually vacate the trees and often migrate considerable distances in search of food. In heavily defoliated stands when the food supply is depleted but not completely consumed before the larvae reach maturity, many succeed in pupating although they are smaller than normal in size. This results in smaller than normal adults, and the number of eggs deposited per female is greatly reduced. Larvae seek sheltered places in which to pupate. Pupae may be found attached by silken threads to limbs and trunks of trees, stones, forest debris, and the like. In heavy infestations, they are often found massed together in large numbers. The pupal stage lasts about 10 days or 2 weeks.

The gypsy moth has long been considered one of the most important forest insects in the United States. Enormous sums of money, probably in excess of 100 million dollars, have been expended since the turn of the century by the Federal Government and the States involved to suppress it and to prevent its further spread. In 1923, a "barrier zone" from 25 to 30 miles wide and about 250 miles long, was established from Long Island to the Canadian border to prevent further western spread of the species by intensive eradication efforts (121). Despite these efforts, outbreaks have continued to occur in the older infested portions of New England, some of which covered tremendous areas, and extensive infested areas occur west of the barrier zone. In 1945, an estimated 1,500,000 acres were defoliated in the New England area. Losses through mortality of defoliated trees have been great. From 1933 to 1952, they amounted to an estimated 2,279,-819 cords and 128,951,000 board-feet of merchantable timber, having a total estimated value of $4,223,556 (*592*).

Gypsy moth damage is not confined to the killing of trees. Heavy losses in reduced growth of surviving trees are also incurred (*592*). Continued defoliation also causes loss of tree vigor, leading to attacks by secondary insects and fungi. Surviving trees are often stunted, ill-formed, and unmerchantable. Further losses result from the reduction in quality of forest sites in stands suffering repeated defoliation.[12] in increased fire damage, in the impairment of watersheds, and in reductions in esthetic, recreational, and wildlife values.

When the gypsy moth was introduced, the insect parasites, predators, and pathogens affecting it in its native habitats abroad were left behind, and it encountered none here that were capable of holding it in check. To remedy this situation, a program of importation of foreign parasites and predators was initiated in 1905 and continued intensively for about 25 years (*128, 387*). Collections representing 45 different species of the parasites and predators were imported, colonies of which were released in infested stands in this country. Nine species of the parasites and two of the predators became established. Two are hymenopterous egg parasites—*Dencyrtus kuwanai* (How.) and *Anastatus disparis* Ruschka; four are tachinid larval parasites—*Compsilura concinnata* (Meig), *Exorista larvarum* (L.), *Parasetigena agilis* (R.-D.), and *Blepharipa scutellata* (R.-D.); three are hymenopterous larval parasites—*Phobocampe disparis* (Vier.), *Apanteles melanoscelus* (Ratz.), and *Monodontomerus aerus* Wlkr.; and two are coleopterous predators—*Calosoma sycophanta* (L.) and *Carabus auratus* (L.). The current status of these enemies of the gypsy moth and effectiveness in its control are discussed by Dowden (*205*).

One of the most important factors affecting heavy gypsy moth populations is the so-called "wilt" disease, caused by a nuclear-polyhedral virus, *Borrelinavirus reprimens*. This pathogen is also a native of Europe. It is believed to have entered this country in gypsy moth larvae imported for the recovery of parasites. During moth epidemics it increases tremendously and practically wipes out populations over large areas. It occurs only rarely in light infestations; thus, is ineffective in preventing outbreaks. Other natural control factors include low winter temperatures—exposed eggs are unable to withstand temperatures lower than —25° F (*697*). Late spring frosts kill newly hatched larvae, and rodents devour large larvae and pupae found on the forest floor. Many larvae also die of starvation in woodlands entirely stripped of foliage before the larvae reach maturity. Bess (*63*) and Campbell (*133*) discuss the population dynamics of the species.

Silvicultural practices designed to promote the health and vigor of stands is helpful in increasing tree resistance to gypsy

---

[12] House, W. P. 1952. Appraisal of damage by the gypsy moth in New England, 1933–52. Unpublished report, U. S. Dep. Agr., Bur. of Entomol. and Plant Quar., Greenfield, Mass., 22 p.

moth damage (*64*). A reduction in the proportion of favored host species also decreases the chances of infestation and limits the degree of population build-up (*53*).

Insecticidal spraying by aircraft has been most widely used in gypsy moth control. Attempts to secure control by spraying an infested stand with the nuclear-polyhedral virus, *Borrelinavirus reprimens* appeared to be successful (*617*). Spraying with the microbial insecticide, *Bacillus thuringiensis thuringiensis* Berliner (*455*) has given promising results. Other promising methods of control include male sterilization by gamma irradiation (*300*), sterilization through the use of chemo-sterilants (*146*), and the use of natural and synthetic sex attractants. The natural female attractant known as gyplure has been isolated, identified, and synthesized (*397*).

The **satin moth**, *Stilpnotia salicis* (L.) (fig. 124), an introduced species first discovered in North America near Boston, Mass., in 1920 (*120*) and in British Columbia during the same year, now occurs throughout most of New England and in the Maritime Provinces of eastern North America. In the West, it has spread southward through western Washington into Northwestern Oregon. The larvae feed on most species of poplar and willow. Adults of both sexes are pure white with a satiny color and have a wingspread of 37 to 50 mm. The head, thorax, and abdomen are black but are so densely clothed with long, satiny-white hairs they appear white. Full-grown larvae are about 34 mm. long. The head is black with a bluish tinge. The body is blackish on top with a row of large white blotches down the middle and a narrow broken line along each side. There is also a transverse row of reddish-brown tubercles on the top of each body segment, each bearing a tuft of yellowish-brown hairs.

Winter is spent in the larval stage. Feeding is resumed in April in New England. Young larvae feed only on the leaf surface, most often on the underside. Partly grown larvae eat small, irregular holes in the leaf, and full-grown larvae devour the entire leaf except the large veins. Feeding is completed by June. Pupation occurs in loosely woven cocoons of silk spun in the leaves or on twigs or other objects. Adults appear in late June and early July. Mostly in July, eggs are deposited on leaves, branches, and trunks of trees or on other surfaces in masses of 100 to 400 eggs each. Each mass is oval, about 9 mm. long, and covered with a glistening white secretion. Hatching occurs in about two weeks. Newly-hatched larvae feed for 5 to 6 days and then spin small webs in which they molt to the second instar. These larvae then feed again for 5 to 6 days. Then they crawl to limbs or the trunk and spin hibernaculae in bark crevices or under loose bark where they remain until the following spring (*123*).

The satin moth is not very important as a forest insect in the Eastern States, although heavy infestations are occasionally reported. From time to time, it seriously defoliates poplars in ornamental plantings. Introduced parasites are generally credited with holding populations to harmless levels (*205*) with some assistance from low winter temperatures, disease, and birds. The hymenopteron, *Apanteles solitarius* (Ratz.), appears to be the most effective parasite; however, the dipteron, *Compsilura con-*

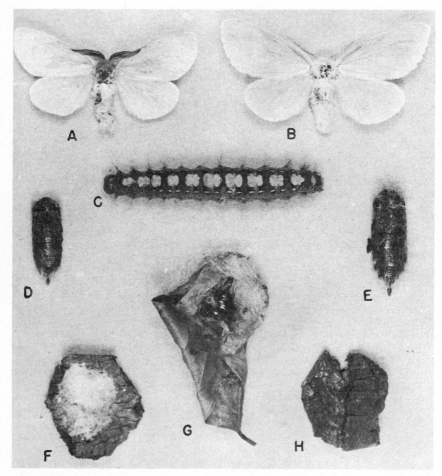

F-519523

FIGURE 124.—The satin moth, *Stilpnotia salicis:* A, male adult; B, female adult; C, larva; D, male pupa; E, female pupa; F, egg cluster; G, cocoon; H, hibernating web on bark.

cinnata Meig. and the hymenopteron, *Eupteromalus nidulans* (Thomson) are also important.

The **brown-tail moth,** *Nygmia phaeorrhoea* (Donov), (fig. 125) an introduced species, was first recorded in North America in Somerville, Mass., in 1897. During the next few years, it increased enormously and spread rapidly. By 1905, it was extremely abundant throughout Rhode Island, eastern Massachusetts, southern New Hampshire, and southwestern Maine, and had been recorded as far north as New Brunswick and Nova Scotia. Ten years later, most of the area east of the Connecticut River, with the exception of northern New Hampshire and Maine, was heavily infested. Infestations also occurred in Vermont and west of the Connecticut River in Massachusetts and Connecticut. Since

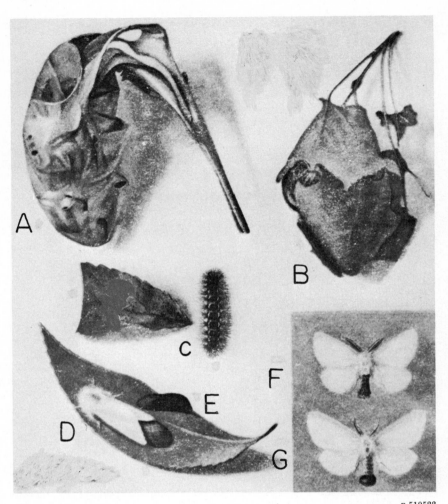

F-519522

FIGURE 125.—The brown-tail moth, *Nygmia phaeorrhoea:* A, a winter nest; B, cocoon in leaves; C, mature larva; D, female depositing egg mass; E, egg mass on leaf; F, male adult; G, female adult.

then, the area and intensity of infestations have declined greatly. Since the late fifties, infestations have been recorded from only a few coastal counties in Maine and New Hampshire and from Cape Cod. During the first several years following its introduction, its hosts were recorded as several species of deciduous trees, principally apple, pear, plum, oak, willow, elm, and maple. At present, infestations occur almost entirely in old, abandoned apple orchards and on beach plum.

Brown-tail moth adults are pure white, except for the tip of the abdomen, which is covered with brown hairs. The female is rather heavy-bodied and has a wingspread of about 37 mm. Males are more slender and somewhat smaller. Full-grown larvae are about 37 mm. The head is light brown; the body is dark brown to almost black with a broken white line on either side and two conspicuous red spots near the posterior end. There are also numerous tubercles with long, barbed hairs and many short, brown hairs on the dorsum and sides. These hairs are poisonous to man and cause a severe rash when they come in contact with the skin.

Adults appear in early July, and the female deposits her eggs in elongate oval masses from 12 to 18 mm. long on the undersides of leaves. Each mass contains about 300 eggs and is covered with brown hairs from the female's abdomen. Young larvae feed gregariously on the surface of the leaves. Later, they tie two or more leaves together with silk near the tip of a branch. Then they spin a web over the outside of these leaves and fasten them securely to the twig, thereby forming a tough, grayish web from 2 to 6 inches long where they spend the winter. Feeding is resumed in the spring, and the larvae become full-grown by mid-June. Pupation occurs in silken cocoons spun usually among the leaves at the tips of twigs (*121*).

The brown-tail moth, although one of the better known forest and shade tree insects in eastern United States, is no longer of economic importance. For some undetermined reason, it has almost disappeared. Introduced parasites, many of which became established (*205*), and a fungus disease probably helped toward its control, but it seems unlikely that they were primarily responsible for its decline.

FAMILY LASIOCAMPIDAE

Tent Caterpillar Moths and Allies

The family Lasiocampidae is represented in North America by less than 30 species, several of which are important economic pests of trees. The moths are medium-sized and stout-bodied; the body, legs, and eyes are hairy; and the antennae are somewhat feathery. The larvae vary in form from nearly cylindrical to very much flattened; they are very hairy.

The majority of important species belong to the genus *Malacosoma* Hubner, and are commonly known as **tent caterpillars**. Four and a possible fifth species occur in eastern United States and eastern Canada. The remaining eleven North American species have a western distribution. The genus was recently revised by Stehr and Cook (*687*). They include keys to the adults, mature larvae, and egg masses of all species. They also discussed their distribution, their hosts, and some of their habits.

Eggs of tent caterpillar moths are laid either in flattened masses on the bark of limbs or trunks of trees or in masses that may encircle small twigs. The number of eggs per mass ranges from 100 to 400, usually from 150 to 250. As the eggs are deposited, they are held in place by a frothy substance called spumaline (*358*). The majority of species also cover their eggs with this material. Hatching occurs in the spring, about the time the new leaves of the host tree appear. Young larvae feed first on egg shells, then on the buds and young leaves. Those of tent-building species also begin immediately to construct a tent on a branch or in a nearby crotch. They do not feed from within the tent, but on the leaves of neighboring branches. As they crawl to these branches, they spin strands of silk which they usually follow in returning to the tent, where they remain during periods between feedings. Species that do not construct tents assemble in clusters on branches and trunks during periods between feedings. Toward the end of an instar they spin nests of silk on branches and trunks on which they congregate to molt.

The larvae usually pass through five or six instars. By the time the last instar is reached, they are no longer gregarious, and they travel extensively in search of food. At this time, they are not very selective in their food requirements and will feed on a wide variety of hosts. When their food supply becomes scarce, they may migrate in search of other food, often for considerable distances. When they reach maturity, they spin cocoons in which to pupate. The cocoons are about 1-inch long, fairly loosely constructed, and white or yellow because of a powdery material dispersed between strands of silk. Cocoons may be found within the old tents, inside logs, beneath loose bark, and between folded leaves.

The **eastern tent caterpillar,** *Malacosoma americanum* (F.) (fig. 126), is generally distributed throughout the eastern half of the United States and southern Canada. Its preferred hosts are wild cherry and apple, but it also attacks a wide variety of other forest, shade, and fruit trees. The adults are light to dark chocolate-brown, the wings are lightly dusted with white scales, and the wingspread varies from about 37 to 50 mm. Each forewing is crossed by two oblique white or yellowish-white lines. The hindwing is uniformly chocolate-brown and crossed by a faint white area. Full-grown larvae have black heads, sparsely clothed with long, fine, light-brown hairs, and are marked with an apparently continuous mid-dorsal light stripe, bordered on each side with longitudinal reddish-brown and black wavy lines. The subdorsal area is marked with a central black area on each segment, crossed by a vertical blue mark posteriorly.

Winter is spent in the egg stage, and hatching occurs about the time the buds of the host tree begin to unfold in the spring. In Florida, adults may appear and lay their eggs even before hatching occurs in the northern parts of the insect's range. The larvae are gregarious. As soon as they hatch, they begin the construction of a tent in a nearby crotch, and continue to enlarge it as they grow. From this tent, the larvae crawl out to the foliage to feed. After feeding, they return to the tent to rest. When they become full-grown, they leave the nest and wander in search of places to pupate. Pupation occurs in tough silken cocoons, dusted with a yellowish powder, on the bark of trees, on fences, on brush and weeds, among dead leaves and other debris on the ground, and even on the sides of buildings. When the adults appear, they lay eggs in essentially a clasping mass on small twigs or branches, or on the trunks of small trees. In the Lake States, eggs are often found on the trunks of very small trees about 6 inches above the ground. There is one generation per year (*102, 600*).

Most of the hosts of the eastern tent caterpillar have little value, thus it usually does not cause economic losses. It may be of some importance, however, when it defoliates commercial size

FIGURE 126.—Eastern tent caterpillar, *Malacosoma americanum:* A, Adults; B, egg masses encircling twigs; C, larvae; D, a typical tent.

black cherry whose wood is of value for furniture (*444*). The species is primarily a nuisance pest. Infested trees in parks, recreational areas, along roadsides, and in the vicinity of homes may be disfigured.

During most years, the eastern tent caterpillar is controlled satisfactorily by its natural enemies. Periodically, however, populations reach outbreak proportions. An effective method of control

329

on isolated trees is to prune off and burn twigs containing egg masses. The destruction of tents on cold, cloudy days when the tents are still small is also effective.

The **prairie tent caterpillar,** *Malacosoma californicum lutescens* (Neumoegen & Dyar) occurs throughout the Great Plains area east of the Rocky Mountains to central Texas. Its hosts are recorded as choke cherry, *Rosa,* willow, wild plum, and *Ribes.* Male adults range from dark reddish-brown to very light yellow; females are yellowish to medium reddish-orange brown. The forewings are crossed by light yellowish lines, and the wingspread is about 37 to 50 mm. Full-grown larvae are about 50 mm. long. The head is blue, mottled with black, and sparsely covered with fine whitish to orange setae. The mid-dorsal area of each abdominal segment is marked with an elongate, somewhat pointed, blue-white dash. These dashes combine to form a broken mid-dorsal stripe.

Eggs are laid in flattish, clasping masses on twigs and branches and are covered with light brown or grayish spumaline. The larvae construct relatively large tents that look like those of the eastern tent caterpillar. Defoliation is usually confined to branches, but during outbreaks trees may be completely defoliated. Because of the low value of its hosts, the species is of minor economic importance.

Malacosoma tigris (Dyar), the **Sonoran tent caterpillar,** occurs in the Southern Great Plains, Southern Rocky Mountains, the Southwest, and Mexico. So far, it is not known to occur farther eastward than central Texas. Its host plants are various oaks and possibly other species. Eggs are laid in encircling bands on very small twigs, occasionally dead twigs. The masses differ from those of other members of the genus in not being covered with spumaline. The larvae construct relatively small tents on which they congregate to molt. They are usually formed near the end of each larval instar. This species does not appear to be of much economic importance, unless it occurs in association with other defoliating species. During recent years, it has combined with the forest tent caterpillar in heavily defoliating oaks in south central Texas.

The **western tent caterpillar,** *Malacosoma californicum pluviale* (Dyar), occurs primarily in western America. However, spotted infestations also occur eastward across central Canada to Quebec. It has also been collected in New Hampshire, New York, and northwestern Minnesota (*687*). Alder, shadbush, willow, choke cherry, birch, apple, plum, cherry, and trembling aspen are known to be attacked. Full-grown larvae are predominantly black and yellow or yellow-orange. The head is mottled blue-black and sparsely covered with fine yellow-orange setae. The dorsum of the abdomen is marked by a stripe formed by a series of elongate blue, white, somewhat pointed dashes, one per segment.

Eggs are laid in flat, clasping masses covered with brown or dark brown spumaline. The tents are similar to those of the eastern tent caterpillar. The species is of little or no economic importance in eastern America.

The **forest tent caterpillar,** *Malacosoma disstria* Hubner, occurs throughout most of the United States and Canada and feeds on a wide variety of hardwoods. In the North and West, trembling aspen is preferred; in the South, tupelo gum, black gum, sweet gum and various species of oak are most heavily defoliated. The adult is stout-bodied, light buff-brown, and has a wingspread of about 25 to 37 mm. The forewings have two darker oblique bands near the middle (fig. 127A). Full-grown larvae have light blue heads mottled with black and sparsely covered with fine, whitish setae. Each abdominal segment is marked dorsally with a yellowish-buff, keyhole-shaped spot which may be divided to form an anterior spot and a smaller posterior spot (fig. 127B). The venter is blue-gray to dark gray, usually with a median spot on each segment, and often with a dark-gray area running full length of the body between the bases of the legs.

Winter is spent in the egg shape and hatching occurs in the spring, about the time the buds on the host tree begin to swell. Young larvae feed on expanding buds; older ones devour the foliage, often completely defoliating the tree. During the first three instars, the larvae are gregarious. At first, all of those from

A AND B COURTESY OF CONN. AGR. EXPT. STA., C, F-506692

FIGURE 127.—Forest tent caterpillar, *Malacosoma disstria*: A, adults; B, full-grown caterpillar, showing key-hole spots along the dorsum; C, caterpillars at rest on trunk and branches of an aspen.

one egg mass often cluster on one leaf or one group of small expanding leaves. Later, they become more widely dispersed on surrounding foliage. Although this species is referred to as a tent caterpillar, it does not construct tents. The larvae do lay down strands of silk along which they travel, however. They also form silken mats on the trunks or branches on which they congregate in masses to rest or to molt (fig. 127C). As they approach maturity, they tend to wander individually over the trees and other vegetation in search of food or places to pupate. Pupation occurs in pale yellow cocoons spun in folded leaves, in bark crevices, on shrubs or other vegetation, and occasionally on buildings. Adults appear from late May in the South to late June and July in the North. Eggs are laid in masses of 100 to 350 in bands 25 to 37 mm. wide which encircle twigs up to 37 mm. in diameter. The eggs are cemented together and are coated with dark brown spumaline. There is one generation per year.

The forest tent caterpillar has been an important enemy of forest, orchard, and shade trees for many years. During the period from 1886 to 1940, five general outbreaks, some of which covered thousands of square miles and lasted for several years, occurred in northwestern United States and eastern Canada. Since the 1930's several outbreaks have also occurred in Virginia, South Carolina, Mississippi and Louisiana (356). In general, tree mortality has not been severe, but losses in reduced increment following defoliation has been great. Studies in Minnesota indicate that about 70 percent reduction in basal area growth of aspen occurs during the first year of heavy defoliation. About 90 percent reduction also occurs during the second year of heavy defoliation, plus about 15 percent reduction during the year of recovery. Total reduction for the 3-year period averages about 58 percent (211). Heavy defoliation of bottomland gums in the South results in substantial mortality and dieback, as well as severe reduction in annual increment. In the Northeast, heavy defoliation in sugar maple orchards not only causes serious injury to the trees, but also a reduction in the quantity and quality of the sap. Outbreaks in recreational areas adversely affect business because of the nuisance created by migrating caterpillars and the midwinter appearance of defoliated trees during the tourist season. Rose (619) and Hildahl and Reeks (353) discuss the effects of defoliation on trembling aspen in Canada.

Outbreaks usually subside after 3 or 4 consecutive years of defoliation. Several adverse environmental factors are responsible for population declines. Freezing weather shortly after the eggs hatch may kill large numbers of larvae. Excessively high temperatures later in the spring may kill large numbers of adults and seriously reduce the viability of newly-laid eggs. Mortality in the late larval instars may be severe or complete as a result of starvation in heavily or completely defoliated stands. A polyhedrosis virus disease sometimes kills enormous numbers of larvae in the late stages of outbreaks. The sarcophagid parasite, *Sarcophaga aldrichi* Park., often becomes extremely abundant during the late stages of outbreaks in the Lake States and greatly aids in their termination (355). The tachinid parasites, *Zenilla protuberans* A. & W. and *Compsilura concinnata* Meig. are also helpful in control, especially in the Northeastern States.

Tolype velleda (Stoll.), occurs from southern Canada south through the Atlantic States to Florida and west to the Lake States. The larvae feed on the foliage of various hardwoods including ash, aspen, basswood, cherry, elm, maple, holly, oak, and apple. The adult has a white head and thorax, a gray abdomen, and a large blackish spot in the middle of the dorsum. The wings are usually gray, sometimes dusky, are crossed by white lines, and have an expanse of 37 to 62 mm. Full-grown larvae are gray with faint longitudinal lines and are about 62 mm. long. The body is flattened and has lateral lappets, each of which has many long hairs, thus forming a fringe along each side of the body. There is a pair of warts, bordered posteriorally by a velvety black band, on the metathorax. Adults appear in September and October. Females lay their eggs in rows and cover them with hairs from the abdomen. Larvae are present from June to August. Pupation takes place in tough, flattened, parchment-like cocoons on the bark. There is one generation per year. This species seldom causes serious injury. The related but smaller species, *T. laricis* (Fitch), feeds on larch. Its range and life cycle are similar to those of *T. velleda*.

The **lappet moth**, *Epicnaptera americana* (Harr.), is generally distributed, but not often common, through the Eastern States and southern Canada. Its hosts are aspen, wild cherry, hickory, birch, maple, oak, and various other hardwoods. Adults are reddish brown and have wingspreads of 30 to 50 mm. The inner angle of the forewing and the costal margin of the hindwing are deeply notched, and there is a pale band edged with irregular dark-brown lines beyond the middle of each. Full-grown larvae are bluish-gray, somewhat mottled above, have lateral lappets, and are about 62 mm. long. There are transverse scarlet bands on the second and third thoracic segments, in each of which are three black dots. Winter is spent in the pupal stage in a tough, flattened cocoon, usually on the bark of the tree. There is one generation per year in the North and a partial second one in the South.

FAMILY ZANOLIDAE

This family is represented in North America by only three species, two of which are encountered fairly often in eastern forests.

Apatelodes torrefacta (J. E. Smith) occurs throughout the eastern part of the United States and feeds on maple, wild black cherry, and various other trees and shrubs. Full-grown larvae have rounded yellowish heads and are about 50 mm. long. The body is whitish to yellow on the dorsum, except for a row or line of more or less connected black spots. It has a row of black spots on each side, is blackish beneath, and is densely clothed with long, fine, white or yellow hairs. Long pencils of hairs, pale at the base and black at the tip, arise from the second and third thoracic and eighth abdominal segments. Larvae are present from June to September, and winter is spent in the pupal stage on the ground.

Apatelodes angelica (Grote) larvae feed on the leaves of ash and lilac from New England and southern Canada to Florida and westward into the Ohio River Valley. Full-grown larvae are 50 to 62 mm. long. The head is rounded, brown, and mottled with light and dark shades. The body is gray and covered with a network of fine wavy black lines, except for the top of the thorax which bears two broad black transverse bands. The tops of segments one and seven bear yellowish-green spots; long brown and white hairs project forward over the head fom the prothorax; and whitish hairs project forward from the middle of the second and third thoracic segments. Most of the rest of the body is sparsely clothed with short white and black hairs. Larvae are found in August and September. Winter is spent in the pupal stage on the ground.

FAMILY GEOMETRIDAE

GEOMETRID MOTHS

This is one of the largest families in the order Lepidoptera, with some 1200 species occurring in the United States and Canada alone. The larvae are all distinguished by their peculiar method of locomotion, which consists of bringing the rear end up to the thoracic legs, forming a loop of the body, and then extending the whole body forward. This characteristic, which results from the absence of prolegs near the center of the body, has given rise to a number of common names for the group such as geometers, measuring worms, inch-worms, loopers, cankerworms, and spanworms. The larvae of many species have the interesting habit of standing nearly erect on the posterior prolegs when disturbed. Motionless in this position, they are almost indistinguishable from small twigs or spurs. All members of the family are foliage feeders, and the majority inhabit forests and areas bordering woodlands.

Brephos infans (Moeschler) occurs from Coast to Coast in southern Canada and in the Northern States south to Pennsylvania. Its hosts are listed as white and gray birches and poplar. The adult is brown-colored and has a wingspan of about 25 mm. Mature larvae are green to reddish-brown and about 25 mm. long. Two fine, yellowish lines run the length of the dorsum, and there are two similar lines plus a broad subspiracular stripe on each side. Larvae are found from May to July, and winter is spent in the pupal stage.

The **fall cankerworm**, *Alsophila pometaria* (Harr) (fig.128), occurs from the Maritime Provinces to Alberta in southern Canada, and throughout the Eastern States south to North Carolina and west to Missouri and Montana. Its preferred hosts appear to be elm and apple, but it also attacks many other hardwoods such as hickory, maple, ash, beech, boxelder, basswood, cherry, and the oaks. The male moth is brownish-gray and has a wingspread of 25 to 35 mm. The forewings are rather glossy with purplish reflections and are crossed by two faint, jagged, whitish bands. The hindwings are grayish-brown, and each has a faint discal dot. Female adults are wingless and about 12 mm. long.

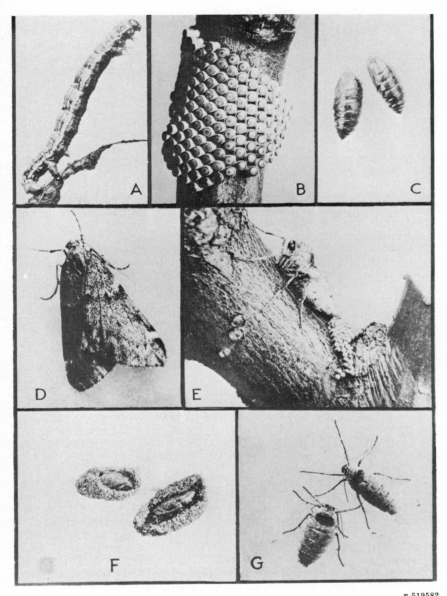

FIGURE 128.—The fall cankerworm, *Alsophila pometaria:* A, larva; B, eggs; C, pupae; D, male adult; E, female adult laying eggs; F, pupae in cocoons; G, female moths.

Full-grown larvae vary from very light green to very dark, brownish-green and are about 25 mm. long. The head and anal segment vary from pale green to almost black, and are sometimes mottled. A median, longitudinal darker stripe runs down the

335

back. Green larvae have longitudinal white lines. There are three pairs of prolegs—a very small vestigial pair on the fifth abdominal segment and larger pairs on the sixth and anal segments.

The fall cankerworm spends the winter in the egg stage, and hatching occurs in late April or early May. Young larvae skeletonize the young leaves at the tips of branches; older ones devour all but the midribs or larger veins of the leaves. They become mature in 5 to 6 weeks and drop to and enter the soil where they make cocoons in which to pupate. Adults emerge in November or December, usually following some freezing weather. Females climb the trees and deposit about 100 eggs in compact, uniform rows of single layers on the smaller twigs and branches. There is one generation per year.

The fall cankerworm is an important pest of forest and shade trees. Outbreaks occur periodically, sometimes covering large, forested areas. Shade trees in urban areas are subject to heavy infestation and may be seriously damaged. Heavy infestations in recreational areas are particularly annoying.

Synchlora aerata (F.) feeds on the foliage of willow and apple in New York State. Full-grown larvae are brownish, have curved appendages on the dorsum, and are about 20 mm. long. Winter is spent in the pupal stage, and there may be two generations per year.

The **Bruce spanworm**, *Operophtera bruceata* (Hulst), occurs from coast to coast in Canada and from New England to the Lake States. In eastern America its preferred hosts are sugar maple, trembling aspen, willow, and beech, but many other hardwoods such as white birch, red oak, pin and choke cherries, alder, and shadbush are also attacked. Serious outbreaks have occurred in both the United States and Canada.

Female moths are light brownish-gray in color and practically wingless; males are light brown and have fully-developed wings. The forewings are semi-transparent, banded with brown or gray, and have an expanse of 25 to 30 mm. Full-grown larvae are bright green except for three narrow yellow stripes on each side; larvae are about 18 mm. long.

In Canada, the winter is spent in the egg stage and hatching occurs in early spring. The larvae feed either openly on leaves or within the shelter of leaves loosely rolled and webbed together with silk. In heavily infested stands, trees are sometimes literally festooned with this silk. Pupation occurs in cocoons in the soil or duff. Adults appear in the fall. The female climbs trees and deposits eggs in bark crevices, under loose bark, or in other hiding places on the tree (*111*). A polyhedrosis virus disease has occurred commonly in New Brunswick infestations.

The **winter moth**, *Operophtera brumata* (L.), an introduced species known to have been present in Nova Scotia since about 1930, now occurs also on Cape Breton and Prince Edward Islands and in New Brunswick. So far, it is not known to occur in the United States. If it continues its recent rate of spread, however, it may soon cross the border. The female moth has a dusky brown to silver gray body with occasional irregular black spots and is practically wingless. Males have fully developed wings with an expanse of 27 to 30 mm. The body is dusky brown with black spots and the forewings are dusky brown with obscure markings.

The most common hosts in Canada are apple, red oak, American elm, red maple, basswood, and eastern hop hornbeam, but a number of other hardwoods are also attacked, such as poplar and willow. Persistent severe attacks result in thin tops, dead twigs and branches, and ultimately the death of trees. Severe defoliation of principal host trees often occurs in Nova Scotia.

Winter is spent in the egg stage and hatching occurs from late April to late May. Young larvae feed first on opening buds and on the undersides of developing leaves. Older larvae feed inside loose leaf rolls. When they become mature, they drop to and enter the ground where they construct cells in which to pupate. Pupation occurs during late June and early July, and the pupae remain in their cells during the remainder of the summer and fall. Adults appear from late October to mid-December. The females climb tree trunks or other objects near their emergence sites and deposit their eggs in bark crevices, under lichens on the trunks or branches, or in other places affording suitable shelter (*178*). Embree (*227*) discussed the population dynamics of the species.

Two imported parasites, the tachinid, *Cyzenis albicans* (Fall.), and the ichneumonid, *Argypon flaveolatum* (Grav.), are providing a considerable degree of control in Nova Scotia (*228*).

The genus *Eupethecia* contains a large number of species, four of which occur in forests of the Eastern States and eastern Canada. *E. palpatata* Pack. occurs on various species of pine, especially white and jack; *E. luteata* Pack., feeds on various spruces, especially white, and other conifers, especially balsam fir and larch; *E. filmata* Pears is found on a wide variety of conifers, especially white spruce and balsam fir; and *E. transcanadata* MacK. which also feeds on a wide variety of conifers, preferably white and black spruce and balsam fir.

Calocalpe undulata (L.), the **cherry scallop shell moth,** occurs on wild and choke cherries throughout much of eastern North America. The adult has a wingspread of about 37 mm. The forewings are marked with 12 whitish, scalloped, parallel lines and a black discal dot; the hindwings are marked with six whitish lines. Full-grown larvae are about 20 mm. long. The body is blackish above with four longitudinal yellow lines, and is straw yellow beneath. The larvae live in nests which they construct by webbing together the leaves toward the end of a branch. Heavily infested trees occasionally are completely defoliated.

Eulype hastata (L.), the **spear-marked black moth,** feeds on birch, willow, and alder from Coast to Coast and north to Alaska. Full-grown larvae are about 25 mm. long. The head is shiny black; the body, dark brown to black, with a row of small black dots and a few white to brick-red spots on each side. In the Northeastern States, larvae are present from June to September, and winter is spent in the pupal stage.

Bapta semiclarata (Walker) occurs on wild cherry in southern Canada and the Atlantic Coastal States. Full-grown larvae are light green and about 18 mm. long. The related species, *B. vestaliata* (Guen.), is known to occur on birch in Maine.

Deilinea erythemaria (Guen) feeds on willow and poplar in the

Northeastern States. Full-grown larvae are about 27 mm. long. They are light green with a reddish stripe on each side of the head, reddish patches on the back, and a red stripe on each side of the body. Winter is spent in the larval stage. The related species, *D. variolaria* (Guen.), is found on willow and trembling aspen in the Northeastern States and southwestern Canada.

Physostegania pustularia (Guen,) occurs on red maple in Maine where it is occasionally abundant. It has also been reported from widely scattered localities in southern Canada. The adult has a wingspread of about 25 mm. and is pure white except for four brownish spots on the margin of the forewing. Full-grown larvae are green and about 15 mm. long. There are two whitish lines down the back, bordered by yellowish-white lines; the skin is quite wrinkled. Larvae are present during May and June.

Semiothisa granitata (Guen.), the **green spruce looper,** feeds on the foliage of various conifers such as white pine, spruce, fir, and hemlock in the Northeastern States and southeastern Canada. Full-grown larvae are about 20 mm. long. The body is light green with brownish tinges on top, and there are two light longitudinal lines on the back. The winter is spent in the pupal stage in the duff. *S. ocellinata* (Guen.) occurs in the Northeastern and Lake States and feeds on honey and black locusts. Full-grown larvae are green except for faint wavy lines of red and are about 25 mm. long. *S. bisignata* (Wlk.) occurs in southern Canada and the Northeastern States and feeds principally on white pine. *S. sexamaculata* Pack., a widely distributed species, feeds on larch.

Eufidonia notataria (Walker) occurs on white pine in the Atlantic Coastal States. In southern Canada, it has been observed mainly on balsam fir and spruce. Full-grown larvae are deep green and about 25 mm. long. There is a light, colored line on the dorsum and two stripes along each side. Larvae are present from July to September, and winter is spent in the pupal stage.

Melanolophia canadaria (Guen.) feeds on the foliage of various hardwoods and conifers such as basswood, paper birch, ash, hemlock, larch, pine, and spruce in the United States and Canada. Full-grown larvae are about 30 mm. long. The body has a broken, purplish line on the top and yellowish stripe suffused with purplish red on each side. Larvae are present from June to early August, and winter is spent in the larval stage in the ground.

Anacamptodes ephyraria (Walker) has been observed feeding on hemlock in the Northeastern States and on several hardwoods in Canada. Full-grown larvae are greenish with reddish-brown tinges and are about 20 mm. long. The head is bilobed and wider than the thorax, and the second abdominal segment is usually swollen at the sides. Winter is probably spent in the egg stage. *A. larvaria* (Guen.) feeds on aspen, paper birch, and alder in the Northeastern States and southern Canada. Full-grown larvae are yellowish-green and about 30 mm. long. There is a reddish band on the second abdominal segment, several reddish blotches on the dorsum, and a pair of blunt tubercles on the eighth abdominal segment. *A. pergacilis* (Hulst) feeds on cypress in the South. During a recent outbreak in Arkansas, several thousand acres were defoliated.

Ectropis crepuscularia (Denis & Schiff.), the **saddle-back looper,** feeds on the foliage of a wide variety of trees in the northern tier of States and from Coast to Coast in southern Canada. South of Canada, it is usually found on hardwoods such as birch, maple, oak, poplar, and walnut. In Canada, it appears to prefer conifers. Full-grown larvae are reddish to chocolate brown and about 30 mm. long. The head is somewhat mottled, and there is a pair of blunt tubercles on the eighth abdominal segment. Larvae are present from May to September in the Northeastern States and the winter is spent in the pupal stage in the ground.

Epimecis virginiaria (Cram.) occurs on sassafras and yellow poplar in the Atlantic Coastal States. The adult is either dark colored to almost black or light gray with a dusting of brown. The forewings are marked with lines and the wingspread is about 50 mm. Full-grown larvae are yellowish to dark brown with 5 pale yellowish longitudinal lines and are about 37 mm. long. Larvae are present during June and July, and they feed at night. There are one and a possible second generation per year.

Phigalia tites (Cram.) occurs in southern Canada westward to Saskatchewan and in several Eastern States. Its hosts include various hardwoods, especially red oak, red maple, basswood, hickory, and elm. Numerous outbreaks have been recorded in mixed oak and maple stands in the Northeastern States. The male moth has a wingspread of 37 mm. The thorax is whitish, and the abdomen is marked with two rows of black dots on the dorsum. The forewings are dotted with dark brown specks and are marked with three blackish lines and a row of black spots along the outer margin. The wings of the female are vestigial and functionless. Full-grown larvae are pinkish with many blackish longitudinal lines and are about 37 mm. long. The thoracic segments are thick, and there are hairy tubercles on all body segments. Eggs are laid beneath the bark on dead branches. Larvae are present from May to July, and winter is spent in the pupal stage in the soil.

The **spring cankerworm,** *Paleacrita vernata* (Peck) (fig. 129), occurs throughout the same general range as the fall cankerworm, also farther southwest and west to Texas, Colorado, and California. Its hosts are about the same as those of the fall cankerworm. Apple and elm are especially favored. Male moths have a wing expanse of about 21 to 30 mm. The forewings are silky with loosely attached, brownish scales, and are crossed by three jagged, dark lines. The hindwings are pale, ashy-gray, and each bears a dusky, discal spot. Each of the first seven joints of the abdomen bears two transverse, dorsal rows of stiff, reddish spines, pointed posteriorly. Female moths are wingless and generally whitish or brown or black. There is a darker stripe down the back and two transverse rows of reddish spines on each of the first seven joints of the abdomen. These spines are often so prominent as to give the dorsum a reddish aspect.

Full-grown larvae are reddish to yellowish-brown, yellowish-green, or blackish and are about 18 to 30 mm. long. The head is light and mottled with brown. The body is usually marked with a yellow stripe just below the spiracles, and a broad greenish-

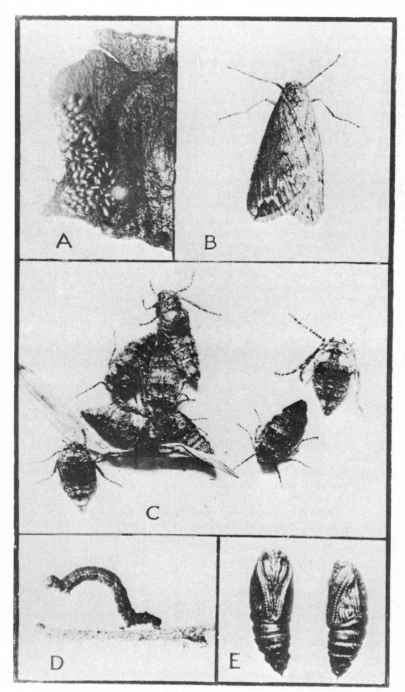

F-519581

FIGURE 129.—Spring cankerworm, *Paleacrita vernata*. A, eggs on inner surface of a piece of bark; B, male moth; C, female moths; D, partly grown larva; E, pupae.

yellow stripe down the middle of the venter. There is a pair of prolegs, one on each of the eighth and anal segments.

Spring cankerworms do not spin cocoons but spend most of the winter as larvae in cells in the soil. Pupation occurs in late winter, and the adults appear about the time frost leaves the ground in early spring. Female moths crawl up the trunks of trees and deposit loose clusters of 100 or more eggs in bark crevices or under bark scales on the trunk or branches. Hatching occurs by early May and the larvae become full-grown by early June. Then they drop to and enter the soil where they remain until late winter or the following spring. Like the fall cankerworm, this species is an important pest of shade trees and in forested areas.

Fall and spring cankerworm populations are normally kept under control by natural control factors. Outbreaks often occur, however, over large areas. Isolated trees can be protected by placing sticky bands around the trunks so as to prevent female moths from climbing them to lay their eggs. (*724*).

The **linden looper,** *Erannis tiliaria* Harr., occurs in southeastern Canada and throughout eastern United States. The larvae feed on the foliage of a wide variety of hardwoods, especially basswood, elm, hickory, maple, oak, birch, and apple. The female adult is light gray to brownish, wingless, about 12 mm. long, and is marked with black spots on the sides and back. Male moths have fully developed wings with an expanse of about 42 mm. The forewings are buff-colored and marked with two transverses, wavy brown bands and a sprinkling of brownish dots. Full-grown larvae (fig. 130) are bright yellow, have rusty brown heads, and 10 wavy black lines running down the dorsum. They are about 37 mm. long.

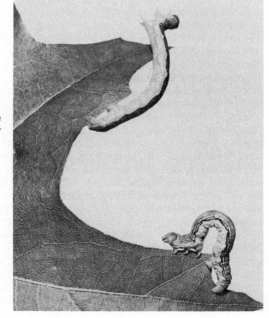

FIGURE 130.—Larvae of the linden looper, *Erannis tiliaria*.

Winter is spent in the egg stage and hatching occurs in April or May. Larvae are present until July, then pupate in cells in the ground. Adults are present from October to December. The females crawl up the trunks of trees and deposit their eggs singly or in small groups in bark crevices. There is one generation per year. Several outbreaks have been recorded in the Northeastern States and Canada. At such times, male moths are attracted to street lights in nearby towns in considerable numbers. Two dipterous parasites, *Pseudotachinomya webberi* Sm. and *Zenillia vulgaris* Fall., commonly attack the larvae. A virus epizootic occurred in an outbreak in Quebec in 1961.

Lycia ursaria (Walker) larvae feed on the foliage of a number of hardwoods such as paper birch, willow, elm, maple, poplar, basswood, ash, wild cherry, and alder in eastern Canada and the Atlantic Coastal States. Willow and paper birch appear to be preferred. The adult is gray, stout-bodied, and has a wingspread of about 50 mm. Both pairs of wings are crossed by diffused, blackish lines. Full-grown larvae are about 50 mm. long. There are four large whitish spots on the front of the prothorax, and the body is marked with numerous longitudinal wavy lines and creamy-white spots. Larvae are present from May to July, and winter is spent as pupae in the ground. This species is occasionally quite common in New England.

Phaeoura quernaria J. E. Smith occurs in oaks in the Atlantic Coastal States. Full-grown larvae are about 50 mm. long. The head is bilobed and angular; the body slate gray, stoutish, and armed with brownish tubercles. The tops of the first two thoracic segments are also marked with reddish brown and black. Larvae are found from June to September; winter is spent in the pupal stage.

Plagodis serinaria (H.-S.) feeds on various hardwoods such as red maple, yellow and white birch, beech, and aspen in the Northeastern States and eastern Canada. Full-grown larvae are about 37 mm. long. The head is bilobed and angular; the body dull brown with blotches of lighter and darker shades and a prominent swollen area on the back of the sixth abdominal segment. Winter is spent in the pupal stage, and adults are present during May and June. *P. phlogosaria keutzingaria* Pack. feeds on ash in the Northeastern States.

Hyperetis amicaria (H.-S.) feeds on beech, yellow and paper birch, willow, and alder throughout much of eastern United States and from coast to coast in southern Canada. There are also records of its feeding on such conifers as larch, white spruce, and balsam fir. Full-grown larvae are green to brownish and about 30 mm. long. The head is rather small and flattened in front, and there are two whitish spots on the tops of all body segments except the first thoracic. Larvae are present from July to early September, and winter is spent in the pupal stage.

The **filament bearer**, *Nematocampa limbata* (Haw.), feeds on the foliage of hemlock, fir, and such hardwoods as maple, oak, gray birch, wild cherry, horse chestnut, and apple in eastern United States and eastern Canada. Full-grown larvae are greenish-brown with reddish-brown heads and are about 18 mm. long. There is a pair of tubercles on the first abdominal segment; a

342

pair of long slender brownish filaments on each side of the second and third segments; a pair of small, rusty red tubercles on the eighth segment; and a broad stripe on the dorsum from the prothorax to the first pair of filaments. Larvae are active from May to July; adults, from late June to August.

The **elm spanworm**, *Ennomos subsignarius* (Hbn.) (fig. 131), occurs occasionally in southern Ontario and throughout eastern United States, west to Michigan, Colorado, and Texas. Its preferred hosts are recorded as hickory, oak, and ash, but it also attacks a large number of other hardwoods (*140*). About 100 years ago, it was best known as a shade tree pest in the larger cities of eastern United States (*343*). In recent years it has been predominantly a forest pest, with widespread severe outbreaks occurring in the southern Appalachians (*238*).

The adult is a powdery white moth with a wingspread of 30 to 37 mm. Full-grown larvae are usually dull, slate black in color except for rusty head capsules; they are slightly more than 50 mm. long.

Winter is spent in the egg stage. Hatching begins in late April in the South. Farther north, it may not start until late May or early June. Young larvae feed on the lower surfaces of leaves, producing shot-hole effects. Older ones eat the entire leaf with the exception of the midrib and petiole. To pupate, mature larvae spin coarse, net-like cocoons of silken threads, often on partly

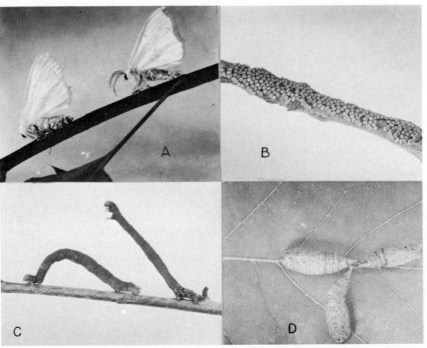

F-500617, 500618, 500615, 500619

FIGURE 131.—Elm spanworm, *Ennomos subsignarius:*
A, adults; B, eggs; C, larvae; D, pupae.

eaten leaves in which to pupate. In completely defoliated stands, cocoons may be spun on exposed branch tips, in leaf axils, in bark crevices, or on stumps or undergrowth.

The elm spanworm is capable of completely defoliating large areas of mixed hardwood forests during outbreaks. This has happened during recent years in the lower Appalachians. During intervals between outbreaks, populations often exist at very low levels. The recent spate of outbreaks in the South was unexpected. A number of insect parasites and predators were found in fairly large numbers during the latter stages of some of the outbreaks and probably helped in bringing them to an end. The hymenopteron, *Telenomous alsophilae* Vier., parasitized and destroyed over 80 percent of the eggs in certain areas (*141*). The predacious beetle, *Calosoma scrutator* (F.), a voracious feeder on lepidopterous larvae, was also abundant in outbreak areas.

Pero honestarius (Wlkr.) occurs on black locust, wild cherry, and larch in the Eastern States. Full-grown larvae are dark brown, with lighter and darker markings; increase in girth toward the rear; and are about 37 mm. long. There appears to be two generations per year. *P. morrisonarius* Hy. Edw. occurs on a wide variety of trees, including fir, spruce, larch, pine, willow, aspen and other trees.

Neptyia semiclusaria (Walker) occurs on fir, larch, pine, spruce, and hemlock in the Northeastern States and on sand pines in Florida (*347*). Full-grown larvae are pale yellow with a wide, orange-red dorsal stripe and thin, longitudinal black and white lines; they are about 50 mm. long. Eggs are deposited in masses under bark scales, and the larvae feed on the old needles. Pupae are found among these needles, some of which are tied together with strands of silk.

The **false hemlock looper**, *Neptyia canosaria* (Walker), occurs on hemlock, fir, white and black spruce, and larch in the Northeastern States and southern Canada. Full-grown larvae are about 25 mm. long. The head is pale whitish or reddish-brown and bears a few black dots; the body is whitish with tinges of yellow or red, black dotted and has a yellowish stripe on each side below which are four or five dark, wavy lines. Larvae are present from June to August.

The **hemlock looper**, *Lambdina fiscellaria* (Guen.), occurs from Newfoundland to Alberta in Canada and south to Georgia in the Eastern States. Its preferred hosts are balsam fir, white spruce, and hemlock. It also feeds on many other species during outbreaks such as larch, red and black spruce, cedar, arborvitae, jack pine, basswood, maple, paper and yellow birch, elm, and wild cherry. In the more southerly portions of its range, infestations develop mainly on hemlock. Outbreaks were recorded in Ohio, Wisconsin, Michigan, New York and Maine during the 1920's and in Massachuetts, New Hampshire and Vermont from 1949 to 1952. The adult is creamy-tan with grayish-brown with a tinge of purple and has a wingspread of about 62 mm. Two irregular purplish-brown lines cross the forewings, and a dot of the same color lies between near the costal margin. Full-grown larvae are usually grayish-green to grayish and are about 30 mm. long. The head and body are flecked with black dots.

Adults are present from around mid-August to early October and deposit their eggs singly or in small groups on moss, lichens, or bark on limbs and trunks. Winter is spent in the egg stage and hatching occurs in June. Young larvae feed on opening shoots; older ones, on old needles. Needles are often chewed off at the base and drop; others, incompletely chewed off, usually dry out, turn brown, then drop. Pupation takes place in bark crevices, or in masses of lichens on or near the bark (*136*).

Hemlock looper outbreaks may develop very suddenly, the most serious ones occurring in mature and over-mature hemlock and balsam fir stands.

Lambdina athasaria pellucidaria (G. & R.) occurs in several Atlantic Coastal States and feeds on pitch, red, shortleaf, and possibly other pines. Several widespread outbreaks have been recorded during the past 60-odd years. The adult is ash gray to smoky in color and has a wingspread of about 37 mm. The forewing is crossed by two irregular diffuse dusky lines and bears a slightly sinuate discal dot. The hindwing is also crossed by a dusky line. Full-grown larvae are pale straw to yellow with black markings and are 25 to 37 mm. long. The body bears faint rows of blackish dots and short wavy lines on the top and sides, and the head is densely marked with light and dark spots.

Adults emerge in May and June and lay their eggs on the needles. The larvae feed on the needles until late September. Winter is spent in the pupal stage in the duff beneath the trees.

Lambdina athasaria athasaria (Walker) occurs on hemlock in several Eastern States. Local outbreaks have occurred in Massachusetts, Connecticut, and Ohio. The adult resembles the adult of *L. athasaria pellucidaria* except for a slightly narrower wingspread. Full-grown larvae are yellowish and about 30 mm. long. The head is marked with irregular brown to blackish spots. The top of the body is lighter than the sides. The sides are marked with wavy lines of dark or reddish brown, interrupted with dashes of white. Winter is spent in the pupal stage on the ground, just beneath the top crust of the leaf mold. Larvae are present from July to late September. *L. endopiaria* (G. & R.) has been observed on oak in the Northeastern States.

The **chain-spotted geometer**, *Cingilla catenaria* (Drury), occurs in eastern Canada and the Northeastern States. It has many hosts including gray and paper birch, oak, poplar, willow, wild cherry, balsam fir, larch, and white spruce. Young white and red pines growing in mixture with the above hosts are also subject to heavy defoliation. Blueberries, huckleberries, and small trees growing in pastures and cutover areas are especially subject to infestation. Local outbreaks have been recorded frequently in the Northeastern States.

The adult has a wingspread of 30 to 42 mm. The head and part of the thorax are orange yellow; the body white with black markings. The wings are smoky white and black spotted. Full-grown larvae are straw-colored and about 50 mm. long. The head and body are dotted with black spots, those on the sides of the body producing chain-like effects. There also are three or four thin lines below these rows of dots. Winter is spent in the egg stage. Larvae are present from June to August.

Deuteronomous magnarius (Gn.), the **notched-wing geometer,** is widely distributed in southern Canada and the Northern States. It feeds on many species of hardwoods such as white ash, basswood, maple, aspen, white birch, beech, willow, and elm. The adult is yellowish and has a wingspread of about 60 mm. The forewing has a reddish tinge, is thickly flecked with brown dots, has a conspicuous lobe near the middle, and is shaded with brown on the outer margin. Mature larvae are yellowish-green and about 50 mm. long. Reddish areas occur on the tops of segments two and five and on the venter of segment three. Adults deposit eggs during August and September. Winter is spent in the egg stage. Hatching begins in May, and larvae are present from May to July or August. This species is sometimes fairly abundant but is seldom of economic importance.

Tetracis lorata Grote occurs on wild cherry in the Northeastern States. Full-grown larvae are about 37 mm. long. The head is grayish, flattened, and square in front; the body, reddish-brown with white markings and a black line running down the middle of the back after the fifth segment. Tubercles are also prominent. Larvae are present from July to September, and winter is spent in the pupal stage.

Abbottana clemataria (J. E. Smith) occurs on basswood, maple, trembling aspen, paper birch, wild cherry, and hemlock in southeastern Canada and the Middle Atlantic States westward to the Mississippi River Valley. Full-grown larvae are purplish brown and up to 60 mm. long. The head is rounded and bilobed; the second and fourth abdminal segments are swollen on top; and there are prominent tubercles on the fifth and ninth abdominal segments. Larvae feed from June to August, and winter is spent as pupae in cocoons in leaves on the ground.

Prochoerodes transversata (Drury) occurs on various hardwoods such as maple, oak, willow, trembling aspen, paper birch, and mulberry in southern Canada and eastern United States. Full-grown larvae are light to purplish-brown and about 50 mm. long. The head is rounded and flattened in front; the second thoracic segment is swollen and streaked with red; and the eighth abdominal segment bears a pair of prominent tubercles. Larvae feed from June to October; winter is spent in the pupal stage; and there are two generations per year.

The **pepper and salt moth,** *Biston* (*=Amphidasis*) *cognataria* (Guen.), occurs in the Northeastern States where it feeds on elm, willow, poplar, black locust, wild cherry, and apple. The adult is dark brown to black and has a wingspread of about 55 mm. Full-grown larvae are about 50 mm. long. The head is deeply cleft, granulated, and flat in front; there are tubercles on each side of the prothorax and on the fifth and eighth abdominal segments. Larvae feed from July to October, and winter is spent in the pupal stage in the ground.

Campaea perlata Gn. is a common species in the Northeastern United States and Canada, and the larvae feed on balsam fir, hemlock, and many species of deciduous trees. *Protobarmia porcelaria* Wlk. is also a common species in Northeastern forests, where the larvae feed on a wide variety of trees including balsam fir, white spruce, larch, jack pine, birch, aspen, and willow.

FAMILY LACOSOMIDAE

Adults of this family are stout-bodied moths with pectinate antennae. The forewings are falcate, bent at the middle, and heavy-veined. The humeral angle of the hindwing is much enlarged, and the frenulum is rudimentary. Two species are known to occur in eastern United States, neither of which is of economic importance. However, they both often attract attention.

Cincinnus melsheimeri (Harr.), **Melsheimer's sack bearer,** occurs fairly commonly on oak, especially scrub oak, from New England to the Lake States and southward. The adult is reddish-gray and has a wingspread of 37 to 50 mm. The body is sprinkled with minute black dots; each wing is crossed by a narrow blackish band and marked by a black discal spot or bar. A newly-hatched larva makes a shelter for itself by drawing two leaves together with strands of silk. Later on it constructs an ellipsoidal portable case of pieces of leaves and silk, leaving a circular hole at each end. It lives in the case but can leave it at will. To move the case, it bites off the strand of silk by which it is anchored and transports it to the new location. When it is at rest the larva anchors the case with silk and stops the openings with its head and rear end. Winter is spent in the pupal stage, and adults appear during May and June.

Lacosoma chiridota Grote feeds on oak throughout much the same range as the Melsheimer sack bearer. Adults are dark yellowish-brown, with deeply scalloped forewings and have wingspreads of 25 to 30 mm.

FAMILY LIMACODIDAE

SLUG CATERPILLAR MOTHS

Limacodid larvae are sluglike in appearance. The head is concealed in the thorax, the thoracic legs are small, and the prolegs are replaced by sucking disks. Pupation occurs in dense, brownish, oval silken cocoons spun between leaves or attached to twigs. Each cocoon has a hole covered by a lid at one end through which the adult emerges.

The **saddleback caterpillar,** *Sibine stimulea* (Clem.), is widely distributed in eastern and southern United States and feeds on a wide variety of trees and ornamental plants. The larva is brownish except for a green patch on the middle of the back which resembles a saddlecloth. In the middle of the back is an oval purplish-brown saddlelike spot. The body is armed along the sides with fascicles of poisonous spines, and has a pair of spiny tubercles at each end (fig. 132).

The **hag moth,** *Phobetron pithecium* (J. E. Smith), feeds on various deciduous trees and shrubs. The larvae are brown, about 10 mm. long, and each bears nine pairs of lateral brown processes. The third, fifth, and seventh pairs are long, curved and twisted, and are suggestive of the disheveled locks of a "hag." These processes are clothed with stinging hairs.

The **oriental moth,** *Cnidocampa flavescens* (Wlkr.) (fig. 133), an introduced species first recorded in this country near Boston,

FIGURE 132.—Larvae of the saddleback caterpillar, *Sibine stimulea*.

Mass. in 1906 (*149*), is still confined to eastern Massachusetts. The adult has a wingspread of 30 to 42 mm. Full-grown larvae are about 22 mm. long and marked with yellow, blue, green, and purple. The larvae feed on a large number of tees, including Norway and sycamore maples, black birch, cherry, apple, pear, plum, oak, aspen, willow, honeylocust, hickory, and hackberry.

Adults deposit their eggs either singly or in groups on the undersides of leaves. Young larvae feed on the lower epidermis of the leaves; older ones consume all but the larger veins. A full-grown larva forms a cocoon by spinning a network of threads around itself and attaching them to the bark in the forks of limbs or twigs. Later it secretes a fluid which fills the spaces between the threads and hardens. Winter is spent as a prepupa in the cocoon. People are severely irritated when they come into contact with the larva's poisonous spines. The tachinid parasite, *Chaetexorista javana* B. & G., was imported from Japan against this species in 1929 and 1930 and has exerted a considerable degree of control.

Prolimacodes badia Hbn. feeds on various hardwoods such as oak, beech, and black cherry in the Northeastern States and southern Canada. It has also been observed feeding on maple in North Carolina. *P. scapha* Harr. feeds on wild cherry and black gum in Massachuetts and New Jersey. *Sisyrosea textula* (H.-S.) feeds on Norway maple and oak; *Packardia geminata* (Pack.) on wild cherry; and *Tortricidia flexuosa* (Grt.) on oak, gray birch, and wild cherry in the New England States.

FAMILY MEGALOPYGIDAE

FLANNEL MOTHS

The bodies of flannel moths are covered with dense coats of scales and long crinkly hairs. The larvae are also covered rather densely with long soft hairs, with an intermingling of poisonous

FIGURE 133.—The oriental moth, *Cnidocampa flavescens:* Upper, adults and cocoons; middle, a defoliated Norway maple; lower, newly hatched and full-grown larvae.

spines. Females deposit their eggs in small batches, usually on leaves, and cover them with hairs from the abdomen.

The **puss caterpillar,** *Megalopyge opercularis* (J. E. Smith), occurs throughout the Southern States where it feeds on various deciduous trees and shrubs. Forest and shade trees commonly infested include oak, elm, hackberry, maple, and sycamore. The adult moth is yellowish-brown, with brownish spots on the wings, and has a wingspread of about 25 mm. The wings bear long, wavy, white hairs, especially along the veins. The larvae are densely clothed with long yellow and reddish-brown or mouse-gray hairs with hairs at the rear end tail-like.

349

Young larvae feed gregariously on the surface of the leaf, skeletonizing it. Older larvae devour the entire leaf. Serious infestations have been recorded in Florida and Texas. Several thousand acres of turkey oak were defoliated during an outbreak in Florida in 1966. Generally speaking, however, the species is most important as a pest of people, because of its poisonous spines (*68*). There may be two generations per year in the more southerly portions of its range. Winter is spent as a pupa in a cocoon spun some place on the host tree. Hand picking of larvae, using gloves, is a common control practice. The tachinid parasite, *Carcelia lagoa* (Towns.), is sometimes abundant in Texas infestations.

The **crinkled flannel moth**, *Lagoa crispata* (Pack.), occurs throughout the eastern half of the United States and feeds on a wide variety of plants, including oak, black locust, birch, cherry, and apple. According to some reports, it occurs most commonly in the northern parts of its range; however, it is known to have completely defoliated shin oak over several hundreds of acres of range land in Texas. The adult is cream-colored, with black wavy lines and brownish, crinkled hairs on the forewings. Full-grown larvae are oval-shaped and about 25 mm. long. The body is covered with long, silky brown hairs which meet in the form of a ridge along the back, and then slope off roof-like on each side. Winter is spent in the pupal stage in a cocoon. The cocoon is unique in being urn-shaped and having a flat, hinged, circular lid which is lifted as the moth emerges. The stings produced by the spines on the larvae of this species apparently are less severe than those produced by related species (*68*).

Norape ovina Sepp feeds on red bud, mimosa, and beech from New Jersey and southern Pennsylvania southward. The adult is a pure white moth with a small amount of crinkly hair. The larvae are spotted and sparsely clothed in tufts of hair.

FAMILY PYRAUSTIDAE

The **grape leaf folder**, *Desmia funeralis* (Hbn.), an important pest of grape, both cultivated and wild, occurs in eastern America and along the West Coast. It also feeds on Virginia creeper and red bud. The adult is black except for a white band on the abdomen of the male and two white bands on the abdomen of the female. The forewings are trimmed with white and have coppery reflections. The wingspread is about 25 mm. The larvae live in tubes formed by rolling over the edges of leaves and tying them with silk. When they become full-grown, larvae are covered with sparse, fine, yellow hairs, are translucent yellow green on the sides, and are 18 to 25 mm. long. The winter is spent in the pupal stage inside the larval tube. There are two generations per year in the South.

The **basswood leaf roller**, *Pantographa limata* G. & R., occurs on basswood in southern Canada and throughout eastern United States. The adult is white, except for shadings of pale yellow and olive or dull-brown markings, and has a wingspread of about 37 mm. Full-grown larvae are bright green, except for black heads and black cervical shields, and are about 25 mm. long. Adults appear during June and July; larvae are present from July to September. Each larva rolls the apical half or more of a leaf into the form of a tube in which it lives (fig. 134). Full-grown larvae spend the winter in cocoons constructed by folding a part of a leaf. The folded leaf drops to the ground with other leaves. Although frequently abundant, this species does not seem to cause serious damage.

Phylctaenia coronata (Hufn.) [=*tertialis* (Gn.en.)], the **elder leaf tier,** larvae feed as leaf rollers on the leaves of elder in the Northeastern States. The adult is brown except for the presence of creamy white spots and streaks, and has a wingspread of 22 mm. Full-grown larvae are translucent, whitish or pinkish, and about 18 mm. long. Winter is spent as a prepupa in a hibernaculum usually spun in the hollow stems or pith of elder. There may be two generations per year. This species occasionally causes serious defoliation.

FAMILY EPIPASCHIDAE

The **pine webworm,** *Tetralopha robustella* Zell., occurs in southern Canada and throughout most of the eastern half of the United States. Its food plants include several species of pines: jack, red, white, Scotch, pitch, Virginia, shortleaf, longleaf, loblolly, and slash. Jack pine is preferred in the Lake States and adjacent parts of Canada. In the Northeast pitch pine is preferred. The adult has a wingspread of about 25 mm. The basal part of the forewing is purple-black, the central part grayish, and the outer part blackish. Full-grown larvae are yellowish-brown, with two, dark-brown, longitudinal stripes on each side, and are about 18 mm. long.

Adults are present from June to August and deposit their eggs on pine needles. Young larvae mine the needles; older ones live in silken tubes which extend through globular masses of brown, coarse frass webbed together by strands of silk (fig. 135). These masses, which are found on the twigs, enclose the needles upon which the larvae feed and range in length from about 3 to 5 inches. Pupation occurs in a cell in the soil. In the northern part of its range, there is usually one generation per year; in the South there may be two (*738*).

The pine webworm is often troublesome in pine plantations. Young seedlings up to 2 feet tall are sometimes completely defoliated and killed by the larvae in a single nest. Ugly nests on the twigs and branches of young pines being grown for the Christmas tree trade sometimes make it impossible to sell them.

Tetralopha asperatella (Clem.) occurs in southeastern Canada and throughout eastern United States. The larvae feed on the foliage of various hardwoods such as sugar, red, and mountain maples, oak, elm, beech, trembling aspen, and willow. The moth is powdery-gray, with the outer half of the forewing somewhat lighter. Full-grown larvae range from pale yellow through shades of green to brown or black and are about 25 mm. long. On sugar maple in Wisconsin, eggs are laid on leaves partly rolled by other insects. When the larvae hatch they feed on these leaves as skeletonizers; older larvae web together groups of leaves, sometimes

FIGURE 135.—Web nest of the pine webworm, *Tetralopha robustella*.

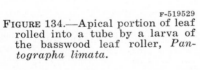

F-519529
FIGURE 134.—Apical portion of leaf rolled into a tube by a larva of the basswood leaf roller, *Pantographa limata*.

F-519532
FIGURE 136.—Characteristic nest of *Tetralopha asperatella* on oak.

including all of the leaves on a branch in a web (fig. 136). Heaviest infestations apparently occur in the more open portions of the crown of trees growing in the most exposed positions in the stand. When the larvae become full-grown, they leave the nest and drop to the ground on strands of silk. The winter is spent as a prepupa in a cocoon spun in the duff on the ground. There appears to be only one generation per year (294).

This species had never been considered economically important until it was shown to be a major factor leading to the development of "maple blight," a condition responsible for the killing of thousands of valuable sugar maples in Wisconsin during the late 1950's.

Other species of *Tetralopha* occurring in eastern United States are *T. militella* Zell., feeding on sycamore; and *T. melanogrammos* Zell., on sweetgum. Another species identified only as being near *T. asperatella* is sometimes abundant locally on beech in New England. The larva is yellowish green and has two pale-brownish stripes running down the back.

FAMILY PHYCITIDAE

This family contains many important tree-infesting species. The larvae differ considerably in their habits. Some feed on rolled or folded leaves; some construct silken cases and feed from inside them; at least one is a predator of scale insects; and many feed as borers in shoots, bark, roots, cones, nuts, or fruits. Members of the family are rather difficult to classify because of the variability of many of their distinguishing characters.

The **pecan leaf casebearer,** *Acrobasis juglandis* (LeBaron), occurs from southern Canada to Florida and Texas, and the larva feeds on the buds, flowers, and leaves of hickory, walnut, butternut, and pecan. The adult is a grayish moth with a wingspread of 14 to 17 mm. The forewing is blackish at the middle of the costa and reddish near the middle of its inner margin. Full-grown larvae are olive green and about 16 mm. long. The larvae feed during two growing seasons. The first summer, they feed on the lower surfaces of leaves. They spend the winter in small cases attached to buds or twigs. The following spring, they resume their feeding by eating into bud after bud and constructing new cases as necessary. Finally, before becoming mature, they move to the leaves to feed. Here, they often chew into the petioles and cause the leaves to break off and fall. This, plus the injury to the buds, often results in serious damage to infested areas (295).

Acrobasis caryivorella Ragonot occurs in southern Canada and throughout eastern United States and the larva feed on the foliage of hickory, walnut, and pecan. The adult has dark bluish-gray to nearly black forewings and a wing expanse of about 20 mm. The larvae are dark grayish-green and about 19 mm. long. In the spring, they feed by boring into new shoots which they tie together with silken threads. Full-grown larvae construct oval cocoons in which they pupate. Two generations per year have been recorded in Texas. In Florida, there are probably three or four generations per year. This species has seriously damaged pecan seedlings in nurseries in Florida and Texas.

The **pecan nut casebearer,** *Acrobasis caryae* Grote, occurs from southern Canada to Florida and westward to Illinois and Texas. Its preferred host appears to be pecan, but it also feeds on hickories. The adult is dark gray, with a ridge or tuft of long dark scales extending across each forewing, and has a wingspread of 18 to 20 mm. Mature larvae are a dirty, olive green and are about 12 mm. long. Winter is spent in the larval stage in a small case near the base of a bud. Later, they bore into tender shoots, causing them to become stunted and distorted. Larvae of the second generation appear in May and bore into newly-set nuts, destroying from two to five nuts each. Larvae of later generations usually feed on the shucks only and cause little or no damage. There are three or four generations per year in the South.

Several other species of *Acrobasis* also occur on forest and shade trees in eastern United States. The **birch tube maker,** *A. betulella* Hulst is common on various species of birch, white birch in particular (in the Northern States and southern Canada) ; *A. rubrifasciella* Pack.—on alder; *A. indiginella* (Zeller)—on hawthorn (in the Northeast) ; *A. demotella* Grote and *A. septentrionella* Dyar—on pecan buds (in Texas) ; and *A. feltella* Dyar—on hickory (in southern Canada and from New England to Illinois).

The genus *Dioryctria* Zeller has a world-wide distribution in the Northern Hemisphere, and the larvae of all species are borers in conifers. Many are highly injurious to seeds and cones. The larval habits of some of the more widely distributed species are quite variable. This suggests that more than one species is involved in certain cases. This can be established only through further taxanomic and biological investigations. The genus has been discussed by Ebel (*217*), Heinrich (*336*), Neunzig and Merkel (*565*), Munroe (*551*), and Neunzig, et al. (*566*).

Dioryctria clarioralis (Walker) occurs throughout the South and infests the vegetative buds, male bud clusters, conelets, and cones of longleaf, slash, loblolly, and shortleaf pines. Moths have forewings marked with wide and nearly black transverse bands near the base, and have wingspreads of 22 to 29 mm. (fig. 137). Larvae are usually yellow-brown to orange-brown, often heavily suffused with gray; they are about 18 mm. long. This was the most common of the moths infesting the cones of shortleaf and loblolly pines in Arkansas in 1960 (*799*). Cone damage is almost identical to that caused by *D. zimmermani*.

Winter is probably spent in the larval stage in conelets. During the spring and summer, the larvae bore into buds, conelets, and cones to feed. A characteristic of this species is the presence of resin-coated silk over the entrance hole in which ejected frass

FIGURE 137.—Adult of *Dioryctria clarioralis*.

is accumulated. Pupation takes place inside hollowed-out cones or conelets or in silken cocoons on uninfested twigs or cone stalks. One generation per year has been recorded in North Carolina. Farther South there may be as many as three per year.

Dioryctria abietella (D & S.) [=*abietivorella* (Grote)] attacks the cones, shoots, and bark of many different conifers, particularly in the genus *Pinus,* and apparently occurs throughout the range of these trees in the Northern Hemisphere. The larvae are among the most destructive pests of slash and longleaf pine cones in the Southern States. Cones infected with the rust *Cronartium strobilinum* are especially attractive (*513*). In the Lake States and southern Canada, red pine cones also are occasionally seriously damaged. The adult (fig. 138) is dark gray with white, zigzag lines bordered by black on the forewings, and has a wingspread of about 20 to 30 mm. Mature larvae are usually reddishpurple with a greenish tinge below, and are about 20 mm. long.

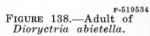

F-519534
FIGURE 138.—Adult of *Dioryctria abietella.*

There appears to be one generation per year in southern Canada; in Florida there may be five or six. Infestations in rust-infected cones are noticeable as early as April in Florida. By mid-June attacks on second-year cones are also apparent.

The **spruce coneworm,** *Dioryctria reniculella* (Grote), occurs throughout most or all of the forested regions of Canada and as far west as the Lake States in northeastern United States. Its preferred hosts appear to be white spruce and balsam fir, but many other conifers including Sitka, Engelmann, red, black, Norway, and Colorado blue spruces, Douglas fir, larch, and jack pine are also attacked. The adult is usually silvery-gray and has a wing expanse of 22 to 26 mm. The forewings are marked with zig-zag white lines and a white discal spot. Mature larvae are reddish or amber brown, have hairy warts on each body segment, and are about 18 mm. long.

In Canada, adults emerge from late June to early August and deposit their eggs singly or in small groups in such places as cracks or fissures in the bark of stems and twigs, in lichens, within the axils of shoots, or between the scales on cones. The eggs hatch in about 10 days, and the young larvae, without feeding, spin hibernaculae in which they spend the winter. When they become active again in the spring, they usually mine one or two needles and then move to and bore into buds, staminate flowers, or cones. During certain years, this species takes a heavy toll of white spruce seed (*495*).

The **Zimmerman pine moth**, *Dioryctria zimmermani* (Grote), as presently identified, is widely distributed in the United States and southern Canada. In the northern part of its range, the larvae feed in the cambial region and outer xylem under the bark of limbs and trunks of all commonly grown species of pines. In the Southeastern States, it feeds almost exclusively within damaged cones of loblolly pine. The adult is gray and has a wingspread of about 25 to 37 mm. The forewing is mottled with zigzag lines of red and shades of gray. Mature larvae from the Northern States are pink to greenish and covered with small black dots, each with a black seta; they are about 18 mm. long. Larvae from the Southeast differ by having the abdominal segments bluish-black above. These differences in habits and appearance of the larvae suggest that not one but two closely related species are involved (*565*).

Adults in the Northern States emerge from mid-July to mid-August and deposit their eggs at the edges of wounds, on resin masses, in bark crevices, or on terminal buds. Hatching occurs in about 8 to 10 days and the young larvae, without feeding, enter bark recesses and spin hibernaculae. Here they remain until the following spring. Feeding begins in May or June, first on the bark, then by tunneling in the cambium area of new growth on terminals or laterals. Damaged terminals usually become "fish-hooked" and turn yellowish-green. Toward the end of June, the larvae leave the new growth and tunnel beneath the bark in the whorl area, girdling branches and leaders. Pupation occurs in resin masses or in the tunnel. Dead tops, dead branches hanging on trees (fig. 139), and burl-like growths on trunks above girdled whorls and pitch masses (fig. 140) are evidence of attack. Infested trees tend to be reattacked again and again, thus becoming so-called brood trees (*614*).

In the Southwest, the winter is spent as young larvae in terminals or second-year cones. Older larvae feed in second-year cones only. Entrance holes in cones are usually filled with loose frass but are not surrounded or covered with resin or webbing. Pupation occurs deep within hollowed out cones and the adults appear in September and October. Infested cones stop growing and turn brown when about half to three-quarters grown.

Zimmerman pine moth damage has been especially serious in Christmas tree plantations of Scotch, red, and Austrian pines in the North Central States and southern Canada in recent years.

Dioryctria amatella (Hulst.) occurs from Virginia to Florida and westward through the Gulf Coast States to Texas and Arkansas. It appears to be most closely associated with longleaf pine, the larvae attacking both the terminals and second-year cones; however, it also attacks second-year cones of loblolly, slash, and shortleaf pines, and stem and branch galls of southern fusiform rust on loblolly and slash pines. The adult (fig. 141) has a wingspread of 27 to 32 mm. and the forewing is dark-brown to black, with prominent patches and zigzag lines of white. Mature larvae are greenish-white with brownish markings above; they are about 25 mm. long.

Winter is spent mostly as young larvae at the base of first-year cones or under expanded terminal needles—occasionally as

F-492959

FIGURE 139.—Damage to young pine by *Dioryctria zimmermani.*

F-492960

FIGURE 140.—Burl - like growths on trunk above gridled whorl, a sign of attack by Zimmerman pine moth.

older larvae in damaged second-year cones. In the Southeast, a high proportion of the overwintering population attacking elongating terminals of longleaf pine in the spring. The tips of these terminals soon turn brown and die. Most of the larvae move to and attack second-year cones by late June, entering them usually near the base. Entrance holes become filled with frass and pitch, and the pitch tends to spread over the outer surface of the cone. By late July, the cones are almost completely browned. If feeding continues in them to the end of the season, they dry out and remain either partially or entirely closed. Pupation occurs either in infested terminals or in hollowed-out cones, and there are several generations per year. This is one of the most abundant species of the genus in the Southeastern States where it occasionally causes heavy seed losses.

F-519535

FIGURE 141.Adult of *Dioryctria amatella.*

357

Dioryctria cambiicola (Dyar) has been found damaging second-year cones and shoots of red pine in southern Canada and the Lake States. The adult has a wing expanse of about 20 to 30 mm., and its forewing is dark purple-brown. Mature larvae are gray to green and about 15mm. long. The larvae apparently feed primarily in the pith of large current-year's red pine shoots and attack cones only when mature (*464*). *D. pygmaeela* Ragonot occurs in eastern United States. It infests the cones of cypress from Maryland to Florida.

Dioryctria disclusa Heinrich larvae feed in the cones of Scotch, red, and jack pines in the Northern States and southern Canada and in the cones of longleaf, loblolly, and scrub pines in the Southeastern States. The adult is bright white, orange, and red and has a wingspread of 17 to 29 mm. In the North, a mature larva is slender, olive-green to buff in color, and about 14 to 18 mm. long. Southern larvae are similar in appearance but are somewhat larger, from 20 to 25 mm. in length.

In the Northern States and Canada, winter is spent as a first-instar larvae in hibernaculae spun beneath bark scales on the branches of red pine. During the spring, the larvae feed first in staminate flowers. Later, they tunnel in second-year cones (*464*). In the Southeast, winter is spent as partly-grown larvae in newly-formed cones. In the spring, the larvae continue their feeding, sometimes destroying two or three cones each. Infested cones have silk attached to their outer surfaces around larval entry holes and to nearby needles. Pupation occurs in damaged cones from mid-May to mid-June, and adults are present from late May to July. There is one generation per year.

The **locust leaf roller,** *Nephopteryx* (=*Salebria*) *subcaesiella* (Clemens), occurs from southern Canada and Maine to West Virginia and westward to Colorado. The larvae feed inside rolled leaves of honey locust and wisteria. The adult is gray and has a wingspread of 25 mm. The forewing is reddish near the base and has a broken, black terminal line. Mature larvae are about 25 mm. long. The head is blackish and the body green, except for a dark line down the middle of the dorsum and for five faint yellow lines on each side. The winter is spent as pupae in silken cocoons among leaves on the ground. This species is quite common at times, but is seldom injurious. *N. virgatella* (Clem.) is a leaf roller on black locust. The larvae resemble those of the locust leaf roller except for their brown heads. *N. subfuscella* (Ragonot) is a leaf roller on sumac from Maine to Texas. The adult is ash gray and has a wingspread of 22 mm. Mature larvae are yellowish-green except for brick-red lines on the dorsum and sides and are about 25 mm. long.

The **lesser cornstalk borer,** *Elasmopalpus lignosellus* (Zeller), a widely distributed species, has damaged black locust seedlings in nurseries in several Southern States. Loblolly pine seedlings in nursery beds in Virginia and Rhode Island have also been damaged. Gall- like growths occur at points of injury on the lower stems of locust seedlings, causing them to die or break off at the ground line. The male adult is ochre yellow to light brown and has a wingspread of 16 to 24 mm. The forewings are long and narrow and marked with several black spots. Mature larvae are greenish-white with interrupted longitudinal stripes of dark brown. The winter is spent either in the larval or pupal stage and there are up to four generations per year in the Deep South.

The **American plum borer,** *Euzophera semifuneralis* (Walker), is widespread and attacks a wide variety of hardwoods, including plum, wild cherry, apple, London plane, mountain ash, walnut, persimmon, mulberry, basswood, poplar, sweetgum, and gingko. Serious infestations have occurred on young London plane trees in newly developed areas on Long Island. The larvae bored in the trunks and larger branches, and were associated with a canker condition.

Euzophera ostricolorella Hulst has been recorded from Long Island to South Carolina and westward to Ohio, Kentucky, Tennessee, and Louisiana. Its preferred host appears to be yellow poplar, but it also attacks magnolia. Heaviest infestations on yellow poplar are found at the base of trees over 10 inches in diameter (*325*). Attacks above a height of 2 feet on the trunk are rare. The larvae feed in the inner bark, excavating tunnels which extend both above and below the ground line. Winter is spent in the pupal stage in the tunnel. There appears to be one generation per year in the North and two per year in the South. Trees of all sizes may be killed by heavy infestations.

Euzophera magnolialis Capps has been observed damaging or killing magnolia seedlings in Florida nurseries. The adult has a wingspread of about 25 mm., and the forewing is puprlish-brown, with black terminal dots. Full-grown larvae are white and flattened, they taper toward the rear and are about 28 mm. long. Attacks occur at the base, the larvae tunneling in the lower inches of the trunk and in the larger roots entering the crown. Heavily infested trees may be girdled and killed (*134*).

Canarsia ulmiarrosorella (Clem.) occurs in southern Canada and throughout eastern United States. The larvae feed on the leaves of elm which they web together with silk. The adult has a wingspread of 15 to 20 mm. The forewings are dusty white and crossed by dark gray or blackish bands. Mature larvae are green, sparsely hairy and about 18 mm. long. Winter is spent in the pupal stage, and there are two generations per year. This species is sometimes abundant enough to attract attention, but is seldom injurious.

Moodna ostrinella Clemens is rather widely distributed in southeasten Canada and eastern United States. In Canada, the larvae have been found in second-year pine cones damaged by other insects. They have also been found in pine cones in Arkansas; in sumac heads in New York, Pennsylvania, and Texas; and in fusiform rust cankers on slash and longleaf pines in Florida. Full-grown larvae vary from yellow with a greenish tinge to bright yellow orange or orange, and are about 8 to 10 mm. long.

Actrix nyssaecolella Dyar is a leaf folder or leaf roller of tupelo from western Pennsylvania to New Jersey and Massachusetts. The adult is powdery gray and has a wingspread of 15 mm. Full-grown larvae are black with yellow heads. Winter is spent in the pupal stage, and larvae are present during July and August.

Laetilia coccidivora Comstock larvae feed on various scale insects. According to some reports, it has aided materially in the control of outbreaks of the pine tortoise scale. It has been recorded from Pennsylvania and Ohio to Florida and Texas.

FAMILY OLETHREUTIDAE

OLETHREUTID MOTHS

This family contains a large number of economically important species of forest insects. Several are particularly important as pests in nurseries and plantations. The larvae differ widely in their feeding habits. Some feed by boring into the buds, twigs, stems, roots, seed, or fruit of their hosts; others feed on the foliage as leaf miners, from within folded leaves, or on the exposed surface. MacKay (*487, 488*) described the known larvae of North American species.

Episimus argutanus (Clem.) is widely distributed and feeds as a leaf roller on sumac, poison ivy, witch hazel, and various other shrubs. The adult has a wing expanse of about 12 mm. and is dull reddish or grayish-brown, mottled with darker colors. Each larva lives in a rolled leaf or between two leaves fastened together with silk. There are two or more generations per year.

The **spruce needle miner,** *Taniva albolineana* (Kft.), occurs from coast to coast in southern Canada and from Maine to North Carolina, Colorado, and Idaho in the United States. Its hosts are white, Norway, Engelmann, Colorado, and black spruce. The adult is dark brown and has a wingspread of about 12 mm. The forewings have three irregular, transverse, broken, grayish-white bands.

Adults are present from mid-May to mid-June. Eggs are deposited so that they overlap in a single row on the undersides of needles in groups of two to twelve eggs each. Young larvae are gregarious and bore into the bases of old needles, hollowing them out. Older larvae feed singly. Shortly after beginning to feed the larvae construct nests composed of dead needles and frass which are held together by fine silk strands. As the larvae develop, their nests are continually enlarged. Winter is spent in the larval stage in the nest. Feeding is resumed on adjacent needles in the spring. Pupation takes place in silken cocoons within the nest during late spring or early summer.

The spruce needle miner is most important as a pest of ornamental spruce, but it also occasionally causes serious defoliation in forest stands. The presence of webs on ornamentals reduces their esthetic value. This can be largely prevented by handpicking or washing the webs from the trees before the buds break in the spring. Webs washed to the ground should be picked up and burned.

Evora hemidesma (Zell.) feeds as a leaf roller on alder, poplar, and willow in southern Canada, and in the Eastern States from Maine to Virginia and Kentucky. The adult is reddish-brown with a darker median band on the forewing and has a wingspread of 12 to 16 mm. Full-grown larvae are dark green to almost black, sparsely hairy, with light-colored tubercles and light-brown

360

heads, and are about 18 mm. long. Larvae are present from May to July.

The **European pine shoot moth**, *Rhyacionia buolinana* (Schiff.) (fig. 142), an introduced species first recorded in North America on Long Island, N.Y., in 1914 (*127*), is now widely distributed in the Northeastern States and southern Canada. Outlying infestations also occur in Washington, Oregon, and British Columbia. Its hosts include Scotch, red, Austrian, mugho, Japanese red, Japanese black, ponderosa, eastern white, jack, pitch, longleaf, and Virginia pines (*527*). Red, mugho, Scotch and Austrian pines are most heavily attacked in eastern United States, especially red and mugho. The adult moth is rusty orange-red and has a wingspread of about 18 mm. The forewings are marked with several irregular, forked, silvery cross lines; the hindwings are plain dark brown, and the legs are whitish.

Adults appear in late spring and fly at night. They lay eggs singly or in groups of two to ten on the bases of buds, on needle fascicles and twig tips, or on the bark of new and old shoots.

F-493841, 493467

FIGURE 142.—European pine shoot moth, *Rhyacionia buoliana*: A, red pine tip with solidified resin mass broken open to show partly grown larvae; B, red pine stand badly damaged by the shoot moth. Note spiked and bushy tops.

Newly-hatched larvae spin resin coated, tentlike webs between needle sheaths and the stems of current year's growth, then they bore through the sheaths and mine the bases of the needles. About mid-summer, the larvae move to buds and construct new resin coated webs. At first, these webs glisten brightly; then they solidify into yellowish-white masses. Feeding ceases in August. Winter is spent in the larval stage in a feeding tunnel in a bud. When activity is resumed in April, the larvae move to undamaged buds and new shoots, construct new tents, and resume feedings. During this period, a single larva may feed on more than one bud or shoot. Larvae reach maturity in May, and pupation occurs inside the burrow or tent in late May or June. Two or three weeks later, the larva works its way out of its chamber. There is one generation per year.

The most important and permanent damage to trees results from spring feeding. Shoots weakened by larval tunneling fall over, but continue to grow. This results in the formation of crooked trunks and branches or "post horns." The killing of terminal and lateral buds results in dead, spike tops. The development of adventitious buds below this dead portion often causes the formation of dense, bushy growth the following season. The killing of the terminal bud and the development of several lateral buds into competing leaders results in forked stems. All open-grown young trees of susceptible species below a height of 20 to 25 feet are subject to attack and damage. Taller trees or trees growing in closed stands are usually not seriously damaged.

Climate is an important factor affecting the distribution and abundance of the European pine shoot moth. Overwintering larvae are killed by temperatures colder than about −20° F. Warm, dry summers followed by mild winters permit maximum survival. Rate of tree growth is also important as damage is usually most severe on slow-growing trees. Introduced and native species of parasites normally destroy about 10 percent of the population. Five introduced species have become established: *Orgilus obscurator* (Nees), *Temelucha interruptor* (Grav.), *Eulimneria rufifemur* Thom., *Pimpla turionellae* (L.), and *Tetrastichus turionum* Htg. *O. obscurator* appears to offer the most promise. Yates (*797*) published a key to the nearctic parasites of the genus.

The planting of susceptible pines on good sites, "snow-depth pruning," and Christmas tree shearing are helpful in reducing damage (*526*). Fumigation in the spring has provided a degree of control on seedlings and larger ornamental specimens (*135*). The reader should consult Agricultural Handbook 331 for details on registered control methods.

Many publications have been issued on the biology, ecology, and control of the European pine shoot moth. In addition to those cited in preceding paragraphs, there are several others that are of special interest (*273, 328, 529, 530, 599, 755*). Articles by Heikkenen [13] and Torgerson [14] are also pertinent.

Rhyacionia adana Heinrich has been recorded from Massachusetts, Pennsylvania, Virginia, Michigan, Wisconsin, and Ontario.

---

[13] Heikkenen, H. J. 1963. Influence of site and other factors on damage by the European pine shoot moth. PhD thesis, Univ. of Mich.
[14] Torgerson, T. P. 1964. The binomics of the European pine shoot moth in Wisconsin. PhD thesis, Univ. of Wis.

Red, jack, and Scotch pine seedlings usually under 3 feet tall in nurseries, plantations, and natural stands and the lower half of trees up to 25 feet tall are attacked. The adult has a wingspread of 15 to 17 mm. The forewing has the outer third red and the remainder gray with four pairs of grayish-white vertical bars.

In Ontario, eggs are laid between needles just above the needle sheath of the needle fascicle. Young larvae spin silken cases between two old needles just above the sheath. Then they enter th needles and mine toward the tip. Later, after new needle growth has begun, they enter and mine the developing shoots. Several larvae may inhabit a single shoot and riddle it with their tunnels. Then they vacate the shoot and move to and destroy the buds. Full-grown larvae crawl down the stem and pupate in cocoons cemented to the stem below the soil surface. There is one generation per year (506). Serious damage has been recorded in red and Scotch pine plantations in Canada and the Lake States.

Rhyacionia rigidana (Fern.) occurs from Georgia to Texas and north to Missouri, New York and Maine. It feeds on pitch, Corsican, Virginia, red, Scotch, loblolly, and slash pines. The adult is similar to the adult of the Nantucket pine tip moth, but is slightly larger and more colorful. The forewings are silver-white with crossbands of silver-white scales, and the hindwings are silver-gray. Its life history is not too well understood; however, there appears to be at least three generations per year in the South. In the North there is probably only one. Damage is also similar to that caused by the Nantucket pine tip moth but apparently differs in the ability of this species to damage trees of large size. Pitch pines up to 15 inches in diameter may be infested, and terminals and laterals of slash pines up to 50 feet tall have been killed.

The **Nantucket pine tip moth**, *Rhyocionia frustrana* (Comst.) (fig. 143), is widely distributed in the Eastern, Central, and Southern States. Its hosts include nearly all species of pines growing within its range, the only exceptions are longleaf and eastern white pines (798). Slash pine is also somewhat resistant, but is occasionally attacked. In the South and Southeast, loblolly and shortleaf pines are preferred; in the Northeast and Mid-Atlantic States pitch, Virginia, and Scotch appear to be favored; and in the Central States, shortleaf is attacked most heavily. Red pine has been infested along the coast of Maine. The adult has the head, body, and appendages covered with gray scales. The forewings are marked with irregular brick-red and coffee-colored patches, the patches being separated by irregular bands of gray scales; the wingspread is 9 to 15 mm.

Winter is spent as a pupa within the injured tips of the host. Adults begin to appear on warm, sunny days in early spring—as early as January in the Deep South. Egg laying begins in a few days, during dusk and darkness. The eggs are deposited on new or old growth needles, in the axils of needles and stems, on developing tips, or on buds. Newly-hatched larvae wander about the shoots looking for suitable feeding sights. Soon, they construct delicate webs in axils formed by developing needles and stems. Then the larva bores into a needle sheath and feeds on the needle, which is then severed. Second instar larvae spin new and larger

F-494206, 494207
FIGURE 143.—Adult and larvae of the Nantucket pine
tip moth, *Rhyacionia frustrana.*

webs between buds, or between buds and needles; they feed in
the buds. When a bud is consumed, the larva moves to another
bud on the same or a different shoot. Eventually, the connective
tissue of the tip is severed, and the damaged portion turns brown.
The larva continues to feed within the shoot and bud. Once having consumed the bud, it bores down the center of the stem. The
larval period lasts for 2 to 4 weeks. Toward the end of this period,
the larva constructs a webbed cell within the shoot in which it
pupates. In the Deep South, there are five or six generations per
year. In the North Carolina, Virginia area, there are three per
year. Still farther north, in Pennsylvania and Ohio, there are only
two per year.

The Nantucket pine tip moth is a major pest of young plants
in the eastern United States. During recent years, it has become
increasingly abundant and destructive as a result of the establishment of large areas of pine plantations and seed orchards.
Damage consists of the retardation of height growth, the crook-
ing or forking of main stems, the reduction of cone crops, and,
occasionally, the death of the tree. Attacks are generally restricted to trees less than 15 feet in height and are most severe in
young plantations, but severe attacks on commercial-size trees
have also been reported.

364

At least 60 species of parasites of the Nantucket pine tip moth have been recorded (*798*), but they are rarely abundant enough to provide satisfactory control. Low winter temperatures in the northern parts of the infested region provide some degree of control by killing overwintering pupae. Damage can also be reduced by limiting the planting of susceptible pines to sites to which they are well adapted. Close spacing and planting under an overstory may also be helpful.

Rhyacionia frustrana bushnelli (Busck), the **western pine tip moth,** occurs from the Dakotas and Nebraska south to New Mexico. Its preferred hosts are ponderosa, red, jack, and Scotch pines. Infestations have been particularly severe in pine plantations in Nebraska (*308*). The adult is indistinguishable from those of the Nantucket pine tip moth, although it tends to be larger. Heinrich (*335*) suggested that it and the true *R. f. frustrana* are one and the same, but Miller (*528*) believes that *bushnelli* may be a distinct species because of its overwintering habit and size. There is one generation per year in the Dakotas and two per year in Nebraska.

In 1925, *Campoplex frustranae* Cush., a common parasite of the Nantucket pine tip moth in the East, was liberated in infested plantations in the Nebraska National Forest. It became established immediately and increased rapidly. By 1930, parasitism at the original liberation point had reached 80%. Unfortunately, the related tip moth, *R. frustrana neomexicana*, which the parasite also attacks but in which it is unable to develop, increased very rapidly in the area about this time, and parasitism of *R. f. bushnelli* declined. This may have happened because the parasite deposited too many of its eggs on *R. f. neomexicana*.

Rhyacionia subtropica Miller, a newly-described species (*524*), occurs throughout the range of slash pine in the South. Typical slash pine, *Pinus elliottii* var. *elliottii*, is the preferred host, but longleaf, loblolly, and tropical pine are also attacked. South Florida slash pine, *P. elliottii* var. *densa*, is fairly resistant. Heavy infestations have been recorded in slash pine plantations on poor sites in Florida; whereas naturally regenerated slash pine seedlings have rarely been infested. Serious losses of grafted slash pine scions in tree improvement programs have been incurred.

Rhyacionia sonia Miller, a newly-described species (*528*), has been recorded from Maine west to southern Manitoba and from South Carolina. Its hosts are jack and pitch pines in the North, and slash and loblolly pines in the South. Superficially, the adult is indistinguishable from those of *R. f. frustrana* and *R. f. bushnelli*. Winter is spent in the pupal stage and there is one generation per year.

The **pitch twig moth,** *Petrova comstockiana* (Fern.), occurs from Maine to North Carolina and west into the Central States. Its hosts include the hard pines, but pitch pine is preferred in the Midwest. The adult is reddish-brown with gray mottlings and has a wingspread of 14 to 20 mm.

In Ohio, eggs are deposited on twigs during May and June. The larvae bore into and downward in the twigs for distances of 3 or 4 inches, and pitch masses form over the entry holes (fig. 144). Winter is spent as a larva under the pitch mass. Development is

F-519519
FIGURE 144.—Larva of the pitch twig moth, *Petrova comstockiana*, in the twig of red pine. Pitch mass covers the opening to the larval gallery.

resumed in May, and pupation occurs under the mass. There is one generation per year. Damaged twigs break off, leading to deformation of infested trees. The braconid, *Agathis pini* (Mues.), has been a major factor in control (*531*).

Petrova virginiana McD. feeds on jack pine in the Lake States and southern Canada. The larvae feed in and hollow out the terminals and adjacent lateral buds. Winter is spent as a larva in the large, central bud. Feeding is resumed about mid-May and pupation occurs in the bud in early June. Damage to terminals and lateral buds results in the death of an entire whorl, causing crooked stems and stag-headedness.

Petrova albicapitana (Busck), the **pitch nodule maker,** occurs in all parts of North America where jack pine grows naturally. Scotch and lodgepole pines are also attacked. The adult is reddish-brown with grayish patches on the forewings, and has a wing-spread of 16 to 23 mm.

Young pines from 1 to 5 feet tall are most heavily infested. Smaller ones are not attacked and taller ones are rarely injured, although signs of attack may be seen in trees up to 30 feet tall. Larvae feed singly under masses of pitch, some of which may be up to 1½ inches in diameter, generally at an internode or fork. As they develop, their feeding may be extended almost to the pith. Two years are required to complete the life cycle, winter being spent in the larval stage. Pupation occurs under the pitch mass.

When an attack occurs at the base of a growing terminal, the shoot may be girdled and killed, or the terminal may survive as a weakened, crooked trunk. Damage in jack, Scotch, and lodgepole pine plantations may be severe. Areas planted entirely during a 1- or 2-year period suffer much less damage than areas planted in small blocks over a period of several years (*723*).

Petrova houseri Miller attacks shortleaf pine in Ohio, West Virginia, and Georgia. The adult is dark gray with light and dark brown areas, has brown, fringed hindwings, and a wingspread of about 12 mm. Prior to its description as a new species (*525*), its damage had been attributed to the pitch twig moth.

The larvae feed in the inner bark of current shoots, usually girdling them. Pitch blisters forming over the entrance holes, average about one-half inch in diameter. Usually, there is only one blister per shoot, and it is situated away from a branch node. Toward the end of summer, the larva bores down to the pith where it spends the winter. Activity is resumed in the spring, and the larva tunnels toward the base of the shoot for a distance of about 1 inch. Pupation occurs beneath the blister. There is one generation per year. Infested shoots usually turn reddish brown, die, and eventually break off. The braconid, *Agathis pini* (Muesebeck), is an important parasite of the species.

The **eye-spotted bud moth**, *Spilonota ocellana* (D. & S.), an introduced species, occurs from coast to coast in the Northern States and southern Canada and south to North Carolina. Its hosts are hawthorn, larch, laurel, oak, and several species of fruit trees. The adult is dark, ashy gray, with a large irregular whitish median band on the forewing and has a wingspread of 12 to 16 mm.

Adults appear in June and early July and lay their eggs on the undersides of leaves. Young larvae feed for a short time on the leaves and then migrate to young twigs where they spin tiny silken hibernaculae in which to spend the winter. Feeding is resumed in the spring on opening buds and unfolding leaves. These are bound together with silk. Pupation occurs in June in silk-lined cocoons. There is one generation per year (*571*). This species is most important as an orchard pest.

Eucosma gloriola Heinrich, the **white-pine shoot borer,** is widely distributed in the Northeastern and Lake States and southern Canada. Its hosts are eastern white, jack, red, Scotch, Austrian, and mugho pines. The adult is coppery-red, with two shining gray transverse bands on the forewings, and has a wingspread of 15 to 18 mm.

Eggs apparently are laid on needle sheaths on new shoots or laterals during May or early June. Young larvae bore into the pith a few inches above the node of the new shoot and construct tunnels several inches long toward the tip. Infested shoots are eventually girdled from the inside (*209*). The full-grown larva bores a hole to the outside through which it escapes and drops to the ground. There it spins a cocoon in the litter or just below the soil surface in which it pupates. Winter is spent in the pupal stage (*132*).

The white-pine shoot borer is a serious pest of young jack pines in the Lake States and Ontario and in white, red, and Scotch pine plantations in New York and Pennsylvania. Infested terminals bend over or break off. Damaged laterals turn yellow, then red, and die gradually as the season advances. Infested trees become bushy after repeated attacks.

Eucosma monitorana Heinrich attacks the cones of various pines in the Northeastern States and southern Canada. The adult is reddish-brown with tan and silver markings on the forewings and has a wingspread of 13 to 16 mm.

In southern Canada, young larvae enter the upper parts of second-year cones in June and bore down the cone axis. They feed on immature seeds until the supply is exhausted and sometimes sever the cone at the base. A single cone may contain up to 25 larvae. Last instar larvae sometimes migrate to and enter relatively fresh cones. At first, they bore around the cone for a short distance. Then they tunnel toward and into the axis where they feed on surrounding seed. Mature larvae vacate the cones during July and drop to the ground to pupate, the stage in which the species overwinters. There is one generation per year (*465*).

Eucosma sonomana Kft., the **jack-pine shoot moth,** occurs in the Lake States and attacks jack pine. The adult has coppery-red forewings and a wingspread of about 18 mm. The larvae are brownish-gray and about 12 mm. long. Young plantation pines from 3 to 12 feet tall are usually attacked, but trees up to 30 feet tall may also be infested. The larvae bore into the pith, 6 to 8 inches above the branch whorl of the previous season, and mine downward for a few inches. Then they move back up the shoot for a few inches, girdle the shoots, bore to the surface and drop to the ground to pupate. By this time, the shoot has wilted and has bent over or broken off (fig. 145) (*473*).

Eucosma cocana Kft., has been recorded as occurring in Massachusetts, Connecticut, Virginia, North Carolina, and Florida, and as probably feeding on the cones of loblolly pine. *E. tocullionana* Heinrich has been recorded from Ontario and New Brunswick, Canada, and from Wisconsin, Massachusetts, New York, Connecticut, Pennsylvania, Virginia, North Carolina, and Ten-

F-492898

FIGURE 145.—Damage to pine terminal by *Eucosma sonomana.*

368

nessee. The larvae feed on the cones of various conifers, such as white pine, spruce, balsam fir, and hemlock (*603*).

Gypsonoma haimbachiana (Kft.), has been recorded from Ontario, from the northern tier of States from New York to Michigan and south through the midwestern states of Missouri, Oklahoma, Arkansas to Mississippi, Louisiana, and Texas. Its hosts are listed as various poplars. The adult is ash gray and has a wingspread of 13 to 17 mm. The basal portion of the forewing is darker than the apical portion. Full-grown larvae are pale and from 13 to 17 mm. long. The head is brownish-yellow; the thoracic shield, brownish-yellow edged with brown; and the anal shield, brown or grayish.

Winter is spent mostly as young larvae either in silk covered, shallow pits excavated in healed-over borer entrance holes, in the margins of corky bark ridges below leaf bases or in depressions of leaf scars. Lesser numbers of late-instar larvae overwinter in hollowed out terminal buds. When the younger larvae resume activity in the spring, they enter the tender, new shoots to feed and complete their development. When the older overwintering larvae resume feeding in the spring, they frequently kill the bud and up to 10 inches of the terminal. There appears to be four or five generations per year in the Mississippi Delta region (*540*).

This is one of the most destructive of the insects that damage young trees of eastern cottonwood. Damaged trees are stunted, have crooked trunks, and produce too many limbs. This leads to a great reduction in the quality and quantity of merchantable pulpwood, sawlogs, or veneer from these trees.

Proteoteras aesculana Riley, the **maple seed caterpillar,** occurs throughout southern Canada and the Northern States, south to Tennessee. The adult is olive-green with yellow, gray, and black markings, and has a wingspread of 11 to 18 mm. The larvae bore in the seeds, leaf stalks, and terminal twigs of horse chestnut and maple and sometimes cause serious injury. Seedlings in nurseries have been heavily attacked. Adults emerge in July and August.

The **boxelder twig borer,** *Proteoteras willingana* Kft., attacks boxelder and maple in many of the Northern and Midwestern States and southern Canada. The adult is white to brownish, marked with streaks, rings, and clusters of yellowish-tan to black scales; it has a wingspread of 11 to 18 mm. The larva destroys dormant leaf buds in the fall and early spring. Later in the spring, it burrows in succulent twigs (fig. 146), causing the formation of spindle-shaped galls (*594*). These galls become woody when they dry out. This usually prevents further terminal growth. Severe damage has been recorded in shelterbelt plantings in the Prairie Provinces of Canada.

The **spruce bud moth,** *Zeiraphera ratzeburgiana* (Ratz.), an apparent introduction from Europe late in the 19th century, now occurs throughout the range of spruce in northern United States and Canada (*595*). In addition to spruce, it feeds on several other conifers, especially fir. The adult is light brown and has a wingspread of about 12 mm. The forewings have darker diagonal markings, and the outer margins are straight. Full-grown larvae are yellowish or grayish green and about 18 mm. long.

F-500805
FIGURE 146.—Larva of the
boxelder twig borer, *Proteoteras willingana*, in a boxelder stem.

Young larvae feed singly in opening buds in the spring or on
tender terminal needles which they web together. Some pupae are
found on the foliage of the trees, but the majority occur immediately below the ground surface. Winter is passed in the egg stage,
and there is one generation per year. *Zeiraphera diniana* Gn.
occurs all the way across southern Canada and possibly in the
northern tier of States. It appears to prefer larch and spruce, but
several other conifers are also infested. *Z. fortunana* (Kft.)
occurs commonly from coast to coast in southern Canada. Infes-

tations also have been found in Maine. It apparently prefers white spruce.

The **maple trumpet skeletonizer,** *Epinotia aceriella* (Clem.), occurs from southern Canada to North Carolina. Its hosts are principally red and sugar maples, but it has also been collected on hawthorn and beech. The adult is white, with dustings of gray or brown and has a wingspread of about 15 mm. Each larva spins a long trumpet-like tube of silk and frass on the underside of a leaf, causing the leaf to fold around it. It feeds from within this tube and skeletonizes the part of the leaf covered by the web, causing it to crumple. Damage is usually not very serious. *E. solandriana* (L.) feeds as a leaf roller on trembling aspen, white birch, and various other hardwoods. It is sometimes abundant in the Northeast and Ontario.

Epinotia nanana (Treit.), an introduced species first recorded in North America in Massachusetts in the early days of this century, now occurs from Maine to Ohio and Michigan and in Ontario, Quebec, and British Columbia, Canada. Its hosts are various species of spruce, especially white, Norway, and Colorado blue. The adult is dark, smoky brown and has a wingspread of about 11 mm. The forewing has a rather blunt apex, which is black and diffused below by a white dash. A blackish band crosses from the middle of the costa to before the anal angle. There are five distinct white spots on the costa of fresh specimens, and the wing is also flecked with whitish scales.

Adults are present during June in Canada and deposit their eggs on the needles. Newly-hatched larvae attack the old needles, boring into them and hollowing them out completely. From the third instar on, they feed in about equal numbers on both old and new needles. A single larva may feed on several needles which it ties together with silk. The winter is spent in the larval stage inside a mined needle. In the spring, the larva moves to a new needle and continues its feeding. Before reaching maturity, it may destroy several other needles, all of which are tied together in bunchs appressed to the twig. Pupation occurs in silken cocoons in hollowed out needles, in old staminate flowers, on the bark, or in litter on the ground. There is one generation per year (*183*). Webs washed from the trees in the spring with a strong stream of water before the buds break has been suggested for control on ornamentals.

Anchylopera plantanana Clemens occurs commonly on sycamore wherever it grows in this country. The adult is whitish with pale reddish forewings and has a wingspread of about 12 mm. Eggs are deposited along the midribs or larger veins on the undersurface of leaves during early spring. Young larvae feed on both sides of the midrib, near the base, and spin fine, silken webs over the leaf surface. Older ones feed beneath these webs and skeletonize the leaf. The winter is spent in the larval stage (*190*).

The **spruce seed moth,** *Laspeyresia youngana* (Kft.), is rather widely distributed in the United States and Canada. It attacks the cones of white, red, black, Colorado, Sitka, and Engelmann spruces. The larvae make tortuous mines near the cone axis, destroying both scales and seeds. White spruce cones are especially susceptible. The adult is smoky brown with four cross bars of shining silver and four shining costal spots on the forewings and has a wingspread of 8 to 11 mm. Full-grown larvae are creamy white and about 10 mm. long.

Winter is spent as a full-grown larva within a cone. Most of the larvae pupate in the spring; some may remain in diapause for 1 to 2 or more years (721). Female moths are reluctant to fly, and as a result, populations tend to build up on old cones bearing trees.

The **hickory shuckworm,** *Laspeyresia caryana* (Fitch), occurs in southern Canada and from the east coast to Missouri and Texas in the United States. The larvae feed on hickory nuts and pecans. The adult is smoky-black and has a wingspread of about 12 mm. Full-grown larvae are creamy white and about 9 mm. long.

Adults appear in early spring (as early as mid-February in Florida) and lay their eggs on the nuts or foliage. Young larvae bore into and feed inside the nuts, thus preventing future nut development. Winter is spent as a larva in the shucks of fallen nuts, and there are from one to four generations per year, depending on locality. Heavy infestations may seriously reduce hickory nut and pecan crops. Gathering and destroying infested nuts during the winter is helpful in control.

Laspeyresia toreuta (Grote) occurs in southern Canada and south in the Eastern States to South Carolina and Texas. It attacks the second-year cones of various pines. The adult is gray-brown with two prominent black-bordered silver bands across each forewing and has a wingspread of 13 to 15 mm. The mature larva is creamy white and about 10 mm. long.

Adults emerge during late May and early June in the mid-South and during late June in Ontario and deposit their eggs in crevices over the cone surface. Young larvae bore into the upper part of second-year cones and enter the seeds to feed; older ones bore around the cone through the bases of scales, feeding on available seeds. Infestations appear to be heaviest on open-grown trees with branches to the ground or on trees in low density stands (439). Winter is spent as a full-grown larva in the woody axis of the cone, and pupation occurs in the spring. A braconid parasite, *Phanerotoma* sp., may destroy a high percentage of the full-grown larvae (465).

Laspeyresia anaranjada Miller occurs throughout the range of typical slash pine, *Pinus elliotti* Engelmann, and its south Florida variety, *P. elliotti* var. *densa* Little and Dorman, in the South. The adult (fig. 147 B) has a wingspan of 14 to 16 mm. The abdomen is pearl-white and the forewings are yellowish orange to rusty orange, with four more or less equally spaced, mostly pearl-white cross bands. The species has been reared principally from mature cones of slash pine, occasionally from longleaf cones, and rarely from loblolly cones.

Eggs are usually laid either singly or in small clusters on second-year cones. Young larvae bore into the cones and feed on the seed, moving from seed to seed, consuming their contents, and lining the tunnels between seeds with silk. A single larva consumes from five to seven seeds. Eventually, the full-grown larva bores into the woody cone axis where it spends the winter. Pupation occurs in the spring, and the adults emerge during April and

FIGURE 147.—Adults of seedworm moths:
A, *Laspeyresia ingens;* B, *Laspeyresia anaranjada.*

May. There is one generation per year. According to estimates, this species destroys from 2 to 10 percent of the seed in open-grown slash pine stands in northeast Florida each year (*514*).

Laspeyresia ingeus Heinrich has been recorded from South Carolina, Georgia, Florida, Alabama, and Mississippi and probably occurs throughout the range of its favored host, longleaf pine. It also infests slash pine to minor extent and may occur occasionally on other southern pines. The adult (fig. 147 A) is grayish-brown and has a wingspread of 17 to 20 mm. Eggs are laid in rows of two to nine eggs each on scale apophyses of 1-year-old cones. Young larvae bore downward through the scales and enter seeds through the micropyle. Larva feeds during the first two instars, each in a seed, vacating it and tunnelling through the cone in search of another seed. Before it reaches maturity the larva may consume two to five additional seeds. A full-grown larva bores into the rachis and usually tunnels toward the base for a distance of 1 to 2 inches. Winter is spent in the larval stage in this tunnel. Pupation occurs in the spring, usually between mid-March and mid-May, and the adult appears about 1 to 2 weeks later. There is one generation per year, except for occasional individuals that enter diapause (*163*). This species causes an estimated loss of 21 percent of longleaf pine seed in the Gulf States region. The related species, *L. erotella* (Heinrich) attacks loblolly pine cones in the Southeastern States.

The **filbertworm**, *Melissopus latiferreanus* (Wlsm.), occurs throughout most of the United States and in southern Canada. The larvae feed in hazelnuts, filberts, acorns, beechnuts, chestnuts, and oak galls. The adult is reddish-brown and has a wingspread of 11 to 20 mm. High percentages of acorn crops may be destroyed during poor seed years.

Paralobesia liriodendrana (Kft.) has been recorded feeding on yellow-poplar in New Jersey and on magnolia in Florida. The adult is brownish or blackish, and there is a tuft or mass of erect, dark-colored scales at the rear of the thorax. Eggs are laid on the leaves from May to September. Young larvae bore into the mid-vein near the petiole and feed in mines during the first instar. Older larvae feed under webs spun on the lower surface of the leaves or between two leaves webbed tightly togther. Pupation occurs undr the web (*593*).

The **locust twig borer**, *Ecdytolopha insiticiana* Zell., attacks black locust throughout eastern United States and in parts of southern Canada. It also occurs in Colorado, Arizona, and California. The adult has a wingspread of about 20 to 25 mm. The forewings are dark, ashy-brown with large, dull, pinkish-white patches on their outer parts. There are also several small, blackish spots near the middle of each of the patches. Full-grown larvae are reddish to straw yellow with a darker dorsal line and are 12 to 20 mm. long.

Adults are present from early May to the end of June and again from July to October. The larvae are twig or stem borers, and cause the formation of elongate galls up to 3 inches long. Winter is passed as a mature larva in a cocoon among the leaves on the ground. In heavily infested areas, seedling mortality may be high. A high percentage of the twigs on larger trees also may be damaged.

Other olethreutids likely to be encountered in eastern forests and their hosts are as follows: *Hedia chionosema* (Zell.)—hawthorn, occasionally red oak and mountain-ash; *Exartema permundanum* Clem.—hickory; *E. quadrifidum*—wild cherry; *Sciaphila duplex* (Wlshm.)—poplar; *Epinotia similana* (Hbn.)—gray birch; *E. lindana* (Fern.)—alternate-leaved and flowering dogwood; and *Griselda radicana* Heinrich—various conifers, principally white spruce and balsam fir.

FAMILY PHALONIIDAE

The moths of this family resemble those of the families Olethreutidae and Tortricidae. Only one eastern species is worthy of mention.

Phalonia rutilana (Hbn.) is an introduced species first recorded in this country in 1878. Its present distribution seems to be limited to southern Canada and from New England to New Jersey and Indiana. Its host plants are various junipers, especially *Juniperus communis* on which it is often abundant. The adult is yellowish and has a wingspread of 10 mm. There are red markings on the head, thorax and forewings, those on the wings occurring as four broad cross bands. The larvae spin webs on the foliage, tying the needles together and forming tubes in which they live and feed. Pupation takes place on the tree in the webbing. The foliage of heavily infested trees may turn brown.

FAMILY TORTRICIDAE

LEAF ROLLER MOTHS

Members of this family eat the foliage of a wide variety of coniferous and deciduous trees of all sizes and ages. Many species are important pests, some extremely so. The larvae either fold or roll individual leaves or parts of leaves or tie several leaves or shoots together forming enclosures in which to rest and feed or from which they move out to feed. The adults are usually small and have wide, oblong, fringed wings. The wing expanse is usually 25 mm. or less and appear bell-shaped while folded. The larvae are usually some shade of green, seldom more than 25 mm. long, and they pupate in flimsy silken cocoons. Just before the pupa transforms to the adult, it works its way partly out of its cocoon.

Adoxophyes furcatana (Wlk.), a leaf roller on sycamore, occurs from New England to Pennsylvania and the Mississippi River Valley. The adult is straw-yellow and has a wingspread of 20 mm. The forewings are marked with five golden brown lines and two irregular light brown bands. The hindwings and their fringes are shiny white. Full-grown larvae are light green, taper toward each end, and are about 18 mm. long.

Amorbia humerosana Clem. occurs from coast to coast in southern Canada and in the Northeastern States south to Pennsylvania. Its hosts include a wide variety of tree species, both coniferous and deciduous. Adults are light gray and have wingspreads of about 25 mm. Larvae are light green except for light brown heads.

Sparganothis acerivorana (MacKay) occurs in southern Canada and the Lake States. In Canada it feeds on several hardwoods, mostly sugar and red maples and also on young Scotch and red pines. In the Lake States, it usually feeds on sugar maple. The adult is reddish-yellow with reddish-brown spots and has a wingspread of about 25 mm. Full-grown larvae are yellowish-green and about 21 mm. long. Winter is apparently spent in the egg stage, and hatching occurs during May of the following spring. Each larva rolls a leaf in which to rest and from which it moves out to feed. Pupation occurs inside the roll.

Defoliation by this species was an important factor leading to the development of maple blight, a condition responsible for the deterioration and death of large numbers of sugar maple trees in Wisconsin during recent years (*294*).

Sparganothis pettitana (Rob.) occurs in southeastern Canada and south and west to Florida and the Mississippi River Valley. The larvae are solitary leaf rollers on various hardwoods, especially basswood and maples. The adult is plain lemon yellow and has a wingspread of about 22 mm. The forewings are sometimes marked with two oblique lines of light brown scales, and the hindwings are white. Full-grown larvae are dull, yellowish-green, with reddish-brown heads and brown to blackish cervical shields.

Sparganothis sulfureana (Clem.) has been observed feeding in the tips and shoots of small red pines in Canada and in the terminals of loblolly pine seedlings in Georgia. Willow, honey locust, apple, and cherry are also attacked. *S. folgidipenna* (Blanchard) occurs over about the same range as *S. sulfureana*. It feeds on white ash, maple, large tooth aspen, and paper birch. *S. dilutocostana* (Wlshm.) occurs commonly on oak in New Jersey and Maine. It has also been recorded feeding on white ash and paper birch in southern Canada. *S. tristriata* Kft. occurs fairly commonly on jack pine in southern Ontario. It probably occurs in the Lake States also.

The genus *Pandemis* Hbn. contains several species which attack a wide variety of hardwoods in eastern America. *P. lamprosana* (Rob.) feeds on beech, paper birch, red and sugar maples, oak, elm, basswood, ironwood, and sassafras from Maine to New Jersey and in southern Ontario and Quebec. *P. limitata* (Rob.)

375

occurs from coast to coast in Canada. It has also been recorded from Maine, Pennsylvania, Georgia, Illinois, and Arkansas. Its hosts include paper birch, willow, oak, basswood, elm, boxelder, alder, and wild cherry.

Archips rosanus (L.), an introduced species, occurs in southeastern Canada, British Columbia and from New England to the Lake States. The larvae are general feeders on a number of deciduous growths. Privet appears to be especially attractive. Adults are dull light-brown to olive-brown and have wingspreads of 17 to 22 mm. Full-grown larvae are dull green and about 18 mm. long. The larvae tie together two or more leaves at the tips of twigs or branches and feed on them during May and June.

The **ugly-nest caterpillar,** *Archips cerasivoranus* (Fitch), occurs from coast to coast in the Northern States and southern Canada. Its preferred hosts are choke and black cherry, but it may also be found on a wide variety of other hardwoods. The adult is dull orange and has a wingspread of 18 to 25 mm. The forewing is irregularly speckled with dark reddish-brown and has three patches of the same color. The hindwing is solid, bright orange. Full-grown larvae are yellowish or greenish yellow except for black heads and cervical shields and are about 20 to 23 mm. long.

Winter is spent in the egg stage. Hatching begins in May, and larvae are present until September, depending on location. They live together in dense nests they construct by webbing twigs and leaves together (fig. 148). In heavily infested areas, these nests

F-519520

FIGURE 148.—Nest of the ugly-nest caterpillar, *Archips cerasivoranus*, on wild cherry.

are often numerous. Some may be large enough to enclose entire small trees.

The ugly-nest caterpillar is usually of little or no economic importance because the trees attacked are usually of low value. However, the presence of its webs on roadside vegetation may be objectionable because of their unsightliness. The cutting and removal of nests provides adequate control in most situations.

The **oak webworm,** *Archips fervidanus* (Clem.), occurs throughout the oak regions of the Northeastern and Lake States and in various parts of southern Canada. Its favored hosts appear to be scrub and bur oaks, but it also feeds on the seedlings and sprouts of several other oaks. The adult is brownish and has a wingspread of 18 to 25 mm. The forewing is yellowish brown with dark patches. The hindwing is uniformly smoky except for a light colored fringe marked with a fine, fasal line. Full-grown larvae are grayish-green and about 20 mm. long. Larvae live together in webs, some of which may be several inches wide and up to 1½ feet long (fig. 149). Occasionally, they are large enough to enclose all of the leaves at the top of a tree. Winter is spent in the egg stage. Larvae appear in midsummer, and pupation occurs within the nest. The species is of little economic importance.

The **fruit-tree leaf roller,** *Archips argyrospilus* (Wlkr.), occurs throughout the United States and from coast to coast in southern Canada. Its hosts include many fruit trees and many forest and shade trees such as ash, hickory, elm, oak, maple, walnut, poplar, birch, basswood, and horse chestnut. The adult is pale yellow to orange red and has a wingspread of 18 to 25 mm. The forewings

FIGURE 149.—Nest of larvae of the oak webworm, *Archips fervidanus.*

are mottled with golden scales, their tips triangular. The hind-wings are fuscous and have dirty white fringes. Full-grown larvae are light green and about 20 to 25 mm. long.

Adults are present from June to August, depending on location. Eggs are deposited in small round or convex masses containing about 100 to 150 eggs each, usually on twigs or small branches. Winter is spent in the egg stage, and hatching occurs in early spring. Young larvae feed on opening buds, blossoms, young fruit, and unfolding leaves which they web together with silk. Later, several leaves may be webbed together, forming a nest in which the larvae live and from which they move out to feed. Pupation occurs in flimsy cocoons spun inside the nest or on the branches or trunk of the tree. A number of outbreaks of this species, some of which covered tens of thousands of acres, have occurred in oak stands in Eastern and Lake States in recent years.

Many other species of *Archips* are also encountered in eastern forests (*266*). A few of these and some of their hosts are as follows: *A. infumatanus* (Zell.)—hickory and pecan; *A. semiferanus* (Wlk.)—oak and witch-hazel; *A. negundanus* (Dyar)—boxelder; *A. rileyanus* (Grote)—hickory and walnut; *A. georgianus* (Wlk.) —oak; *A. griseus* (Rob.)—oak and hickory; *A. magnolianus* (Fern.)—yellow cucumber tree; and *A. purpuranus* (Clem.)— basswood, paper birch, trembling aspen, willow, and black cherry.

The **spruce budworm**, *Choristoneura fumiferana* (Clemens) (fig. 150), occurs in the region of North America extending from Virginia to Labrador and westward to the MacKenzie River Valley, Yukon Territory, Canada (*688*). Until recently, it had been considered present throughout the ranges of spruce and fir in North America. Forms occurring in western Canada and western United States are now considered different species (*269*). Balsam fir is the preferred host of the spruce budworm. To a lesser degree, it also feeds on white, red, and black spruce, and on larch, pine, and hemlock (*47*).

Spruce budworm adults are smaller than the adults of other spruce-fir feeding species. In series, they are mostly gray with a few ochreous-gray specimens. The male has a wingspread of 21 to 26 mm; the female, 22 to 30 mm. Full-grown larvae are about 20 to 23 mm. long. The head is usually almost entirely dark brown; the prothoracic shield is brownish-yellow with some diffusion of brown pigment or is entirely dark brown; and the anal shield is brownish-yellow. Pupae are light to reddish-brown except for darker bands and spots.

Spruce budworm adults are active from late June to early August, depending on location, and the females deposit their eggs in elongate masses of two to sixty eggs each, the eggs overlapping like shingles on a roof. A large proportion of the masses are usually found on needles near the periphery of the crown. The eggs hatch in about 10 days under normal conditions. After a period of 1 to 2 days during which they are dispersed throughout the tree and stand, the larvae spin hibernaculae in suitable sites and molt to the second-instar. While the majority of hibernaculae are found on the branches of host trees, some are also found in mined buds, in flower scars, under bark scales, or under lichens. Many larvae become dislodged while searching for overwintering sites

F-493456, 495235, 501800

FIGURE 150.—Spruce budworm, *Choristoneura fumiferana:* A, adult;
B, eggs; C, larvae on twig of balsam fir.

and drop down on silken threads. At this time, they may be blown considerable distances by the wind, often into uninfested stands.

379

In the spring, after several days of warm weather, but before balsam fir buds expand, the overwintering larvae emerge and start to feed. The new buds of staminate flowers are attacked first if present; otherwise, the larvae bore into old needles. After a short period of feeding here, the larvae move to the ends of branches and bore into expanding, vegetative buds. Later, they feed on the new foliage of developing shoots. When about half-grown, they begin tying the tips of two or more twigs together with silk, forming a small nest. During this period, old needles are avoided until all of the new ones are eaten or cut through. Feeding is usually completed during late June or early July. Pupation usually takes place within the last-formed nest but some occurs at twig axils. Adults appear in about 10 days and are subject to considerable dispersal by the wind. The female does not fly until she has deposited one or two egg masses. Wind dispersal may be the most important factor influencing population trends in any given area (543).

In light or moderate infestations, spruce budworm injury is restricted to the partial loss of new foliage, especially in the upper portion of the crown. Damaged needles on webbed branch tips turn reddish-brown by mid-summer. In heavy, persistent infestations, all of the new foliage may be consumed (fig. 151) for several successive years, and opening vegetative buds and developing shoots may be killed in their formative stages. Top killing usually occurs after about 3 years of severe infestation,

F-492901
FIGURE 151.—Balsam fir defoliated by the spruce budworm, *Choristoneura fumiferana.*

and tree mortality, after about five years. In sustained outbreaks, nearly complete mortality of the merchantable volume of balsam fir may occur by the 8th year (55). During widespread outbreaks, the magnitude of these losses is great: It is estimated that 225 million cords of pulpwood were destroyed in an outbreak which occurred in Quebec, New Brunswick, Maine, and northern Minnesota from 1910 to 1920.

Much has been learned about the factors or conditions conducive to the development and decline of spruce budworm outbreaks. For example, it was determined many years ago (700) that outbreaks generally begin in extensive and continuous areas of mature and overmature balsam fir. Later, it was learned that even when these conditions prevail, at least three or four summers of clear, dry weather are necessary for populations to explode (313). Much has also been learned about factors tending to hold populations in check during intervals between outbreaks or which assist in bringing them under control once they are underway (543).

The spruce budworm has many natural enemies, including parasites and predators, birds, mites, spiders, and several pathogenic organisms. Their effectiveness in control is always important, but it is greatest only after another agent, such as weather or starvation, has reduced the budworm population considerably (521). A number of authors have evaluated the control effectiveness of natural enemies in specific outbreaks (206, 207, 400, 483, 79, 80).

Other important natural control factors affecting the spruce budworm are: (1) the loss of young larvae through competition for new foliage in heavy infestations; (2) loss of young larvae as a result of cooler than normal temperatures and late frosts in the spring; (3) loss of large larvae through starvation following complete defoliation; and (4) loss of adults through dispersal.

A number of management practices have been suggested for reducing the chances of spruce budworm outbreaks. These include: the utilization of balsam fir (700); the regulation of age classes to prevent the occurrence of large areas of overmature fir (310); and the favoring of less susceptible species, such as spruce. The removal of overstory mature balsam fir was suggested for preventing outbreaks (757, 496); management plans and risk-rating systems for selective cutting were presented (497, 498, 758); and risk-rating systems for the Lake States were devised (45, 306). The budworm and forest management in the Maritime Provinces of Canada was discussed by Balch (23).

For further information on the spruce budworm, the reader is referred to McKnight's review of the literature (491) which covers 370 citations on the species and the two related species, Choristoneura occidentalis Freeman and C. biennis Freeman.

The **jack pine budworm**, Choristoneura pinus Freeman, is known to occur in Nova Scotia, Ontario, Manitoba, and Michigan. Its hosts include various species of pine, especially jack and red. The adult has a wingspread of 15 to 28 mm. The head, thorax, and forewing are ochreous-tawny; the forewings, distinctly masculate; and the hindwings, entirely smoky with dark basal lines through their white fringes. The full-grown larva has a shiny light brown to black head, a dark brown "collar" separated from the head by a narrow white band, a reddish brown bcdy with yellowish sides and two rows of white dots along the back, and it is about 20 to 22 mm. long (fig. 152). Pupae are pale green when just formed; later, they become dark reddish brown, and they are about 12 mm. long. This species was considered to be a racial form of the spruce budworm until it was described as a new species in 1953 (*265*).

Jack pine budworm adults are present from early July to early August and lay their eggs in clusters of about 40 eggs each. Hatching occurs in about 10 days. A few days later, the young larvae, without feeding, spin hibernaculae under bark scales on the trunk or larger limbs, or between needles. Then they molt to the second instar, the stage in which they remain throughout the remainder of the summer, fall, and winter. In the spring, about the time the staminate flowers are shedding their pollen, they emerge and begin feeding on the pollen. Some usually remain in the flower clusters throughout the entire feeding period, but the majority migrate to new foliage on which they feed, once it is well developed. The needles are not consumed entirely, but are usually clipped off at the base and webbed together. Pupation occurs among the needles or between webbed shoots.

The jack pine budworm usually does not cause heavy mortality of merchantable jack pine, but it may cause top killing and stag-headedness. During outbreaks, however, heavy losses in poles, saplings, and reproduction may result. In heavily infested stands, young understory red and white pines also are often severely

F-506744

FIGURE 153.—Pupae of the large aspen tortrix, *Choristoneura conflictana*, in webbed leaves.

F-501801

FIGURE 152.—Larva of the jack pine budworm, *Choristoneura pinus*, feeding on needles of jack pine.

defoliated and killed. Fortunately, outbreaks usually last only 2 to 4 years.

Cutting practices designed to remove the jack pines that most commonly produce staminate flowers are helpful in preventing outbreaks (359). These trees are usually coarsely branched and large crowned, or suppressed and slow growing. The growing of hard pines in fully stocked stands or in groups; the elimination of large-crowned, "wolf" trees; the utilization of trees before they become mature; and the encouragement of species suited to the site are also recommended (309). Parasites and a polyhedral virus disease aid in the control of infestations following periods of heavy defoliation. Rapid declines in populations have also been attributed to decreases in staminate flower production.

A new subspecies, *Choristoneura pinus maritima* Freeman, has been found feeding on Virginia and pitch pines in Pennsylvania, Massachusetts, New Jersey, and Kentucky. Adults are larger and redder than those of the jack pine budworm (269).

The **large aspen tortrix**, *Choristoneura conflictana* (Wlk.), occurs throughout the range of trembling aspen in Canada and eastern United States south to New Jersey and Ohio. Several other hardwoods also serve as hosts such as balsam poplar, largetooth aspen, paper birch, willow, and alder. The adult is dull, light gray in color and has a wingspread of 25 to 35 mm. Full-grown larvae are usually dark green, sometimes almost black, and are 12 to 21 mm. long. The prothoracic shield is reddish-brown to black; the thoracic legs, black.

In Canada, eggs are laid in flat clusters usually on the upper surfaces of leaves in June or July. First instar larvae feed gregariously on leaf surfaces during July, spinning much silk and webbing the surfaces together (fig. 153). Later they move to the trunk in search of hibernation sites in rough bark or under moss. Here they molt and spend the winter in the second instar. The following spring, they climb the trees and mine the swelling buds. Later, they roll leaves and feed within the enclosures. Pupation occurs within the rolls, and adults begin to emerge in June (606). Many outbreaks have occurred in aspen stands in Canada. Serious defoliation has also been recorded in New England, New York, and Michigan.

The **oblique-banded leaf roller,** *Choristoneura rosaceana* (Harr.), occurs in southern Canada and throughout most of the United States. It is recorded as a general feeder on the foliage of deciduous trees and shrubs. In Canada, it occurs most frequently on trembling aspen, paper birch, and willow but has also been observed feeding on Scotch pine. In New York, it has seriously damaged coniferous seedlings in nursery seedbeds (652). Seedlings most seriously affected were those of white, Scotch, and red pines. The infestation is believed to have resulted from an invasion of the nursery from larvae developing on weeds or other vegetation surrounding the nursery. The adult is reddish-brown and has a wingspread of 18 to 20 mm. The forewings are marked with three dark-brown oblique bands. Full-grown larvae are greenish and about 9 mm. long.

Winter is spent as young larvae in tightly-woven cases under bud scales or loose bark, or between leaves. The following spring, the larvae feed first on the surface of unfolding leaves. Later, each larva ties two or more leaves together with silk and feeds from within the case. Adults may appear as early as June, and there may be two generations per year, depending on location.

Choristoneura fractivittana (Clem.) feeds on sugar maple, beech, paper birch, red maple, elm, and red oak in southern Canada and from Massachusetts to Wisconsin and Colorado. It is sometimes mistaken for *C. rosaceana. C. houstonana* (Grote) attacks various species of *Juniperus,* especially red cedar, and is a pest in windbreak and ornamental plantings in western Kansas (*337*).

The **red-banded leaf roller,** *Argyrotaenia velutinana* (Wlk.), occurs in southern Canada, mostly in the southeastern part, and throughout eastern United States, westward to Iowa, Missouri, and Texas. In Canada and Maine it occurs commonly on various conifers, especially white, red, and black spruces, balsam fir, and larch. In the United States, it occurs on a wide variety of deciduous trees. Damage is often serious in apple orchards. The adult has a wingspread of 12 to 16 mm. The forewing is marked with a band that widens as it runs from the middle of the costa to the outer third of the inner margin. Full-grown larvae are pale green and about 15 to 18 mm. long. Winter is spent in the pupal stage among leaves and debris on the ground, and there may be three or four generations per year. A granulosis virus disease which tends to retard larval development has been reported in Virginia. Eggs are sometimes heavily parasitized by *Trichogramma minutum* Riley.

The **pine tube moth,** *Argyrotaenia pinatubana* (Kft.), feeds on various conifers, mostly white pine, in southern Canada, the Northeastern States, Florida, and Louisiana. The adult is small, slender, and grayish; it has a wingspread of 14 mm. The forewings have broad, orange to reddish-ochreous patches and are crossed by two whitish, oblique lines; the hindwings are smoky; and the abdomen is gray, blackish, or mouse-colored with ochreous, apical tufts. Full-grown larvae are 10 to 14 mm. long.

The larva lives within the tube it constructs by drawing from five to 20 needles together and fastening them with silk. It feeds on the tips of these needles (fig. 154). Winter is spent in the pupal stage within the tube. There may be two generations per year. Heavily infested pines often have a ragged appearance. This may be objectionable where valuable ornamentals are involved.

The **hickory leaf roller,** *Argyrotaenia juglandana* (Fern.), occurs in southern Canada and throughout the Eastern States. Its principal host is hickory but it will feed on plum and *Viburnum.* The adult is dark brown and has a wingspread of 18 to 25 mm. The front wings are marked by two parallel, oblique, blackish bands. Full-grown larvae are pale to translucent, with pale green heads tinged with brown; larvae are about 20 mm. long. They feed from within longitudinally rolled leaves and pupate beneath the bark on the trunk of the tree.

Argyrotaenia quercifoliana (Fitch) occurs in southern Canada and south to Florida and Texas. The larvae feed on the foliage of red, black, white, scrub, and pin oaks. The adult is cream-yellow marked with light brown dots and has a wingspread of 16 to 24 mm. The forewings are marked with two oblique brown bands, and the hindwings are white. Full-grown larvae are light green except for amber-yellow heads and are about 20 mm. long. This species sometimes causes serious defoliation locally.

Several other species of *Argyrotaenia* are recorded as feeding on eastern trees (*266*): *A. occultana* Freeman—on spruce and occasionally balsam fir and larch (in Canada and New York); *A. mariana* (Fern.)—on paper birch, willow, choke cherry, elm, pear, *Vaccinium*, and possibly oak (from eastern Canada to Florida); *A. quadrifasciana* (Fern.)—on hawthorn, shadbush, plum, and pear (in southeastern Canada and from Maine to Missouri); and *A. alisellana* (Rob.)—on oak (from southern Canada to Florida).

Croesia albicomna (Clem.) [=*semipurpurana* (Kft.)] feeds on various oaks from southeastern Canada and Massachusetts to Minnesota and Texas. Adults have wingspreads of about 12 mm. The forewings vary in color from almost solid yellow to yellow with dark brown markings. The full-grown larva is dirty white to light green, except for a pale head and brown to black thoracic legs, and is about 12 mm. long.

Eggs are laid individually on the bark of second-year wood of branches in late June and early July and hatch in April of the following year. Newly-hatched larvae enter unopened buds and feed on the young leaves. Older ones fold together sections of leaves and feed inside the folds. When they reach maturity in May, they spin down to the ground and pupate in the litter. Adults appear a week or two later (*51*).

Serious outbreaks have occurred in the Northeastern and Middle Atlantic States in recent years. During 1964 and 1965, approximately a half million acres of red oak were severely defoliated in Pennsylvania alone, resulting in considerable tree mortality.

The **black-headed budworm**, *Acleris* (=*Peronea*) *variana* (Fern.), occurs from coast to coast in Canada and southward into the United States. In eastern United States and Canada, balsam fir is its preferred host, but during epidemics, white and sometimes red and black spruces and hemlock may also be defoliated (*475*). The adult is predominantly mottled gray with various brown, white, or gray ragged bands across the wings. Some individuals have a white, yellow, or orange stripe down each wing. The wingspread is about 19 mm. Full-grown larvae are bright green and about 12 to 16 mm. long.

Adults appear during August and September and deposit their eggs singly on the undersides of needles, mostly on the upper branches. The winter is spent in the egg stage. Hatching occurs in the spring, and the young larvae burrow into the expanding buds. As the new needles grow, the larvae web together a few of them and feed within. Once the new needles are devoured, the larvae feed on the old ones. Pupation occurs within webbed masses of partially eaten and damaged needles.

In eastern America, extensive outbreaks tend to occur at intervals of 10 to 15 years in stands where maturing balsam fir is dominant, but they usually subside before many trees are killed.

Acleris chalybeana (Fern.) has been recorded from Ontario, Quebec, Wisconsin, Maine, New York, and Pennsylvania. The larvae feed on the foliage of sugar, red, and mountain maples, yellow birch, beech, and ironwood. The adult is grayish and has a wingspread of 21 mm. Full-grown larvae are light green and from 17 to 21 mm. long. In Wisconsin, winter is apparently spent as first or second instar larvae in hibernaculae on the twigs. During June, the majority of them were found in rolled leaves previously occupied by larvae of *Sparganothis acerivorana;* the remainder rolled their own leaves. Pupation occurs inside the roll. Damage by this species appears to have been one of the factors contributing to the development of maple blight, a condition leading to the deterioration and death of large quantities of sugar maple trees and saplings during recent years (*294*). *A. logiana* (L.) skeletonizes the leaves of paper and river birches. Larvae are dull green, with the head, cervical shield, and front legs black; they have black warts on the prothorax. They usually feed singly inside folded leaves. Sometimes, they are found between two leaves folded together. *A. tripunctana* (Hbn.) feeds on paper birch.

Aphelia alleniana (Fern.) normally feeds on weeds and clovers, but may also attack and injure small seedlings in coniferous plantations. Seedling losses have been severe in the Lake States and southern Canada. The larvae tie the shoots of the seedlings togther and feed from within the sheath on the stems and new needles during May and June. Injured seedlings become twisted and deformed. Winter is spent in the larval stage, and there is one generation per year.

Xenotemna pallorana (Rob.) also normally feeds on weeds and clover, but it also occasionally damages seedlings in young coniferous plantations in the Lake States and southern Canada. It is widely distributed in eastern United States, occurring from New England to the Lake States, Missouri, and Texas. The larvae draw the young shoots of seedlings together, fastening them with loose silk. Then, they feed on the young needles and tunnel into the shoot. Heavy damage to young white, red, jack, and Scotch pines has been recorded during May and June in Michigan. There are two generations per year in Ontario. Winter is spent as larvae in hibernaculae spun within folded leaves (*503*).

FAMILY COSSIDAE

CARPENTERWORM MOTHS

Carpenterworm moths have fairly heavy, spindle-shaped bodies, and narrow, pointed wings. The larvae excavate large galleries in the wood of trees, often causing serious injury.

The **leopard moth**, *Zeuzera pyrina* (L.), an introduced species, is known to occur from the Philadelphia area to northern Massachusetts. Its favored hosts are elm, maple, ash, beech, walnut, oak, chestnut, poplar, willow, apple, pear, and plum, but it will attack scores of other species. The female is heavy-bodied and has a wingspread of 62 to 75 mm. Full-grown larvae are about 50 mm. long. The body is usually pale yellow but may have a pinkish tinge. It is also sparsely hairy and dotted with brown or black tubercles.

Adults are present from late spring until fall. Eggs are deposited either singly or in small groups in bark crevices. Young larvae bore directly into twigs, branches, or the trunk and feed in the heartwood. When a larva becomes too large for a twig or branch, it vacates it and migrates to a larger one. As the larva feeds, it pushes chips, matted excrement, and frass to the outside through the entrance hole. Pupation takes place within the tunnel, and the life cycle requires 2 years (*386*).

The leopard moth may cause considerable damage to its host. Damaged twigs wilt and break off; small branches break and hang down; larger branches are girdled (fig. 155) and may break in the wind; and small seedlings are killed. Ugly scars appear on the trunks of large trees where the bark dies and splits over wounds. The removal and destruction of infested twigs, branches, and heavily infested trees is a recommended control practice. Borers in valuable shade trees can be killed by probing their tunnels with flexible wires.

The **pecan carpenterworm**, *Cossula magnifica* (Strecker), occurs throughout the Southern States. Its hosts are pecan, oak, and

FIGURE 155.—Elm branch nearly severed by larvae of the leopard moth, *Zeuzera pyrina*.

FIGURE 154.—Larval tube and larval feeding damage by the pine tube moth, *Argyrotaenia pinatubana*.

hickory. The adult is grayish with brown markings and has a wingspread of 37 mm. Full-grown larvae have pinkish bodies sparsely clothed with short, fine hairs and are about 37 mm. long.

Adults appear in May and June and deposit their eggs on the bark of small twigs. Newly-hatched larvae bore into the twigs and tunnel in the pith. Later, they emerge and migrate to larger branches or the trunk where they enter and excavate tunnels several inches long. Frass is extruded through holes that are about 6 mm. in diameter in the trunk; it can usually be found in small heaps at the base of infested trees. Winter is spent in the larval stage, and pupation occurs in the tunnel in the spring. There appears to be one generation per year.

Acossus centerensis (Lint.) and *A. populi* (Wlk.), the **aspen carpenterworm,** also occur in eastern United States. *A. centerensis* bores in poplars from New Jersey to Illinois. *A. populi* is found in poplars and cottonwoods from coast to coast.

The **carpenterworm,** *Prionoxystus robiniae* (Peck.) (fig. 156), is widely distributed in the United States and southern Canada where it breeds in various hardwoods. In the Eastern and

F-498365

FIGURE 156.—Eggs, larva, pupal case, and adults of the carpenter-worm, *Prionoxystus robiniae.*

Southern States, the oaks, particularly those of the red oak group, are most heavily damaged. In the Prairie States, green ash is the chief host. Other hosts are black locust, elm, maple, willow, cottonwood, and occasionally fruit trees and ornamental shrubs (*327*). The adult is dark, slightly mottled, stout-bodied, and has orange and black hindwings. The female is lighter colored and considerably larger than the male and has a wingspread of 75 mm. The posterior half of the hindwing of the male bears a large yellowish to orange spot with a black border. Full-grown larvae are greenish-white, are nearly naked, bear simple setae, and are 50 to 70 mm. long. The head is shiny brown and armed with powerful, nearly black mandibles. The thoracic legs are yellowish, and three-jointed, and each bears a curved, pointed tarsal claw.

Carpenterworm moths begin to appear in late April in the South, the last week of May in the Central States, and the first week of June in more northerly regions. The female deposits upwards of 450 to 800 eggs in groups in bark crevices, near wounds, or under vines, lichens, or moss. Young larvae bore directly to the inner bark, or enter it through openings, and feed there until about half-grown. Then they bore into the wood, their tunnels angling upward in the sapwood and straight upward in the heartwood. Feeding may be finished in one year in the Deep South but may continue for 3 or 4 years in the North. Tunnels are kept open and enlarged as needed by the growing larvae; eventually they may reach a diameter of 18 mm. and a length of 375 mm. Mature larvae line their tunnels with loose, silky, yellowish-brown webs. Pupation occurs at the upper end of the tunnel. Before completing its transformation to an adult, the pupa wriggles to the mouth of the tunnel and continues until its head and thorax are protruding. Even after the adult has formed and departed, the pupal case usually remains in place, sticking out of the opening.

Carpenterworms seldom kill trees outright; although, heavily riddled, small trees may be broken off by the wind. The greatest damage results from the degrade of lumber cut from infested trees. The overall value of rough-cut, oak lumber may be reduced by as much as 15 percent. Open-grown trees, or trees growing on poor sites such as dry ridge tops or ridge slopes, are especially subject to attack and damage.

Little is known about natural control of the carpenterworm. It is believed, however, that predation by woodpeckers on larvae and kingbirds on adults frequently accounts for the destruction of fairly large numbers. Insect parasitism appears to be inconsequential. No satisfactory method of control in the forest is known, although the removal or killing of heavily infested weak, deformed, cull trees should, however, be helpful in reducing the intensity of infestations. Shade trees can be protected by painting injuries with wound dressing. Larvae in small trees can be killed by probing their tunnels with a wire.

The **little carpenterworm**, *Prionoxystus macmurtrei* (Guer.), a species very similar to the carpenterworm, is widely distributed in eastern Canada and eastern United States. The larvae are borers in oaks, and their habits are similar to those of the carpenterworm. They spend their first summer in the outer layers of bark and the second in the sapwood. During the third summer, they bore in the woody part of the tree, making a labyrinth of crossing and recrossing tunnels. The third winter is spent in the pupal stage in the tunnel. This species attacks all parts of the tree over 1 inch in diameter, and trees infested continuously become badly honeycombed. Fortunately, infestations are usually very local.

FAMILY COSMOPTERYGIDAE

Chrysoclista linneella (Clerck), an introduced European species, was first reported in this country in 1928 when it was found infesting linden trees near New York City. Other infestations were later found in surrounding parts of New York and New Jersey, and near Boston, Massachusetts. Its current distribution is not known. Full-grown larvae are whitish, with light brown heads and are about 6 mm. long. Adults are present from late May to mid-June and are thought to lay their eggs on the branches of their host. The larvae bore into and tunnel the bark. Winter is spent in the larval stage, and pupation occurs in the spring in cells formed in the galleries close to the surface of the bark.

The **palm leaf skeletonizer,** *Homaledra sabalella* (Chamb.), feeds on many varieties of palms, particularly Canary Island date palm and sabal palmetto, in the Southern States. It is often quite injurious in Florida. The larvae feed in groups of 35 to 100 larvae each under webs of silk on both the upper and lower surfaces of the leaf (*173*). Eggs are usually laid in masses on the interleaf husks. There are no hibernation stages and there may be up to five generations a year. Cutting out and burning of all interleaf husks and infested fronds is helpful in control.

FAMILY WALSHIIDAE

Aenea ostryaealla Chmb., a leaf miner of ironwood, has been recorded from New York, Kentucky, Ohio, and southern Ontario. Its eggs are laid on the undersurface of leaves, near the midrib. The larvae feed in the tissues of the leaf between two lateral veins, and form blotch-type mines. Full-grown larvae vacate the mines in the fall and drop to the ground where they spin thin, loosely woven silken cocoons in the litter. Winter is spent in the pupal stage (*458*).

FAMILY GELECHIIDAE

WAX MOTHS

Wax moths are small and have narrow forewings. The outer margins of the hindwings are usually concave. The larvae of some feed in folded or rolled leaves webbed together; others feed as leaf miners; still others feed in buds, seeds and cones, and roots. A few species are quite destructive.

Coleotechnites (=*Recurvaria*) *apicitripunctella* (Clem.) occurs in Quebec and in the Northeastern States. Its known hosts are hemlock and cypress. The adult is buff yellow to whitish and has a wingspread of 12 mm. The forewings are marked with blackish spots and dots, and the hindwings are fringed. The larva is greenish, sometimes with a brownish tinge, and is about 6 mm. long. Adults are present from early June to mid-July. The larvae feed for the rest of the summer and fall. They mine the leaves and web them together, forming broad, flat nests. A nest may contain six or eight mined leaves where the larvae spend the winter. Feeding is resumed in the spring, and pupation occurs in late spring or early summer. There is one generation per year. Local outbreaks occur occasionally.

Coleotechnites (=*Recurvaria*) *thujaella* (Kft.), occurs from New Jersey to New Brunswick and westward to Saskatchewan, in Canada. The larvae are leaf miners on arborvitae. The adult is creamy white with heavy dustings of black and brown scales and has a wingspread of about 9 mm. There are three oblique blackish bands, a number of costal and terminal dots, and a shaded apical region on each forewing. Eggs are deposited from late June to early August between scale-like leaves on growing tips. The larvae bore into the tips and mine along the twigs, causing the foliage to turn brown. Winter is spent in the larval stage in a mine, and there is one generation per year. Ornamental arborvitae is subject to serious injury.

Coleotechnites (=*Recurvaria*) *piceaella* (Kft.) occurs commonly from Maine to Colorado and from the Maritime Provinces to Alberta in Canada. Its hosts are white, Colorado blue, Engelmann, Norway, red, and black spruces. The adult is light gray and has a wingspread of 10 to 13 mm. The head and thorax are pale yellow to whitish. The forewings are buff or ochreous near the base, shading to fuscous at the apex, and are marked with dark gray, diagonal crossbands and a few conspicuous black spots. The hindwings are broad and gray with a silvery sheen; the abdomen and legs are ochreous, sprinkled with gray. Full-grown larvae are reddish to cinnamon brown and about 8 mm. long.

Adults are active from June to late July, depending somewhat on season and locality. Eggs are laid singly or, rarely, in groups of two or three either between the axils of current year's needles, in insect-damaged or mechanically-damaged needles, in insect-damaged cones, or in spent staminate flowers. Some also may be deposited at the base of needles or inserted between the scales of sound cones. The larvae feed as miners in healthy needles, in needles and cones damaged by other insects, in spent staminate flowers, and in dead needles on shoots damaged by late spring frosts (494). Winter is spent in the larval stage, and there is one generation per year. Damage is usually not very injurious, but may be important on ornamentals.

Other eastern species in the genus *Coleotechnites* include *C. juniperella* (Kft.) which mines the needles of red cedar and common juniper in the Northeastern States; *C. dorsovittella* (Zell.) which feeds on sweetgum; and *C. variella* (Chambers) which feeds on cypress. Heavy infestations of the latter species have killed the top 2 or 3 feet of cypresses up to 20 feet tall in Ohio.

The **pine needle miner**, *Exoteleia pinifoliella* (Chambers), occurs in southeastern Canada and south to Georgia and Texas.

Jack, pitch, and shortleaf pines are preferred hosts, but it has also been observed feeding on Virginia, Scotch, scrub, longleaf, loblolly, and red pines. The adult has a wingspread of about 9 mm. The forewing is reddish to golden brown and is marked by four narrow, grayish bands. The hindwings are wider than the forewings. Full-grown larvae are pinkish and about 6 mm. long.

Females deposit their eggs in recently vacated, mined needles from May to July, depending on location. Young larvae vacate the old mined needles and bore into the bases of current year needles, killing them within 2 or 3 weeks. Older larvae mine in both old and new needles, killing the apical portions beyond the entrance holes. Winter is spent in the larval stage, and there may be two or more generations per year (*248*). Forest-grown trees are occasionally infested heavily, but are seldom injured seriously. On the other hand, heavy infestations on ornamentals or in plantations may be serious. The mite, *Pediculoides ventricosus*, appears to be an effective predator in some areas. It is reported to have destroyed over 75 percent of late instar larvae in infestations in North Carolina (*40*).

Exotelleia dodecella (L.), the **pine bud moth**, was discovered in the Niagara Peninsula, Ontario, in 1928 and now occurs throughout southern Ontario. So far as known, it has not yet crossed the border into the United States. Its preferred hosts appear to be Scotch and mugho pines, but several other pines such as eastern white, red, jack, and Austrian may be attacked in heavily infested areas. Old Scotch pines, particularly those growing along roadsides, are highly subject to attack. Infestations on such open-grown trees may persist for years. Heavy infestations cause a thickening or browning of the needles, followed by branch malformation. Eventually, the needles thin out. A high proportion of the buds on young trees may be killed.

Eggs are laid on current-year and 1-year-old shoots in late July or early August. The larvae feed on the needles during the first season; the following spring they feed on the buds. Winter is spent in the third instar in mined needles (*504*).

Exoteleia chillcotti Freeman is a common needle miner of longleaf pine in Louisiana. Bennett (*60*) discussed the morphology of the pupa.

Exoteleia nepheos Freeman, first recorded in southern Canada in 1958, is also known to occur in Ohio. Its known hosts are red and Scotch pines and, rarely, Mugho pine. The adult is small and inconspicuous and has a wingspread of less than 12 mm. Mature larvae are pale yellow with a reddish hue and are about 6.5 mm. long. Winter is spent in the larval stage.

Adults are present from early July to early August in Ontario (in Ohio they may appear as early as June 1). Eggs are laid singly, or, rarely, in clusters of two to four, on the sheaths of previous year's needles or, occasionally, under loose bark scales of twigs. Newly-hatched larvae bore into the tips of the needles. The remainder of the summer is spent mining the needle, and winter is spent in the tunnel. In the spring, the larvae vacate their tunnels and either re-enter the same needles, adjacent needles, or swelling buds. Larval growth is completed in May, and pupation occurs in the flowers or shoots of the tree. There is one generation per year (*459*).

Larval feeding stunts the growth of new shoots, giving the branches of infested pines a tufted look. Infestations in Ontario have been reported on pines from 10 to 25 feet tall.

Anacampsis innocuella (Zeller) occurs in southern Canada and from Massachusetts to Colorado and Texas. The larva is a leaf-roller on poplars, willow, and cherry. The adult is ash-gray or slightly darker and has a wingspread of 18 to 22 mm. A pale, wavy, transverse line crosses the forewing well beyond the middle. Behind it, the color darkens and there are three dots in the cells and two in the fold. The larva is translucent green.

Larval feeding and leaf rolling begin in Ohio about the time the leaves of bigtooth aspen begin to develop. Prior to pupation in May or June, the larva severs the petiole of the rolled leaf, causing it and the enclosed larva to drop to the ground. Rolls containing two or more leaves tend to remain on the tree. Adults appear during the last half of June. It is believed that winter is spent in the egg stage on twigs of the host (*523*).

Anacampsis rhoifructella (Clem.) feeds on *Viburnum* and sumac in the Northeastern States. The adult is grayish-brown and has a wingspread of 15 mm. Markings on the forewings resemble those on *A. innocuella*. Larvae are pale brown to dark brownish-red. On sumac, they live in silken galleries within fruit clusters in the spring and feed in the fruit spikes.

The **palmerworm**, *Dichomeris ligulellus* (Hbn.), occurs in Canada and in the Northern States from Maine to Minnesota. Its hosts are various hardwoods such as apple, plum, pear, cherry, hazel, basswood, and oak. Full-grown larvae are greenish and translucent, and about 12 to 15 mm. long. There is a pair of narrow, whitish lines down the back, and a wider one runs along each side.

Eggs are laid on the undersides of leaves in early spring. The larvae feed on and skeletonize the leaves, either in exposed positions or within folded or rolled leaves. Pupation occurs either in these rolls or in ground litter. Adults appear during July or August and apparently live until the following spring. Although most important as a pest of apple orchards, this species is capable of seriously defoliating oak during outbreaks.

The **juniper webworm**, *Dichomeris marginellus* D. & S., an introduced species, occurs in many eastern and western states and in southern Canada. Its hosts include various species of *Juniperus*, such as Irish juniper, common juniper, and red cedar. The adult is brownish with white front and rear margins of the forewings, and has a wingspread of 15 mm. Full-grown larvae are light brown and from 12 to 15 mm. long.

Adults are present during June and July, and deposit their eggs in leaf axils of new growth. Newly-hatched larvae feed first as needle miners, entering the upper surface of the needle near the axil. Mined needles turn brown and die. Dead needles are incorporated in webbing constructed between branchlets. Larvae continue to use mined needles as protective retreats while developing. During July, larvae crawl from primary mined needles and feed on adjacent needles, eventually constructing silken tubes from holes in needles to other nearby needles. Webbing area is expanded from July to September. Entire trees up to 8 feet tall may be completely webbed (fig. 157). Winter is spent in the larval stage in a silken case. The larvae resume feeding in the spring, becoming full grown and pupating from mid-May to early June (*569*). Trees grown as ornamentals or in permanent plantings may be seriously damaged by this species. The cutting out and removal of webbed masses of foliage is a helpful control practice.

Fascista cercerisella (Chambers) feeds on redbud from Delaware and Maryland to Illinois and southward. The adult is velvety black except for its white head and a white collar. The forewings are slightly bronzed and marked with three costal spots and several white terminal points. The larvae feed on leaves which they web together. There are at least two generations per year.

Battaristis vittella (Busck) is widely distributed throughout eastern United States and southern Canada. It has been reared from the buds of mugho pine; from the cones of Scotch, Austrian,

F-519583
FIGURE 157.—Defoliation by the juniper webworm, *Dichomeris marginellus.*

and longleaf pines; and from cecidomyid galls on loblolly pine. The adult has bright red eyes; the forewings are cinnamon-brown and traversed by gray bands; and the wingspread is 8 to 10 mm. Mature larvae are slender and from 4 to 6 mm. long. Winter is spent in the larval stage in a tunnel in a bud or cone. Pupation occurs in the spring, and adults appear by May.

FAMILY OECOPHORIDAE

This family contains a large number of moderately small moths, only a few are ever very injurious to trees in eastern United States. The larvae of most species either roll, tie, or web together the leaves on which they feed. Gates-Clarke (*282*) revised the family several years ago.

Machimia tentoriferella Clem. occurs rather commonly in the Northeastern States and southeastern Canada. Its hosts are various hardwoods such as birch, ash, maple, oak, honey locust, mountain ash, hickory, elm, and wild cherry. The adult is light-ochreous and has a wingspread of 18 to 20 mm. The forewing is dusted with black and marked with two black discal dots, a spot of black in the fold, a broken postmedial line parallel to the outer margin, and a series of black terminal dots. The larva is green and has a large head and tapering body. It lives and feeds inside a folded leaf.

Psilocorsis faginella (Chmb.) occurs in eastern Canada and the Northeastern States. The larva feeds principally as a leaf tier on American beech. Other hosts include the birches, maple, and red oak. Embree discussed its biology in Nova Scotia (*226*).

Full-grown larvae have reddish-brown heads, pale green bodies, and are about 12 mm. long. Eggs are laid singly on the undersides of leaves. During the first three instars, the larvae feed together and skeletonize the leaves near the veins. Older larva usually feed singly from within the silken tubes they spin. Full-grown larvae drop to the ground and crawl under fallen leaves, where they pupate and overwinter. *Psilocorsis reflexella* Clem., *P. obsoletella* (Zell.), and *P. quercicella* Clem. occur on oaks in the Eastern States. *P. fletcherella* Gibson has been observed feeding on trembling aspen in eastern Canada. It probably occurs in the Northeastern States also.

Other tree-infesting species of oecophorids in eastern United States are as follows: *Agonopterix pteleae* Barnes & Busck—on the common hop tree; *A. robiniella* (Pack.)—on black locust; *A. argillaceae* (Wlsm.)—on willow; *A. nigrinotella* (Busck)—on prickly ash; *Bibarrambla allenella* (Wls.)—on white birch and oaks; and *Depressaria betulella* (Bsk.)—on white birch and hophornbeam.

FAMILY BLASTOBASIDAE

Blastobasid moths are small with long antennae. Long scales on the head often cover the face and base of the antennae. The scape of the antenna is broad and armed with a fringe of bristles, and the hindwings are narrower than the forewings. The larvae feed either in the cones, nuts, and seeds of various trees; as scavengers in hollowed out nuts or insect galls; or as predators on scale insects.

Valentinia glandulella (Riley), the **acorn moth,** feeds in acorns, hickory nuts, and chestnuts in southern Ontario and southward throughout the oak region of the Eastern and Central States. Larvae are grayish-white or yellowish, with blackish marks on top.

Holcocera lepidophaga Clarke larvae feed mainly in male flower buds and flowers or among the basal scale leaves of young cones and vegetative buds of slash and longleaf pines in Florida. It has also been recorded from Massachusetts. The adult has a wing-spread of 11 to 17 mm. The head is ochreous-white, with slight infuscation posteriorly; the antennae are ochreous-white with narrow, dark annulations; and the forewings are ochreous-buff. The larvae of *Zenodochium coccivorella* Chambers are internal parasites of female scale insects of the genus *Kermes* in Florida.

FAMILY GLYPHIPTERYGIDAE

The **apple-and-thorn skeletonizer,** *Anthophila pariana* Clerck, an introduced species first recorded in New York State, is now known to occur in Virginia west to Indiana, and north to southern Canada. The larva feeds mostly on the leaves of apple, pear, and hawthorn; but mountain ash, birch, willow, plum, and sour cherry are also attacked. The adult is dark reddish-brown with a purplish tinge and has a wingspread of 12 mm. The forewings are often marked with faint, pale bands and wavy, black lines. Three or four white spots are usually along the costal margin. Full-grown larvae are yellowish-green with prominent black tubercles and are about 12 mm. long.

Young larvae skeletonize the undersurfaces of the leaves under loose webs. Older larvae move to the upper surfaces and draw the opposite sides of leaves together with silk. They feed inside the fold, consuming everything but the lower epidermis and larger veins. Damaged leaves curl, turn brown, and fall by early September. Pupation occurs in cocoons spun in the angles or folds of leaves, on weeds or other objects, and even in cracks of buildings. There are three and possibly four generations per year.

The **mimosa webworm,** *Homadula anisocentra* Merrick (=*albizzae* Clark), an introduced species first reported in the United States at Washington, D. C., in 1942, is now widely distributed from New Jersey and Pennsylvania southward to Florida, Alabama, and Mississippi, and westward to Kansas and Nebraska. Its hosts are mimosa and honeylocust trees. The adult has a wingspread of about 12 mm. The forewings are mouse-gray, except for a silvery luster and a stippling of black. Full-grown larvae are pale green to dark brown in color, are marked with five longitudinal white lines, and are about 12 mm. long. Pupae are yellowish-brown and about 6 mm. long. They are found in whitish, silken cocoons.

Winter is spent in the pupal stage in the soil or in other protected places. Adults appear by June, and the female deposits her eggs on flowers or foliage, or on the bark of small branches and twigs. Egg laying continues throughout the season. First and second instar larvae spin webs around flowers and leaves, within which they live and feed (fig. 158). Adjacent surfaces of webbed leaves may be skeletonized, turn brown, and die. Older larvae feed on the tender, terminal leaves. Pupae of this generation are formed in the webbing of infested trees. Second generation adults appear during late July and early August and deposit their eggs on webs formed by first generation larvae. In heavily infested areas, the larvae of this generation may completely defoliate their hosts. Some of the second generation larvae pupate in cocoons spun in webs on trees, and the adults appear during the fall. Other larvae move to the soil or other protected places, pupate, and spend the winter (756).

The mimosa webworm is a serious defoliator of ornamental plantings of mimosa and honey locust. The thornless variety of honey locust is heavily attacked in nurseries. Season-long protection against attack has been obtained by the use of systematic insecticides (198).

FAMILY AEGERIIDAE

CLEARWING MOTHS

Members of this family are known as clearwing moths because the greater parts of one or both pairs of wings are without scales, thus leaving them clear or transparent. The forewings are long and narrow, with the outer margins short and the anal veins reduced. The hindwings are somewhat broader than the forewings, and the anal areas are well developed. In some species, the two sexes are colored differently. Many species bear a striking resemblance to bees or wasps. The adults are swift fliers and are most often seen around flowers. The larvae are ivory-white and mostly unmarked. They bore in the roots and basal stalks, the trunks, or branches of trees and shrubs, and vines, or in the stems and roots of herbaceous plants. A few form galls, others are inquilines in galls, and some inhabit injured areas on the trunks or branches of their hosts. A number of species are important pests

FIGURE 158.—Webs formed by the mimosa webworm, *Homadula anisocentra.*

of forest and shade trees and ornamentals. The family has been treated by Engelhardt (*2303*) and MacKay (*489*).

The **hornet moth**, *Aegeria apiformis* (Clerck), an introduced species first observed in North America around 1880, is now known to occur in Massachusetts, Connecticut, New York, New Jersey, Pennsylvania, and California. Its hosts are poplar and willow. The larvae bore in the roots, trunks, or large limbs. The adult is brownish-black except for yellow markings on the head and sides of the thorax; it has a wingspread of 34 to 44 mm. It also has black and yellow bands on the abdomen and brown legs. Because of its close resemblance to the giant hornet, it is known as the hornet moth. Full-grown larvae are white with reddish heads and are about 30 to 50 mm. long. They excavate extensive tunnels in their hosts, causing swellings to occur. Young trees are often killed. Two years are required to complete the life cycle. The first winter is spent in the larval stage in the wood; the second, as a larva in a cocoon in wood borings in or close to the base or roots.

Aegeria tibialis (Harr.) attacks poplar and willow from New York to Nova Scotia and in the Midwestern States. Adults are distinguished by their black abdominal segments, all but the second and fourth of which have narrow posterior yellow margins. Full-grown larvae are 40 mm. or more long. Infestations are located well down on the trunk or in the roots.

The **dogwood borer**, *Synanthedon* (=*Thamnosphecia*) *scitula* (Harris), occurs in southeastern Canada and throughout the eastern half of the United States. Although normally a bark borer in oaks, it also attacks a wide variety of other deciduous hardwood trees, and shrubs, and sometimes pine. It is often an important pest of flowering dogwood and pecan. In the South, it is commonly called the **pecan borer**. Abnormal growths such as woody galls, excrescences due to fungi, rusts, blight, and bruises and healing wounds are attractive as points of attack. Galls, such as those produced by the cynipid *Andricus cornigerus* on black and pin oaks, sometimes occur in the thousands on a single tree, and nearly every one will be infested by this borer (*230*).

The adult is a small, blue-black moth with yellow banded legs and yellow stripes on segments two and four of the abdomen. The wings are transparent with blue-black margins, and the wing spread is from 14 to 20 mm. The larvae are whitish with brown heads and are up to 14 mm. long.

Eggs are laid from late spring to mid-summer on rough bark or around wounds. The larvae enter the bark through openings and feed in the cambial area. Infested areas are sometimes up to 2 feet or more in length and may contain up to 50 larvae each on the larger trees. A single larva can kill a dogwood 4 inches in diameter in one year. There are one and possibly two generations per year, depending on locality. Keeping the bark smooth, especially at the base of branches has been recommended for control on dogwood (*737*).

The **rhododendron borer**, *Synanthedon* (=*Ramosia*) *rhododendri* Beutenmuller, attacks rhododendron and sometimes laurel and azalea in the Atlantic Coastal States. The adult is blackish, except for various white and yellow markings, and has a wingspread of 10 to 15 mm. Mature larvae are up to 15 mm. long. The winter is spent as a full-grown larva in the stem of its host. Pupation occurs in the spring, and the adults appear during May and June. Eggs are deposited on the bark, and the larvae bore into the stems, causing ugly scars and sometimes killing large branches and small plants. Cutting out and burning of infested parts of plants is a recommended control practice.

Several other species of *Synanthedon* (=*Thamnosphecia*) also occur in eastern America. *S. geliformis* (Wlk.) is a bark borer in dogwood and pecan. It also infests *Andricus* galls on oaks and diseased and injured tissues of various other plants. *S. pyri* (Harr.) attacks apple, hawthorn, shadbush, and mountain-ash. The larvae excavate shallow, tortuous tunnels in and beneath the bark of trees usually injured by storms and disease, causing the bark to blister and peel. *S. pictipes* (Grote & Robinson) breeds in peach, wild plum, and in fungus growths on wild plum. It is a major pest of peach. *S. viburni* Eng. larvae bore under the bark of *Viburnum*, preferably in injured areas or galls. *S. acerrubri* is a bark borer in maple, preferably in branches and often in wounds and scars caused by other insects. *S. sapygaeformis* (Walker) has been recorded infesting woody galls in oaks in Florida. *S. castanea* (Beutenmuller) bores in the trunks of American chestnut, preferably in bruised areas.

Thamnosphecia rubrofascia (Hy. Edw.) larvae excavate long, sinuous tunnels in the bark of sour gum from Maryland to Florida. Injuries and healing wounds on well matured trees are preferred. *T. sigmoidea* (Beut.) attacks low-growing willows in bays, along streams, and in depressions in sand dunes of coastal and lake regions. Infestations are often heavy.

The **maple callus borer**, *Sylvora* (=*Conopia*) *acerni* (Clem.), is widely distributed in southern Canada and throughout eastern United States south to Florida. Its hosts are sugar and red maples. The adult is amber-colored and has a wingspread of 20 to 25 mm. The head is orange-yellow and there is a red tuft of hairs at the posterior end of the yellow-banded abdomen. Full-grown larvae are white and from 14 to 19 mm. long.

Adults appear in May and June and deposit their eggs in roughened places on the trunk, preferably on or near wounds. The larvae bore through the bark and in to the sapwood. Slightly wounded trees are often severely damaged. Winter is spent in the larval stage and pupation occurs in the spring. Just before it changes to an adult, the pupa wriggles part way out of its burrow. When the adult emerges, the cast pupal skin is left sticking out of the bark. There is one generation per year. Smoothing of roughened bark areas, removal of borers from under the bark in the spring, and painting of wounds are recommended control practices. The southern form, *S. a. buscki* Eng., attacks silver maple in Florida and Georgia.

The **pitch mass borer**, *Vespamima* (=*Parkarmonia*) *pini* (Kellicott), occurs in eastern Canada and eastern United States southward to Georgia and Tennessee and westward through the Great Lakes region. Its preferred host appears to be white pine but it also attacks Austrian and Scotch pines and spruce. The forewings are blue-black, with a metallic green luster, and have an expanse of 25 to 30 mm. There is an orange band on the fourth abdominal segment and a tuft of orange scales at the tip of the abdomen. Mature larvae are white to pink and 25 mm. long.

Eggs are deposited on the bark during June and July, usually near a wound, on old scars, or just below a branch. The larvae bore in the inner bark and sapwood, excavating more or less transverse tunnels and cause copious flows of pitch. This pitch accumulates in masses 3 to 4 inches in diameter at the entrance hole. Pupation occurs in the pitch mass, and when the moth emerges the empty pupal case is left sticking out of the mass. The life cycle requires 2 to 3 years. Although not a killer of trees, this species causes some lumber degrade as a result of its activities. No practical control methods are known for use on forest grown trees. Borers in shade, ornamental, or park trees may be removed with a knife.

The **persimmon borer,** *Sannina uroceriformis* Walker, occurs from southern Maryland to Kansas, Texas, and the Gulf Coast and feeds as a larva in the solid wood of the base and tap roots of persimmon. The adult is mostly bluish-black and has a wingspread of 28 to 32 mm. Full-grown larvae are up to 30 mm. long. Trees growing in cut over areas and in hedge rows are particularly subject to infestation. Young trees in nurseries are also damaged seriously at times. The life cycle requires 2 or 3 years.

The **lilac borer,** *Podosesia syringiae syringiae* (Harris) (fig. 159), occurs throughout the eastern half of the United States and Canada. It attacks lilac and privet and other trees and shrubs of *Oleaceae.* The adult has a wingspread of 26 to 38 mm. Southern adults have the thorax and abdominal segments two and three almost entirely chestnut-red, only narrowly edged with black. Northern ones have these parts mostly brown-black with edgings of yellow or chestnut-red. The larvae bore into the main stems of lilac and privet, causing them to wilt, take on an unhealthy appearance, or break. Winter is spent in the larval stage, and there is one generation per year. Borers in lilacs can be killed by inserting a flexible wire or injecting a fumigant into their burrows.

The **ash borer,** *Podosesia syringiae fraxini* (Lugger) (fig. 160), occurs from Texas north through the Midwestern States to Manitoba and Saskatchewan. It attacks green, white, red, and Euro-

FIGURE 159.—Adult, pupal case, and larval tunnel of the lilac borer, *Podosesia syringiae syringiae.*

COURTESY OF DUKE UNIV. SCH. OF FOREST.

FIGURE 160.—Adult and larval galleries of the
ash borer, *Podosesia syringiae fraxini.*

pean ash. The adult is blackish and has a wingspread of 28 to 34
mm. The forewing is opaque with hyaline streaks between the
veins to the wing base, and the fringe is dark brown. The hindwing is transparent, with yellowish-brown veins and a sordid
brown fringe darkening toward the base. The larvae tunnel in
branches and trunks, excavating galleries several inches long.
Winter is spent as a larva in the tunnel. Young shade trees and
trees growing in shelterbelts may be seriously damaged. Control
is difficult, but the cutting and burning of infested trees should
be helpful.

Paranthrene palmii (Hy. Edw.) (fig. 161) occurs from the
New York area to Florida and along the Gulf Coast at least to
Mississippi. Its hosts are various species of oaks. In Mississippi,
it shows a preference for red oaks, especially Nuttall and cherry-
bark oaks (*680*). Eggs are deposited in bark crevices at the base
of the tree, preferably in trees over 12 inches d.b.h. The larvae

F-519923-22
FIGURE 161.—Adult and larva
of *Paranthrene palmii.*

401

bore through the bark and into the wood. Here they excavate relatively uniform galleries up to 9 mm. in diameter and 4 inches long. The first inch or two the gallery slopes upward, then it continues straight up. The life cycle in Mississippi requires 2 years. The major hazard associated with the work of this borer is the possibility that rot and stain producing fungi will enter the larval galleries and degrade the butt logs.

Paranthrene simulans simulans (Grote) occurs from Nova Scotia to Maryland, Illinois and the Lake States. It has also been recorded from black, red, and pin oaks. The larvae bore into solid wood, constructing galleries up to 2 inches long. It, or a closely related species, has also been found infesting natural oak growth and 2- to 5-inch nursery stock in Long Island. The larvae, generally one to four per tree, bore into the wood of the trunk from 1- to 2-feet above the ground and then tunnel upwards 2- to 3-inches in the center of the trunk.

Paranthrene dollii dollii (Newm.) bores in the base and root collar area of young cottonwoods and black willow in the Deep South. The adult is brown with dark wings and yellow cross-bands on its abdomen and has a wingspread of about 37 mm. Eggs are laid in bark crevices. The larvae bore in the wood and pith, constructing open tunnels up to 6 inches long. Heavily infested trees are weakened and subject to wind breakage. Damage is often severe in cottonwood nurseries and plantations in Mississippi where there are two generations per year. The closely related species, *P. d. castanea* (Beut.) also occurs in the Deep South. Its hosts, habits, and damage are much the same as those of *P. dollii dollii*.

Paranthrene tricincta (Harris) larvae bore in the branches and terminals of young cottonwoods in the Deep South, weakening them and causing some to break. There are two generations per year. *P. tabaniformis* (Rott.), an introduced species with similar hosts, habits, and life cycle, occurs in the Northern States.

Conopia proxima (Hy. Edw.) larvae bore in the cones, branches, and exposed roots of low-growing willows in moist or shady locations. *C. bolteri* (Hy. Edw.) also attacks low-growing willows. *C. acerrubri* (Engelhardt) attacks various poplars. The larvae feed under the bark and cause slight swellings. Local outbreaks have been recorded.

FAMILY YPONOMEUTIDAE

Moths of this family are small, usually brightly patterned, and have rather broad wings.

The genus *Argyresthia* contains a number of leaf mining species. The adults have wingspreads of about 25 mm. While at rest, their wings are folded close to the body, their front legs are extended forward, and their hind legs are slanted upwards at 45° angles.

Argyresthia freyella Wlshm. is generally distributed in eastern Canada and south and west to the Middle Atlantic States and Missouri. Its hosts are red cedar and arborvitae. The adult is whitish and has a wingspread of about 8 mm. The forewings are golden with silvery spots and bands and a black dot at the apex of each. The larvae feed in mines which they extend along main branches and branchlets. Winter is apparently spent in the mine as a full-grown, yellowish-green to green larva, and there is one generation per year. Pupation takes place in cocoons spun on leaves or branches in the spring. Damage to ornamentals and nursery seedlings appears to be less than that caused by the related species, *A. thuiella*. *A. auveoargentella* Brower also attacks arborvitae. It resembles *A. freyella* except that its cocoons are whiter and larger.

The **arborvitae leaf miner,** *Argyresthia thuiella* (Pack.), feeds on arborvitae throughout much of the same areas as that occupied by *A. freyella*. The adult is light gray to white and has a wingspread of about 8 mm. The forewings are marked with brown and there is a black spot in the middle edge of the distal end of each. The larva is about 3 mm. long. The head and cervical shield are shiny black, the body is green with a reddish tinge, and the legs and anal plate are black. Adults appear from late May to mid-July, and the female deposits her eggs in the axils of branchlets or along the edges of leaves. Newly-hatched larvae bore into th leaves and feed in them as miners for the rest of the season. Winter is spent in the larval stage in the mine and pupation and adult emergence occurs in the spring. Outbreaks in Maine have severely damaged forest stands of arborvitae. Damage to ornamentals and nursery seedlings is often serious. Heavily defoliated trees may be killed (*107*). Silver (*647*) discussed arborvitae leaf miners in New Brunswick.

Larvae of **the apple fruit moth,** *Argyresthia conjugella* Zell., bore in the fruit of mountain ash, shadbush, *Crataegus*, apple, plum, and cherry in the Northeast. The adult is dark gray and has a wingspread of 10 to 12 mm. The forewings are dark gray, very slender, crossed by black and silver-white bands and each bears a yellowish-white spot on the outer margin. *A. laricella* Kft. larvae bore in the shoots of larch in southern Canada and the Lake States.

The **ailanthus webworm,** *Atteva aurea* (Fitch), feeds on the foliage of ailanthus throughout the Southern States and north to New York and the Lake States. The adult is orange to brownish and has a wingspread of 25 to 30 mm. The forewings are bright yellow, and each one has four rows of round yellow spots on a blue background. The larvae feed on leaves enclosed in frail, silken webs. This species is often common in the South. *Zelleria haimbachi* Busck feeds rather commonly on jack pine in southern Ontario. It may occur in the Lake States.

FAMILY HELIOZELIDAE

Shield Bearers

Shield bearer moths are rather small and have lanceolate wings. The larvae are strongly flattened and spend most of their lives mining the leaves of their hosts.

The **tupelo leaf miner,** *Antispila nyssaefoliella* Clem., feeds on tupelo throughout the eastern part of the United States. The adult is dark brown and has a wingspread of 7 to 8 mm. The pale green larvae feed within leaf tissues, forming blotch-like mines. A full-grown larva spins a cocoon within the mine and then cuts through the upper and lower layers of the leaf around the cocoon, forming a case. The case, which encloses the larva and cocoon, drops to the ground. Once there, the larva fastens the case to some object by means of silken threads and then pupates. Heavily infested trees may turn completely brown by mid-summer.

Coptodisca splendoriferella (Clem.) also occurs in eastern United States. Larvae mine the leaves of apple, cherry, and related hosts. They pupate in cases attached to the limbs and trunks of their hosts.

FAMILY COLEOPHORIDAE

CASEBEARER MOTHS

Nearly 100 species of casebearer moths occur in North America. The adults are plain, little moths with markings limited to dustings of lighter or darker colored scales. The wings are narrow and have an expanse of 12 mm. or less. The larvae of all species feed within leaf mines in the first instar. At the end of this instar, each larva constructs a portable case in which it lives thereafter. The larvae of certain species continue to feed as miners after the first instar. Without leaving the case, the larva mines in a circle or from each side of the point of entrance into the leaf. The larvae of other species feed externally in the later instars. Their cases are constructed from parts of the mined leaves and are lined with silk. They are enlarged by the larvae as needed, thus providing shelter at all times. The winter is spent as a partly-grown larva in a case which is usually fastened securely to a twig or branch with silk.

Coleophora tilaefoliella Clem. constructs a black case on basswood. *C. atromarginata* Braun occurs on southern red and swamp white oaks. Its case is black with white markings on the underside. *C. querciella* Clem. occurs on white and swamp chestnut oaks. Its case is grayish with a black patch on the top near the rear end. *C. alniella* Hein. has been observed on beech in New York. *C. ulmifoliella* McD. feeds on various species of elm in southern Ontario and possibly occurs in the Lake States.

The **pecan cigar casebearer**, *Coleophora caryaefoliella* Clem., occurs from New England to Florida and west through Texas. Its hosts are pecan, walnut, and various hickories. The adult is brownish and has a wingspread of about 10 mm. The larval case is brown, smooth, cigar-shaped, and about 6 mm. long. The winter is spent as a partly-grown larva in the case. Feeding is resumed in the spring on opening buds and young foliage. Damage is often serious (*295*).

The **elm casebearer**, *Coleophora limosipennella* (Dup.), an introduced species first observed in the vicinity of New York City in 1901, is widely distributed in the Northeastern States and also occurs in southern Ontario. Its hosts are English, Scotch, and various native elms. The female adult is buff, covered with gray markings, and has a wingspread of about 12 mm.

Adults appear in late July and lay their eggs on the leaves of their hosts. The larvae feed within mines in the leaves at first.

Then they emerge and construct tiny cases in which they migrate to the twigs where they spend the winter. Feeding is resumed in the spring with each larva eating out a tiny circular hole in a leaf and then, without leaving its case, mining out an area between the larger veins as far as it can reach. The case is enlarged as needed to accommodate the growing larva, eventually reaching a length of 9 to 10 mm. This species is primarily a pest of shade and ornamental trees. The mined parts of laves turn brown and, where numerous, are unattractive. Fortunately, outbreaks are usually limited.

The **larch casebearer,** *Coleophora laricella* (Hbn)., an introduced species, was first recorded in North America in Massachusetts in 1886. It now occurs throughout most of the range of tamarack, *Larix laricina,* in North America, west to central Minnesota and northwestern Ontario. In 1957, an infestation was also discovered on western larch, *L. occidentalis,* in Idaho (*191*). The adult is silvery to grayish-brown, has narrow wings fringed with long hairs, and a wingspread of about 9 mm. Full-grown larvae are about 6 mm. long. The pupa is colored brown. This species is one of the most serious defoliators of larch in North America. Outbreaks have been occurring at about 8 year intervals in eastern Canada. One was also recorded in the Lake States in the late 1940's and early 1950's. Heaviest losses result from reduced growth. Trees completely defoliated for 2 or more years in a row may be killed.

Eggs are deposited singly on needles in early summer and hatch in about 2 weeks. The newly-hatched larva bores directly into a needle and continues to mine it until late summer. Then the larva lines a hollowed section of the needle with silk and chews the section free at both ends. thereby forming a case. The remaining larval period is spent in the case, which is enlarged as needed. A single larva may mine several needles before the needles fall. Before the onset of cold winter weather, the larva migrates to an outer twig or branch to which it fastens its case, usually at the base of a bud. Several cases may be found grouped together around the bases of spurs from which new needles arise in the spring. The most serious damage is done by the large larvae as they feed on newly developing foliage during the spring. Adults emerge from late May to early July, depending on locality and season. There is one generation per year.

The larch casebearer is attacked by more than 50 species of native parasites in eastern America, but none are particularly effective in control. Two introduced hymenopterous parasites, *Agathis pumilus* (Ratz.) and *Epilampsis laricinellae* (Ratz.) are now widely distributed and are believed to be quite helpful in control.

The **birch casebearer,** *Coleophora fuscedinella* (Zell.) (=*salmani* Heinr), an introduced species first observed in North America in Maine in 1927, is now known to occur throughout the Northeastern States and from Newfoundland and New Brunswick to southern Ontario, Canada. Its favored hosts are paper, gray, and European white birches. Eggs are laid along the mid-ribs and larger veins on the undersides of leaves in July. Young larvae enter the leaves and feed as miners for several days; then they emerge and construct cases in which they live and feed thereafter. Winter is spent in cases firmly attached to the bark, usually in crotches of limbs. In the spring, the larvae feed on buds and young leaves, mining as far as possible without leaving their cases. Infested leaves tend to shrivel. During recent years, this species has been abundant in Quebec, New Brunswick and northern Maine. Many stands of white birch in New Brunswick were completely defoliated in 1968.

The **cigar casebearer,** *Coleophora serratella* (L.) (=*fletcherella* Fern.), is principally a pest of apple in the Northern States, but it also attacks cherry, hawthorn, plum, quince, and pear. It is most injurious in the spring when the larvae feed on expanding foliage, flowers, fruit, and fruit stems. The adult is dark gray to grayish-brown and has a wingspread of about 12 mm. The larval case is brown, shaped like a cigar, and about 8 mm. long. The life cycle and habits are similar to those of the pecan cigar casebearer.

FAMILY GRACILLARIIDAE

Leaf Miners

The family Gracillariidae, the largest of the leaf-mining families of Lepitoptera, is represented in North America by more than 200 species (*225, 559*). The adults are tiny and beautifully arrayed in shining scales and plumes, and their more or less lanceolate wings are overlaid with glistening scales of silver or burnished gold. While an adult is at rest, the front part of the body is raised and the wing tips touch the surface on which it sits. Early instar larvae are very flat and usually feed first within mines in the leaves. Later, some feed mostly on the leaf tissues from within tentiform mines or they skeletonize the leaf from shelters made by folding over parts of leaves.

The full-grown larvae of most species spin silken cocoons, usually within feeding mines or shelters, in which to pupate. Winter is spent either as larvae, pupae, or adults, depending on the species.

The **solitary oak leaf miner,** *Lithocolletis* (=*Cameraria*) *hamadryadella* (Clem.), occurs throughout much of eastern United States and southeastern Canada. Its hosts are various species of oak, especially those in the white oak group. The adult has a wingspread of about 6 mm. The forewings are pale with bronze patches, and the hindwings are silvery with broad fringes of hairs. Young larvae are tiny, flat, and taper toward the rear. Full-grown ones are cylindrical and about 5 mm. long. The larvae feed singly, forming irregular blotch-like mines just below the upper leaf surface. A single leaf may contains several contiguous mines (fig. 162). Winter is spent in the larval stage in leaves on the ground and there are several generations per year. Injury to forest trees is of minor importance, but the beauty of shade trees may be seriously reduced.

The **gregarious oak leaf miner,** *Lithocolletis* (=*Cameraria*) *cincinnatiella* (Chamb.), occurs throughout the same range as that of the solitary oak leaf miner, and it feeds on the same hosts. The adults and larvae of the two species are similar in appearance, but the feeding habits of the larvae differ. Larvae of this species are gregarious and feed together, forming large brownish-yellow mines, several of which may be found on a single leaf. Winter is spent in the pupal stage in leaves on the ground, and there are two or more generations per year. Heavy infestations have been reported in oak stands in the Central States, causing severe browning and premature dropping of infested leaves over large areas.

Many other species of *Lithocolletis* attack a wide variety of deciduous trees in eastern America. *L. salicifoliella* Chambers occurs in Canada and probably throughout most of the United States. Its preferred host appears to be trembling aspen. Martin (*502*) discussed its biology in Canada. *L. crataegella* Clem. mines the leaves of apple, hawthorn, wild cherry, plum, and quince. Heavily infested trees become ragged and scorched in appearance. *L. lucetiella* Clem. mines the leaves of basswood. The mine is nearly square. *L. hamameliella* Busck mines the upper surface of witch hazel leaves. It probably occurs wherever witch hazel grows. The mines are circular or somewhat irregular. *L. bethunella* Chamb. mines the leaves of oak in Delaware. *L. trinotella* Braun mines the undersides of the leaves of red and Norway maples; *L. aceriella* Clem. produces large white mines in the upper sides of red and sugar maple leaves. *L. robiniella* Clem. produces digitate mines in the upper surfaces of black locust leaves. *L. ostensackenella* Fitch forms blotch mines in black locust leaves. The **aspen blotch miner,** *L. tremuloidiella* Braun, con-

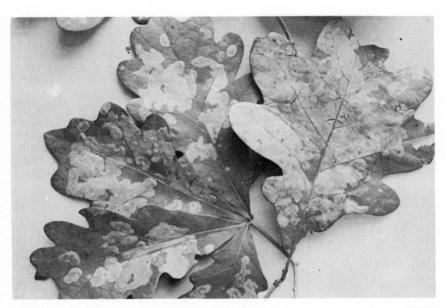

FIGURE 162.—Oak leaves with the blotchy mines characteristic of attack by the solitary oak leaf miner, *Lithocolletis hamadryadella.*

407

structs oval mines in the leaves of aspen. It is occasionally quite abundant in the Lake States and Maine. *L. corylisella* Chamb. mines the leaves of hazel in Maine.

Marmara fasciella Chamb. is widely distributed, probably occurring throughout the range of its host, white pine. Eggs are laid on the bark of branches of the host. Young larvae bore through the bark and construct linear mines in the inner bark. Winter is spent as a larva in the mine; pupation occurs during late spring, and adults begin to appear in late May. Several other species of *Marmara* have been recorded mining the inner bark of twigs of balsam fir, oak, willow, and other trees (*258*).

Phyllocnistis populiella Chamb., the **aspen leaf miner,** is widely distributed in southern Canada and the Northern States. It feeds on various species of poplar, especially trembling aspen. In the Eastern States, it has been recorded as far south as West Virginia. Eggs are laid near the tips of young leaves in the spring. The larvae form tortuous mines in the leaves (fig. 163), mostly on one side of the midrib (*154*). Noticeable infestations have been observed in Maine.

Phyllocnistis liriodendrella Clem. larvae mine the undersides of young leaves of yellow poplar and *P. magnoliella* Chamb., the undersides of young leaves of magnolia. The mines originate near the outer margins of the leaves and continue tortuously until large portions of the upper surfaces are detached. The damaged areas have a bluish cast. *P. liquidambarisella* Chamb. mines the leaves of sweet gum.

The larvae of *Parectopa robiniella* Clem. feed in the leaves of black locust, forming triangular, blister-like mines.

Callisto geminatella (Pack.), the **unspotted leaf miner,** occurs throughout the Northern States, west and south to Colorado, Virginia, and Arkansas. Its hosts are apple, quince, pear, sour cherry, wild cherry, plum, and hawthorn. Eggs are laid on the undersides of the leaves, and the larvae devour all of the tissues between the upper and lower surfaces of the leaves. Four generations per year have been recorded in Virginia.

Gracillaria negundella Chamb. occurs throughout eastern America west to the Prairie Provinces of Canada and feeds on boxelder. Early instar larvae feed within mines in the leaves. A partly grown larva vacates its mine and moves to the tip of a lobe of the leaf, which it then turns over and attaches to the lower surface with silk, thus forming a shelter. It then feeds from within the shelter. There appears to be at least two generations

F-506745

FIGURE 163.—Small-track mines of *Phyllocnistis populiella,* the aspen leaf miner.

per year as far north as Canada. Heavily infested trees may be seriously damaged.

The **lilac leaf miner**, *Gracillaria syringella* (F.), an introduced species, occurs in many of the Northeastern States and southeastern Canada. Its hosts are listed as lilac, black ash, privet, and euonymus. The adult has a dark brown body and a wingspread of about 10 mm. The forewings are brownish except for six irregular transverse patches of yellow, and the hindwings are grayish-brown. Full-grown larvae are pale yellowish, translucent, and about 8 mm. long. Early instar larvae feed gregariously inside the leaves and produce blotch-like mines. Later, they abandon their mines and roll or web several leaves together which they feed on from within this shelter. There are two generations per year. Injured portions of infested leaves dry up and become unsightly. Raking and destruction of fallen leaves is a good control practice.

Gracillaria sassafrasella Chamb., the **sassafras leaf miner**, feeds on the leaves of sassafras. The larvae feed first within mines. Later, they vacate their mines, move to nearby leaves, bend their tips over, and feed from inside the folds. Mature larvae vacate these folds and form split, capsule-like cases on the undersides of other leaves in which to pupate. *G. azaleella* Brants. larvae bend the tips of azalea leaves downward and feed from inside the folds. Injured leaves wilt and die. *G. packardella* Chamb. larvae mine the undersides of sugar and Norway maple leaves in the early instars. Older larvae feed on the surface of the leaves. Other eastern species of the genus and their hosts include *G. bimaculatalla* Ely on maple; *G. purpuriella* Chamb. on poplar and willow; *G. quercinigrella* Ely on oak; and *G. pulchella* Chamb. on yellow birch and alder.

FAMILY LYONETIIDAE

This family contains numerous species of tiny moths, the majority of which belong to the genus *Bucculatrix* Zeller. At least 18 species are known to feed on trees in eastern America (*97*).

Adults of the genus *Bucculatrix* have the vertex of the head rough or tufted, and the face smooth and produced into a point extending below the eyes. The wings are lanceolate and broadly fringed with markings of brown, black, or silver. Larvae are cylindrical and greenish and have well-developed legs and prolegs. Pupation occurs within longitudinally ridged or ribbed silken cocoons.

Bucculatrix pomifoliella Clem., the **apple bucculatrix**, is widely distributed in southern Canada and eastern United States. Its hosts are apple, black cherry, shadbush, and hawthorn. Full-grown larvae are dark yellowish-green tinged with red, have brown heads, and are about 6 mm. long. Winter is spent in cocoons spun on the lower surfaces of twigs, foliage, or fruit. The color of the cocoons differs according to the larval host— white on apple, pale tannish-ochreous on shadbush, reddish-brown on black cherry, and dark brown on hawthorn. There is one generation per year in the North and two in the South.

The **birch skeletonizer**, *Bucculatrix canadensisella* Chambers, is a common species in southern Canada and throughout the birch-growing regions of the eastern States from Maine to North Carolina and Minnesota. Paper birch appears to be the favored host, but several other birches and possibly alder are also attacked. The adult has a brown and white body and a wingspread of about 9 mm. The forewings are marked with diagonal white bars and the hindwings have broad fringes of hair. Full-grown larvae are yellowish-green, with hairs projecting from white tubercles, and are about 6 mm. long.

Adults are active from late June to late July and lay their eggs singly here and there over the leaves. Hatching occurs in about two weeks and the young larvae enter the leaves to feed, forming serpentine mines. Three or four weeks later they emerge through the lower surface and spin webs within which they molt. After molting, they leave the webs and feed externally as skeletonizers until they reach maturity. Full-grown larvae drop to the ground and spin short, brown cocoons in which they spend the winter on the undersides of fallen leaves or other debris. There is one generation per year.

Outbreaks occur at frequent intevals, often over large areas, and last for 2 or 3 years. Defoliation may be severe but it seldom causes much tree mortality. The defoliated trees may be so seriously weakened, however, that they are attacked and killed by the bronze birch borer.

The **oak skeletonizer**, *Bucculatrix ainsliella* Murt., occurs from southern Canada and the Lake States to North Carolina and Mississippi. Its hosts are various species of oak and chestnut. The adult has a wingspread of 7 to 8 mm. The forewing is largely blackish, with paler areas outlining an oval, blacker patch on the inner margin. Full-grown larvae are yellowish-green and about 5 mm. long.

The winter is spent in the pupal stage in cocoons. The cocoons are white, about 3 mm. long and ridged longitudinally. Adults are active in April and May and again in July and August. Eggs are laid on the undersides of leaves. First-instar larvae enter the leaves to feed, forming serpentine or blotch mines. Older larvae feed externally on the lower surface, often completely skeletonizing the leaves (fig. 164) (*287*). Two generations per year have been recorded in Michigan and Massachusetts. Outbreaks occasionally occur over large areas.

Other widely distributed species of *Bucculatrix* and their hosts are as follows: *B. packardella* Chamb.—various oaks and occasionally beech; *B. quinquenotella* Chamb.—oaks; *B. luteella* Chamb.—white oak; *B. recognita* Braun—various white oaks, preferably bur, and *B. coronatella* Clem.—black birch.

FAMILY PSYCHIDAE

BAGWORM MOTHS

Members of this family have the interesting habit of spending the entire larval stage within silken bags. The bag is usually strong, tough, and camouflaged by an outer layer containing bits of twigs and leaves. Newly-hatched larvae begin to spin bags about their bodies as soon as they start to feed and they continue

410

F-519521

FIGURE 164.—Red oak leaves skeletonized by larvae of the oak skeletonizer, *Bucculatrix ainsliella.*

to enlarge the bags as they grow. An opening is maintained at the top of the bag, through which the head and several segments of the body protrude when the larva is moving, feeding, or enlarging its case. There is also a smaller opening in the bottom end of the bag, through which excrement drops out. About 24 species have been recorded from eastern United States (*185*). Jones and Parks (*406*) discussed the species occurring in Texas.

Oiketicus abbotii Grote occurs over much of the Atlantic and Gulf Coastal Plains from North Carolina to Texas. It feeds on many species of trees such as cypress, live oak, bayberry, sycamore, elm, hackberry, sweetgum, and willow. It is noted for the rather large bag, from 69 to 70 mm. long, which the larva constructs. Small twigs used in its construction are placed in a circular pattern around it. *Fumaria casta* (Fall.) feeds on lichens, mosses, and the beech scale, *Cryptococcus fagi,* in Massachusetts. The larvae occasionally climb up on the sides of houses in such large numbers that they are a nuisance. *Basicladus celibatus* (Jones) frequently attaches its bags to the lower trunks of oaks and pines in coastal areas from North Carolina to Florida. The larvae are general feeders on low vegetation and may feed on trees.

The **bagworm,** *Thyridopteryx ephemeraeformis* (Haw.), is widely distributed in eastern United States, and attacks a wide variety of trees. Arborvitae and red cedar appear to be preferred, but many other conifers and hardwoods such as pine, spruce, black locust, sycamore, willow, maple, elm, basswood, poplar, oak, cypress, and persimmon are also attacked. The male moth is sooty black, densely hairy, and has a wingspread of about 25 mm. Females are wingless, have no functional legs, eyes, or antennae, and are almost maggot-like in appearance. The body is soft, yellowish-white, and practically naked except for a circle of woolly

411

hairs at the posterior end of the abdomen (*384*). Full-grown larvae are dark brown and about 18 to 25 mm. long. The head and thoracic plates are yellowish and spotted with black.

Male bagworm moths emerge in the fall, fly to the females, and mate. The female remains in her larval bag and deposits her eggs either in or outside the pupal case. Winter is spent in the bag in the egg stage and the eggs hatch during the following May or June. The larvae feed on the surface of leaves at first; later entire leaves are consumed. Mature larvae attach their bags to twigs (fig. 165) with silk, and pupate in them. There is one generation per year.

The bagworm is most important as a pest on shade trees and ornamental shrubs growing in yards and hedges, along the streets of cities and towns, and in parks and other recreational areas. Large numbers of arborvitae and other conifers are lost each year as a result of complete defoliation. Many others only partly defoliated are weakened and rendered unsightly. Damage to forest trees is usually not very severe (*444*); however, heavy infestations do occur occasionally in stands of cedar and black locust, especially in the Deep South.

Low winter temperatures, bird predation, and parasitism by the ichneumonid, *Itoplectis conquisitor* (Say), are often particularly effective in bagworm control. Handpicking and burning of overwintering bags is also helpful in control, especially on small trees and ornamentals (*790*).

F-508522

FIGURE 165.—Larval cases of the bagworm, *Thyridopteryx ephemeraeformis*, attached to the twigs of an infested tree.

Cryptothelea gloverii (Packard) occurs from South Carolina to Florida and westward along the Gulf Coast. Its hosts are recorded as two species of scale insects, and persimmon, oak, hickory, *Acacia* sp., *Crataegus* sp., and *Citrus aurantium*. The male moth is dark or dark red and has a wingspread of 14 to 18 mm. Females are 9 to 10 mm. long. Their cases may be covered with fragments of scale insects, bark, fruit rinds, or leaves.

FAMILY NEPTICULIDAE

This family includes the smallest of the Lepidoptera, the adults of some species having wingspreads of only 3 mm. Because of their minute size, their retiring habits, and their irregular flight, they are seldom seen. The larvae of most species are leaf miners; a few construct mines in the bark of their hosts. Many of the more common deciduous trees in eastern United States serve as hosts for one or more species. The larvae are slightly flattened, and their heads are rather deeply retracted into the prothorax. When full-grown, the majority vacate their mines, drop to the ground, and spin dense, flattened cocoons in the duff (*96*).

The genus *Nepticula* Von Heyden contains many leaf mining species. Eggs are deposited on either surface of a leaf, usually along the side of a vein. The larvae of certain species mine only one side of a leaf; some mine either side; and some mine different sides at different periods of larval life. The mines may be linear and gradully widen as they are extended, or, at some point, they may enlarge suddenly into a blotch. Winter is spent in the larval stage. There are one to four generations per year, depending on the species. Heavy outbreaks of *N. sericopeza* Zell., an introduced species that mines the seed pods and leaf petioles of Norway maple, have been recorded in Maine. Damaged leaves and seed pods drop prematurely. There are two and perhaps three generations per year.

The genus *Ectodemia* Busck contains a number of species, the larvae of which either form galls on leaf petioles or twigs or mine the bark of various trees. Members of the genus have only one generation per year. *E. populella* (Busck) forms pea-sized globular galls on the petioles of poplar leaves. *E. heinrichi* Busck larvae excavate flattened oval, spiral mines in the bark of young branches of pin oak.

Obrussa ochrefasciella Chamb., the **hard maple bud borer,** bores into and destroys the buds of hard maple. The larvae spend the winter in axillary buds and migrate to the main buds in the spring. Kulman (*446*) discussed the biology and importance of the species.

FAMILY INCURVARIIDAE

The **maple leaf cutter,** *Paraclemensia acerifoliella* (Fitch), is the only member of this family of economic importance in eastern forests. It occurs in southeastern Canada and in the Northeastern States south to Virginia and west to Illinois. Its favored host is sugar maple, but the larvae also feed on the leaves of red maple, beech, birch, elm, and hophornbeam. The adult has long, narrow, pointed wings and a wingspread of 8½ to 13 mm. The forewings are steel blue and fringed with black; the hindwings are pale smoky brown, translucent, and bordered with a pale brown fringe of long hairs. There is a dense tuft of bright orange-yellow hairs on the top of the head, the thorax is steel blue, the legs whitish, and the abdomen dark brown. First instar larvae are flattened, about 1½ mm. long, and they taper from the front to the rear. Full-grown larvae are slender, flattened, and usually dull white with amber brown heads and a broad longitudinal stripe. They are about 6 mm. long. Pupae are light yellow-ish brown, about 5 to 6 mm. long. Abdominal segments two to eight bear transverse rows of short, stiff, backward-pointed spines on the back.

In Canada, adults appear in the spring about the time the leaves open and deposit their eggs singly in pockets on the undersides of the leaves. When the larvae hatch, they bore into the leaf tissues and feed as miners for about 10 days to 2 weeks. Then, each larva cuts a round disc out of the leaf and makes an oval, movable case in which it resides as a casebearer. As it grows, it cuts out larger oval pieces and attaches them to its case. In order to feed, it attaches the case to a leaf and reaches out from it in a circle as far as it can. The uneaten center of this circle often drops out, leaving a hole up to ½ inch in diameter in the leaf. When the larvae become full-grown, they drop to the ground to pupate. Winter is spent in the pupal stage, and there is one generation per year (*620*).

The maple leaf cutter is often a pest in sugar maple stands, especially in sugar maple orchards. The trees may be severely defoliated, often for several years in succession.

FAMILY HEPIALIDAE

HEPIALID MOTHS

Hepialid moths sometimes attract attention late in the day when they are seen flying swiftly in a zigzag manner, close to the ground. They are medium to large in size, with rather long, stout abdomens and wingspreads of 25 to 100 mm. The better known species are yellowish to brown or ashy-gray with silvery-white spots on the wings. The larvae are long-headed and nearly naked, have 5 pairs of prolegs, and normally live as root borers. *Sthenopis argenteomaculatus* (Harr.) breeds in the base of the trunk and roots of alder in the Northeastern States; *S. thule* (Stkr.) breeds in the roots of willow.

FAMILY ERIOCRANIIDAE

Larvae of the very small species, *Mnemonica auricyonia* (Wlsm.), mine the leaves of oak, chestnut, and chinquapin in the Eastern States. The mines are often blotch-like and may encompass up to one-fourth of the leaf area. Damage is sometimes a matter of concern to owners of Asiatic chestnut orchards.

414

Order DIPTERA

Flies

The Diptera constitute one of the largest orders of insects. The majority of species differ from other insects to which the term "fly" is applied, such as the sawflies, stone flies, and dragonflies, by the fact that they possess only one pair of wings, the forewings. Their hindwings are reduced to small knobbed structures called halteres. The majority of species are soft-bodied and small to minute in size. The larvae, commonly known as maggots, are legless and vary in form from slender and elongate to stout and cylindrical. The pupae may be free, loosely enclosed, or held immobile in the last larval skin. In the latter case it is known as a puparium.

Many species of Diptera are destructive pests and are of great economic importance. Blood-sucking forms such as the mosquitoes, black flies, punkies, horse flies, and others are serious pests of man and animals. Some of these as well as some of the scavanger species, such as the house fly, are important vectors of the causative organisms of such serious diseases as malaria, yellow fever, filariasis, dengue, sleeping sickness, and dysentery. A number of others are important pests of agricultural crops; a few are pests of trees and ornamental plants; and many are important parasites or predators of injurious species of insects.

Several native and introduced species are highly effective parasites of some of our most destructive tree-defoliating insects, especially of the order Lepidoptera. A few aquatic species, some of which are nuisance pests in the adult stage are economically important as fish food in the larval stage.

Several comprehensive treatments of the order Diptera have been published. Curran's revision (181) of Williston's Manual (769) is especially useful in the classification of adults. Brues, Melander and Carpenter (114) published a key to families. Stone, et al (695) issued a catalog of the species occurring in North America north of Mexico.

Family CULICIDAE

MOSQUITOES

Mosquitoes are important pests of man and animals. Not only are their bites extremely annoying, but they transmit many of the most serious diseases of man and animals, such as malaria, dengue, yellow fever, and encephalitis. As nuisances, they often seriously interfere with public enjoyment of parks, vacation sites, and other recreational areas. Woods workers, fishermen, hunters, vacationers, and hikers are also hounded by them. The health of domestic animals and wildlife suffers with serious losses of weight and disease.

A total of 22 genera and 117 species of true mosquitoes occur in the United States and Canada. (693). The larvae and pupae live in standing or slowly moving bodies of water that range in size from small accumulations held by plants to vast salt marshes. Many of the most important species belong to the genera *Anopheles, Aedes, Culex, and Psorophora*. King, et al. (*417*) discussed the mosquitoes of the Southeastern States.

FAMILY CERATOPOGONIDAE

SANDFLIES, PUNKIES, "NO-SEE-UMS"

This family contains a number of species of very tiny flies, usually 1 to 4 mm. in length, that feed on the blood of man and animals. They are often abundant in the vicinity of fresh water inlets along the seashore or near fresh water streams, ponds, and pools. Woods workers, hikers, hunters, fishermen, picnickers, and others frequenting these areas often find their presence almost intolerable because of their very burning and painful bites. Populations are heaviest during late summer. At this time, these flies bite chiefly in the evening and very early in the morning. Wirth (*786*) records 27 genera and some 300 species as occurring in America north of Mexico.

FAMILY CHIRONOMIDAE

MIDGES

Midges are small, slender flies, rarely over 10 mm. in length. They resemble mosquitoes, but do not have fringes of scalelike hairs on the wings. They differ also by the discontinuation of the costal vein at the end of the third vein. Midges are frequently seen in great swarms, dancing in the air, usually in the evening. The larvae of most species are found in the water of streams, usually attached to the surface of stones, sticks and other objects. Many are red and are commonly known as bloodworms. Midge larvae are fed upon by many fresh water fishes and other aquatic animals. Sublette and Sublette (*696*) published a list of the species occurring in America north of Mexico.

FAMILY SIMULIDAE

BLACK FLIES

Black flies occur in nearly all parts of the United States and Canada. In different parts of their range they have various common names such as buffalo gnats and turkey gnats, as well as black flies. The females feed on the blood of man and animals and their bites cause swellings, itching, and sometimes bleeding. Their habit of hovering about the face and getting into the eyes, ears, and nostrils makes them a nuisance. When they appear in large numbers, birds and animals may be literally smothered by flies drawn into their air passages. In the woods and mountains of northern United States and Canada, they are often so abundant in the spring that they are almost unbearable. Black flies have also been incriminated in the transmission of several diseases of wild and domestic birds.

416

Black flies usually lay their eggs on grass and other materials just below the surface of water in swiftly flowing streams. The larval stage is spent in the water, usually attached to sticks, stones, or living vegetation. Adults are not strong fliers and are usually encountered in large numbers not too far from streams. Sometimes, however, the wind blows them a considerable distance. Stone (*694*) published a list of species occurring in America north of Mexico.

FAMILY BIBIONIDAE

MARCH FLIES

March flies are slender-bodied, stout-legged, rather hairy, and have short, many jointed antennae. They are usually dark colored, but may be marked with red or yellow. Full-grown larvae are distinguished by a fully developed false segment armed with spines behind the head. The common name, March flies, has been applied to the group because of the frequent appearance of the species, *Bibio albipennis albipennis* Say, in large numbers in March. The larvae usually feed on decaying vegetable matter, but a few feed on the roots of grass and other plants.

FAMILY MYCETOPHILIDAE

FUNGUS GNATS

Fungus gnats are moderately small, slender, delicate, mosquito-like insects. The antennae have 12 to 17 segments, the wings are large, the coxae are prominent and elongated, and the tibiae are armed with spurs. The adults are often common in dark, humid habitats in wooded areas. Many species breed on mushrooms or on fungi growing on trees and logs. A number of others are predacious and are found under bark or in the galleries of wood boring insects.

FAMILY CECIDOMYIIDAE

GALL MIDGES

There are about 1200 species of Nearctic cecidomyids, of which several hundred are known to attack various trees and shrubs (*256*). The oaks are especially favored as hosts but several other species of trees are also infested, such as willow, elm, maple, walnut, and the pines. The larvae of about two-thirds of the Nearctic species cause the formation of galls or pronounced swellings by their feeding (*241*). Others feed in such places as patches of pitch exuding from injured limbs, in the excrement of insects, birds, and mammals, and in galls produced by other insects. A few are predators on small insects such as asphids, mites, psyllids, and scales.

Gall midges are small, mosquitolike flies with relatively long antennae and legs. Young larvae are slender, somewhat flattened, and taper toward each end. Full-grown larvae are distinguished by the presence of a sclerotized structure, commonly known as a spatula, on the underside of the front end.

The **balsam gall midge,** *Dasineura balsamicola* (Lint.), produces swollen, oval galls about 3 mm. in diameter near the bases of needles of balsam fir and Fraser fir. It probably occurs wherever its hosts grow in North America (*293*). Damage in Christmas tree plantations may be severe. *D. gleditchiae* (O. S.) produces oblong, padlike galls on the new leaflets of honeylocust. Damage is sometimes rather severe to thornless honeylocust seedlings in nurseries in the Midwest. *D. pseudacaciae* (Fitch) attacks the young leaves of black locust and causes them to fold. *D. communis* Felt produces greenish or reddish pouch galls on the veins of red and sugar maple leaves.

The **boxwood leaf miner,** *Monarthropalpus buxi* (Laboulbene), an introduced species, occurs from Rhode Island south to Delaware and Maryland. Its hosts are different varieties of boxwood, the tree boxwood and the glossy leafed boxwood, in particular. Adults are orange yellow and about 2.5 mm. long. The larvae feed within the tissues of the leaf, causing blisterlike blotches up to 2.5 mm. long by fall. Heavily infested leaves turn gray or yellowish-brown and often drop prematurely.

Contarinia juniperina Felt, the **juniper midge,** is a pest of red cedar and other junipers in the Midwest. Adults are very small, only about 1.5 mm. long, and have bright red abdomens. Eggs are laid on the needles of new growth, near the tips of twigs. Larvae bore into the twigs at the bases of the needles and kill the portion beyond the entrance hole (*324*). Heavily infested trees turn brown in the fall and most of the infested twigs break off during the winter. The hymenopterous parasite, *Platygaster pini* Fouts, is reported to have exerted a high degree of control of an outbreak in Missouri during the late thirties.

Contarinia negundifolia Felt, the **boxelder gall midge,** produces fleshy galls on the leaves of boxelder. It has been recorded from Virginia, the Lake States, and the Prairie Provinces of Canada. Wilson (*779*) discussed its biology in Michigan. Other fairly common species of *Contarinia* include *C. virginianiae* (Felt), which feeds on the fruit of choke cherry, causing it to become swollen and deformed; and *C. canadensis* Felt, which produces galls on the leaves of ash.

Asphondylia ilicicola Foote larvae feed in the berries of American holly, and the infested berries remain green all winter. It has been recorded from New Jersey, Maryland, Virginia, and West Virginia (*352*). The related species, *A. azalea* Felt, produces the so-called pinkster bud gall on rhododendron.

Thecodiplosis piniresinosae Kearby, the **red-pine needle midge,** has been recorded causing the formation of gall-like structures in the bases of needle fascicles of red pine in Wisconsin (*411*). Damaged needles turn brown in the fall and drop during the winter. The laterals and terminals of heavily infested trees may be killed. Heavy infestations appear to be confined to slow growing trees.

Cecidomyia piniinopsis O. S., the **gouty pitch midge,** causes swellings and malformations on the twigs of Virginia and pitch pines in eastern America. Dead needles, dead or dying twigs, and distorted, twisted terminals are evidence of its attack. Eaton and Yuill (*215*) discussed its biology and control. The larvae of *C. resinicola* (O. S.) (fig. 166) are found in small patches of fluid resin exuding from wounds caused by their feeding in Virginia pine. *C. reeksi* Vockeroth larvae are found in similar situations in jack pine. *C. cupressi* (Schweinitz) feeds in the seeds and causes a leaf gall on bald cypress.

Several other species of *Cecidomyia* also attack a variety of eastern trees. *C. catalpae* Comst. larvae feed on the young leaves and seed pods of *Catalpa*. Damaged leaves wilt and fall prematurely, and the terminals of heavily infested trees may be dwarfed and stunted. *C. poculum* O. S. produces clusters of pale or red saucerlike galls that are attached by slender stalks to the undersurfaces of oak leaves. *C. pellex* O. S. produces reddish-brown bullet galls on ash. *C. ocellaris* (O. S.) causes the yellow galls margined with red that are often seen on the upper surface of red maple leaves. *C. verrucicola* O. S. produces wartlike galls on the leaves of basswood. *C. foliora* Rssl. and Hkr. produces marginal fold galls on the leaves of black, red, and pin oaks. Finally, *C. cerasiserotinae* O. S. produces bright red or yellow irregular bud or terminal galls on wild cherry.

Oligotrophus papyrifera Gagné larvae feed in the buds of paper birch in the Lake States, causing the formation of galls (fig. 167). The galls are comprised of the basal portions or all of one or two

F-501805
FIGURE 166.—Resin masses caused by feeding activity of larvae of *Cecidomyia resinicola*.

419

leaf petioles and either a bud or a part of the stem near the bases of the petioles (*782*). Damaged leaves fall prematurely and buds and branches are killed. Trees from 2 to 30 feet tall are attacked. The younger ones are often badly deformed. The related species, *O. betulae* (Winn.) feeds on and destroys the seeds of beech.

The **willow beaked-gall midge**, *Mayetiola rigidae* (O.S.), produces apical, beaked galls on the lower branches of many species of willow (fig. 168). In Michigan, eggs are laid singly on or near the buds of the host. Newly-hatched larvae penetrate the bud and a gall begins to develop by the end of the first larval instar and continues to enlarge until fall. Winter is spent as a larva inside the gall, and pupation occurs in the spring. The gall deforms the stem and occasionally a galled branch dies or breaks off (*781*).

Many other species of gall midges have been recorded attacking various species of eastern trees. A few of the more common ones are as follows: *Parallelodiplosis florida* (Felt)—produces elongate, pocketlike swellings on the veins and midribs of scrub and pin oak leaves; *Obolodiplosis robiniae* (Hald.)—causes the margins of black locust leaves to fold; *Caryomyia holotricha* (O. S.), *C. sanguinolenta* (O. S.), and *C. tubicola* (O. S.)—produce galls on hickory; *Cincticornia pilulae* (Beut.)—produces subglobose or globose, irregular, wrinkled, reddish galls on red oak leaves; *Janetiella coloradensis* Felt—causes swellings at the bases of scrub pine needles; *Prodiplosis morrisi* Gagne—feeds on the

F-519914
FIGURE 168.—Gall produced on willow by the willow beaked-gall midge, *Mayetiola rigidae*.

F-519915
FIGURE 167.—Damage to paper birch by the cecidomyid, *Oligotrophus papyrifera*.

young leaves of cottonwood in the South, causing them to turn black, unfold improperly, and drop off frequently. Terminal growth is sometimes severely stunted. *Mycodiplosis alternata* Felt —produces clublike swellings on small twigs of dogwood. This sometimes kills several inches of the damaged twigs.

Aphidoletes thompsoni Mohn, a European predator of the balsam woolly aphid, has been imported and is established in aphid-infested stands of Fraser fir in the Southern Appalachians.

FAMILY XYLOPHAGIDAE

Ichneumon Flies

These flies, as their common name suggests, often resemble members of the hymenopterous family, Ichneumonidae. The adults are usually observed feeding on sap, the nectar of flowers, or other liquid matter in forested or wooded areas. The larvae appear to be either predators or scavengers in rich soil, in decaying vegetable matter, under the bark of trees, or in decaying logs. *Erinna lugen* Loew larvae may occur in large numbers under the bark of elm in association with the elm borer. The larvae of *E. abdominalis* Loew feed on beetle larvae under the bark of pine.

FAMILY STRATIOMYIDAE

Soldier Flies

Soldier flies are brightly colored, moderately large, nearly bare, and thinly pilose. Many species are wasplike in appearance but the majority are broad and greatly flattened, and their wings lie parallel upon each other while at rest. These flies occur chiefly in wooded or forested areas or in meadows near water. Many are attracted to flowers. The larvae are usually terrestrial but sometimes aquatic and act mostly as scavengers. *Zabrachia polita* Coq. has been reared from decaying pine logs and from beetle infested elm logs.

FAMILY TABANIDAE

Horse Flies and Deer Flies

Many members of this family are important blood-sucking pests of livestock and wild animals. Some species also attack man and can be extremely annoying. Their bites are sharp and painful, and many are capable of removing considerable quantities of blood from their hosts, especially when they attack in force. They may also transmit such animal diseases as anthrax, anaplasmosis, surra, swamp fever, and tularemia.

Most of the large horse flies usually seen belong to the genus *Tabanus*. These flies breed mostly in marshes, swamps, bogs, and ponds. The largest and best known species is the **black horse fly,** *T. atratus* Fab. The adult is up to 25 mm. long and its bite can result in the loss of a considerable quantity of blood. In addition to the amount swallowed by the insect, as much as 100 cc. of blood may ooze from the puncture after the fly has left. Other important species include: the **striped horse fly,** *T. lineola* Fab., *T. costalis* Wied., *T. abactor* Philip, *T. quinquevittatus* Wied., *T. sulcifrons* Macq., and *T. nigrovittatus* Macq.

Deer flies belong to the genus *Chrysops* and are smaller than horse flies. They are active during the hottest weather and are often quite abundant during rainy spells. More than 60 species occur in eastern United States. *Diachlorus ferrugatus* (Fab.) is a common and notorious pest in swampy areas from New Jersey to Florida and Louisiana, especially in the Carolinas.

FAMILY RHAGIONIDAE

SNIPE FLIES

Snipe flies are commonly found in the woods, especially in moist areas. The majority are brownish or gray; others are black with spots or stripes of white, yellow or green. Both the adults and larvae feed on other insects. Adults of the genus *Symphoromyia* fly persistently about the head and are very annoying because their bites are painful.

FAMILY ASILIDAE

ROBBER FLIES

Robber flies are mostly large to very large (fig. 169). Some have long, tapering abdomens; others are stout-bodied and resemble bumblebees. All are rather hairy. They are predacious on other insects and occasionally on their own kind. The larvae of *Tolmerus notatus* (Wield.), *Leptogaster flavipes* Loew, *Laphria index* McAtee, *L. flavicollis* Say, and *L. thoracica* (F.) have been collected from decaying wood infested with cerambycid and other coleopterous larvae. Larvae of certain other species feed on grasshopper eggs and white grubs.

FIGURE 169.—Adult of a robber fly, *Asilus sericeus.*

FAMILY BOMBYLIIDAE

BEE FLIES

These flies are moderately large, densely hairy, and look like bees. The adults are nectar and pollen feeders. The larvae of certain species are parasitic on the larvae of other insects, especially of the orders Lepidoptera, Hymenoptera, and Coleoptera. Others feed on the egg pods of grasshoppers.

FAMILY EMPIDIDAE

DANCE FLIES

Members of this family are commonly known as dance flies because of their habit of flying up and down, up and down, in swarms in the woods, along streams, or on the shores of ponds and lakes. The flies range in length from 1 to about 15 mm. and probably are all predatory, mostly on small Diptera. The larvae live in damp earth, in decaying wood or other vegetation, under the bark of trees, or in the water. They are probably all predators. *Tachydromia* sp. has been reared from white pine leaders infested with the white pine weevil.

FAMILY DOLICHOPODIDAE

LONG-LEGGED FLIES

Members of this family are very small, long-legged flies, rarely more than 10 mm. long. Adults are predacious on other insects and are found on the foliage or trunks of trees, or on damp earth, usually in swamps or along lightly shaded streams. Most of the larvae appear to be aquatic, but those of a few species occur under the bark of trees where they feed on other insects. *Dolichopus vittatus* Loew has been reared from beetle infested hickory, and *Medetera* sp. from beetle infested larch.

FAMILY PIPUNCULIDAE

BIG-HEADED FLIES

Pipunculids are small, dark flies with large heads composed mostly of large approximated eyes. The larvae are small, elliptical, thick, depressed, naked, and narrowed at each end. They are parasitic on various families of Homoptera, especially the Cicadellidae.

FAMILY SYRPHIDAE

FLOWER FLIES

This is one of the largest families in the order Diptera, and it is almost entirely beneficial to man (*516*). The adults are strongly attracted to flowers and play important roles in the cross-pollination of plants and trees. The larvae of many species feed on and aid in the control of many destructive insects such as aphids, scales, psyllids, spittlebugs, mealybugs, and lepidopterous larvae. A few species are plant feeders but they are seldom injurious.

Adults are usually brightly colored and are frequently striped, spotted, or banded with yellow. Some resemble wasps; others look like small bumblebees. The males have the peculiar habit of hovering almost completely motionless in the air and then darting swiftly to one side when disturbed. The maggots of insect feeding species are sluglike. The body tapers toward the front end and the body contents are visible through the integument. Wirth, Sedman, and Weems (787) published a list of the syrphids occurring in America north of Mexico.

FAMILY CONOPIDAE

THICK-HEADED FLIES

Conopid flies are thinly pilose or nearly bare, elongate, and of moderate size. The head is broader than the thorax, and the abdomen is elongated and constricted. The antennae are 3-segmented, the third segment bearing a dorsal arista. Adults fly slowly and are usually seen around flowers. The larvae are solitary internal parasites, mainly of Hymenoptera. One species parasitizes grasshoppers and crickets.

FAMILY TEPHRITIDAE

FRUIT FLIES

Fruit flies are fairly small and usually have spotted or banded wings. The larvae are usually pale yellowish and taper slightly toward the front. Eggs of most species are deposited in healthy, living tissue and the larvae feed in various parts of plants. Certain species produce root and stem galls and a few are leaf miners. Others develop in fleshy fruits or in the seeds or ovaries of flowers. Many species are highly destructive of fleshy fruits and vegetables throughout the world. A few of the species occurring in the woodlands or forests of eastern United States are discussed below.

The **apple maggot,** *Rhagoletis pomonella* (Walsh), an important pest of apple, also breeds in the fruit of hawthorn, choke cherry, plum, and dogwood. The adult is dark colored and a little smaller than the house fly. Each wing is crossed by four dark bars which merge together. Three or four white bands run across the dorsum of the abdomen. The **cherry fruit fly,** *R. cingulata* (Loew), breeds in the fruit of wild cherry. Adults are black except for yellow margins on the thorax, two white cross bands on the abdomen, and a dark band on each wing. They are smaller than house flies. The **black cherry fruit fly,** *R. fausta* (O. S.), breeds in wild cherry throughout the same area as does the cherry fruit fly. Adults resemble those of the cherry fruit fly except for the abdomen which is entirely black. The **walnut husk fly,** *R. completa* Cresson, breeds in the husks of black walnut in the Central States. Feeding by the larvae produces a slimy condition which causes the husks to turn black, stick to and stain the shell. Nuts with damaged shells cannot be sold even though the contents are sound. The wings of the adult are transparent with dark cross-bars. *Toxotrypana curvicauda* Gerstacker breeds in papaya in Florida and Texas.

FAMILY CHAMAEMYIIDAE

The larvae of a number of species in several genera of these small, grayish flies are predators of aphids, scale insects, and mealybugs. One species, *Leucopis obscura* Hal., a native of Europe, was introduced into Canada against the balsam woolly aphid in the early thirties. It quickly became established and, following additional colonizations, spread over most of the infested areas in eastern Canada and into northern New England. Since 1954, colonies have been released in aphid-infested stands in Vermont, New Hampshire, New York, and North Carolina, and the Pacific Northwest. It is usually found on heavily infested trees only, where it feeds mostly on adults that have laid many eggs. *Cremifania nigrocellulata* Cz., another European species, also imported into eastern Canada and the Pacific Northwest against the balsam woolly aphid, is now established. A fairly large number have developed on stem-infested trees, but their spread has been very slow.

FAMILY LONCHAEIDAE

Adults of this family are shiny black and about 5 to 6 mm. long. The larvae are very small and are covered by minute spines. These flies act mostly as scavengers or as predators on other insects. *Lonchaea polita* Say has been reared from bark-beetle infested wood. *L. corticis* Taylor has been recorded as an important parasite of the white pine weevil (*467*).

FAMILY DROSOPHILIDAE

Vinegar Flies

These are the flies that are so often seen around spoiled fruit, slime fluxes, and fungi. Usually yellowish except for black markings on the abdomen, adults seldom exceed 5 mm. in length. Few if any species are of importance as enemies of forest, shade, or ornamental trees. There is a possibility, however, that certain species are involved in the transmission of the oak wilt fungus, *Chalara quercina* (*315*).

FAMILY CHLOROPIDAE

Chloropid Flies

These flies are small to very small and bare to nearly bare insects. Some species are brightly colored with yellow and black. The larvae of certain species parasitize or prey on other insects;

425

others have been found feeding in the seeds and cones of conifers. Adults of the genus *Hippelates* are attracted to the eyes of man and animals and are very annoying. Certain species are also reported to transmit yaws and pinkeye. *Gaurax apicalis* Mall., *Oscinella coxendix* (Fitch), *Madiza glabra* Fall., and *Hippelates* sp. have been reared from the leaders of white pine infested by the white pine weevil (*467*).

FAMILY AGROMYZIDAE

LEAF MINER FLIES

These flies are very small and light or dark colored. The body covering ranges from sparse bristles to dense hairs. The larvae are plant feeders; some mine the cambium, but the majority mine the leaves. Frick (*270*) published a synopsis of North American species.

Larvae of the genus *Phytobia* Lioy feed in the cambium of living trees, making long, thin, gradually widening mines (fig. 170). These mines sometimes originate in the top of the tree and extend all the way to the base and into the roots. They cause defects known as pith-ray flecks. Heavily infested logs may be rendered unfit for some uses.

Phytobia setosa (Loew) attacks red and sugar maples (*320*). Adults are small and dark colored. The larvae are opaque-white and about 16 mm. long. *P. pruinosa* (Coq.) infests wild cherry, maple, and black and river birches. Adults are about 3 to 4 mm. long; the larvae are up to 30 mm. long. This species apparently lays its eggs in the forks of branches near the tops of trees and the larvae tunnel all the way down into the roots. *P. amelanchieris* (Greene) attacks shadbush and *P. pruni* (Gross.), wild cherry.

The **holly leaf miner,** *Phytomyza ilicicola* Loew, is a serious pest of American holly in eastern United States. The adult is a small, grayish-black fly about 25 mm. long. The female punctures leaves with her ovipositor and feeds on the juices exuding from the wounds. She also deposits eggs in the undersurfaces of leaves in

FIGURE 170.—Cambium miner work: Left, streaklike, longitudinal mines on trunk and roots of infested trees; right, "pitch-fleck" defects in the wood.

426

punctures made near the midrib. The larvae mine the tissues between the leaf surfaces. The mine is hairlike at first but gradually widens as the larva continues to grow. Eventually it becomes blotchlike (fig. 171). Heavily infested leaves become unsightly and usually drop prematurely. Leaves damaged by feeding punctures become roughened, twisted, and stunted. The winter is spent in the larval stage in the mine. Pupation occurs from early March to early April and the adults emerge from mid-May to late June. There is one generation per year.

FIGURE 171.—Injury by the holly leaf miner, *Phytomyza ilicicola:*
Left, undamaged leaves; right, mined leaves.

Several other members of the family also mine the leaves or produce galls on their hosts. *Japanagromyza viridula* (Coq.)—produces blotch mines in the leaves of red oak; *Melanagromyza schineri* (Gir.)—causes the formation of slight swellings on the smaller twigs of poplar; *M. tiliae* (Couden)—produces swellings about half an inch long on the twigs of basswood; *Phytobia posticata* (Meigen)—produces blotch mines in the leaves of sweetgum; and *Phytomyza clara* (Melander)—produces blotch mines on *Catalpa bungii.*

FAMILY ANTHOMYIIDAE

Members of this family are quite similar in appearance to those of the family Muscidae. The maggots vary in habits, some feeding on the roots of plants, some as scavengers, and others as parasites of other insects. The **seed corn maggot,** *Hylema platura* (Meigen), damaged red cedar seedlings in a forest nursery in Tennessee (*766*). In this case, the larvae chewed through the bark of the main stem just below the ground line and fed on the roots. Large numbers of seedlings were killed.

427

FAMILY MUSCIDAE

HOUSE FLIES, STABLE FLIES, AND ALLIES

Flies of this family vary in length from 2 to 12 mm. Some are yellowish or black in color, but the majority are gray or brown. There are several economically important species, such as the well-known **house fly**, *Musca domestica* L., the **stable fly**, *Stomoxys Haemetobia irritans* (F.), and the **tsetse flies.** Fortunately, tsetse flies, which transmit the organisms responsible for sleeping sickness and other diseases, are native to Africa and do not occur in this country. A number of species in the genus *Muscina* are parasites of various species of Coleoptera.

FAMILY HIPPOBOSCIDAE

LOUSE FLIES

Louse flies may be winged or wingless. Many look like lice. The body is flat and leathery-looking, and the legs are short, strong, and broadly separated by the sternum. The tarsi are short and armed with strong claws, and the abdomen is saclike. All species feed on birds and mammals. The best known member of the family is the **sheep ked**, *Melophagus ovinus* (L.), an important parasite of sheep. Other important species are *Lynchia americana* (Leach)—parasitizes grouse, hawks, and owls; *Olfersia fumipennis* (Sahl.)—attacks the bald eagle; species of *Ornithoica* and *Ornithomyia*—feed on various small birds; and species of *Lipoptena*—parasitize deer.

FAMILY CALLIPHORIDAE

THE BLOW FLIES

Blow flies have metallic blue, green, or yellow bodies and are usually about the size of house flies. The arista of the antenna is plumose at the tip and the hindmost posthumeral bristle is almost always longer than the presutural bristle. In the maggots, or larvae, the posterior spiracles are flush. A few species are economic pests, but the majority serve a useful purpose in helping to rid the landscape of such undesirable materials as dead animal bodies and animal excrement.

The **screw-worm**, *Cochliomyia hominivorax* (Coquerel), a long time pest of livestock in the Southwest, was first recorded from the Southeastern States in 1933. Since then, or until its eradication from the region through the mass release of sexually sterile male flies (*457*), it caused tremendous losses to livestock. Big game, such as deer, and smaller animals, such as racoons, rabbits, and opossums, have also been attacked and injured. The female deposits up to 300 eggs around wounds; the maggots feed on the tissues, and produce foul smelling wounds. This attracts additional flies and compounds the infestation. Heavily infested animals may die within a few weeks unless the maggots are killed and the wounds treated.

Other blow flies occasionally attacking living animals include *Phaenicia sericata* (Meigen), the **greenbottle fly**, the **black blow fly,** *Phormia regina* (Meigen), and the **secondary screw-worm,** *Cochliomyia macellaria* (Fab.). They also oviposit on wounds or sores. Larvae of the genus *Protocalliphora* are blood-sucking parasites of nestlings.

FAMILY SARCOPHAGIDAE

Flesh Flies

Larvae of this family feed on a wide variety of foods. A number of species are scavengers, feeding on dead insects, dung, and other decaying materials. Some species are parasitic in various insects. Adults are 6 to 12 mm. long; the sides of the face are hairy; the aristae of the antennae are feathery for about half their length; there are 3 black stripes on the thorax; and the abdomen is checkered. The larvae have their posterior spiracles located in a pit.

Sarcophaga aldrichi Park., an important parasite of the forest tent caterpillar, occurs in southern Canada and from New England to the Lake States and Southern Appalachians. It suppresses significantly forest tent caterpillar outbreaks in the Lake States. Living young are normally deposited on cocoons and the larvae feed as scavengers on the prepupae or pupae inside the cocoons (*355*). Full-grown larvae are about 13 mm. long. The adults are strong, active fliers and during tentcaterpillar outbreaks may occur in enormous numbers, swarming over everything, livestock and people included. During intervals between outbreaks, the species is hard to find. In the Southern States, the related species, *S. houghi* Aldrich, parasitizes the forest tent caterpillar and elm spanworm.

FAMILY TACHINIDAE

Tachina Flies

The family Tachinidae contains many of the most important species of insect parasites. All species appear to be internal parasites of many kinds of insects, especially Lepidoptera, but also various species of Coleoptera, Hemiptera, Orthoptera, and Hymenoptera (*629*).

Tachinid flies look very much like overgrown house flies but differ in having an entirely bare bristle on each antennae. The maggots are clothed with minute spinules, and the posterior spiracles are flush with or raised from the adjacent area.

The majority of species are oviparous, but a few give birth to living young. Eggs are deposited on the skin of the host, on leaves or other parts of plants on which their hosts feed, or on the soil. Living young are deposited on or under the skin of the host, on leaves and other parts of plants frequented by their hosts, or on the ground. The number of generations per year varies from 1 to 10, depending on species and climate.

A large number of native species and a few introduced species parasitize various native and introduced species of eastern forest insects. More than 125 species have been recorded attacking lepidopterous larvae in this country (*638, 639*). A few of the more important introduced species are discussed here.

Compsilura concinnata (Meigen) (fig. 172) was imported against the gypsy and brown-tail moths in the early days of this century. It is now widely distributed throughout most of the Northeast and in southeastern Canada where it attacks at least 200 species of Lepidoptera. Parasitization of the gypsy moth averages from 10 to 50 percent in much of the infested area. Even higher percentages are recorded in brown-tail and satin moth infestations (*205, 177, 751, 124*).

Blepharipa scutellata (R.-D.) (fig. 173), a parasite of the gypsy moth, was imported and became established by 1911. In most of the areas where it occurs, it parasitizes from 5 to 25 percent of the gypsy moth population. As far as known, it confines its attack to the gypsy moth in this country, whereas in Europe it has several lepidopterous hosts. Burgess and Crossman (*124*) discussed its life history and habits.

Parasetigena agilis (R.-D.) and *Exorista larvarum* (L.) were imported against the gypsy moth from 1924 to 1933. *P. agilis,* a single brooded species, is probably the most important parasite of the nun moth in Europe. *E. larvarum,* a multi-brooded species, attacks about 45 different hosts in Europe. Both species are now important parasites of the gypsy moth throughout the generally infested area in the United States. *E. larvarum* is also a parasite of the satin moth and brown-tail moth in this country.

Two species, *Townsendiellomyia nidicola* (Tns.) and *Carcelia laxifrons* Vill., were imported against the brown-tail moth during

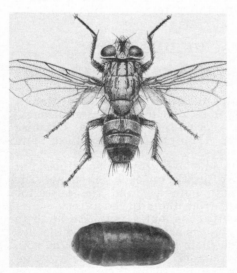

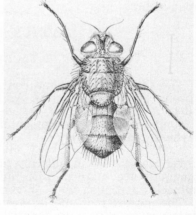

FIGURE 173.—Adult of *Blepharipa scutellata,* a parasite of the gypsy moth and other defoliators.

FIGURE 172.—Adult and puparium of *Compsilura concinnata,* a parasite of the gypsy moth and other defoliators.

the early days of this century. *T. nidicola* quickly spread throughout the infested area. During recent years it has frequently parasitized an average of 17 percent of overwintering brown-tail moth larvae. *C. laxifrons* also occurs throughout the infested area. Unfortunately, it parasitizes a very low percentage of the population.

Chaetexorista javana B. & B., a native of Japan, was imported against the oriental moth in 1929 and 1930. As early as 1933, parasitism in the infested area around Boston, Massachusetts averaged 60 percent. *Erynniopsis rondanii* Towns., a native of Europe, has been successfully introduced into California against the European elm leaf beetle. Colonies have also been liberated against the beetle along the Atlantic Seaboard but without success. *Drino bohemica* Mesn., a native of Europe, was successfully introduced into Canada against the European spruce sawfly during the thirties and forties. This is probably the same species that was introduced into the United States around 1906 as *Sturmia inconspicua* (Meig.) against the gypsy moth, brown-tail moth, and red-headed pine sawfly (*205*). It was recovered at gypsy moth colonization sites for several years thereafter, but it apparently did not become permanently established. It probably occurs now in northern Maine as a result of spread from New Brunswick and Quebec, where it appears to be one of the most effective parasites introduced against the European spruce sawfly.

FAMILY OESTRIDAE

WARBLES OR BOT FLIES

Warble or bot flies are all parasitic on animals, and several are serious pests. They are best known as enemies of domestic animals, but many species also attack various species of wild animals. The adults are medium- to large-sized flies and resemble small bees. *Cephenomyia pratti* Hunt. and *C. phobifer* (Clark) are serious enemies of deer. Various species of the genus *Pseudobogeris* infest squirrels, rabbits, cats, and meadow mice. Cattle are subject to serious infestations by the **northern cattle grub,** *Hypoderma bovis* (L.) and the **common cattle grub,** *H. lineatum* (Villers).

Order HYMENOPTERA

The order Hymenopt ra is one of the largest and most important orders of insects. Besides a large number of harmful species, the order contains a far greater number of beneficial species. Bees, wasps, and ants are among the better known groups. Beneficial forms include the well-known honeybee, plus a large number of less familiar forms. Most of the species are parasites of other insects, and many are important pollinators of plants. Among harmful species are the sawflies. Many of them are important pests of forest and shade trees and young trees in nurseries and plantations.

The winged members of the order characteristically have four membranous wings, the front pair larger and more completely veined than the hind pair. The hindwings have a row of tiny hooks along the anterior margin by which they are attached to the front wing. Some forms, such as the common ant, are wingless. The ovipositor is usually well-developed and in the higher forms is modified into a sting.

The order is divided into two suborders—Apocrita (=Clistogastra) and Symphata (=Chalastogastra) (550). Each of these, in turn, is divided into a number of superfamilies.

Suborder SYMPHATA (= CHALASTOGASTRA)

Members of the suborder Symphata are distinguished by having the abdomen of the adult broadly joined to the thorax—the first abdominal segment is not modified into a petiole as in the suborder Apocrita. The ovipositor of the female is well-developed and fitted for making incisions in the leaves or stems of plants. In the majority of species it is saw-like. Because of this, these members of the suborder are known as sawflies.

The larvae of all species, except for the family Orussidae, are phytophagous, the majority feeding externally on the foliage. The remainder bore into stems, fruit, wood, or leaves to feed. Orussid larvae are parasitic on wood-boring coleopterous larvae. While external leaf-feeding larvae look like lepidopterous larvae, they have only one ocellus on each side of the head and have six or more pairs of prolegs on the abdomen, none of which bear hooks or "crochets."

The suborder Symphata is represented in the United States and Canada by approximately 1,000 species, many of which are highly destructive of forest and shade trees and of young trees in nurseries and plantations.

SUPERFAMILY MEGALODONTOIDEA

Family XYELIDAE

Members of the family Xyelidae are medium-sized to small sawflies, most less than 19 mm. long. They differ from all other sawflies in having the third antennal segment longer than all of the remaining segments combined and in having three marginal cells in the forewing. Unlike all other sawflies, except the Pamphiliidae, they have the costal cell divided by a longitudinal vein.

The genus *Xyela* Dalman contains several species which feed as larvae on the developing pollen of the male strobili of various species of pines. The adults are usually found on the catkins of willow and alder and occasionally on the pollen of pines. Only 16 species are known in the world (119). *X. bakeri* Konow—reared or collected from longleaf, slash, and jack pine (known to occur from Maryland to North Carolina as well as in Florida and Texas); *X. minor* Norton—known hosts are Virginia, slash, and longleaf pines (in Virginia and from Florida to Texas); *X. obscura* (Strobl)—known hosts are jack, Virginia, slash, and longleaf pines from southern Canada to Florida and Texas); *X. alpigena* (Strobl)—recorded from white pine and spruce (southern Canada, New York, Maryland, and Illinois); *X. styrax* Burdick—recorded from Virginia pine (Maryland and Virginia).

Ebel (*218*) discussed the species occurring on slash and longleaf pines.

Pleroneura brunneicornis Rohwer occurs in eastern Canada and in the Northeastern States from Maine to Michigan. Its hosts are listed as balsam and white firs. Full-grown larvae are white and from 4 to 7 mm. long. The true legs are weakly developed and the prolegs consist of nothing more than slight swellings. In New Brunswick, Canada, adults are found during late May. Eggs are deposited in tightly packed needle clusters on expanding buds, and the larvae feed in tunnels excavated in the center of new shoots. These shoots stop growing, turn brown, and drop. Later on, they resemble frost-killed shoots. Winter is spent in the pupal state in oval cocoons in the soil, and there is one generation per year (*749*).

An unidentified species of *Pleroneura* (or possibly *Xyela*) has been recorded attacking loblolly, shortleaf, and slash pine in Georgia. Eggs are deposited on new shoots and the larvae feed on the tissues of the shoots, causing the formation of spindle-shaped galls. Full-grown larvae vacate the galls and drop to the ground. Pupation occurs in cells in the soil. The curculionid, *Conotrachelus caroliniensis*, breeds in and hollows out the vacated galls. This weakens the shoots and causes them to break in the wind.

Several species of *Megaxyela* Ashmead have been observed feeding as larvae on hickory, and the larvae of one species of the genus *Macroxyela* Kirby feeds on elm.

FAMILY PAMPHILIIDAE

WEB-SPINNING SAWFLIES

The family Pamphiliidae is represented in North America north of Mexico by four genera and 85 or more species, better than half of which occur in eastern America. The adults are moderately large with long, many-segmented antennae. The abdomen is flattened and has sharp lateral margins; the ovipositor of the female is short. Larvae have the venter flattened and are about 15 to 25 mm. long. The thoracic legs are well-developed, but abdominal legs are absent. The larvae of certain species are gregarious and feed together in nests which they prepare by webbing together leaves of their hosts. Others roll the edges of leaves or spin silken tubes in which to live (*519*).

The **pine false webworm**, *Acantholyda erythrocephala* (Linn.), an introduced species first recorded in Pennsylvania in 1925, now occurs from Connecticut to New Jersey and Pennsylvania, in the Lake States, and in New Brunswick. Its preferred hosts are white and red pines, but it also attacks several other pines, including Scotch, Austrian, mugho, Swiss Mountain red, and Japanese red. Female adults have orange-red heads and steel-blue bodies; males are almost entirely steel-blue. Full-grown larvae are pale greenish-gray and about 16 to 20 mm. long. The head is clay-yellow with dense, small dark brown spots, and there are longitudinal stripes of purplish red on the dorsum, venter, and sides.

Winter is spent in the larval stage; pupation occurs in early spring, and adults appear from about mid-April to mid-May. Eggs are deposited in short rows of three to 10 eggs each on the previous year's needles. The larvae spin loose webbing about themselves and feed gregariously on the old needles. Young larvae cut the needles off just above the bundle sheaths and pull them into the webbing, where they are consumed. Older larvae feed singly from within individual silken tubes spun around themselves along twigs. Considerable amounts of frass and bits of needles usually adhere to the exterior of these tubes (fig. 174). Full-grown larvae drop to and enter the ground for hibernation. There is one generation per year. Heavy infestations sometimes develop locally, causing severe defoliation.

FIGURE 174.—Damage and webbing by the pine false webworm, *Acantholyda erythrocephala.*

Acantholyda zappei (Rohwer), the **nesting-pine sawfly,** occurs in southern Canada and the Northeastern, Central, and Lake States. Its hosts are various species of pines such as red, jack, Austrian, pitch, and Japanese red. A full-grown larva is green, with a brown head and a dark green dorsal stripe, and is about 18 to 25 mm. long. Eggs are laid singly on young needles of the current year's growth from late June to early July. Young larvae spin webs about themselves and fasten the outer threads to the needles. Needles are cut off near the base and drawn into the web where they are consumed. Webs are increased in size as the larvae develop and may reach a length of 5 inches by the time the larvae are full-grown. Winter is spent as mature larvae in cells in the soil, and pupation occurs in the spring. There is one generation per year (*802*).

Acantholyda circumcincta (Klug) has been recorded from Georgia and Florida. During 1968, it defoliated approximately 100 acres of sand pine in Florida.

Additional eastern species of *Acantholyda,* along with known hosts and known areas of distribution, include the following: *A. apicalis* Westw.—loblolly pine (in North Carolina, Mississippi, and Florida) ; *A. pini* Rohwer—red pine (in southern Canada and from New York to North Carolina) ; *A. angulata* (MacGillivray) —white, pitch, jack, Austrian, and Japanese red pines (from southeastern Canada and Maine to Pennsylvania and Minnesota) ; *A. luteomaculata* (Cresson)—white and jack pines, preferably white (in southeastern Canada and from New Hampshire and Massachusetts to Ohio and Minnesota) ; *A. maculiventris* (Norton)—balsam fir and white spruce (in southern Canada and from Maine to North Carolina).

Cephalcia fascipennis (Cresson) occurs in Canada, Maine, New Hampshire, and West Virginia. Its hosts are listed as blue and white spruce. Full-grown larvae have a black head and thorax and a green body. They are about 25 mm. long. Ornamental spruce and hedges are sometimes rendered unsightly by the presence of larval nests (*224*). *C. fulviceps* (Rohwer) feeds on jack and red pines in southern Canada, New Hampshire, Connecticut, and New Jersey. *C. marginata* Middlekauff feeds on young red pines in Quebec, New York, Massachusetts, Connecticut, Pennsylvania, Virginia, and West Virginia. Daviault (*182*) discussed its life history.

The **plum web-spinning sawfly,** *Neurotoma inconspicua* (Norton), occurs in southeastern Canada and from New England to Montana in the United States. Its hosts are listed as hawthorn and various wild plums and wild cherries. The adults are black with supraocular spots, their wings are hyaline with faint bands beneath the stigma, and their legs are mostly reddish brown beyond the coxae. The larvae are gregarious and web together the foliage (the webs are somewhat similar to those of the fall webworm). Heavily infested trees no more than 6 feet tall may support up to 25 webs, some of which may enclose entire branches. Such trees may be completely defoliated.

Neurotoma fasciata (Norton) occurs in southern Canada, and in the Eastern States from New Hampshire to Florida, westward to Illinois and Michigan. Its hosts are listed as wild black and pin cherries. The full-grown larva has a shiny black head and prothoracic plates and a deep green body, and is about 18 mm. long. The larvae are gregarious and construct dirty, brown nests on the branches and shoots of young trees especially. Larvae overwinter in cells in the soil. Some of these larvae pupate in the spring. The remainder do not pupate until late fall or the following spring. The related species, *N. crataegi* Middlekauff, feeds on hawthorn from Massachusetts to Michigan and Illinois.

SUPERFAMILY TENTHREDINOIDEA

Sawflies

Members of the superfamily Tenthredinoidea are commonly called sawflies because of the sawlike ovipositor of the female. The ovipositor is composed of three main pieces held within protecting sheaths. The upper piece is a rigid lance with grooves along which the other two pieces slide. The last two consist of thin plates with their flat inner surfaces together. Each plate is usually shaped like a long acute triangle with the edge of one long side along a groove of the lance. The edge of the other long side is saw-toothed. The narrow base of the lance is the point from which springs the rod that attaches the blade to the abdomen and controls its movements.

Sawfly larvae resemble lepidopterous larvae but are usually naked. A few, however, are spined, hairy, or covered with a gummy or waxy secretion. The best single feature for distinguishing sawfly larvae from lepidopterous larvae is the presence of only one eye on each side of the head—lepidopterous larvae have six on each side. When disturbed, the larvae of certain sawfly species curl up and lie on their sides, whereas others hold their abdomens aloft over their heads or raise the head and thorax. The majority are external feeders on foliage, either eating entire leaves or skeletonizing them. Some feed from within webbed nests; a few feed within mines in the leaves, leaf petioles, and twigs; some produce galls on the leaves or shoots; and a few feed on catkins, buds, or fruits. When they reach maturity they either spin cocoons or construct cells in which to pupate. Cocoons may be spun on leaves, twigs, or other parts of the host, or they may be spun in the litter or soil beneath the trees. Cells are formed in pith, bark, and brashy wood, or in the ground. Leaf mining species sometimes form their cocoons within their mines.

Sawfly adults frequently resemble small bees or wasps, except for their antennae, which differ in the number of joints. The antennae may also be feathered, clubbed, threadlike, forked, or may bear spurs on some of the joints. It is rather difficult to separate the adults into species because the females are variable, with the variations in related species overlapping, while the males are monotonously alike. It is often much easier to separate the larvae into species.

Sawflies comprise one of the most destructive groups of insect defoliators in eastern forests. Outbreaks occur frequently and sometimes spread over large areas and persist for several years before subsiding. Damage is often severe, especially in coniferous plantations. During the past several years, outbreaks of an increasing number of species have been reported, possibly as a result of the establishment of more and more pine stands in planting programs. Ross (*622*) published a list of the species in the superfamily occurring in America north of Mexico.

FAMILY PERGIDAE

The family Pergidae contains only one genus, *Acordulecera* Say, and 13 species, all of which occur in eastern United States.

Full-grown larvae are greenish with light or blackish heads and distinct lateral lobes, and measure less than 12 mm. long. Each body segment bears transverse rows of slight tubercles armed with short, stiff setae. The larvae feed gregariously on the foliage of oak, butternut, hickory, hawthorn, and pecan and occasionally are abundant enough to attract attention. Adults appear in May and June; larvae are present from June to August, and winter is spent in cocoons in the ground. There is usually one generation a year, but some species occasionally have a partial second.

FAMILY ARGIDAE

ARGID SAWFLIES

The family Argidae is represented by eight genera and 32 species in the United States and Canada, the majority of which occur in the Eastern States. The adults are medium- to small-sized, stout-bodied sawflies. They can be recognized by their three-segmented antenna, the third segment of which is very long and sometimes U-shaped or Y-shaped. The more common species are also usually either reddish-brown or bluish-black, with more or less dark brown wings. Larvae are yellowish-green or red and are usually spotted. The body is rather thick-set, widest on abdominal segments one to three, tapering toward the rear end, and the venter is flattened.

The **birch sawfly,** *Arge pectoralis* (Leach), is widely distributed in the Northeastern States and southern Canada. Its preferred hosts are various birches, especially gray and paper. It also has been recorded feeding on willow. Full-grown larvae are about 18 mm. long. The head is reddish-yellow with a spot on each side; the body yellowish, with six rows of black spots on top and three on each side. Adults appear during June and July and deposit their eggs in slits cut in the margins of leaves. Larvae are present from July to September, and winter is spent as full-grown larvae in cocoons spun in the litter on the ground. The species is of no economic importance, although it occasionally becomes abundant enough to cause noticeable defoliation over limited areas.

Additional species of argid sawflies likely to be encountered on trees and shrubs in the Eastern States are as follows: *Arge clavicornis* (Fab.)—willow, birch, and azalea; *A. scapularis* (Klug)—elm and birch; *A. coccinea* (Fab.)—sumac; *Sterictiphora prunivora* (Dyar)—cherry; and *Arge* sp.—elm and oak.

FAMILY CIMBICIDAE

CIMBICID SAWFLIES

The family Cimbicidae is represented in the United States and Canada by 12 species, some of which have been recorded feeding on trees in the Eastern States. The adults are large; the antennae are clavate with an abrupt enlargement at the tip. The tibiae are without preapical spurs; however, there are single apical spurs on the front tibiae. Full-grown larvae have large heads, and their bodies taper toward the rear. During life they are covered with a waxy bloom.

437

The **elm sawfly,** *Cimbex americana* Leach, is the largest of the North American sawflies. It is widely distributed, occurring from coast to coast in southern Canada and throughout the Northeastern States west to Colorado. The larvae feed primarily on the foliage of elm and willow, but are also observed occasionally on basswood, birch, maple, poplar, and alder. The antennae of the adults are tinged with orange, the head and thorax black, the wings smoky brown, and they are about 25 mm. long. The female's abdomen is usually steel-blue, with three or four yellowish spots on each side and a faint whitish spot near the thorax. In the male, the whitish spot near the thorax is distinct, but there are no yellowish spots on the sides. Full-grown larvae are yellowish-white or greenish-white and about 43 mm. long, with a pebbly skin and a black dorsal stripe. While feeding, the larva usually coils its rear end around a stem or twig; at rest it usually lies coiled up like a snail fig. 175).

FIGURE 175.—Larva of elm sawfly, *Cimbex americana.*

Adults appear from about mid-May to mid-August, and the eggs are deposited in pockets cut into leaf tissues. Larvae occur from June until October, depending on location. When they become full-grown, they crawl to the ground and spin tough, papery cocoons in the litter or just below the surface of the soil. Winter is spent in the larval stage, and pupation occurs in the spring. There is one generation per year.

The elm sawfly is of minor importance as a defoliator of forest trees, but occasionally seriously defoliates shade tree elms. Willow also has been heavily attacked in the Northern Great Plains area. The larvae partially or entirely defoliate the trees, while the adults chew the thin, tender bark of twigs, girdling and killing them.

Trichiosoma triangulum Kirby occurs fairly commonly in the Eastern States. The larvae are solitary feeders on the foliage of birch, poplar, willow, and wild cherry. At maturity, they are about 37 mm. long. The head is creamy white, the body greenish-white, and the eye spots and spiracles blackish. The life cycle is similar to that of the elm sawfly.

FAMILY DIPRIONIDAE

CONIFER SAWFLIES

The family Diprionidae includes many of the most serious defoliators of conifers. The majority of species are native to the continent but several of foreign origin are well established. The family is divided into two subfamilies, Monocteninae and Diprioninae, and five genera (*550*). Adults are described as follows: Antennae composed of 13 or more segments, serrate in the female, and pectinate or bipectinate in the male. Mesosterno-plural sutures atrophied, mesoscutellum with anterior margin **V**-shaped, posterior margin with an exremely narrow and cordlike postergite (*621*). The larvae usually range in length from about 18 to 25 mm. The body is usually whitish, yellowish or grayish with brown or black stripes or rows of more or less distinctly separated spots (*801*).

Many species of diprionids are serious pests in both forest stands and plantations. Outbreaks occur periodically, sometimes over extensive areas, resulting in loss of growth and sometimes tree mortality (*11, 160*).

The genus *Monoctenus* Hartig is represented in the United States and Canada by four species, all of which occur in eastern America on *Juniperus*. None are considered serious pests of forest or shade trees. *M. melliceps* (Cresson) occurs in southern Canada and in the Northeastern States west to Kansas. Its hosts are red cedar, arborvitae, and juniper. Full-grown larvae are dull green and about 18 mm. long. The head is light brown; the body is marked with three dark longitudinal stripes; and the legs are black. Adults appear in May, and larvae are active during June and July.

The genus *Neodiprion* Rohwer contains many of the most destructive species of sawflies. During recent years outbreaks of several species have occurred, resulting in serious damage to young pines on thousands of acres of pine plantations in eastern United States. Some outbreaks spread over millions of acres of forested areas before subsiding. Atwood and Peck (*12*) and Ross (*623*) discussed the taxonomy of the genus and Krombein (*442*) published a check list of North American species.

The **red-headed pine sawfly**, *Neodiprion lecontei* (Fitch), occurs in southeastern Canada and throughout eastern United States. Its preferred hosts are jack, red, shortleaf, loblolly, slash, longleaf, pitch, and Swiss Mountain pines. White pine, larch, deodar cedar, and Norway spruce may also be defoliated, especially where they are growing close to trees of preferred species. Full-grown larvae are about 22 to 25 mm. long. The head is reddish and the body is yellowish-white, with six rows of black spots (fig. 176).

Winter is spent in the prepupal stage. Pupation occurs in early spring and the adults appear in a few weeks. Eggs are deposited in the tissues of current or previous year's needles, a single female depositing up to 100 eggs. The larvae feed gregariously on new and old needles and usually completely defoliate one branch be-

RED-HEADED
PINE SAWFLY

a shows a cluster
of larvae feeding
on a pine twig; b,
adult male. (a and
b, about natural
size.) c and d are
the female and
egg niches in a
needle, respec-
tively. e, Mature
larva. f: f, Co-
coon. (c, d, e, and
f, all greatly en-
larged.)

Cushman '51

FIGURE 176.—Red-headed pine sawfly.

fore moving to another. They also feed frequently on the tender bark of young twigs. Sometimes they completely defoliate a tree, with defoliation progressing from the top downward, before they reach maturity. When this happens, they may abandon the tree and migrate for distances of several yards in search of new foliage. Full-grown larvae drop to the ground, enter the soil, and spin tough, reddish-brown cocoons in which they spend the winter. In the South there may be five generations per year; in the Northern States and Canada there is only one.

The red-headed pine sawfly is one of the most widespread and destructive of the pine sawflies. It usually feeds on young trees, preferably on trees from 1 to 15 feet tall (474). In the southern portions of its range, it seems to prefer trees growing in shaded areas. In Canada, eggs are typically laid on trees in full sunlight and often on the leaders. Damage is most severe in young plantations and nurseries and to reproduction and ornamentals. Outbreaks occur frequently through the area of infestation. From 1935 to 1953, a total of 73 were recorded throughout eastern United States, 36 of which were widespread (58).

Among the more important natural control factors affecting the species are parasites, a polyhedrosis virus disease, and temperature extremes during the larval stage. The egg parasite, *Closterocerus cinctipennis* Ashm., and the larval parasite, *Spathimeigenia aurifrons* Curran, are often quite effective. The European parasite, *Dahlbominus fuscipennis* (Zett.), was liberated in infested stands in Tennessee, Alabama, New York, and Michigan in the late thirties and early forties. It has been recovered only in Michigan.

A number of management practices have been suggested for preventing damage in plantations by the red-headed pine sawfly: (1) Do not plant hard pines under hardwoods or closer than 25 feet to hardwood borders; (2) remove hardwood overstories before the planting of pines; (3) replant pines in areas of poor survival; and (4) promote early closure of plantations by planting pines with spacing not greater than 6 by 6 feet (in the North Central States).

Neodriprion pratti pratti, the **Virginia pine sawfly,** has been recorded from New Jersey and Maryland to North Carolina and westward to Illinois. Its hosts are listed as Virginia, pitch, jack, shortleaf, loblolly, and red pines. Newly-hatched larvae are pale green, with black head capsules, and are about 3 mm. long. Full-grown larvae (fig. 177) are spotted or marked with longitudinal black stripes and are from 16 to 23 mm. long.

Winter is spent in the egg stage, and hatching occurs in early spring. Newly-hatched larvae feed gregariously on previous year's needles, beginning about one-half inch below the tip. Feeding in groups of 2 to fifteen larvae each, they consume the outer portion of the needle, leaving the inner vascular tissue intact. After the first two instars, the larvae consume entire needles, except for the basal portion within the sheath. They may also feed on portions of developing buds and on the tender bark of twigs. By mid-May they become full grown and drop to the ground. Here they spin cocoons in the surface litter or in the soil. Pupation occurs in September and the adults appear in October and November.

F-519912
FIGURE 177.—Larvae of *Neo-diprion pratti pratti*, the Virginia pine sawfly.

Eggs are deposited individually within slits made by the female ovipositor along the flat sides of needles, usually before the end of November. There is one generation per year (*634, 536*).

Prior to the development of an outbreak in Maryland, Virginia, and North Carolina during the late fifties, this species was not considered an important pest in the Middle Atlantic States. Surprisingly, the outbreak occurring at that time swept over more than 14 million acres of pine and pine-hardwood type before it subsided. Tree mortality was not serious although some scattered killing was reported, but growth loss was severe.

White-footed mice and ants destroy large numbers of cocoons and prepupae in heavy infestations. The hymenopteron, *Exenterus canadensis* Provancher, is also an effective parasite of uncocooned prepupae on the ground (*86*). *Dahlbominus fuscipennis* (Zett.), an introduced parasite of sawfly cocoons, has been liberated and established in infested stands in Virginia. A native polyhedrosis virus has destroyed up to 70 percent of sawfly larvae when applied from an airplane (*485*).

The **jack-pine sawfly**, *Neodiprion pratti banksianae* Rohwer, occurs in southeastern Canada from New Brunswick to Manitoba, and in the Lake States. Jack pine is the favored host, but red and Scotch pines are occasionally attacked by larvae if they are growing with heavily infested jack pine. Full-grown larvae are yellowish-green and about 22 mm. long. The head is black and there are two longitudinal pale greenish-gray stripes running down the back. There is also a single row of 11 black spots on each side.

Winter is spent in the egg stage and hatching occurs in May or June. The larvae feed gregariously on previous year's needles only. Feeding is completed by early July. The larvae then drop to the ground and spin cocoons in the duff and top layers of the soil. Adults appear in late August and early September and lay three to five eggs in each needle, with the full compliment of eggs on the needles of one twig. There is one generation per year.

All sized trees are attacked, but small trees with open crowns are more susceptible to damage than trees in closed stands. Even aged stands and plantations are especially attractive. Mortality from a single defoliation seldom occurs, but it may result from several successive defoliations. Generally, the most serious damage results from gradual reduction in vigor and growth of the affected trees. Late spring frosts and a polyhedrosis virus disease are often effective in the control of heavy infestations. Direct and preventive methods of control are discussed by Ewan (*233*).

Neodiprion pratti paradoxicus Ross has been recorded from Maryland to Nova Scotia and Ontario. Its hosts are pitch, Scotch, shortleaf, and jack pines. Full-grown larvae have black heads, and the body is marked with very pale lateral stripes. Supraspiracular spots are usually partially or entirely atrophied in the middle of the body. Widespread outbreaks have occurred in pitch pine and shortleaf pine stands in New Jersey during recent years.

Neodiprion taedae taedae Ross [=*americanum* (Leach)], the **loblolly pine sawfly**, has been recorded from Maine and eastern Virginia. Its favored host is loblolly pine, but it also occasionally feeds on shortleaf pine. Full-grown larvae are greenish-white and about 22 mm. long. The head is reddish-brown, and there is a dull grayish-green longitudinal stripe on each side of the dorsum. There is also a row of black spots just above the spiracular line which extends from the second thoracic to the ninth abdominal segments, and there are two black blotches on top of the tenth segment.

Winter is spent in the egg stage, and hatching occurs in late April or early May. The larvae feed on old needles and reach maturity in about 30 days. In late September, they drop to the ground and tunnel in for several inches, where they spin cocoons. Adults appear about mid-October and lay their eggs, in rows in the sides of needles. There is one generation per year (*345*).

Since the new foliage is not eaten, infested trees are not completely defoliated or killed. Infestations occur more commonly in understocked pine stands where the trees retain their lower branches.

Neodiprion taedae linearis Ross., the **Arkansas pine sawfly,** long recognized as a pest of loblolly pine in Arkansas, is now known to occur also in Louisiana, southeast Texas, Mississippi, South Carolina, Missouri, Ohio, and Illinois. As far as known, loblolly and shortleaf pines are its only hosts, loblolly preferred. Full-grown larvae are dull green and about 25 mm. long. There are heavy black stripes along each side and often two lighter stripes below the heavier, black ones.

Winter is spent in the egg stage. Hatching occurs from early March to early May, depending on location. Young larvae feed gregariously in groups, often encircling the needles about half way from end to end, and partially girdling them. Infested terminals soon take on a reddened appearance. Older larvae feed singly or in pairs and consume the entire needle, leaving short stubs on the branch. They still retain their gregarious habit, however, and move in a group from branch to branch (fig. 178). For the most part, only the older foliage is eaten, but on shortleaf pine the terminal buds and tender bark on the new growth are also occasionally eaten (*162*). Full-grown larvae drop to the ground and spin mahogany-colored cocoons in the litter or topsoil. Pupation occurs in October or November and the adults appear immediately. Eggs are laid in slits cut into the needles, usually two to ten per needle. Each female lays from 90 to 120 eggs, often all in the needles of one twig (*742*).

This sawfly is found chiefly on medium-sized or large trees in forest stands. Several outbreaks have been recorded. One, which lasted from 1945 to 1948, spread over a gross area of about 3 million acres in Arkansas before it subsided. Defoliation causes a reduction in growth, especially if the tree is defoliated during successive years, and tree mortality may occur (fig. 179). Important natural control factors are a polyhedrosis virus disease, cold, rainy weather in the spring, and two larval parasites, the dipteron, *Anthrax sinuosa* (Wied.), and the hymenopteron, *Exenterus canadensis* Provancher.

The **Swaine jack-pine sawfly**, *Neodiprion swainei* Middleton, one of the most important of the pine-infesting sawflies in eastern Canada, is known to have been present in the Lake States since the early fifties. It is now widely distributed in the Upper Peninsula, Michigan, and in north-central Minnesota and Wisconsin. Jack pine is its favored host, but red, Scotch, and white pines growing in close proximity to heavily infested jack pines are also subject to defoliation by migrating larvae. Full-grown larvae differ in color in different portions of the infested region. Those found in the Lake States have bright orange heads and yellow bodies and there usually are two longitudinal pale stripes on each side. Bright yellow specimens without stripes are also occasionally found.

In the Lake States, winter is spent as full grown larvae in cocoons in the litter or top soil, and pupation and adult emergence occurs in early to late spring. Eggs are laid in current year's

FIGURE 178.—Larvae of *Neodiprion taedae linearis*, the Arkansas pine sawfly.

F-486626
FIGURE 179.—Large pines defoliated and killed by *Neodiprion taedae linearis*, the Arkansas pine sawfly.

needles, one to three eggs per needle, during June or July. The larvae are gregarious and feed primarily on old foliage, usually on exposed trees during July and August, until they become mature and drop to the ground. There is one generation per year (*48*).

Several outbreaks have occurred in jack pine stands in Ontario and Quebec, and heavy tree mortality has occurred. Furthermore, practically all surviving mature trees over many square miles remained stag-headed for several years. Some of the most severe infestations in the Lake States have occurred in jack pine plantations and windbreaks. Aerial application of a polyhedral virus spray provided satisfactory control for at least one year in tests conducted in Quebec (*654*).

The **red-pine sawfly,** *Neodriprion nanulus nanulus* Schedl, occurs in many Northeastern States west to Wisconsin and in southeastern Canada west to Saskatchewan. Its favored hosts are red and jack pines, but it also feeds on white, Japanese red, and mugho pines. Full-grown larvae are dull grayish-green to black on top, greenish-white beneath, and about 18 mm. long. The head is black and two olive-green stripes run down the back to a darker area near the rear end. There are two longitudinal dark stripes on each side, with the upper one a little darker than the lower one.

Winter is spent in the egg stage. Hatching occurs in early May, and larvae are present until July or August, depending on location. They are gregarious and usually consume all of the mature needles from one branch before migrating to another. Mature larvae drop to the ground and spin cocoons in the duff. Adults emerge in early fall and deposit their eggs in slits in the round face of current season's needles near the tips of well-exposed branches.. The female does not lay her entire complement of eggs in the needles of a single twig—sometimes only one needle per twig is chosen. There is one generation per year (*409*).

Little or no mortality results from a single defoliation because only the older needles are eaten, but where defoliation continues for several years a high percentage of the affected trees may be killed. Overmature trees are particularly susceptible to damage.

The **white-pine sawfly,** *Neodiprion pinetum* (Norton), occurs throughout the range of eastern white pine, its preferred host, in eastern United States and southern Canada. Pitch, shortleaf, red, and mugho pines are also attacked at times. Full-grown larvae are pale yellow and about 25 mm. long. The head is black and four rows of black spots extend from the head to a black spot at the posterior end.

In the spring, the female deposits her eggs in needles, three to four per needle, and the full complement is placed in the needles of a single twig. The larvae feed gregariously on both old and new needles, and when one branch is defoliated they migrate to another. When they reach maturity they drop to the ground and spin cocoons in the soil. Winter is spent as a mature larva in a cocoon spun in the soil and pupation occurs in the spring. There is one, and sometimes a partial second, generation per year, depending on location.

The white-pine sawfly attacks trees of all sizes both in plantations and in forest stands. Because the larvae feed on both old and new needles, they are capable of completely defoliating a tree. Widespread outbreaks occur occasionally, whereas local ones are reported almost every year.

The **balsam-fir sawfly,** *Neodiprion abietis* (Harris), occurs from New England to the Lake States and Missouri and from coast to coast in southern Canada. Its favored host is balsam fir but it also attacks black and white spruces. Full-grown larvae are dark green and are from 18 to 25 mm. long. The head is black and the body is marked with six longitudinal dark stripes or bands on the back, the lowest of which may be broken up into small dots or spots.

Winter is spent in the egg stage and hatching occurs in May or June. Newly-hatched larvae feed gregariously on old needles, eating only parts of the needle. Feeding is completed in about 1 month. The mature larvae then spin tough, silvery or light brown cocoons on the needles or in the litter on the ground. Adults appear from late July to early September and lay their eggs singly in slits cut in the edges of the needles. There is one generation per year.

Balsam fir growing in open stands, in pastures, along lake shore lines in Ontario, and on islands off the coast of Maine is often heavily defoliated. Trees are seldom killed by a single defoliation but some are killed by repeated defoliations. Spruce trees in farm shelterbelts and ornamental plantings in the Prairie Provinces of Canada have also been damaged. The introduced parasite, *Dahlbominus fuscipennis* (Zett.), has destroyed up to 40 percent of cocoons in the duff in Maine. Cocoons spun among the needles on the trees in the same stands escaped parasitization.

Neodiprion abbotii (Leach) has been recorded in Ontario, Wisconsin, Virginia, North Carolina, South Carolina, Georgia, and Florida. Its hosts are listed as loblolly, slash, longleaf, shortleaf, red, and Carribean pines. The full-grown larva has a brown to black head with a light spot on the frons and the thorax and abdomen are pale green. There are also four dark green to black lateral stripes.

Winter is spent as a mature larva in a cocoon and pupation occurs in the spring. Adults emerge as early as late March in the South. Eggs are laid in single rows of 15 to 20 eggs each mostly on 2-year-old needles, the eggs of a row almost touching each other. Newly-hatched larvae feed gregariously; older ones tend to feed singly. Mature larvae spin cocoons on the needles of the tree. There appears to be at least three generations per year in the South. First generation larvae are found in May; second generation larvae during July and August; and third generation larvae from October to December (*346*).

Light defoliation by this species may not be noticeable because of the tendency of the large larvae to wander in search of needles on which to feed.

Neodiprion rugifrons Middleton occurs in southern Canada and the Lake States and feeds on jack pine. Full-grown larvae have orange-brown to bright orange heads with black eyespots. The prothorax is yellowish-green to light olive-green with dark markings. A dark lateral stripe extends backward along each side from the prothorax to the ninth abdominal segment. The question as to whether this is a true species, or whether it is a member of a group known as the "Virginianius complex" is not settled. The complex consists of three species, *N. virginianus, N. rugifrons,* and *N. dubiosus.*

Winter is spent in cocoons in the soil. Adults emerge in May and June and lay their eggs in 1-year-old or older needles. There are one or two generations per year. The larvae of the first generation feed in colonies on previous year's needles, while those of the second generation feed on foliage of all ages.

In heavy infestations, jack pine may be completely defoliated by September or October. Planted pines from 3 to 20 feet tall may be killed. Trees in isolated stands and windbreaks are also subject to severe damage (*767*).

The **European pine sawfly**, *Neodiprion sertifer* (Geoff.), an introduced species first recorded in North America at Somerville, New Jersey, in 1925 (*636*), is now widely distributed. It has been recorded from New England to Michigan and southwestern Ontario, and south and southwest to southern Ohio, southern Illinois, and southwestern Iowa. It has many hosts, particularly Scotch, red, jack, Japanese red, Table-Mountain, and mugho pines. Eastern white, Austrian, ponderosa, shortleaf, and pitch pines also are fed on to some extent when they occur in mixture with more favored species.

Full-grown larvae are grayish-green and from 18 to 25 mm. long. The head, thoracic legs, and upper part of the anal plate are black and there is a longitudinal light stripe down the back.

447

There are also two light and one intense green or black stripes on each side.

Winter is spent in the egg stage and hatching occurs from early April to mid-May. The larvae feed gregariously on previous year's foliage (fig. 180) and devour all of the needles on one branch before moving to another one. New needles are never eaten. Larvae may also feed on the bark of new shoots. This may result in shoot deformation or death (*777*). When an entire tree is defoliated before the larvae reach maturity, it is vacated and the larvae crawl to other trees to feed. Full-grown larvae either drop to the ground and spin tough, light to dark golden brown cocoons in the duff, or they spin them in protected locations on the tree. Pupation occurs during late August or early September and the adults appear from early September to late fall. Eggs are laid in slits cut in the edges of current year's needles in needle clusters near the end of a branch. Six to eight eggs are usually laid in a single needle and about 10 to 12 needles in a single cluster are usually infested. There is one generation per year.

F-519945
FIGURE 180.—Colony of larvae of the European pine sawfly, *Neodiprion sertifer*. Larvae hanging head downward were killed by a polyhedral virus.

Trees defoliated by the European pine sawfly are seldom killed, since the new foliage is never eaten and the tree is never entirely stripped of its foliage. Bark feeding may cause some twig mortality but it is not serious. Losses in height and diameter growth may be severe however, especially following repeated defoliations. Damage is most severe to Scotch pines grown as Christmas trees in plantations.

During the late thirties and early forties, colonies of the two European parasites, *Dahlbominus fuscipennis* (Zett.) and *Exenterus abruptorius* (Thunberg), were received from Canada for release in eastern infestations of this sawfly. *D. fuscipennis* became established in New Jersey and within a few years became rather abundant locally (*299*). *E. abruptorius* also became established in New Jersey. So far, neither species has given adequate control. A supply of a European polyhedrosis virus of the sawfly was also received from Canada for use in its control (*66*). It has proved to be very effective when applied as a spray either by aircraft or by knapsack or hydraulic sprayers. Lyons (*466*) reviewed the literature on the biology, ecology, and control of the European pine sawfly.

Neodiprion excitans Rohwer occurs from Virginia to Florida and west to Texas. Loblolly and shortleaf pines are its preferred hosts. Slash, longleaf, pond, and Sondregger pines are also attacked but to a much lesser extent (*709*). The full-grown larva is olive-green and about 25 mm. long. (fig. 181). Its head is glossy black, there are two longitudinal black stripes on the dorsum, a row of black spots on each side, and a large black spot on the last abdominal segment.

Winter is spent mostly in cocoons, but occasionally in the egg stage or as older larvae. Adult appearance begins in early spring and continues until it reaches a peak in late summer. Egg laying begins in March by the female inserting her eggs in slits cut near the bases of needles. Needles closest to the tips of exposed shoots are chosen during spring and fall, whereas needles on shaded shoots are chosen during hot weather. The peak of egg laying occurs in July or August in east Texas and from late August to October in the Southeast. Newly-hatched larvae are gregarious, often with several encircling a single needle. Older larvae feed singly or in pairs on a single needle, preferably older needles. They usually eat most of the needle, leaving only a stub. Sometimes they attack the needle at the base first, causing the remainder of the needle to fall. When a branch is completely defoliated, the larvae migrate in groups to other branches or trees. Full-grown larvae either drop to the ground and spin tough, light to dark brown cocoons in the duff or loose topsoil, or remain on the tree and spin their cocoons on twigs, needles, or

F-514368

FIGURE 181.—Larva of *Neodiprion excitans*.

beneath loose bark scales. There are four or five generations per year (*347, 346, 709*).

Infestations usually occur on medium to large trees in moderately to densely stocked stands, but they are also occasionally found on seedlings and saplings. Because of the lateness of the season when the larvae are most active, heavily infested trees may remain without needles throughout the winter. Heavily defoliated trees are weakened and rendered susceptible to attack by bark beetles, especially *Ips* spp., and wood borers. Tree mortality as a result of defoliation has not been reported. Several outbreaks have been recorded in Florida and Texas in recent years, most of which subsided after one season. A polyhedral virus disease and several parasites and predators apparently are highly effective in bringing outbreaks to an early end.

A number of other species of *Neodiprion* also occur in eastern forests: *N. nigroscutum* Middleton occurs on jack pine in the Lake States and Ontario. Full-grown non-feeding larvae are gray-pink with a tinge of yellow on the lateral margins (*49*). *N. pinirigidae* (Norton) feeds on pitch and shortleaf pines from New Jersey to Maine. The full-grown larva is dull green, has a double longitudinal black line on the dorsum and a broken black stripe on each side. Sometimes a double row of black dots occur below each lateral stripe. *N. warreni* Ross occurs on shortleaf pine in Arkansas. Full-grown larvae have almost entirely black heads and broad black longitudinal stripes on the dorsum. An outbreak was recorded in 1958. *N. merkeli* Ross attacks slash pine in southern Florida. The head of a full grown larva is reddish above the eyes and sooty black below, with a reddish infusion. *N. hetricki* Ross has been observed feeding on loblolly pine in Virginia and pond pine in South Carolina. The head of the larva is black, subdorsal lines are solid, and supradorsal lines are composed of separate spots or beaded lines. *N. compar* (Leach), feeds on red and jack pines in southeastern Canada, Virginia, North Carolina, and Georgia. *N. maurus* Rohwer occurs on jack pine in southeastern Canada and the Lake States.

The genus *Diprion* Schrank is represented by only three species in the United States and Canada and all three are of foreign origin.

The **introduced pine sawfly,** *Diprion similis* Hartig, was first recorded in North America at New Haven, Connecticut, in 1914. It now occurs from Maine to Virginia, in the Central and Lake States, and in southern Ontario and Quebec. White pine appears to be its favored host but Scotch, red, jack, and mugho pines are also commonly attacked. Full-grown larvae (fig. 182) are about 20 mm. long. The head is shiny black and the body is dark brown or black with a double black stripe down the dorsum and black and yellow spots on the sides.

Winter is spent in the prepupal stage. Pupation occurs in early spring and the adults appear from May to mid-June. The females are reported to possess a potent sex attractant (*161*). Eggs are laid in rows of about 10 eggs each and deposited in slits cut in the edge of old needles. Young larvae feed gregariously; older ones, singly. First generation larvae feed on old needles only, while the larvae of later generations eat both new and old needles. Young larvae eat only the outer, tender parts of needles; older ones consume the entire needle and nibble the bark. First generation cocoons are usually spun among the needles, at the bases of small branches, or in bark crevices on the trunk, and pupation occurs in late July. Second generation larvae feed until September and then spin cocoons on the tree or in the duff. Under favorable conditions some pupate and emerge in late fall to produce a partial third generation. The remainder do not pupate until the following spring. Because of some overlap between the first and second generations, all stages of the sawfly may be found during the summer (*778, 520*).

Heavily infested trees may be completely defoliated in one season. When this happens late in the season after the buds are formed, many branches and occasionally trees may be killed. The introduced parasite, *Monodontomerus dentipes* (Dalm.), is occasionally very effective in control. Up to 75 percent parasitization has been recorded in New Jersey. Second generation larvae and cocoons located above the snow line on trees are particularly susceptible to low winter temperatures.

Diprion frutetorum (Fab.) was discovered in North America in Massachusetts and Rhode Island in 1932, and now occurs throughout many of the Northeastern States and in southeastern

FIGURE 182.—Larvae of the introduced pine sawfly, *Diprion similis*.

Canada. Its favored hosts are red and Scotch pines, but it may also attack various other hard pines. Full-grown larvae are light green with reddish brown heads and are about 20 mm. long. The body is marked with six longitudinal dark green stripes, two on the dorsum and two on each side (fig. 183).

Winter is spent as a full-grown, cocooned larva and pupation occurs in the spring. Adults appear from late May to late July. Eggs are laid in slits cut in the needles. The larvae feed singly, preferably on the older needles. Because of their greenish color they blend into the background and are difficult to see. Usually, the first sign of infestation is the presence of frass and green needle fragments on the ground beneath the tree. Heavy infestations occur occasionally in pine plantations (*637*).

The **European spruce sawfly**, *Diprion hercyniae* Hartig, was first recorded in North America near Ottawa, Canada, in 1922. In 1929 it was found in the United States on Mount Washington, New Hampshire. By the late thirties it had spread throughout the eastern spruce forests. White spruce appears to be the favored host; however, red, black, and Norway spruces also are attacked. Young larvae are yellowish-green; older larvae are darker green, marked with five longitudinal white lines, and about 20 mm. long (fig. 184). During the last instar, the white lines are absent and the body is somewhat shortened.

In the Northeastern States there may be 1 or 2 or a partial third generations per year, depending on location. Farther north there is only one. In the Northeastern States, adults of the first generation appear from early May to early June. Eggs are laid in slits cut in old needles and hatching occurs within a few days. Larvae of all ages feed singly. Young larvae feed by chewing out small pieces of the needle or by eating all but the vascular bundle. Older ones consume the entire needle. Old needles are usually preferred, but full-grown new needles may be eaten also. Second

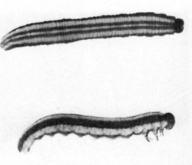

F-519578

FIGURE 183.—Larvae of *Diprion frutetorum.*

F-519573

FIGURE 184.—Larva of European spruce sawfly, *Diprion hercyniae.*

generation adults appear in early July or later and lay their eggs in needles. Hatching occurs shortly thereafter, and the larvae feed for 3 or 4 weeks. At maturity, they drop to the ground and spin cocoons in the litter in which they spend the winter. In the northern portion of the species range, some remain in diapause for several years before pupating (604).

The European spruce sawfly found conditions favorable for a rapid increase in numbers once it gained a foothold in the spruce forests of North America. In 1932, serious infestations were found over an area of about 2,000 square miles of the Gaspé. Two years later evidence of defoliation was also apparent in Quebec, New Brunswick, and adjacent areas in the United States. By 1935, the Gaspé outbreak covered about 6,000 square miles, and tree mortality in some areas had reached serious proportions. Conditions continued to worsen through 1937, but in 1938 a general reduction in population levels was reported from nearly all regions. The downward trend in populations continued and by 1942, they had declined to medium or light intensity in all but a few restricted localities. The collapse of the outbreak was caused by an accidentally introduced polyhedral virus disease (26). The virus was first observed in Canadian infestations in 1930, but it was not until 1938 that numerous diseased larvae became noticeable in parts of New Brunswick. Four years later it had brought the widespread outbreak under control. Since then populations have been fluctuating at very low levels and the sawfly is no longer considered an economic pest (561).

During the thirties and forties, the Canadian Government imported and liberated approximately 20 species of parasites in infested areas (484). Substantial numbers of these parasites were also released in the United States. Two species of cocoon parasites and five species of larval parasites became established (205).

FAMILY TENTHREDINIDAE

The family Tenthredinidae is represented by more than 350 species in the United States and Canada, the majority of which occur in eastern America. The larvae are all leaf feeders, leaf miners, gall formers, or fruit borers. Many species are important pests of forest and shade trees and forest plantations.

The antennae of the adults have seven to ten segments and range in shape from setaceous and filiform to clavate. The mesothorax is without sterno-pleural sutures, the anterior of the scutellum is V-shaped, and the posterior margin usually has a distinct posttergite. The tibiae are without pre-apical spurs, and the apical spurs of the front tibia usually have the longer spur cleft at the apex. The larvae range in length from 10 to 37 mm. and are usually largest in diameter at the thorax. The body is greenish or variously colored, sometimes with distinct markings, and is either smooth, glabrous, setiferous, tuberculate, or spinous (621, 801).

Heterarthrus nemoratus (Fall.) (=*Phyllotoma nemorata* [Fall.]), the **birch leaf-mining sawfly,** an introduced species first recorded from North America in 1905, is now widely distributed in the Northeastern States and southeastern Canada. Its hosts are various species of birch, with gray, paper, yellow, and European white being preferred. The full-grown larva is somewhat flattened and whitish, with the head and joints of the thoracic legs brownish, and is about 10 mm. long.

In Maine, winter is spent in the larval stage and pupation occurs in late spring. Female adults (no males have been found) appear during June and early July and deposit their eggs singly in slits cut in the edges of mature leaves, apparently at all levels in the tree. The larvae feed in the tissues between the upper and lower surfaces of the leaf, producing large blister-like or blotch mines free of frass (fig. 185). Each full-grown larva constructs a cocoon or hibernaculum within its mine. The leaf then falls to the ground and the larva remains in its hibernaculum throughout the winter. There is one generation per year (*591*).

Heavy infestations of the birch leaf-mining sawfly occurred in Maine during the 1920's and 30's, and severe defoliation of birch occurred in many areas. Very little tree mortality occurred, but there was a considerable loss in annual growth. During this period several species of parasites were imported against the sawfly (*204*), two of which, *Kratochviliana laricinellae* (Ratzeburg) and *Phanomeris phyllotomae* Muesebeck, became established.

The **birch leaf miner**, *Fenusa pusilla* (Lepeletier), an introduced species first recorded from North America in Connecticut in 1923, now occurs in southeastern Canada and from Maine to New Jersey and west to Ohio and the Lake States. Full-grown larvae are somewhat flattened, yellowish-white in appearance, and about 6 mm. long. Black spots occur on the venter of the thorax and the first abdominal segment.

F-519525

FIGURE 185.—Mines and hibernaculae of *Heterarthrus nemoratus*, the birch leafmining sawfly, in leaf of paper birch.

Winter is spent as full-grown larvae in cocoons in small earthen cells 1 or 2 inches below the soil surface. Pupation occurs in the spring and the adults begin to appear about mid-May. Eggs are deposited singly in slits cut in the central areas of young leaves, usually near the tips of branches. The larvae feed on the tissues between the leaf surfaces. At first, they feed singly, forming small kidney-shaped mines near the egg. Then, as they increase in size, the mines of different larvae coalesce and form large, hollowed-out brown areas in the leaf. These areas (fig. 186) wrinkle and turn brown. Full-grown larvae chew their way out of the leaf and drop to and enter the ground where they form earthen cells in which to pupate. There are three or four generations per year in the southern portions of the infested region (*271*).

Outbreaks occur frequently in the Northeastern States and result in the browning of birch stands over wide areas. Some tree killing may occur, but the greatest damage is the weakening of affected trees, which leads to attack by other insects.

The **elm leaf miner,** *Fenusa ulmi* Sundevall, an introduced species, occurs in southeastern Canada and the Northeastern States west to the Lake States. Its preferred hosts are English, Scotch, and Camperdown elms. American elm is also attacked occasionally. Full-grown larvae are about 6 mm. long, flattened, and whitish with a greenish cast. The head is brown and the legs are encircled with brown.

Winter is spent as full-grown larvae in brown papery cocoons in the topsoil. Pupation occurs in the spring and the adults appear in May, usually during the first half of the month. Eggs are laid in the upper surfaces of leaves. The larvae mine the tissue between the leaf surfaces, causing large blotch or blister-like mines. Several attacks may occur on a single leaf. When this happens, the various mines may coalesce and the entire leaf be hollowed out (fig. 187). These leaves soon wither and fall. Where only a small portion of a leaf is mined, the surfaces dry out and crack,

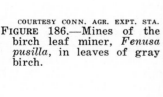

FIGURE 186.—Mines of the birch leaf miner, *Fenusa pusilla*, in leaves of gray birch.

COURTESY CONN. AGR. EXPT. STA.
FIGURE 187.—Mines of the elm leaf miner, *Fenusa ulmi*, in elm leaves.

leaving holes in the leaf. The larvae usually become mature in late June. Then they vacate their mines and drop to and enter the ground to spin their cocoons. There is one generation per year. This species appears to be most injurious to small trees in nurseries and ornamental plantings.

The **European alder leaf miner,** *Fenusa dohrnii* (Tischbein), an introduced species, occurs in southeastern Canada and throughout the Northeastern States. Its hosts are listed as alders, especially the introduced European alders. Winter is spent in the larval stage in cocoons in the ground. Pupation occurs in the spring, and the adults appear and lay eggs during late May and early June. The larvae feed in the tissues of the leaf, forming blotch mines. Full-grown larvae drop to the ground to pupate, and a second generation of adults appears from late July to early September. They also lay eggs and give rise to a second generation of larvae. These become full-grown by late fall and then enter the ground to spend the winter.

Profenusa thomsoni (Konow), possibly an introduced species from the Far East, is widely distributed in southeastern Canada and from Maine to Illinois and Wisconsin. Its hosts are gray, paper, and yellow birches. In Ontario, female adults were observed in late July and early August and laid eggs in the tissues of leaves. The larvae mined the tissues, forming light-colored, blotch mines. Up to 40 larvae were found in a single mine. When all of the tissues of a leaf were consumed, all of the larvae, regardless of age, vacated the mine and dropped to the ground. Of these, only those in the latter part of the fifth instar were able to enter the soil and survive. In light infestations, sucker growth up to about 4 feet tall in shaded locations was preferred. In contrast, trees up to 35 feet tall in all types of habitats were attacked in heavily infested areas. Damage was not considered severe because defoliation occurred late in the season (*505*).

Profenusa mainensis Smith, a newly-described species (*655*), has been observed mining the leaves of oak, primarily red oak, in Maine during recent years. Full-grown larvae are about 6 mm. long and have prognathous, octagonal heads more than twice as wide as long. Winter is spent as mature larvae in cells in the duff.

Adults appear in the spring and the female lays her eggs on the upper surfaces of the leaves. The larvae bore into the leaf and mine the tissues, causing blotching and severe browning. Heavily infested leaves may drop by September, leaving bare branches in the top of the tree.

Profenusa canadensis (Marlatt) has been recorded mining the leaves of hawthorn and cultivated cherry in Massachusetts, New York, and Wisconsin. Serious infestations have occurred in Massachusetts and New York. *P. lucifex* (Ross) attacks white oak in Maine and bur oak in Ontario.

Messa populifoliella (Townsend) mines the leaves of poplar from New Brunswick southwestward through the United States to Arizona.

The **pear-slug,** *Caliroa cerasi* (L.), an introduced species, occurs from coast to coast in southern Canada and northern United States. Although best known as a pest of cherry and pear in the United States, it also feeds occasionally on hawthorn, plum, quince, mountain ash, black cherry, and shadbush. Full-grown larvae are tadpole-shaped, slug-like, and about 12 mm. long. The body is covered with a shiny, olive-green material secreted by the larva.

Winter is spent in earthen cells or in cocoons composed of grains of earth and a substance secreted by the larvae. Pupation occurs in June. Eggs are deposited singly in small semi-circular slits cut in the leaf tissue. The larvae feed mostly from the upper surface of the leaf, eating the parenchyma only. Heavily infested trees appear as if scorched, and their leaves drop prematurely. Full-grown larvae drop to the ground and form cells in the soil in which pupation occurs. Adults appear in 2 or 3 weeks and lay eggs. Larvae of this generation are present in August and September. When they become mature, they also drop to the ground. There are two generations per year throughout most of the infested portions of the United States.

Caliroa lineata MacGillivary, the **pin oak sawfly,** has been recorded in New Jersey, North Carolina, and Missouri. Its hosts are pin, white, and various red oaks, preferably pin. Full-grown larvae are slug-like, yellowish-green, and about 12 mm. long. The head and thoracic legs are shiny black. There appears to be at least two generations per year in New Jersey *(319)*. Both larvae and adults may be found almost any time from late May or early June until late September. The larvae feed on the lower surfaces of the leaves, leaving only the upper surface and a fine network of veins. Defoliation is usually noticed first in the tops of trees. Late in the season heavily infested trees may be completely defoliated.

Caliroa (near) *quercuscoccineae* (Dyar) has been recorded feeding on pin oak in Massachusetts and North Carolina. Full-grown larvae are shiny green and about 12 mm. long. Adults appear to be most numerous in October. Eggs are laid in slits cut in the lower surface of the leaf. They are placed singly in rows along the sides of the midribs and larger veins, and all hatch within a few days after being laid. The larvae feed on the epidermis of the leaf, leaving it almost colorless and transparent. Evidence of feeding is apparent during late summer. There may be two generations per year, and the winter may be spent in the larval stage (*40*).

The **larch sawfly**, *Pristiphora erichsonii* (Hartig), probably an introduced species, was first recorded in North America at Boston, Massachusetts, in 1880. It now occurs in all Canadian Provinces, in Alaska, and all of the northern tier of States except Ohio, Indiana, and Idaho. Its hosts are listed as tamarack and Western, European, Japanese, and Siberian larches. In eastern America, tamarack is most seriously infested. Full-grown larvae (fig. 188), are whitish beneath and gray-green along the dorsum, have jet black heads, and are about 16 mm. long. Female adults are black and from 6 to 9 mm. long. The abdomen has a broad orange band, tapers sharply posteriorly, and is keeled longitudinally along the midventral line.

In the Lake States, winter is spent in the prepupal stage in the ground. Pupation occurs in the spring and the adults appear from mid-May to August, depending on temperature and location. Eggs are laid in rows under the bark of current terminal, lateral twigs. Hatching occurs in about 8 days, and the larvae move back to the foliage on older twigs, where they usually feed in groups. Feeding is completed in about 20 days and the mature larvae drop to the ground, enter the duff, and spin tough, papery, brown cocoons. Because of the long period of adult emergence, feeding larvae, cocooned larvae, pupae, and adults all may be found at the same time in early summer. Normally, there is one generation per year. Occasionally, however, small numbers of second-generation adults are produced. A small number of larvae enter diapause and require 2 years to complete one generation (*210, 307*).

Larch sawfly larvae eat the needles on older twigs, and where the attack is heavy, the entire tree may be defoliated. These trees do not die readily from defoliation, however, because of their ability to refoliate within the same season. Normally, during outbreaks the affected trees are characterized by thin foliage, reduced radial and terminal increment, reduced production of normal shoots with a tendency toward adventitious growth, and branch mortality. Marked loss of radial increment occurs after 4 to 6 years of outbreak, and after 6 to 9 years of moderate to heavy defoliation, tree mortality occurs. Many widespread outbreaks have been recorded since 1880 and losses have been severe. Since the middle fifties, an estimated volume loss of 40 percent in valuable sawtimber and pulp stands has occurred in managed forests in Minnesota. Between 1910 and 1926 in Minensota an estimated one billion board feet was killed.

Overwintering cocooned sawfly larvae are destroyed in enormous numbers by small mammals, especially shrews and voles. High surface water in tamarack bogs also destroys large numbers at times. Many species of parasites occur but only two, the imported ichneumon, *Mesoleius tenthredinis* Morley, and the tachinid, *Bessa harveyi* (Townsend), have been prevalent during the current outbreak which began in about 1938. Initially, *M. tenthredinis* was quite effective in control; however, the sawfly developed an immunity to it in central Canada, Minnesota, and Wisconsin (*208*).

The **mountain ash sawfly,** *Pristiphora geniculata* (Hartig), a probable introduction from Europe, was first recorded in North America at Haines Falls, New York, in 1926 (*635*). It is now known to occur in New Jersey, New York, Pennsylvania, Michigan, all of the New England States except Rhode Island, and in all eastern provinces of Canada west to Ottawa, Ontario. Its principal hosts are American and European ash. It also occurs occasionally on showy mountain ash and the hybrid, *Sorbaronia hybrida*. Full-grown larvae are pale greenish to yellow with yellow heads and yellow thoracic legs. All body segments except the last are marked with black spots of uneven size and shape (fig. 189). The spots occur in irregular rows, four along each side of the body and two broken ones down the dorsum.

In eastern Canada, winter is spent in the prepupal stage. Pupation occurs in the spring and the adults appear from late May to early July. Eggs are deposited in slits cut around the edges of leaflets and hatching occurs in about 1 week. Newly-hatched larvae straddle the edge of the leaf and feed around the periphery. When disturbed they raise their abdomens in the form an "S". Larvae of the first two instars are gregarious. Later, especially in the fourth and fifth instars, they often feed singly. They usually consume all of a leaflet except the midrib. When they have consumed one leaflet they move to another. Feeding is completed in about 2 or 3 weeks and the larvae drop to the ground. Here they spin cocoons in the duff and top soil. About 20 percent of these pupate and appear as second generation adults in July (*257*).

The mountainash sawfly is primarily a pest of shade and ornamental trees. The esthetic values of these trees is seriously reduced by defoliation, but they usually survive even when completely defoliated.

Other species of *Pristiphora* occurring in eastern forests include *P. chlorea* (Norton) on oak, *P. siskiyouensis* Marlatt on birch, and *P. sycophanta* Walsh on willow.

The **yellow-headed spruce sawfly,** *Pikonema alaskensis* (Rohwer), is widespread, occurring from Maine and New Brunswick to Idaho, British Columbia and Alaska. Its hosts are white, black, red, blue, Norway, and Engelmann spruces (*772*). Full-grown larvae (fig. 190) are olive-green above and lighter green below and are about 18 mm. long. The head is chestnut-brown or reddish-yellow and is sometimes mottled with various shades of brown. Each side of the body bears a gray-green longitudinal stripe near the midline of the dorsum, a broad one beneath this, and a darker one farther down. There is also a dark line or spot just above the base of each leg.

In Maine, winter is spent as full-grown larvae in tough, dark brown cocoons. Pupation occurs in the spring, and the adults appear from late May to mid-June. Eggs are deposited in slits cut in current season's needles, usually at the base and usually only one per needle. Sometimes they are also found on tender bark of the stem between needles. Young larvae feed on the new needles. Older ones move on to and devour the old needles. While feeding, their rear ends curve downward or upward. The larvae become full-grown in July and drop to the ground. Here they spin

459

FIGURE 188.—Larvae and cocoons of the larch sawfly, *Pristiphora erichsonii.*

F-495242

FIGURE 190.—Dorsal and lateral views of larvae of the yellow-headed spruce sawfly, *Pikonema alaskensis.*

F-519576

FIGURE 189.—Larvae of the mountain ash sawfly, *Pristiphora geniculata.*

cocoons in the duff or top soil. There is one generation per year (*554*).

The yellow-headed spruce sawfly is most injurious to shade trees and ornamentals, to nursery stock, and to young trees in plantations, as well as naturally regenerated cutover areas, in shelterbreaks, and windbreaks. Open-grown trees older than 5 years are especially susceptible to injury, the majority being killed by 3 or 4 consecutive years of moderate to heavy defoliation. Trees in natural or closed stands are practically immune to attack and damage.

The **green-headed spruce sawfly,** *Pikonema dimmockii* (Cresson), also occurs from coast to coast in southern Canada and from Maine to Idaho, and feeds on various species of spruce. Populations are usually low and apparently cause little injury.

460

The **willow sawfly,** *Nematus* (*=Pteronidia*) *ventralis* Say, occurs in southeastern Canada and south and west in the Eastern States to Georgia and Montana. Its favored host is willow, but it also feeds on poplar. Full-grown larvae are black or greenish-black, with large light yellow spots on the sides of the body, and are about 18 mm. long.

Winter is spent in the prepupal stage in cocoons in the litter or top soil beneath the trees. Pupation and adult emergence occurs in the spring. Eggs are deposited in pockets cut in the tissues of the leaves. Young larvae feed in colonies, eating small holes in the leaves. Later, entire leaves are eaten. There are usually one to five generations per year depnding on location. In the northern areas some individuals may remain in diapause up to 20 months before completing their development.

The willow sawfly occasionally heavily defoliates willows in ornamental plantings and along streams. Basket willows in the South have been damaged severely.

Nematus salicisodoratus Dyar occurs in the Eastern States west to Illinois. It also feeds on willow and poplar. Full-grown larvae are light green and about 15 mm. long. The head is black and there are three longitudinal rows of closely spaced black spots on the dorsum. There are also two rows of black spots on each side; those in the lower row are larger. Winter is spent in the prepupal stage in cocoons on the ground. Pupation occurs in the spring, and adults of the first generation appear in late May or June. Larvae of this generation are found in June and July. Adults of a second generation appear from late July to early September. This species is often abundant locally in the Northeastern States.

Approximately 40 additional species in the genus *Nematus* have been recorded from eastern forests (Muesebeck, et al.). Known hosts of a few species are as follows: black locust—*N. abbotti* (Kirby) and *N. tibialis* Newman, white birch—*N. hyalinus* (Marlatt) and *N. pinguidorsum* Dyar, poplar—*N. fulvicrus* Provancher and *N. populi* (Marlatt), hophornbeam—*N. ostryae* (Marlatt), and willow—*N. limbatus* Cresson.

Trichiocampus irregularis (Dyar) occurs in southeastern Canada and southward through the New England States, and feeds on willow. Full-grown larvae are yellow, sparsely clothed with hairs, and about 18 mm. long. The head is almost entirely black and there are two rows of black spots on each side of the body. The related species, *T. gregarius* Dyar feeds on poplar in the Eastern States.

Trichiocampus viminalis (Fallen), an introduced species, occurs across southern Canada and the Northern States. Its hosts are various species of poplar and willow. Full-grown larvae are orange-yellow, sparsely clothed with yellow hairs, and about 18 mm. long. Each side of the body is marked with two rows of more or less rounded black spots. Those of the lowest row are smaller (fig. 191).

Winter is spent in the prepupal stage in cocoons in the duff beneath the trees. Pupation occurs in the spring and the adults appear in May. Young larvae feed side by side on the leaves.

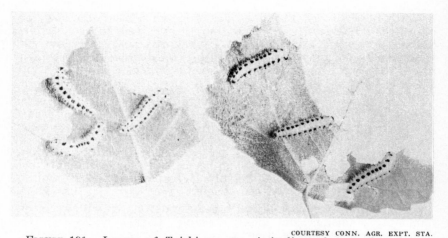

FIGURE 191.—Larvae of *Trichiocampus viminalis* on leaves of poplar.

Older ones tend to scatter and eat all but the midribs and larger veins. They become full grown in June or early July. Some pupate and give rise to a second generation of adults in August; the remainder do not complete their development until the following spring. Carolina and Lombardy poplars grown for ornamental purposes may be seriously defoliated.

The **dusky birch sawfly,** *Croesus latitarsus* Norton, occurs in eastern Canada and south through the Eastern States to Florida. Its hosts are various species of birch, preferably gray birch. It has also been found feeding on alder and cherry in Canada. Full-grown larvae are yellowish-green with shades of black and are about 24 mm. long. There is a row of more or less distinct black blotches on each side and a series of black spots in the subspiracular area.

Winter is spent in the prepupal stage in a cocoon in the topsoil. Adults appear during May and June, or earlier in the Deep South. There may be several overlapping generations per year and larvae may be found from spring until fall. The larvae are gregarious and feed along the edges of the leaf (fig. 192). Colonies are often found defoliating small saplings, but this usually does not occur over wide areas.

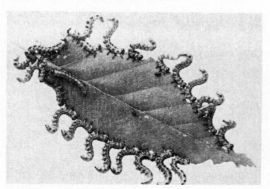

FIGURE 192.—Larvae of the dusky birch sawfly, *Croesus latitarsus*.

The **striped alder sawfly,** *Hemichroa crocea* (Fourcroy), probably an introduced species, occurs from coast to coast in southern Canada and northern United States. Its hosts include various species of alder and occasionally birch. Full-grown larvae are yellowish and about 20 mm. long. The head is shiny black, and there is a dark brown subdorsal stripe on each side running from the second thoracic to the tenth abdominal segment. Two broken subspiracular stripes composed of blotches and dashes extend along each side to the ninth segment.

Winter is spent in the prepupal stage in cocoons just beneath the surface of the soil. The cocoon is very thin-walled and is formed within a cell made by cementing together particles of soil and sand. Adults appear during late May and deposit their eggs in slits cut in the sides of the midrib on the undersurface of leaves. The larvae are gregarious and usually eat all but the midrib and larger veins of the leaf. They become full grown in July, and, during late July and August, adults of a second generation appear. Larvae of this generation are found during August and September. There are two generations per year. This species occasionally severely defoliates alder in the Lake States, Northastern States, and Canada.

The **maple petiole borer,** *Caulocampus acericaulis* (MacGillivray), an introduced species, is known to occur in the Northeastern States south to New Jersey. The larvae feed by boring into and tunneling the petioles of leaf stems of maple. Full-grown larvae are light yellow with light brown heads and are about 8 mm. long.

Winter is spent in the larval stage in a cell 2 or 3 inches below the surface of the soil. Adults appear early in May and deposit their eggs near the bases of the petioles of maple leaves. The larvae tunnel in the petioles until they break, usually near the leaf blade, and the leaves fall (fig. 193). After the petioles break, the larvae continue to feed for about a week to 10 days in those portions of the petioles remaining on the tree. When these also break and fall, the larvae vacate them and enter the soil to pupate. There is one generation per year.

Damage by the maple petiole borer is slight. Nevertheless, heavy infestations on valuable shade trees may be undesirable because of the presence of large numbers of dead leaves on them during the summer.

The **brown-headed ash sawfly,** *Tomostethus multicinctus* (Rohwer), occurs in southern Canada and throughout eastern United States west to the Great Plains. Its hosts are red and white ash trees. Full-grown larvae are greenish- or yellowish-white and from 14 to 20 mm. long.

Winter is spent in the prepupal stage in cocoon-like cells in the top soil. Adults appear as early as April in the southern portions of its range and lay their eggs in slits cut along the outer margin of young leaflets, several eggs per leaflet. Young larvae chew holes in the leaflets, and the older ones consume them entirely. Larvae become full grown and move to and enter the ground by late May in the South. Farther North, they become full grown at progressively later dates. Pupation occurs in the spring and there is only one generation per year. The larvae are such voracious feeders that they may completely defoliate a heavily infested

FIGURE 193.—Petiole of maple leaf severed by larvae of the maple petiole borer, *Caulocampus acericaulis.*

tree in a week. Shade trees are especially subject to serious defoliation (*448*).

The **black-headed ash sawfly,** *Tethida cordigera* (Beauvois), occurs throughout much the same area as the brown-headed ash sawfly. The habits, food plants, and life histories of the two species are also very similar. Full-grown larvae are whitish with a yellowish tinge and are about 18 mm. long. The head is shiny black, and the thoracic legs are blackish-brown. This species is occasionally a pest of shade trees.

Eriocampa juglandis (Fitch) (previously misidentified as *Blennocampa caryae* (Norton), the **butternut woolly worm,** occurs in southern Canada and throughout the Northeastern States. Its hosts are butternut, black walnut, and hickory. Full-grown larvae are green, with indistinct black spots on the sides and are about 18 mm. long. The body is covered with flocculent white tufts which rub off when touched, and the head is white with black eye spots. The larvae feed gregariously, often causing considerable defoliation locally. When they become full grown they move to and enter the ground, where they form cocoons composed of particles of sand and earth cemented together. Winter is spent in the cocoons and there is one generation per year.

The genus *Hoplocampa* Hartig is represented in eastern America by a number of species, all of which presumably feed as larvae in the fruit of their hosts. Eggs are laid in the calyx of flowers and the larvae bore into and hollow out the developing fruit. Some of the eastern species and their known hosts are as follows: *H. oskina* Ross—hawthorn in the Central States, *H.*

halcyon (Norton)—shadbush in the Northeastern States and southeastern Canada, *H. pallipes* MacGillivray—shadbush in the Lake States, *H. lacteipennis* Rohwer—choke cherry in southeastern Canada and the Northern States, and *H. montanicola* Rohwer —choke cherry in the Northern States and southern Canada.

The genus *Anoplonyx* Marlatt contains only eight species, two of which occur in eastern United States and Canada. The larvae of all species feed on various species of larch. Full-grown larvae of the two eastern species, *A. canadensis* Harrington and *A. luteipes* (Cresson), are green in color and range in length from about 9 to 15 mm. The thorax is larger than the abdomen, producing a humpbacked appearance and causing the body to taper posteriorally (*93*).

The genus *Euura* Newman is represented in eastern United States and Canada by 16 species, and all are gall makers on various species of willow. Larvae are usually yellowish or greenish-white with black eye spots, and the head is often tinted brown. All species apparently have one generation per year. Winter is spent as full-grown larvae either in cocoons in the ground or in galls on the host. Adults appear in the spring and lay their eggs in the shoots. Larvae feed on the tissues and become enveloped in galls. When they become full grown, some of them vacate the galls and drop to the ground to pupate; others remain inside their galls. Galls usually consist of a somewhat woody swelling of the twig. Sometimes an entire shoot is enlarged. In other cases, the gall appears as an abrupt swelling on one side of the shoot. These galls may cause economic loss when they occur where normal twig development of willow is important.

The genus *Macremphytus* MacGillivray is represented in eastern forests by five species all of which feed as larvae on dogwood. Full-grown larvae are creamy-yellow on top with grayish-black crossbands or spots, and the legs and venter are yellowish. The head is shiny black, and the body is covered with a white powdery secretion.

SUPERFAMILY SIRICOIDEA

FAMILY SIRICIDAE

HORNTAILS

Members of the family Siricidae are commonly known as horntails because of the presence of a hornlike projection on the last abdominal segment of the adult. This process is short in the male; in the female it is much longer and often spear-shaped. The ovipositor of the female is long and fitted for boring. In this respect it differs from the ovipositor of sawflies which consist of sawlike plates. Horntails attack both hardwoods and coniferous trees. A few species have been recorded infesting vigorous trees, but they usually prefer trees or parts of trees that are dead or in a badly weakened condition. Horntail larvae are parasitized by several species of ichneumon wasps of the genus *Megarhyssa* Ashm. Two of these, *M. atrata atrata* and *M. macrurus macrurus,* are of special interest because of their striking appearance. Using their extremely long ovipositors, the females bore deep holes into the wood and deposit their eggs on or near horntail larvae in their galleries.

Horntail adults are medium to large in size and are usually metallic blue or black in color. Some are vari-colored with combinations of black, red, and yellow. The head, thorax, and abdomen are of equal width; the wings are well developed; the antennae are long and filiform, with about 15 segments; and the anterior tibia is armed with a single apical spur, cleft at the apex.

Damage caused by members of the family can be prevented or reduced by the prompt utilization or submersion in water of infested logs and by kiln drying of green lumber sawed from infested logs.

The genus *Sirex* L. is represented by four eastern species. *S. juvencus* (L.) occurs in eastern Canada and the Northeastern and Midwestern States. Its hosts are listed as pine, fir, and spruce. *S. abbottii* Kirby has been recorded breeding in larch in New York and Georgia. The **blue horntail**, *S. cyaneus* F., attacks spruce and pine in southern Canada and the northern tier of eastern States. *S. edwardsii* Brulle has been taken from pitch pine in the Atlantic Coast States. *S. nigricornis* F. attacks shortleaf pine from New York to Ohio and Florida.

The genus *Urocerus* Geoffrey is represented by three eastern species. *U. albicornis* (F.), the **white-horned horntail**, attacks many species of conifers and occurs throughout boreal America. Adults are blue-black or black and about 25 to 30 mm. long. The middle of the antennae, cheeks, bases of the tibiae, and tarsi are white. White spots also occur at times on the sides of the abdomen. This species has also been observed attacking freshly sawed lumber. *U. flavicornis* (F.), the **yellow-horned horntail**, attacks spruce and other conifers in New England and Canada. Adults are black and from 20 to 37 mm. long. Females have the first, sixth, and part of the seventh abdominal segments yellow; males have the second through fifth segments orange-yellow. *U. cressoni* Norton, the **black and red horntail**, occurs from eastern Canada to Georgia and breeds in poplar.

The **pigeon tremex**, *Tremex columba* (L.), is the most common of the horntails. It occurs throughout nearctic America and breeds in a wide variety of dead or weakened deciduous trees such as beech, maple, birch, elm, hickory, oak, and sycamore. The adult female is 37 to 50 mm. long. The head, antennae, and thorax are reddish and black; the abdomen is black with ocher yellow bands and spots along the sides; and the wings are smoky brown with an expanse of 50 mm. or more. Males are reddish, with some black, and are about 18 to 37 mm. long. Full-grown larvae are whitish, cylindrical, and about 50 mm. long. The abdomen ends in a short, strongly sclerotized and compressed process armed with two pairs of small teeth.

The female bores through the bark to a depth of about 12 mm. in the wood to deposit her eggs. Although laid singly, several eggs may be found near each other in a limited area. The larvae feed by excavating tunnels entirely in the wood. This frequently weakens the tree and leads to wind breakage. Pupation occurs at the end of the larval tunnel and the adults emerge through circular holes about 8 mm. In diameter. There appears to be one generation per year.

FAMILY XIPHYDRIIDAE

The family Xiphydriidae is represented in the United States and Canada by only six species, all of which occur in eastern United States. The adults are somewhat similar to those of the family Siricidae, but are only about 12 to 18 mm. long, and the female ovipositor sheath is seldom longer than the last tergite. Adults are reddish, black and yellowish, or entirely black. Full-grown larvae are about 18 mm. long and the abdomen ends with a brown concave prong ornamented with teeth on the underside. As a rule, the larvae feed in moderately sound to partly decayed wood of deciduous trees. Few, if any, are ever very abundant.

Eastern species and their known hosts and distribution are as follows: *Xiphydria abdominalis* Say—basswood, maple, and elm from southern Canada to North Carolina and Iowa; *X. maculata* Say—maple in Canada and most of the United States except the Gulf States; *X. tibialis* Say—elm, birch, beech, American hornbeam, and hawthorn in southeastern Canada and the Northeastern States; *X. hicoriae* Rohwer—hickory and elm in southeastern Canada and from Massachusetts and New Jersey to Illinois; *X. mellipes* Harris—beech, birch, and alder across southern Canada and the Northern States.

FAMILY ORUSSIDAE

Eight species of the family Orussidae have been recorded from the United States and Canada, five of which occur in eastern United States. The adults are somewhat similar to those of the Siricidae, but are much smaller, ranging from only about 8 to 14 mm. in length. As far as known, the larvae are all parasitic on woodborers of the coleopterous family Buprestidae.

SUPERFAMILY CEPHOIDEA

FAMILY CEPHIDAE

Stem Sawflies

The larvae of all members of this family and superfamily are borers in the stems of plants such as grasses or berries, or in the tender shoots of trees and shrubs. Only 12 species are recorded from the United States and Canada. Adults are slender-bodied and seldom more than 18 mm. long. The body is black or dark colored, occasionally marked with narrow yellow bands. The antennae are filiform, with 20 to 30 segments, and are either spindle-shaped or club-shaped. The front tibia has a single apical spur, cleft at the apex.

The **willow shoot sawfly,** *Janus abbreviatus* (Say), occurs in southern Canada and from New England to Virginia and South Dakota. Its hosts are willow and poplar. Full-grown larvae are white, cylindrical, and about 12 mm. long. The thoracic legs are indistinctly jointed and fleshy. There is a single pair of small prolegs on the last abdominal segment and a short, tubular prong on the tip of the abdomen. Adults appear in late May and June and the females deposit their eggs in punctures in the shoots of their hosts. Sometimes they girdle and weaken the shoots above the oviposition site. The larvae feed by boring down through the pith which kills the shoot for varying distances. Winter is spent within the shoot in cocoon-like structures.

The genus *Periclista* Konow is represented in eastern forests by eight species which feed as larvae on the leaves of oaks and hickory. The larvae are usually light green or have the dorsum grayish, and are armed with rows of small, single, two-pointed spines.

Suborder APOCRITA (=CLISTOGASTRA)

Members of the suborder Apocrita have the base of the abdomen constricted into a slender petiole or "waist." The constricted portion is comprised of the first abdominal segment which is fused to the thorax. Thus, what appears to be the first segment of the abdomen is actually the second. The adult female is equipped with a piercing ovipositor. In some species it is used as a tool for boring deep holes into the wood in which eggs are deposited; others use it for thrusting eggs into the bodies of other insects; in still others it is connected to poison glands and is used as a sting. The larvae are usually grublike or maggotlike. Some feed as parasites or predators on other insects and some feed on plants. Adults feed chiefly on flowers, sap, or other plant materials; some parasitic species feed occasionally on body fluids of the host.

Considered as a whole, members of this suborder are far more beneficial than harmful. Only a few species are harmful to trees or wood products. A number are injurious to tree seed and cone crops. Some species of ants are destructive of young trees in nurseries, plantations, and natural regeneration areas, while others are destructive of finished wood products.

SUPERFAMILY ICHNEUMONOIDEA

This superfamily constitutes one of the largest groups of parasitic insects and from the point of view of effectiveness in holding in check the numerous pests that infest plants, it probably takes first rank (*144*). It is comprised of three families (Stephanidae, Braconidae, and Icheneumonidae), and these have been broken down into more than 30 subfamilies, hundreds of genera, and thousands of species. Only a small portion of the important species parasitic on forest insects are mentioned. A complete listing of the species known to occur in the United States and Canada has been published by Meusebeck, et al. (*550*) and Krombein (*442*).

FAMILY STEPHANIDAE

This very small family of rather rare insects is represented in eastern forests by only one genus and three species. They are usually collected on dead trees and all are presumed to be parasitic on wood-boring Coleoptera. The adult is odd looking, having a spherical head situated at the end of a long neck, bearing crowns of teeth.

FAMILY BRACONIDAE

The family Braconidae comprises one of the major groups of insect parasites. The majority of species are parasitic in the larvae of Lepidoptera, but a large number are also parasitic of several other orders, especially the Coleoptera. Braconid adults are seldom more than 15 mm. long. They resemble those of the family Ichneumonidae in lacking a costal cell but differ in not having more than one recurrent vein. Many species pupate in silken cocoons on the outside of the body of the host, whereas others spin cocoons entirely apart from their hosts. There are from one to many generations per year, depending on the species. In some species the life cycle may be completed in less than 2 weeks (*144*).

In addition to the large number of native species attacking forest insects, several species have been imported from abroad against important introduced pests. A few of these are discussed briefly below.

Agathis (=*Bassus*) *pumilis* (Ratz.) was imported into the United States and Canada against the larch casebearer during the thirties. It is now widely distributed throughout eastern Canada and Northeastern United States and is providing a high degree of control in some areas. It has also been established in Idaho where the casebearer was discovered on western larch in 1957. Winter is spent in the larval stage within the host and there is one generation per year.

Meteorus versicolor (Wesm.), a parasite of the brown-tail moth and various other species of Lepidoptera, was introduced into the United States early in the century, and is known to have been established since 1909. It is now widely distributed throughout the range of the brown-tail moth in New England, but appears to be of little value in its control. Attempts to establish it on the satin moth in the Northeast have failed. It is established on the satin moth in the Pacific Northwest, however, where it is considered an important control factor (*205*).

Apanteles lacteicolor Vier., a parasite of the brown-tail moth in Europe, was introduced and established in the United States in 1908, and is now generally distributed throughout the range of its host. Studies made several years after its establishment showed a parasitization of 7 percent of overwintering larvae over a wide area. Winter is spent within young brown-tail moth larvae. The adults appear in the spring, and two generations may develop in alternate hosts (*549, 124*).

Apanteles melanoscelus (Ratz.), a European parasite of the gypsy moth, was introduced into New England in 1911 and 1912 and became established very quickly. Later, it was recolonized widely and is now generally established over the infested area of New England. Parasitization is sometimes fairly high in spots. Its abundance is greatly reduced in the spring by hyperparasites which attack overwintering cocoons.

Apanteles solitarius (Ratz.) was introduced into New England against the satin moth in 1927 and soon became established throughout the infested area. Parasitization as high as 67 percent has been recorded. The winter is spent either as a first-instar larva in a satin moth larva or as a prepupal larva in a satin moth cocoon. Thus, two separate broods of adults arise from the overwintering generation, each of which produces a second generation during the summer (*577*).

Phanomeris phyllotomae Mues. was imported into New England and New York in the early thirties against the birch leaf-mining sawfly. It became established but its effectiveness in control has not been determined. There is one generation a year (*204*).

Orgilus obscurator (Nees) was imported by the United States and Canada in the thirties against the European pine shoot moth and is now widely distributed in most shoot moth infested areas. Percentage parasitization is quite variable but often high in the United States, ranging from very low to as high as 50 percent. Significant levels of parasitization have also been recorded in parts of Canada. Winter is spent as a first instar larva within the hibernating host larva and there is one generation per year.

FAMILY ICHNEUMONIDAE

ICHNEUMONS

There are approximately 2500 described species of ichneumons in the United States and Canada, and probably at least 5,000 undescribed ones (*716*). The family has been divided into 14 subfamilies and 53 tribes and subtribes (*550*). All members of the family are parasites of the larvae and pupae of holometabilous insects, or of spiders, spider egg sacs, or pseudoscorpions. The majority of insect hosts belong to the order Lepidoptera, but many species of Hymenoptera, especially the sawflies, and several species of Coleoptera are also attacked.

Ichneumon adults vary greatly in size, form, and coloration. They resemble slender stinging wasps, but differ in having the antennae longer and with more segments, in having the trochanter two-segmented, in having the female ovipositor permanently extruded, and in lacking a costal cell in the front wing. They also resemble adult braconids but differ in having two recurrent veins in the front wing instead of just one.

Forest and shade tree insects are parasitized by a great many species of ichneumons, far too many to mention here (*550*). The majority are native to this continent and attack native hosts. In addition to these, a number of species have been introduced from abroad against several important introduced hosts (*205*).

Aptesis basizonia (Grav.), a European parasite of sawfly cocoons, was introduced originally into Canada against the European spruce sawfly during the thirties, and several colonies were made available for liberation in the United States as well as Canada against both the European spruce sawfly and the European pine sawfly. It became established on the European pine sawfly, which it parasitizes heavily at times. It has not been recovered from the spruce sawfly in the United States.

Exenterus abruptorius (Thnb.), an important parasite of the European pine sawfly in Europe, was imported into Canada during the thirties against the European spruce sawfly and European pine sawfly. Colonies were later made available for release in the United States. Recoveries were made from the pine sawfly several years after liberation in New Jersey.

Mesoleius tenthredinis Morley was imported into Canada from England in 1910-11 and liberated against the larch sawfly. A colony was also released against the sawfly in the Great Lakes region. It became established and for many years effected considerable control. Gradually though, the host developed an immunity to the parasite in many portions of its range, thereby greatly reducing its effectiveness. So far, this immunity does not seem to have developed in the more easterly infestations into which the parasite has spread.

Pimpla turionellae (L.), a European parasite of the pupae of many Lepidoptera, was imported against the European pine shoot moth during the thirties. It has not been recovered in the United States but is apparently established in southern Ontario.

Temelucha interruptor (Grav.) was imported from England and Europe against the European pine shoot moth during the thirties. It became established and was recovered in Connecticut, New Jersey, and southern New York in 1937. Ten years later, however, it had almost disappeared, being collected at only one point in Connecticut.

Eastern forest insects also are attacked by numerous native species of ichneumonid parasites. *Itoplectis conquisitor* (Say) parasitizes a tremendous number of species, and is especially important. *I. 4-cingulatus* (Prov.) and *I. viduata* (Grav.) also attack a great many species. *Megarhyssa lunator* (F.) is a conspicuous parasite of horntail larvae. The female is equipped with an extremely long ovipositor which is used as a drill for laying eggs in horntail larval galleries deep in infested wood. The ovipositor often becomes caught in the wood and the female, unable to escape, dies.

SUPERFAMILY CHALCIDOIDEA

This superfamily contains more species than any other superfamily in the order Hymenoptera. It contains, among its families, probably a majority of all entomophagous insects, with an extremely wide range in form, habits, host preferences, and host relationships. These comprise the majority and are mostly beneficial, but there also are a number of phytophagous species, many of which are economic pests. The species occurring in the United States and Canada are divided into 21 families and more than 460 genera (*588*).

Practically all of the more common orders of insects serve as hosts for the parasitic and predacious members of the Chalcidoidea, with the Lepidoptera, Diptera, Coleoptera, and Homoptera being preferred. The majority of the injurious tree-infesting species in this country are those which destroy the seeds of their hosts.

Chalcids are mostly small to minute in size—some are less than one-fourth of a millimeter in length. The antenna is elbowed, the pronotum does not extend back to the tegula; the trochanter is two-jointed; the forewing is without either a stigma or closed cells, and the ovipositor issues some distance before the apex of the abdomen.

FAMILY MYMARIDAE

This family is represented by more than 100 species in the United States and Canada, the majority of which occur in the east. All members of the family are internal parasites in the eggs of other insects, particularly of Homoptera. Adults are mostly black or yellowish in color and are extremely minute in size, usually less than 1 mm. long.

Polynema striaticorne Gir. is an important parasite of several species of membracids. It also attacks various aphids and other insects. Balduf (*30*) discussed its bionomics in Ohio and Illinois. *Acmopolynema bifasciatipennis bifasciatipennis* (Girault) parasitizes the eggs of several species of tree crickets. *Ooctonus aphrophora* Milliron attacks the Saratoga spittlebug.

FAMILY TRICHOGRAMMATIDAE

The family Trichogrammatidae consists of extremely small insects all of which are internal parasites in the eggs of other insects. Hosts have been recorded from the orders Lepidoptera, Coleoptera, Hymenoptera, Neuroptera, Diptera, and Hemiptera, but the Lepidoptera are preferred. Muesebeck, et al. (*550*) list 40 species as occurring in the United States and Canada.

Trichogramma minutum Riley parasitizes the eggs of a great many species of insects, including many important enemies of trees. The following is only a partial list of important eastern hosts: locust leaf miner, gypsy moth, brown-tail moth, orange-striped oak worm, the saddled prominent, walnut caterpillar, satin moth, hickory shuckworm, European pine shoot moth, Nantucket pine tip moth, forest tent caterpillar, spruce budworm (as many as 75 percent of spruce budworm eggs may be attacked), black-headed budworm, bagworm, elm sawfly, fall webworm, yellow-headed spruce sawfly, and the fall cankerworm (*588*).

The adult is less than ½ mm. long, and it inserts its eggs directly into host eggs. During warm weather, the life cycle may be completed within 9 to 16 days and there may be a dozen or more generations per year.

FAMILY EULOPHIDAE

Adults of this family are very small, ranging in length from 1 to 3 mm. Well over 100 species are known to parasitize tree-infesting insects, several of which are important pests (*588*). A number of foreign species have been imported into the United States and Canada in efforts to control several species of introduced pests.

Kratochviliana (=*Chrysocharis*) *laricinellae* (Ratz.) (fig. 194), a parasite of the larch casebearer and the birch leaf-mining sawfly was introduced into New England and Canada in the late twenties and thirties. It now appears to be widely established. Adults are bright, metallic green with pale yellow legs, and are about 2 to 3 mm. long. There may be 3 generations per year in the casebearer, but there are only one and a partial second in the sawfly. This species is not an effective parasite of the casebearer because it sometimes also acts as a secondary parasite and attacks the more effective introduced parasite, *Agathis pumilis* (*204*). Its effectiveness in controlling the birch leaf-mining sawfly is unknown.

Dahlbominus fuscipennis (Zett.), a parasite of several species of sawflies in Europe, was introduced into Canada in 1934 for release against the European spruce sawfly. The following year, shipments were received from Canada for release against the same species in Maine. Since then, releases have been made against several other sawflies in Canada and the United States. So far, it has been recovered in this country from the European spruce sawfly in New England, the European pine sawfly in New Jersey, the red-headed pine sawfly in Michigan, the Virginia pine sawfly in Virginia, *Neodiprion pratti paradoxicus* and *N. pinirigidae* in New Jersey, the red-pine sawfly in Wisconsin, the balsam-fir sawfly in Maine, and *Diprion frutetorum* in Connecticut (*205*).

Adults are 2.3 to 2.8 mm. long. The head, thorax, and abdomen are black; the wings have a smoky tinge; the legs are white to light brown, except the femur which is black; and the antennae are elbowed and black, except for a white scape in the female. This species is an external parasite of sawfly larvae and of sawfly pupae within their cocoons. There are from two to seven generations per year, depending on location. It has never become a very effective parasite of the spruce sawfly. Yet, almost 50 percent parasitization of the European pine sawfly has been recorded locally in New Jersey.

Coccophagus insidiator (Dalman), a European parasite of the introduced European elm scale was discovered at Ithaca, New York, in 1924 where it was parasitizing the scale quite heavily. It had apparently been introduced into the area by accident. The female is an endoparasite of the scale; the male an ectoparasite

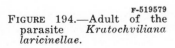

F-519579
FIGURE 194.—Adult of the parasite *Kratochviliana laricinellae.*

473

of the larval stage of the female parasite. There may be three to five generations per year.

The genus *Tetrastichus* contains a large number of important parasites of important forest insect pests. Descriptions of most North American species and information on their distribution and hosts were published by Burks (*125*).

Tetrastichus turionum (Htg.) was imported during the thirties and released in New England, New York, and New Jersey against the European pine shoot moth. Several years later it was also released in Ontario. It is known to occur in Massachusetts, New Jersey, on Long Island, and in southern Ontario. The adult is a tiny, iridescent, blue-green insect. The antennae are brown and the apices of the femora and the tarsi are light yellow or white. This is a pupal parasite and it has one generation per year. So far, it has been of no consequence in control of the shoot moth in this country.

Tetrastichus brevistigma Gahan is a pupal parasite of the elm leaf beetle. Adults are black with a slight, metallic, greenish tinge and are only about .5 to 1.5 mm. long. An average of 12 parasite larvae develop in each pupa and there are three or four generations per year. Parasitization as high as 50 to 80 percent occurs commonly in the vicinity of Boston, Massachusetts, where it was introduced from California. *T. holbeini* Gir. and *T. rugglesi* Roh. attack several species of *Chrysobothris* and *Agrilus,* respectively. *Dimmockia incongrus* (Ashm.) parasitizes the gypsy moth and many other species of Lepidoptera. *Elachertus cocoeciae* (How.) parasitizes various species of Lepidoptera. Members of the genus *Hyssopus* Gir. parasitize several species of shoot and tip moths and seed and cone infesting insects.

FAMILY ELASMIDAE

This family is represented in North America by one genus and 17 species, all of which occur in eastern United States. They are parasitic on lepidopterous larvae or hyperparasitic on ichneumonid or braconid parasites of lepidopterous larvae.

FAMILY THYSANIDAE

This family is also represented by one genus and 17 species in the United States and Canada. As far as known, they either attack various species of scale insects, whiteflies, and other Homoptera, or they attack other chalcid parasites of Homoptera.

FAMILY ENCYRTIDAE

This is a large family of parasites. Insect hosts are widely distributed among the various orders, but the majority of species are parasitic on aphids, scales, and whiteflies. Adults are 1 to 2 mm. long.

Ooencyrtus kuwanai (Howard), a parasite of gypsy moth eggs, was introduced into the United States in 1908 and 1909 from Japan (*175*). The adult is black and about 1 mm. long. Winter is spent in the adult stage, during which mortality may be severe.

Surviving adults appear during April and lay their eggs in the overwintering eggs of the host. There may be one or two spring generations; for the entire year there may be four or five generations. This species is an important parasite of the gypsy moth in the southern portion of its range. Parasitization of 40 to 50 percent frequently occurs in Massachusetts and Connecticut.

Habrolepis dalmani (Westw.) is sometimes fairly common as a parasite of the golden oak scale in this country. It has been introduced into New Zealand from New England and is credited with having saved the oaks in that country. *Kermes pubescens,* another oak scale, is attacked by at least five other species of encyrtids. The European fruit lecanium is attacked by more than 20 different species. The San Jose scale and oystershell scale each are also attacked by several species.

FAMILY EUPELMIDAE

Members of the family Eupelmidae parasitize a wide range of insects including Coleoptera, Orthoptera, Diptera, Lepidoptera, Hymenoptera, Hemiptera, and Homoptera. Many other species are hyperparasitic and a few are phytophagous.

Anastatus disparis Ruschka, an egg parasite of the gypsy moth in Europe and Japan, was introduced into New England in 1906, and quickly became established (*175*). It is now generally distributed throughout the infested parts of New England. Adult females are marked with green and brown, have two broad fuscous bands on the wings, and are 2 to 3 mm. long. Males are greenish black, with hyaline wings, and are only about 2 mm. long. The winter is spent as a full-grown larva within the gypsy moth egg. Adults appear in June and July and lay their eggs in egg masses of the host. Hatching occurs quickly and larval development is rapid, the hibernating stage being reached within about 2 weeks. Yet, there is only one generation per year. This species is usually scarce in areas where the egg parasite, *Ooencyrtus kuwanai,* also occurs. Interspecific competition may be the cause.

A few other species of eupelmid parasites and some of their hosts are as follows: *Eupelmella vesicularis* (Retzius)—gypsy moth, satin moth, forest tent caterpillar, European pine shoot moth, and several species of pine sawflies; *Eupelmus cyaniceps amicus* Girault—*Dioryctria disclusa,* Nantucket pine tip moth, bagworm, and the smaller European elm bark beetle; *E. cyaniceps cyaniceps* Ashm.—European pine shoot moth, Nantucket pine tip moth, and the bagworm; *E. pini* Taylor—white pine weevil; *E. allynii* (French)—various species of tree crickets; and *Metapalma spectabile* Westwood—buprestid and cerambycid borers.

FAMILY EUCHARITIDAE

The family Eucharitidae is comprised of only six genera and 27 species. As far as known, all species are parasitic on the pupae of ants. Adults are distinguished by the configuration of the scutellum, which is frequently produced backward in the form of powerful spines.

FAMILY PERILAMPIDAE

This is a small family with only two genera and 31 species in the United States and Canada. Its members are secondary parasites of various Diptera, Hymenoptera, Orthoptera, and Neuroptera. The pupae of tachinid, braconid, and ichneumon parasites are especially attractive.

Perilampus hyalinus Say, a common species throughout the United States, is a secondary parasite of a large number of insects in which it develops at the expense of many species of primary tachinid and ichneumonid parasites. The adult is bright, metallic, bluish-green and is from 2 to 4 mm. long. The thorax is large and the abdomen triangular. Peck (*588*) lists more than 20 species of Orthoptera, 16 species of Lepidoptera, 12 species of sawflies, and many species of ichneumonid, sarcophagid, and tachinid parasites as hosts. Smith (*657*) discussed its biology as a secondary parasite of the fall webworm.

FAMILY TORYMIDAE

Most members of this fairly large family are parasites of gall-forming insects. A number of others are parasitic on various lepidopterous larvae; quite a few feed in the seeds of various plants; and some act as hyperparasites.

The genus *Torymus* Dalman contains a large number of species that parasitize the immature stages of gall-forming cynipids and cecidomyids. *T. rugglesi* Milliron has been collected from the seeds of American holly in Delaware.

Members of the genus *Megastigmus* Dalman are all phytophagous, developing in the seeds of plants. Eastern species include *M. amelanchieris* Cush.—on shadbush; *M. laricis* Marcovitch—on larch; and *M. specularis* Walley—on balsam fir. The latter has destroyed up to 40 percent of balsam fir seed during certain years in eastern Canada.

The genus *Monodontomerus* contains several important parasites of various species of Lepidoptera and sawflies. *M. dentipes* (Dalman), a European species which probably entered this country with its European host, the introduced pine sawfly, is now widely distributed in southeastern Canada and in northern States from Maine to the Lake States. It is not only an effective parasite of the introduced pine sawfly, but also an important parasite of several other sawflies attacking conifers. It spends the winter as a prepupa inside the host cocoon. Adults appear over a fairly long period in the spring and lay their eggs through the host cocoon, depositing several upon the prepupa. There are probably two generations per year.

Monodontomerus aerus Walker was introduced into New England from 1906 to 1910 against the gypsy and brown-tail moths. It was released originally as a primary parasite but is much more common as a hyperparasite, attacking both hymenopterous cocoons and tachinid puparia. It is also parasitic on the white-marked tussock moth and the eastern tent caterpillar.

476

Other species of *Monodontomerus* recorded as parasites of important forest insects in the Eastern States include *M. indiscretus* Gahan—on the birch leaf-mining sawfly; *M. montivagus* Ashm.— on the spruce budworm; *M. minor* (Ratz.)—on the eastern tent cateripillar, the cecropia moth, and the spruce budworm; and *M. japonicus* Ashm., an introduced species—on the European spruce sawfly.

FAMILY PTEROMALIDAE

The family Pteromalidae is the largest in the superfamily and its members act as parasites or hyperparasites of almost all orders of insects. The adults are minute, black or metallic green or bronze insects. Many have a more or less triangularly shaped abdomen.

Schizonotus sieboldi (Ratz.), a primary parasite of the imported willow leaf beetle and several allied species of Chrysomelidae, is widely distributed in eastern United States. The larva feeds externally on the pupa of its host. High percentages of parasitization were recorded over a 3-year period in the vicinity of Boston, Massachusetts, but host populations were not materially reduced (*203*).

Dibrachys cavus (Walker), a hyperparasite of many primary parasites, occasionally acts as a primary parasite. It is extremely destructive of many beneficial parasites. In common with the adults of many other parasites, the adults often feed at puncture holes made by their ovipositors. This results in the death of many larvae that are not parasitized.

FAMILY EURYTOMIDAE

This family contains a number of both phytophagous and entomophagous species. Many form galls in the stems of grasses and other plants; some are parasites of gall-forming Diptera and Hymenoptera; a few are egg parasites of Orthoptera; and others are parasites of various tree-infesting Coleoptera. Adults are usually black and the abdomen is rounded or oval and somewhat compressed.

Eurytoma pissodis Girault is one of the most important parasites of the white pine weevil. The adult is dull black on the thorax, glossy black on its shining abdomen, has conspicuous red eyes, and is from 3 to 6 mm. long. Eggs are laid on full-grown weevil larvae and winter is spent as a prepupa within the pupal cell of the host. Parasitization of at least 50 percent has been recorded in some white pine weevil infestations.

Species parasitic on other important forest insects include the following: *Eurytoma verticillata* (F.)—on the European pine shoot moth; *E. pini* Bugbee—on the European pine shoot moth, Nantucket pine tip moth, bagworm, and *Rhyacionia rigidana; E. tylodermatis* Ashm.—on the hickory shuckworm, European pine shoot moth, and Nantucket pine tip moth; and *E. magdalidis* Ashm.—on the southern pine beetle and *Pityophthorus liquidambarus.*

FAMILY CHALCIDIDAE

The family Chalcididae contains many primary and secondary parasites of Lepidoptera, Diptera, Coleoptera, and Orthoptera. The adults of certain species are fairly large and conspicuous; all are solitary in habit; and practically all develop inside their hosts.

A few of the more important species and their hosts are: *Haltichella rhyacioniae* Gahan—the Nantucket pine tip moth, *Rhyacionia rigidana,* and the western pine tip moth; *H. xanticles* (Walk.)—the European pine shoot moth and the oak skeletonizer; *Phasgonophora sulcata* Westw.—the bronze birch and the flatheaded apple tree borers; *Trigonura elegans* Prov.—several species of woodborers including the flatheaded apple tree borer, the red elm bark and black elm bark weevils; *Spilochalcis albifrons* (Walsh)—numerous hosts including the locust leaf and arborvitae leaf miners, and the larch casebearer; *S. flavopicta* (Cresson)—the Nantucket pine tip moth; *S. mariae* (Riley)—the bagworm and several species of Saturnid moths; *Brachymeria compsilurae* (Cwfd.)—tachinid flies, especially *Compsilura concinnata* and *Blepharipa scutellata* (*202*) ; and *B. ovata* (Say)—a wide variety of lepidopterous hosts including the white-marked tussock moth, hemlock looper, and bagworm.

SUPERFAMILY CYNIPOIDEA

The superfamily Cynipoidea consists of very small, dark-colored wasps. Many species are gall makers or gall inquilines. The remainder are parasitic on other insects. Weld (*754*) divides the superfamily into four families—Ibaliidae, Liopteridae, Figitidae, and Cynipidae. The liopterids are mostly exotic, and their habits are unknown.

FAMILY IBALIIDAE

Members of this family are all parasitic on horntails of the family Siricidae. Four species are recorded from eastern United States—*Ibalia anceps* Say, *I. ensiger* Norton, *I. maculipennis* Haldeman, and *I. scalpellator* Westw.

Ibalia maculipennis Hald., a common species in eastern United States and southeastern Canada, is a parasite of the pigeon tremex. The adult is marked with a yellow and dark-brown pattern, has two conspicuous dark-brown to black bands on the forewings, and is about 12 mm. long.

FAMILY FIGITIDAE

This family is represented in eastern America by 30 species. The majority are parasitic in dipterous puparae; a few are parasitic in the cocoons of chrysopids.

FAMILY CYNIPIDAE

THE GALL WASPS

This large family of several hundred species consists largely of species which produce galls on their plant hosts in which they live and feed during the larval stage. Many others live in galls produced by other insects, and a few are parasitic on other insects. The adults are small to extremely small and usually black. They are distinguished by the abdomen which is oval, shining, somewhat compressed, and almost covered by the first tergite. Many gall-forming species produce two quite different generations per year. One generation develops during the summer in one type of gall. Adults appear in the fall and consist entirely of parthenogenetic females. Eggs laid by these females give rise to larvae which produce an entirely different kind of gall. Adults of this generation, consist of both males and females, and may be quite different in appearance from those of the first generation.

It is estimated that 86 percent of the known gall-forming species produce galls on oaks and are confined to them (419). There are 717 species listed as occurring in the United States and Canada, 76 percent of which form galls on oaks (550).

The females deposit their eggs in the tissues of all parts of the host, from the roots to the flowers. Gall production is believed to result from the reaction of the cambium and other meristematic tissues to stimuli produced by the larvae. The great majority of species are of little or no economic importance. However, certain species which produce large irregular galls on the smaller branches are capable of causing injury (fig. 195). Infested branches may be disfigured or even killed. Occasionally, entire trees are killed. On the other hand, galls produced by certain other species are economically valuable: Some have long been used in the manufacture of ink and in dyeing and tanning; others serve as a source of winter food for bees. One, the deciduous oak gall, is occasionally abundant enough on black oak in Missouri to be used as food for hogs, cattle, sheep, turkeys, and chickens (418, 420). Some of the more common and important gall-forming species are discussed below.

Callirhytis floridana (Ashm.) occurs from Virginia to Florida and Missouri and Arkansas. It produces slender, elongate swellings from 12 to 75 mm. long on branches close to the ground of Chapman, post, and dwarf post oaks. Large acreages of dwarf post oaks were nearly all killed during an outbreak in eastern North Carolina in 1935 (420).

Callirhytis punctata (O. S.), the **gouty oak gall**, occurs from southern Canada to North Carolina and Illinois. It produces galls (fig. 196) on the twigs and smaller limbs of scarlet, pin, and black oaks. These galls are about 12 to 38 mm. long and they frequently occur so close together that they form practically continuous masses. This species has alternate generations. The first produces small blisterlike galls on the leaves near the veins in the spring. The second produces gouty galls during the summer. In heavy infestations, twigs, fairly large branches, and even entire trees may be killed. Shade trees are especially subject to damage.

Callirhytis cornigera (O. S.), the **horned oak gall,** occurs from southern Canada to Georgia and Iowa. It produces galls on the twigs of pin, scrub, black, blackjack, and water oaks. Injurious infestations have been observed on roadside and woodland oaks in the Niagara area of Canada.

Callirhytis (=Andricus) gemmaria (Ashm.), the **ribbed bud gall,** occurs from Massachusetts to Florida, Illinois, and Texas. It produces somewhat conical, strongly ribbed galls about 5 mm. long on the twigs of black oaks. These galls sometimes occur in such large numbers as to cause infested twigs to split and die. Entire young trees are sometimes killed.

Callirhytis operator (O. S.) occurs from New England to Virginia and Texas and causes the formation of woolly galls on the staminate flowers of various oaks. When the adults emerge, they oviposit in immature acorns. This results in the formation of so-called **acorn pip galls** within the acorn cups. In heavy infestations, acorn crops are reduced. *C. futilis* (O. S.) produces globose, grayish galls up to 4½ inches long on the main roots of young white oaks just below the ground line.

Neuroterus quercusbatatus (=batatus) (Fitch), the **oak potato gall** (fig. 197), occurs from Ontario and Rhode Island to Florida

F-520107
FIGURE 195.—Heavy infestation of galls on twigs of Nuttall oak in the Mississippi River Delta region.

and Illinois on white oaks. There are two generations per year. Adults of the first generation emerge in May from galls produced on the preceding year's growth. Second generation adults emerge from green galls. Females of this generation lay their eggs in the same galls from which they emerge.

Neuroterus floccosus (Bass.), the **oak flake gall**, produces small, hemispherical galls from 1.5 to 3.5 mm. in diameter on the lower surface of terminal leaves of white oaks. These galls are covered with white hairs and often occur in large numbers on a single leaf. Heavily infested leaves curl and are unsightly on shade trees.

Neuroterus noxiosus (Bass.), the **noxious oak gall**, occurs on swamp white oaks from New England to Virginia and in the Central States. Heavily infested trees may be severely disfigured.

Amphibolips confluenta (Harr.), the **large oak-apple gall** (fig. 198), occurs from southern Canada to Virginia. It produces galls on the leaves or leaf petioles of various oaks, principally red, black, and scarlet. These galls are quite large, from 12 to 50 mm. in diameter, and greenish to brownish in color, depending on age. The related species, *A. fulginosa* Ashm., produces globose galls on the sides of willow and laurel acorn cups in Florida.

FIGURE 196.—Gouty oak galls caused by *Callirhytis punctata*.

FIGURE 197.—Oak potato gall on white oak caused by *Neuroterus quercusbatatus*.

FIGURE 198.—Large oak-apple gall caused by *Amphibolips confluenta*.

Dryocosmus quercuspalustris (O. S.) (=*Callirhytis palustris*), the **succulent oak gall**, occurs from southern Canada and New England to Iowa and Florida. It produces somewhat circular, succulent galls from 9 to 12 mm. in diameter on the leaves or axils of staminate flowers of red oaks. The galls are fleshy walled and hollow, except for a free-rolling cell about 2.5 mm. in diameter.

Xanthoteras forticorne (O. S.) (=*Biorhiza forticornis*), the **oak fig gall**, produces galls on the leaves, twigs, and stems of white oaks in the Eastern States north of Virginia. Early in the season they are reddish and bladderlike. Sometimes they occur in dense clusters several inches long around a twig. When they do, the irregular masses look like pressed figs.

SUPERFAMILY PROCTOTRUPOIDEA

As far as known, all members of this superfamily are parasitic on the immature stages of other insects. The group as a whole seems to be rather poorly known, and most of the North American species are still undescribed. The adults of the majority of species are black, often shiny, and small to extremely small in size. The smaller ones resemble chalcids, but differ in having the pronotum extend laterally to the tegulae and the ovipositor issue from the end of the abdomen. In many of the smaller species, the wings are almost veinless; in others, the wings are entirely absent.

FAMILY EVANIIDAE

Members of this small family of spider-like wasps are parasitic in the egg capsules of cockroaches. Adults are about 10 to 15 mm. long and are distinguished by very small, oval abdomens attached by petioles to the propodeum considerably above the base of the hind coxae. The majority of described species occur in eastern United States.

482

FAMILY AULACIDAE

The family Aulacidae consists of slender ichneumon-like wasps, with the female ovipositor about as long as the body. A number of species are parasitic on wood-boring insects; the remainder are parasitic in the nests of bees and wasps in twigs or wood. *Pristaulacus rufitarsis* (Cress.) is a parasite of the hemlock borer and poplar borer in eastern America; *P. bilobatus* (Prov.) is also parasitic on the hemlock borer. *Aulacus burquei* (Prov.), *A. digitalis* Townes, *A. lovei* (Ashm.), and *A. pallipes* Cress are parasitic on various species of *Xiphydria*. Several species in the genera *Gasteruption* and *Rhydinofoenus* are parasitic in bee's and wasp's nests in twigs or wood.

FAMILY PELECINIDAE

This family appears to be represented in North America by only one species, *Pelecinus polyturator* (Drury), a parasite of May beetle larvae. The female is a large shiny black insect, often up to 62 mm. long. The abdomen is slender, about five times as long as the head and thorax combined, and is without a sting. Males are much smaller and have the posterior of the abdomen swollen.

FAMILY CERAPHRONIDAE

A number of species in this family have been taken from colonies of ants. Various others are known to be hyperparasitic on various hymenopterous and dipterous parasites. One of the latter, *Conostigmus virginicus* (Ashm.), is a parasite of *Blepharipa scutellata* (P.-D.), an introduced parasite of the gypsy moth.

FAMILY DIAPRIIDAE

This is a large family of very small black wasps, most of which appear to be parasitic on immature Diptera. Adults of most species can be recognized by the location of the antennae, which arise on a shelflike protuberance in about the middle of the face. *Psilus politus* (Say) has been recorded as parasitic on the cherry fruit fly. *Trichopria tabanivora* Fouts is a parasite of horseflies. Apparently, only a small percentage of the species in the family have been described.

FAMILY SCELIONIDAE

As far as known, all members of this large family of small insects are parasitic in the eggs of other insects. Species attacking some of the more important forest and shade tree insects are as follows: *Telenomus dalmani* (Ratz.) and *T. hemerocampae* Wilcox—the white-marked tussock moth, *T. californicus* Ashm.—the satin moth, *T. geometriae* Ashm. and *T. alsophilae* Vier.—the fall cankerworm, *T. bifidus* Riley—the fall webworm, *T. catalpae* Mues.—the catalpa sphinx, *T. dalmani*—the hemlock looper, *T.*

alsophilae—the elm spanworm, and *T. clisiocampanae* Riley—forest tent and eastern tent caterpillars.

FAMILY PLATYGASTERIDAE

The majority of species in this family are parasites of Diptera, especially of the families Cecidomyiidae and Tipulidae. A number of others are also important as enemies of mealybugs and whiteflies. The introduced species, *Allotropa burrelli* Mues., an important parasite of the Comstock mealybug, has been widely released in eastern United States. Two native species, *A. ashmeadi* Mues. and *A. convexifrons* Mues., also are important parasites of the Comstock mealybug.

SUPERFAMILY CHRYSIDOIDEA

FAMILY CHRYSIDIDAE

Members of this family are brilliantly metallic-blue and green wasps and are popularly known as gold- or cuckoo-wasps. The majority of species are external parasites of various wasps and bees. A number of species deposit their eggs in the cells of their hosts, and the larvae either feed on the original occupants of the cells or on the food prepared for them.

Chrysis shanghaiensis Smith, the only species known to be parasitic upon lepidopterous larvae, was introduced into Massachusetts from Japan in 1917-18 against the oriental moth, also an introduced species. Recoveries were made the year following its release (*576*), but it has not been recorded since that time.

FAMILY CLEPTIDAE

This family is represented in North America by two genera and seven species. The genus *Cleptes* Latrielle contains six species, all of which are western in distribution and all of which apparently parasitize various sawflies. The genus *Mesitiopterus* Ashm. is represented in eastern United States by the single species, *M. kahlii* Ashm., an egg parasite of the walkingstick.

SUPERFAMILY BETHYLOIDEA

FAMILY BETHYLIDAE

Members of the family Bethylidae are parasitic almost exclusively on the larva of Lepidoptera and Coleoptera. More than 100 species have been recorded from the United States, about two-thirds of which occur in the eastern portion of the country. The adults are small to medium in size. Females are often wingless and antlike and differ so much in appearance from the males that the two sexes are not easily correlated.

A number of species of the genus *Scleroderma* Latreille are often parasitic on larvae of the family Cerambycidae. Additional species of importance as parasites of forest insects and their hosts are: *Pseudobrachium mandibulare* (Ashm.)—the black carpenter

484

ant; *Perisierola punctaticeps* (Kieffer)—the hickory shuckworm; *Goniozus electus* Fouts—Nantucket pine tip moth; and *G. longinervis* Fouts—the western pine tip moth.

SUPERFAMILY SCOLIOIDEA

FAMILY TIPHIIDAE

TIPHIID WASPS

The family Tiphiidae contains a number of important parasites of scarabaeid larvae in the soil. As far as known, all species are external parasites, usually feeding on the final larval instar of the host. The adults of most species are moderate in size, hairy, and black. The remainder are mostly black and yellow. A number of species have been imported against several introduced pests.

Tiphia inornata Say is one of the commonest and most important parasites of white grubs in the United States. Infestations are heaviest during the years when full-grown white grubs are present. At other times, they are usually very low (*788*).

Tiphia vernalis Rohwer was introduced against the Japanese beetle from Japan and Korea during the period 1924-1933. It became established and now plays an important role in control of the beetle in certain parts of the East, especially in Pennsylvania (*143*). *T. popilliavora* Rohwer, also introduced against the Japanese beetle during the twenties and thirties, is now well established from New Hampshire to Virginia and Ohio. *T. asericae* A. & J. was introduced against the Asiatic garden beetle and *Serica peregrine* during the twenties. It is well established in Pennsylvania.

FAMILY MUTILLIDAE

VELVET ANTS

Members of the family Mutillidae are commonly known as velvet ants because the females are wingless, have heavy coatings of fine hairs, and are usually observed running back and forth over the ground. In certain regions they are also known as 'cow-killer ants.' Adults are usually brightly colored with red, orange, or yellow markings, and some of the females are 25 mm. or more long. The majority of species are parasitic on ground-nesting bees and wasps (*518*). A common species in the South, where members of the family are most common, is *Dasymutilla occidentalis occidentalis* (L.). Because of their large size, velvet ants are capable of inflicting painful stings.

FAMILY SCOLIDAE

The family Scolidae is represented by about a dozen species in eastern United States and, as far as known, all species are external parasites of Scarabaeid larvae in the soil. White grubs are especially susceptible to attack. The adults are large, hairy, and usually black except for spots or bands of yellow or red, and their wings are often dark brown with purple or green iridescence. *Campsomeris annulata* (Fab.), a native of China and Japan, was introduced against the Japanese beetle in the twenties but did not become established.

FAMILY SAPYGIDAE

As far as known, all members of this family are parasitic on the larvae of leaf-cutting bees. Less than a dozen species are recorded from eastern United States. Adults are moderate in size, short legged and usually spotted or banded with yellow.

FAMILY FORMICIDAE

The Ants

Ants are among the most abundant and widespread of all insects and they are found in practically all terrestrial habitats. The majority of species nest in the soil, while many others build their nests in wood, in timbers, in or under the bark of decaying trees, or in hollow stems of plants. Some of the more primitive species feed on insects or other small animals which they are able to kill. Many others feed on sweet fluids such as sap exuding from wounds, on nectar, or on honeydew produced by other insects. Certain leaf-cutting species cultivate fungi on which they feed.

Ants differ from their near relatives in having the abdomen divided into two distinct regions, the pedicel and the gaster; and in having the antennae elbowed, with the first segment greatly elongated in the females and workers. They also differ from termites, with which they are often confused, by having a strong constriction or "waist" between the thorax and abdomen and by having two pairs of wings of unequal size.

Ants are social insects and live in nests or colonies containing from a few to several thousands of individuals each. A colony consists of three castes—females, males, and workers. Females generally are winged, the wings being discarded after they mate. Males are usually smaller than females and generally retain their wings until death. Workers are wingless and are usually smaller than the females or males.

With the exception of the carpenter ants and certain leaf-cutting species, ants are of minor importance as enemies of trees or wood products. Many species, however, are nuisance pests in forested areas, especially in picnicking or other recreational areas. Several publications on the biology and control of carpenter ants are available (*277, 632, 649, 660*).

The **black carpenter ant,** *Camponotus pennsylvanicus* (DeGeer), nests in standing live and dead trees, rotting logs, and stumps, telephone and telegraph poles, and the wood of houses and other buildings. It is widely distributed in eastern United States and Canada, occurring from North Dakota to Quebec and Ontario and south to Texas and Florida. These are large ants (fig. 199), the workers ranging in length from 6 to 13 mm. The body color is typically black, but in some individuals the pleuron, petiole, and legs are reddish. The gaster is covered with dense, long, appressed, pale yellowish and ashy pubescence. Body hairs are suberect or erect, yellowish, and moderately abundant.

The black carpenter ant does not eat wood. It simply removes it in order to produce galleries which serve as its nest. Its natural food consists largely of dead and live insects, honeydew, sap, juices of well-ripened fruits, and refuse. It also feeds on various household foods such as different kinds of sweets, raw and cooked meats, and fruits.

Live trees are occasionally infested but usually only when the ants are able to enter them through cracks, scars, knot holes, and decayed or other faulty places. Once inside the tree, they remove the faulty wood and often extend their galleries into adjacent soundwood. A wide variety of trees such as poplar, cherry, white and pitch pine, balsam fir, elm, willow, and red, white, scarlet, black, and post oaks have been found infested. Infestations frequently are located near the base but may occur very high in a tree. Infested trees are often subject to serious injury. They are frequently weakened to the point that they are subject to windbreakage. The wood also may be rendered worthless for lumber or pulpwood (fig. 200).

Houses also are often invaded by carpenter ants coming from nests located nearby outdoors. Possibilities of this happening are greatest where houses are located in the vicinity of trees, logs, or stumps. Entry is usually gained through openings around the foundation or from tree branches in contact with the house. The woodwork may be attacked in any number of places, but the most commonly damaged parts are supporting timbers, porch pillars, sills, girders, joists, studs, window casings, and external trim. The galleries are similar to those constructed by termites. They differ in that they run across the grain, are sandpaper smooth,

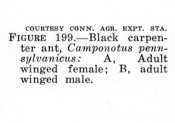

COURTESY CONN. AGR. EXPT. STA.
FIGURE 199.—Black carpenter ant, *Camponotus pennsylvanicus:* A, Adult winged female; B, adult winged male.

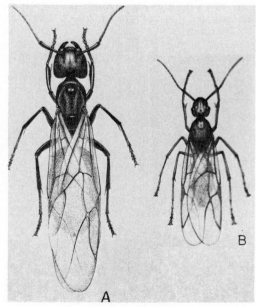

FIGURE 200.—Cross-section of an oak log showing galleries made by carpenter ants.

and are kept free of frass. The presence of large black ants running about the house; swarms of large black, winged ants about the house in the spring; piles of sawdust-like borings; slit-like holes in woodwork such as window and door casings; and faint rustling sounds in walls, floors, woodwork, and flush-panel doors are all evidences of infestation in a house. Where infestations are of long standing, damage to structural timbers may be severe and require extensive repairs. Telephone and telegraph poles also are subject to serious damage (fig. 201) (*272*).

Overwintering males and females in colonies over 3 years old engage in nuptial flights from May to late July. Fertilized females then establish nests in cavities, usually under the bark of a tree,

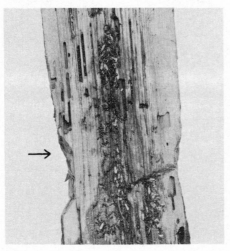

FIGURE 201.—Colony of carpenter ants in a 2-foot section of a telephone pole in winter. Arrow indicates ground level.

log, or stump and seal themselves in. Here they rear their first broods of workers to maturity on salivary secretions. These workers, being inadequately fed, are smaller than normal. Subsequent broods are fed by the workers, and individuals are larger. Long-established colonies contain workers of various sizes, some of which are extraordinarily large. Such colonies may consist of a reproductive female, scores of winged males and virgin females, and several thousand workers.

Tightly-constructed houses with concrete foundations, good clearance, and full basements are fairly safe from invasion by black carpenter ants. The removal of all wood from near or under a house site prior to construction, making certain that infested wood is not brought into the house, and the cutting back of branches in contact with the house are also helpful in preventing infestations in buildings.

The **red carpenter ant**, *Camponotus ferrugineus* (Fab.), occurs over much of the same portion of the United States as the black carpenter ant, but it is apparently less common. It appears to prefer wooded areas where it normally nests in or beneath well-rotted logs and stumps. Under these conditions, it often extends its galleries for considerable distances in the soil. Nests are also found in dead, standing trees and apparently, rarely in houses. The workers are about the same size as those of the black carpenter ant. Most of the thorax, petiole, base of the gaster, and much of the legs are yellowish ferruginous. The remainder is black. Hairs and pubescence are more golden yellow than those of the black carpenter ant, especially on the gaster. This species has caused considerable damage to standing white cedar in Minnesota (*305*).

The **Florida carpenter ant**, *Camponotus abdominalis floridanus* (Buckley), occurs from North Carolina to Florida and Alabama. It is one of the most important house-infesting species in Florida. Workers are about 5.5 to 10 mm. long. The head is reddish, the thorax and petiole yellowish or yellowish-red, the scape and gaster blackish or black, and the body is covered with many long yellowish hairs. This species builds its nests in various places such as in the ground beneath objects, in dead branches in trees, in and beneath rotting logs and stumps, and sometimes in the woodwork of porches, roofs, kitchen sinks, and paneling. Outdoors, the ants feed largely on living and dead small insects, and on honeydew which they secure by tending aphids, mealybugs, and scales. Indoors, they feed on such items as molasses, honey, and liver.

Camponotus nearcticus Emery usually nests in small colonies in dead twigs and branches of trees, in or beneath the bark of dead and living trees, in insect galls and pine cones, in the hollow stems of plants, and in wooden posts. Nests have also been found in the woodwork of houses, especially in roofing. It occurs from New York to Ontario, North Dakota and Colorado and south to Mississippi and Florida. Workers are about 4.5 to 7.5 mm. long, and their bodies are usually black and rather shiny.

Camponotus rasilis Wheeler occurs from South Carolina to Florida and Texas, but is apparently most common in the Gulf Coast States. It nests in small colonies in tunnels made by borers in the twigs and branches of various hardwoods; in insect galls;

in cavities in the stalks of plants; under the bark of trees; and in logs, stumps, wooden posts, and houses. Galleries in branches may be anywhere from 1 inch to over 5 feet long. Workers are 4 to 9 mm. long. The head, thorax, and petiole are usually yellowish-red or reddish, and the gaster is blackish or black. *C. caryae discolor* (Buckley), a species similar in appearance and habits to *C. rasilis,* has been recorded from Ohio to Kansas and Iowa and south to Texas and Florida. It is most common in the lower Mississippi Valley. *C. castaneus* (Latreille) occurs throughout the South but is most common in the Southeast. It nests in rotten logs and stumps or in the soil. Workers are yellowish to yellowish-red and from 7 to 10 mm. long. *C. tortuganus* Emery occurs in the southern half of Florida and apparently nests in small colonies in rotting wood or in the soil beneath stones. It also occurs in houses where it may be a pest. *C. mississippiensis* M. R. Smith has been found nesting in the new growth of white ash branches in Mississippi. Galleries are apparently limited to one year's growth. *C. pylartes fraxinicola* M. R. Smith nests in the dead branches of various hardwods. It has been recorded from Mississippi.

The **Texas leaf-cutting ant,** *Atta texana* (Buckley), is a serious pest of pine seedlings in east Texas and west-central Louisiana. It also defoliates and damages a wide variety of other plants, including orchard trees. Injury to pines is especially severe during the winter when there is a dearth of other green foliage.

Texas leaf-cutting ants are rusty-red in color. The head is strongly bi-lobed; the antennae are 11-segmented and without a well-defined club; the thorax bears three pairs of prominent spines on top, with the anterior ones the largest; and the legs are extraordinarily long. The queen is about 18 mm. long; workers, from 1.5 to 12 mm. long.

Nests of the Texas leaf-cutting ant are constructed in the ground, usually in well-drained stand or loamy soils and commonly on slopes facing the south or west (*59*). The interior of the nest may reach a depth of 20 feet and its outer surface may occupy up to one-tenth of an acre. It may contain a thousand or more entrance holes. Nest areas are usually marked by many crescent-shaped mounds, up to 5 to 14 inches high and a foot in diameter. Each mound surrounds an entrance hole (fig. 202). The nest consists of many cavities connected by narrow tunnels. There are vertical tunnels that extend to mound openings and lateral tunnels that lead outwards, sometimes for a hundred yards or

F-482847
FIGURE 202.—Mounds of the Texas leaf-cutting ant, *Atta texana.*

490

more. Above ground, sharply defined foraging trails sometimes extend hundreds of feet to the plants under attack. Ants move in procession along these trails, each carrying a fragment of leaf or other material to the nest. These fragments, which may be several times the size of the ants carrying them, are borne upright over the head like a parasol.

The ants do not eat the foliage which they remove from plants. Instead, they cut it up into small fragments, shape it into small pellets, and carry it into their underground chambers. Here it is placed upon so-called gardens where it serves as a medium for the growth of a fungus. It is this fungus which serves as the food of the colony. During summer most of the foliage is brought into the nest during the night; whereas, during fall, winter and spring most of it is brought in during the day, unless it is too cold or wet.

Winged males and females appear during May and June and fly from the colony and mate. Mated females lose their wings and dig into the soil where they establish nests. Here they become the queens of new colonies.

A pelleted bait has given good control when scattered over portions of nests where excavation mounds are concentrated (567). The reader should consult Agricultural Handbook 331 for details on the control method.

The **Allegheny mound ant,** *Formica exsectoides* Forel, is a serious pest of young white pines, red pines, Scotch pines, red cedars, and spruces in the Eastern and Northeastern States. It nests in the ground and constructs mounds which may be up to 4 feet in height and 6 feet across. In forested areas, these mounds are most often found in openings or along the edges of stands. All vegetation, excepting large trees, may be destroyed in an area 40 to 50 feet in diameter around a mound. Trees from 2 to 15 years old are especially susceptible to attack. Damage may be severe in forest plantations. The adult ant is about 3 to 6 mm. long. The head is reddish brown and about as wide as long; the thorax is reddish brown and feathered; the anal region is reddish and surrounded by a fringe of hairs; and the legs are sometimes brownish or dark red.

The Allegheny mound ant does not feed on trees or other vegetation. Its food consists of living and dead insects and honeydew excreted by various species of sucking insects. It appears that the only reason it attacks vegetation is to kill it to keep it from shading the mounds. Trees are killed by the injection of formic acid into their tissues. Apparently this results in the coagulation of cell contents and the prevention of downward movement of foods in the inner bark (590).

The life history of the Allegheny mound ant is not too well understood, but it is known to forage for food from April to September and to spend the winter in its nest. There are several generations per year and both queens and workers are known to live for several years.

Crematogaster cerasi (Fitch) occurs from southern Canada to Georgia. Its nests are found in the ground, in rotting stumps, logs, or branches, and in empty nuts on the ground. Nests also may be found in various parts of houses such as the roof, siding, ceiling, and porch, but most often in and around door and window frames. *C. clara* Mayr occurs from Indiana to New Jersey and south to Texas and Florida, but is most common in the lower Mississippi Valley. Its nests are found in cane stems, branches, trees, rotten stumps and sometimes in the woodwork of houses. *C. lineolata* (Say) occurs in southern Canada and throughout eastern United States. It constructs fairly large nests, usually in the soil, but also in logs, stumps, dead trees, or in the woodwork of houses. When alarmed, the workers bite fiercely and give off a repulsive odor. *C. laeviuscula* Mayr and *C. ashmeadi* Mayr have been recorded nesting in various dead hardwoods in Mississippi.

The **Argentine ant,** *Iridomyrmex humilis* (Mayr), an introduced species first recorded in this country at New Orleans in 1891, now occurs in many localities in the Southern States and California. Local infestations have also been found in St. Louis, Baltimore, and Chicago (*660*). Indoors, it feeds on almost every kind of food, especially sweets, meats, pastries, fruit, eggs, dairy products, animal fats, and vegetable oils; outdoors, it feeds partly on honeydew produced by aphids, mealybugs, and scale insects. By fostering and protecting the latter insects from many of their enemies, they encourage the development of heavy infestations which are capable of causing serious damage to affected plants. They also remove seeds from seed beds and feed on the sap or fruit juices from various trees and plants.

Argentine ants are more or less uniformly light brown or brown in color; the antennae are 12-segmented and without a club; and the petiole scale is well developed and inclined. Workers are from 2.2 to 2.6 mm. long and when freshly crushed emit a stale, greasy, musty odor. Nests occur in all sorts of places—in the soil, in rotten wood, in cavities in trees, and in refuse piles, bird nests, beehives, and other places. The number of ants present in well-established infested areas is beyond comprehension. Fortunately, they are usually of minor importance as pests in forested areas.

Iridomyrmex pruinosus (Roger) occurs throughout the Eastern and Southern States north to New York and Wisconsin. It nests in the ground and under the bark of logs and stumps and is sometimes a nuisance in houses. The odor of freshly crushed workers resembles the odor of rotten coconut.

The genus *Solenopsis* Westw. is represented by seven species in the United States, six of which occur in the Southeastern States. Nests are usually constructed in the soil, but also sometimes in rotten wood and in houses. The workers are aggressive and practically omnivorous. Several species are serious economic pests. They may remove seeds from seed beds; kill young quail and poultry and even small game; gnaw into vegetables, fruits, and flowers; make large ugly mounds in fields, parks, playgrounds, and recreational areas; and damage young nursery trees.

The **imported fire ant,** *Solenopsis saevissima richteri* Forel, an introduced species, first officially recorded in the United States at Mobile, Alabama, in 1930, now occurs from North Carolina to Florida, Texas and Arkansas, exclusive of Tennessee. Workers are about 2.8 to 6 mm. long and are usually reddish in color, except for a blackish gaster. Queens are about 9 mm. long.

Imported fire ant mounds are found in almost all kinds of soil, but most commonly in open areas. Few if any are ever found in heavily timbered areas, especially in hardwood stands. An average mound is about 1 foot high and 2 feet across; some are up to 3 feet tall. The larger ones are usually dome-shaped or conical, and may contain more than 100,000 ants. In heavily infested areas there may be more than 60 nests per acre. Nests also are found in rotting logs, around tree trunks, and occasionally under buildings. Green (312) discussed the biology of this species.

For more comprehensive treatments of ants, the reader is referred to publications by Wheeler (759), Smith (659), and Creighton (174).

SUPERFAMILY VESPOIDEA

This superfamily is comprised of two families, the Vespidae and the Pompilidae. Many species are social in habit and live together in colonies; others are solitary and live alone. The adults generally feed on nectar, sap, or similar materials, whereas the larvae feed on other insects or spiders. A few species are of some importance as pests of forest or shade trees; quite a number of others may create problems when they occur in abundance in picnicking areas, campgrounds, or other recreational areas.

FAMILY VESPIDAE

HORNETS, YELLOW JACKETS, AND POTTER WASPS

The family Vespidae contains the well known stinging wasps, hornets, and yellow jackets. More than 350 species have been recorded in North America north of Mexico, about one-third of which occur in eastern United States. Considered as a whole, these insects are not very important as forest pests since very few of them are capable of inflicting serious injury to trees. Adults of the family differ considerably in size and appearance, but all are distinguished by the very long discoidal cell in the forewing, and by their common habit of folding their wings longitudinally while at rest. Some of the more common species live in nests or colonies containing a few to several hundreds or thousands of individuals. Bohart (87) published a synoptic catalog of species occurring in America north of Mexico.

Social species construct nests out of papery material consisting of wood or foliage chewed up and elaborated by the insect. Hornet nests contain several to many tiers of hexagonal cells enclosed in a papery envelope and are usually attached to the limbs of bushes or trees or to the eaves of buildings. They are roughly spherical in shape and are often quite large, measuring several inches in diameter. Yellow jackets also construct nests of papery material, but these are usually placed out of sight in the ground, in stumps, or under objects. An exit hole leads to the outside. Wasp nests usually consist of a single horizontal comb or layer of cells attached to a support by a slender stalk. They may be found in all sorts of places such as under the eaves of roofs, under porches, in open sheds, and on bushes, shrubs, and trees. The adults of all members of the family feed commonly on nectar, ripe fruits, sap, and honeydew. The larvae feed on other insects provided by the adults.

The **giant hornet,** *Vespa crabro germana* (Christ), an introduced species, has been recorded from Quebec and Massachusetts to South Carolina. According to reports, hollow trees, hollow posts, sheds, barns, porches, and even attics are preferred as nesting sites. These nests occasionally become very large, reaching a length of 3 feet and a diameter of 20 inches. There are many reports of damage to trees and shrubs by the adults (*643*). They may girdle small twigs, and they gnaw holes in the bark of larger branches, possibly in search of nest-building materials and possibly in search of sap. Injuries have been reported to lilac, birch, ash, and horsechestnut. The adult possesses a long sting and a large poison sac. It is probably capable of inflicting painful stings, but does not appear to be as likely to attack when disturbed as is the bald-faced hornet.

The **bald-faced hornet,** *Vespula maculata* (Linn.), a well known member of the family, is widely distributed in the United States and Canada. Adults are 12 to 19 mm. long and largely black, with white or yellow markings on the face and thorax, and with the posterior third of the abdomen white. It commonly attaches its nests to the limbs of trees or bushes, also occasionally to the walls and windows of houses. These nests may reach a diameter of 15 inches and contain up to five thousand hornets each. Bald-faced

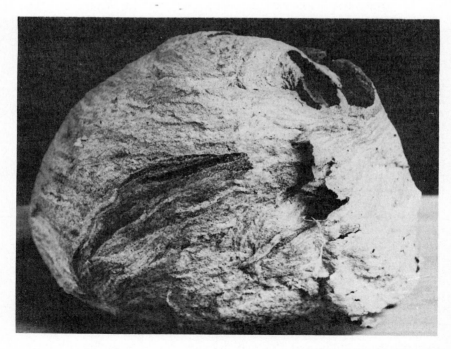

FIGURE 203.—Nest of the yellow jacket, *Vespula arenaria arenaria.*

hornets attack at once when their nests are disturbed and are capable of inflicting extremely painful stings.

Vespula arenaria arenaria (Fab.) is probably the most common species of yellow jacket in eastern United State.. It also occurs throughout the remainder of the United States, and in Canada, and Alaska north to the Arctic Circle. Adults are black and yellow with black predominating. The legs are yellow with the femora mostly black, and the length is about 12 mm. Nests (fig. 203) are usually built in the ground, with an exit hole leading to the outside. This species also inflicts severe stings and it often attacks in force when its nest is endangered. It is a common species around picnic tables where it is often a nuisance.

The genus *Polistes* Latreille contains the familiar wasps whose nests are so frequently encountered hanging under the eaves of buildings and in various and sundry other places. They differ in appearance from the hornets and yellow jackets in having long and spindle-shaped abdomens. The nest consists of a single comb suspended by a peduncle, and it is not enclosed in an envelope. It is usually rather small, although some may be several inches in diameter. The adults of a number of species collect lepidopterous larvae as food for their young and, where abundant, are apparently capable of exercising a considerable degree of control of their hosts. Like hornets and yellow jackets, these insects are vicious stingers, and their nests should be approached with caution.

FAMILY POMPILIDAE

Members of this family are predacious or parasitic on various species of spiders. The adults are often seen visiting flowers and are noted for their extreme activity and ability to run. Their nests are usually found in the ground, but some consisting of mud cells are constructed under logs or stones and in other protected places such as holes in wood.

SUPERFAMILY SPHECOIDEA

All members of this superfamily are predacious on other insects. The majority of species nest in burrows in the soil; the remainder build nests of clay, mud, or sand, or in the stems of plants or various kinds of cavities in which they store paralyzed prey which serves as food for their progeny. Host preferences are varied, including spiders and most of the more common orders of insects. Adults generally can be recognized by the structure of the pronotum which does not extend back to the tegulae, by their unjointed trochanters, by the absence of dilation in the hind tarsus, and by the simple pubescence of the head and thorax.

FAMILY AMPULICIDAE

This family is represented in North America by only two genera and three species. As far as known, they nest in twigs, under bark, and under litter on the ground. Their prey consists of immature cockroaches.

FAMILY SPHECIDAE

This family is represented by 86 genera and scores of species in the United States and Canada. The majority are solitary nest-building wasps which provision their nests with other insects or spiders. Many species nest in the ground; some construct nests of mud and attach them to the ceilings or walls of buildings or to the lower surfaces of other objects; others construct their nests in the stems of plants. Adults are distinguished by the presence of an anal lobe and several closed cells in the hindwing, the presence of seven exposed tergites on the abdomen of the male, the failure of the hypopygium to enclose the sting in the female, and the lack of dilation of the hind tarsus. In a few species, such as the familiar dirt-daubers, the petiole of the abdomen is greatly lengthened.

The **cicada killer,** *Sphecius speciosus* (Drury), which provisions its nest with adult cicadas, is the most conspicuous member of the family. The adult female is a large, black or yellow wasp up to 37 mm. long. There are prominent black and yellow bands or spots on the abdomen and the ovipositor or stinger is long and curved. Adults are usually present from midsummer to early fall and they burrow into the ground for nesting purposes. The female paralyzes a cicada by stinging it and then carts it to her nest, stores it in a cell, and deposits an egg between its legs. When the larva hatches it feeds on the cicada. There is one generation per year.

Cerceris fumipennis Say provisions its nests with a wide variety of wood-boring buprestids. Species of the genus *Psen* Latrielle prey on various membracids, cereopids, and leafhoppers. *Crossocerus ambiguus* (Dahl) preys on various species of tree-infesting cicadellids (*184*); *Stictia carolina* (Fab.) is frequently seen hovering over livestock in search of horseflies.

FAMILY DRYINIDAE

This is a small family of rare insects. As far as known, all species are parasitic on the nymphs of Homoptera, especially the membracids, cicadellids, flatids, and cercopids. The females of certain species are wingless and antlike. Also, in most species they differ so much in appearance from the males that the two sexes can be associated only by rearing them.

During the larval stages, these insects are internal parasites of the abdomen of their hosts. Usually one or more external gall-like cysts develop on the integument of the host. These cysts which may be as large as the abdomen of the host, contain the parasite larvae. *Aphelopus theliae* Gahan, a parasite of the membracid, *Thelia bimaculata,* which feeds on young black locust, lays a single egg in a nymph of its host. Polyembronic development takes place and from 50 to 75 parasites are produced in the nymph. When they reach maturity, they bore through the body wall and drop to the ground to pupate (*278*).

SUPERFAMILY APOIDEA

BEES

It has been estimated that more than 2,500 species of bees occur in North America, many of which, such as the honeybee and bumble bee, are so common as to require no description. Fortunately, none of these insects are particularly injurious to forest or shade trees. On the contrary, as a group they are highly beneficial because of the prominent role so many of them play in the pollination of flowers. While the majority of species provision their nests with pollen and honey, a few lay their eggs in the cells of other bees where their young live as inquilines or parasites and feed on food stored by their hosts. Members of the superfamily are distinguished by the following characteristics: the pronotum does not extend back to the tegulae; the trochanter is single-jointed; the hind tarsi are dialated or thickened; and the head and thorax are covered with feathery hairs.

FAMILY MEGACHILIDAE

LEAF-CUTTING BEES

Leaf-cutting bees are small to medium and black, blue, brown, gray, metallic, or purplish. Some are marked with yellow. They build their nests in rotten wood, in holes in solid wood, and in the hollow stems of plants, and they line the walls of their cavities with circular or oval-shaped pieces of leaves cut from various species of plants. A few species have been recorded damaging shade trees and ornamentals in various parts of the country; otherwise, the group is non-injurious.

FAMILY APIDAE

BUMBLE, CARPENTER, AND HONEY BEES

The family Apidae is represented by more than a thousand species in the United States and Canada. It has been divided into three subfamilies—Anthrophorinae, Xylocopinae, and Apinae.

The subfamily Anthrophorinae contains the so-called mining or digger bees and the cuckoo bees. A number of species collect pollen and nest in the ground. Certain others, such as the cuckoo bees, are parasitic in the nests of other bees. The adults are usually wasp-like in appearance. Members of the subfamily Xylocopinae construct their nests in wood or plant stems and are commonly known as carpenter bees. The genus *Xylocopa* Latreille contains the carpenter bees. The adults look like bumble bees but differ in having the dorsum of the abdomen largely bare. They nest in solid wood. The subfamily Apinae contains the well-known bumble bees and honey bees.

Considered as a whole, members of the family are far more beneficial than harmful. Many species are highly efficient plant pollinators, and the importance of the honey-producing honeybee is too well-known for discussion. The only destructive members of the family are the carpenter bees, several species of which attack and damage wood in use.

The **carpenter bee**, *Xylocopa virginica virginica* (=*virginica*) (Linnaeus), is an important pest because of its habit of tunneling into the solid wood of beams, rafters, telephone poles, or structural timbers. This may lead to structural damage, especially when the same piece of timber is attacked for several years. Dead but sound wood of cypress, cedar, white and hard pines, and California redwood that has been softened by weathering, seems to be preferred. The adult, which is about 25 mm. long, bores a hole about 9 mm. in diameter straight into the wood for a short distance, then makes a right angle turn and follows the grain of the wood for a distance of 6 to 8 inches. Sometimes two bees use a common entrance hole. When this happens the tunnel is extended in opposite directions from the entrance hole. Eggs are deposited singly in separate chambers in the tunnel, each of which is largely provisioned with pollen. Each larva lives and feeds in its chamber until mature. Adults feed on pollen during daylight hours. Females spend the night in their burrows, and males, under boards or in other protected places. Winter is spent as young adults in their tunnels. There is one generation per year.

Living bees in tunnels can be killed by running a stiff wire all the way to the end of the tunnel.

Two other species of carpenter bees, *Xylocopa virginica texana* Cresson and *X. micans* Lepeletier, also occur in eastern United States. The former is found from Maine to Michigan and south to Florida and the Gulf of Mexico. The latter occurs from North Carolina to Florida and westward along the Gulf Coast.

INSECTS AND TREE DISEASES

Insects are involved in or are directly responsible for the transmission of many serious diseases of forest and shade trees in eastern United States. Some of these diseases, such as Dutch elm disease and elm phloem necrosis, are among the most destructive tree diseases known. The majority are caused by various species of fungi. One is of virus origin. A few, such as Dutch elm disease and elm phloem necrosis, attack living, healthy trees and kill them quickly. Many stain the sapwood of coniferous trees, usually of felled timber. They also occur occasionally in living trees weakened by environmental conditions and hasten their death. Others cause the decay of sapwood or heartwood of dead, dying, and felled conifers.

Fungus diseases are transmited by insects through the direct transfer of spores from infected to healthy trees or wood. The bodies of insects emerging from diseased material become contaminated with the spores and when the insect attacks healthy material spores are rubbed into the wounds. Wind-borne spores also gain entry into healthy trees through insect-produced wounds. Viruses, such as the one responsible for elm phloem necrosis, are most often transmitted by species of sucking insects.

Dutch elm disease.—This disease is caused by the introduced fungus, *Ceratocystis ulmi* (Buisman) C. Moreau. It was first recorded in North America in Ohio in 1930. Three years later it was found in the New York City area. It is now known to occur on the east coast from New England south to the Carolinas, Alabama, and Mississippi and west to the Rocky Mountains (*763*). Its hosts are listed as both native and exotic species of elm, American elm especially. Its principal insect vectors are the smaller European elm bark beetle and the native elm bark beetle (*150*). Root grafting may also account for local tree-to-tree spread, particularly among closely spaced street trees.

The first symptoms of Dutch elm disease are the wilting and yellowing or drying of the foliage. This is followed immediately by defoliation and death of the affected branches. Diseased trees commonly die within a single growing season, but some may die gradually, branch by branch, over a period of several years. Diseased trees develop a brown discoloration in the water-conducting vessels in the wood. In early spring, this occurs as brown streaks in the wood just under the bark of diseased branches (fig. 204). Later in the growing season, it appears as brown spots or as a partial or complete brown circle in one or more outer rings of the wood.

Dutch elm disease is one of the most destructive tree diseases known. It kills both wild and planted elms but is best known as a killer of valuable shade tree elms. Since its discovery, it has killed too many of these trees to count. Currently, the value of trees killed and the cost of their removal is estimated at $100 million each year. A considerable amount of research has been devoted to the control of the bark beetles responsible for its spread (*763*).

F-519563

FIGURE 204.—Cross-section of an elm branch affected with Dutch elm disease, showing brownish discoloration in outer ring of sapwood.

Elm phloem necrosis.—This is a virus disease of American and winged elms (*702*). It occurs in the Midwest in an area bounded by latitudes 30° and 40° North, and by longitudes 80° and 100° West. The virus is transmitted by the white-banded elm leafhopper, or through root grafts of trees growing close together. The insect sucks up the virus while feeding on the sap of a diseased tree. Later, the virus is transmitted when the insect feeds on a healthy tree. This leafhopper is widely distributed in eastern United States.

Foliar symptoms of elm phloem necrosis vary but are somewhat similar to those produced by drought, girdling, and certain other tree diseases. Symptoms may first appear on a single branch or a portion of the top; usually, there is a gradual decline of the tree. In large trees, there is usually a slight scarcity of foliage in the top or at the outer tips of branches. This is followed by a scarcity of foliage throughout the crown. The leaves turn yellowish-green, then yellow, and some on the lower suckers become dry and brown. Defoliation follows soon thereafter, and the tree dies. This occasionally happens within 3 to 4 weeks but it usually requires a year or a year and a half. Before the tree dies, a typical discoloration of the phloem develops. In large trees this discoloration is usually found only in large roots and the lower part of the trunk. In most small trees, and occasionally in large ones, it may be found in the upper part of the trunk and occasionally in branches. The discoloration (fig. 205) is at first yellow. Later, it turns to "butterscotch" and often contains scattered dark flecks. Still later, the phloem becomes brown and necrotic. Moderately discolored phloem has a faint odor of wintergreen, a

F-520108
FIGURE 205.—Typical discoloration of the phloem of an elm tree infected with elm phloem necrosis.

F-519951
FIGURE 206.—Shade tree elms killed by phloem necrosis virus.

500

distinguishing characteristic of the disease. Death follows the dying of the roots.

Elm phloem necrosis is an extremely destructive disease. During epiphytotics such as occurred in the Central States in the late thirties and forties, it has killed enormous numbers of valuable shade tree elms in many cities and towns (fig. 206). More recently, however, it has been at a low ebb.

Beech bark disease.—A destructive disease of American and European beeches and all their varieties is caused by the fungus, *Nectria coccinea* var. *faginata* Lohman, Watson, and Ayres. The pathogen gains entry into the tree through tiny ruptures in the bark caused by the feeding of the beech scale. The scale, and probably the fungus, is of foreign origin. The disease, which was first recorded at Halifax, Nova Scotia in 1920, now occurs throughout the Maritime Provinces of Canada and south through the beech-growing areas of New England to Central New York and eastern Pennsylvania.

The fungus may infect large areas on scale-infested trees, completely girdling and killing them. Trees only partially girdled may remain alive in a weakened state for many years, or they may be broken by the wind. On some trees, the fungus may be confined to strips or spots on the bole where it produces cankers. Parts of the crowns of these trees become chlorotic and die.

The beech bark disease is destructive. In many stands it has killed more than half the beech, and the commercial value of many of the survivors has probably been seriously reduced. Shigo (*646*) discussed possible methods of control.

Oak wilt.—This disease is caused by the fungus, *Ceratocystis fagacearum* (Bretz). It occurs over a wide area, from Nebraska and Kansas to the Carolinas and Pennsylvania, and, as far as known, attacks all native species of oak regardless of size, age, or vigor. The fungus spreads from infected trees to adjacent healthy trees through natural root grafts, and there is considerable evidence that insects are responsible for spread over longer distances: fungus spores have been recovered from the bodies of several species of insects after they fed on fungal mats, and some of these are known to feed on sap at fresh wounds on healthy trees (*116, 170, 314*).

Oak wilt is potentially a very serious disease (fig. 207). Given the proper conditions for an epiphytotic, it could cause heavy losses in the vast oak forests of eastern United States. It has already caused considerable damage in many oak woodlots and forest stands in Wisconsin, Minnesota, and Iowa. Methods of control are discussed by Fowler (*260*).

Persimmon wilt.—This fast-killing disease of common persimmon, *Diospyros virginiana* L. in the Southeastern States, is caused by the fungus, *Cephalosporium diospyri* Crandall, which produces masses of spores beneath the bark of infected trees. In smooth-barked trees the spores occur in such large masses that the overlying bark is raised in the form of blisters. When these blisters break, the spores are released and then blown away by the wind. In rough-barked trees the spores are produced in the cambium region and are released when the bark begins to disintegrate or is removed or broken off.

Wind is undoubtedly the major agent of spore dissemination, but some spread is also probably effected by insects such as the bostrichid, *Xylobiops basilaris* (Say). The adults of this species, some of which attack healthy trees, become contaminated when they emerge through spore masses on dying trees. Feeding injuries on the terminals and twigs by adults of the twig girdler, also serve as entry courts for wind-borne spores (*172*).

Blue stains.—In 1928, it was suggested that blue-staining fungi were probably introduced into pines by bark beetles and that they played important roles in the killing of trees (*166*). This was later confirmed (*564*). Blue-staining occurs mostly in felled timber but also may be found in beetle-infested trees weakened by fire, drought, and other adverse factors.

Ceratocystis minor (Hedgc.) Hunt one of the most important of the blue-staining fungi in eastern United States, is introduced into pine trees by the southern pine beetle. It does not cause decay but stains the wood which may greatly reduce its market value. In living trees, it also interferes with transpiration, and the trees die from the top downward.

Ceratocystis ips (Rumbold) C. Moreau is introduced into southern pines by the engraver beetles, *Ips calligraphus* and *I. grandicollis,* and it produces a stain that spreads inward from the beetle galleries toward the heartwood (fig. 208). This fungus has also been found in living and felled red pines in the Lake States attacked by *I. pini* and *I. grandicollis* (*450*).

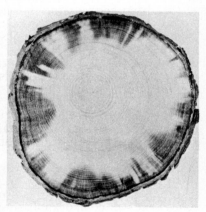

FIGURE 208.—Cross-section of bole of shortleaf pine killed by *Ips calligraphus,* showing development of blue-stain fungus, *Ceratostomella ips,* in sapwood.

F-519913
FIGURE 207.—Oak tree killed by the oak wilt fungus, *Ceratocystis fagacearum.*

Rumbold (*626*) discussed the interrelationships of bark beetles and blue-staining fungi. Bramble and Holst (*95*) discussed the fungi associated with the southern pine beetle in killing short-leaf pines. Nelson (*563*) reported the effect of blue-staining fungi on southern pines attacked by bark beetles.

Several species of ambrosia beetles carry staining fungi on their bodies and, since they attack hardwood logs and lumber in large numbers, are considered to be important stain disseminators (*733*).

LITERATURE CITED

1. Abrahamson, L. P., and Norris, D. M.
    1966. Symbiotic interrelationships between microbes and ambrosia beetles. I. The organs of microbial transport and perpetuation of *Xyloterinus politus*. Entomol. Soc. Amer. Ann. 59 (5) : 877–880, illus.
2. Aldrich, R. C., Bailey, W. F, and Heller, R. C.
    1959. Large scale 70 mm. photography techniques and equipment and their application to a forest sampling problem Photogram. Eng., Dec., p. 743–754, illus.
3. ———, Heller, R. C., and Bailey, W. F.
    1958. Observation limits for aerial sketch-mapping southern pine beetle damage in the southern appalachians. J. Forest. 56 (3) : 200–202, illus.
4. Alexander, R. D.
    1957. The taxonomy of the field crickets of the eastern United States (Orthoptera: Grylldae: Acheta). Entomol. Soc. Amer. Ann. 59 (6) : 584–602, illus.
5. Amman, G. D.
    1962. Seasonal biology of the balsam wooly aphid on Mt. Mitchell, North Carolina. J. Econ. Entomol. 55 (1) : 96–98, illus.
6. ———
    1966. *Aphidecta obliterata* (Coleoptera: Coccinellidae), an introduced predator of the balsam woolly aphid, *Chermes piceae* (Homoptera: Chermi, dae), established in North Carolina. J. Econ. Entomol. 59 (3) : 506–508.
7. ——— and Speers, C. F.
    1964. Release of predators of the balsam woolly aphid in North Carolina. U.S. Forest Serv. Southeast. Forest Exp. Sta. Res. Note SE-32, 4 p.
8. Anderson, L. D., and Papp, C. S.
    1961. The larger elm leaf beetle, *Monocesta coryli* (Say) (Coleoptera: Chrysomelidae). Entomol. Soc. Wash. Proc. 63 (3) : 203–207, illus.
9. Anderson, R. F.
    1964. Forest and shade tree entomology. 428 p., illus. New York: John Wiley & Sons.

10. Anderson, W. H.
    1952. Larvae of some genera of Cossoninae (Coleoptera: Curculionidae). Entomol. Soc. Amer. Ann. 45(2): 281–309, illus.
11. Atwood, C. E.
    1961. Present status of the sawfly family Diprionidae (Hymenoptera) in Canada. Entomol. Soc. Ont. Proc. 1960, 91: 205–215.
12. ———— and Peck, O.
    1943. Some native sawflies of the genus *Neodiprion* attacking pines in eastern Canada. Can. J. Res. 21 (Sec. D): 109–144, illus.
13. Baerg, W. J.
    1947. The biology of the maple leaf scale. Ark. Agr. Exp. Sta. Bull. 470, 14 p., illus
14. ————
    1959. The black widow spider and five other venomous spiders in the United States. Ark. Agr. Exp. Sta. Bull. 608, 43 p., illus.
15. ————
    1961. Scorpions: biology and effect of their venom. Ark. Agr. Exp. Sta. Bull. 649, 34 p., illus.
16. Bailey, J. W
    1928. The Chilopoda of New York State with notes on the Diplopoda. N.Y. State Mus. Bull. 276: 5–50, illus.
17. Bailey, S. F.
    1940. The distribution of injurious thrips in the United States. J. Econ. Entomol. 33(1): 133–136, illus.
18. Baker, E. W., and Wharton, G. H.
    1952. An introduction to Acarology. 465 p. New York: The MacMillan Co.
19. Baker, J. M.
    1963. Ambrosia beetles and their fungi, with particular reference to *Platypus cylindrus* Fab. Symbiotic Assocs. Soc. Gen. Microbiol. 13th Symp., p. 232–265, illus. Cambridge University Press.
20. Baker, W. L.
    1941. Effect of gypsy moth defoliation on certain forest trees. J. Forest. 39(12): 1017–1022, illus.
21. ————
    1948. Transmission by leafhoppers of the virus causing phloem necrosis of American elm. Science 108: 307–308.
22. ————
    1949. Studies on the transmission of the virus causing phloem necrosis of American elm, with notes on the biology of its insect vector. J. Econ. Entomol. 42(5): 729–732.
23. Balch, R. E.
    1946. The spruce budworm and forest management in the Maritime Provinces. Can. Dep. Agr. Entomol. Div. Processed Pub. 60.

24. ——
    1952. Studies of the balsam woolly aphid, *Adelges piceae* (Ratz.) and its effects on balsam fir, *Abies balsamea* (L.) Mill. Can. Dep. Agr. Pub. 867, 76 p., illus.

25. ——
    1960. The approach to biological control in forest entomology. Can. Entomol. 92 (4) : 297–310.

26. —— and Bird, F. T.
    1944. A disease of the European spruce sawfly, *Gilpinia hercyniae* (Htg.) and its place in natural control. Sci. Agr. 25 (2) : 65–80.

27. ——, Clark, R. C., and Brown, N. R.
    1958. *Adelges piceae* (Ratz.) in Canada with reference to biological control. Tenth Int. Cong. Entomol. Montreal, Proc. 1956, 4 : 807–817.

28. ——, and Mitchell, R. G.
    1967. Balsam woolly aphid, *Adelges* (=*Dreyfusia, Chermes*) *piceae* (Ratz.). *In* Important Forest Insects and diseases of mutual concern to Canada, the United States and Mexico. A. G. Davidson and R. M. Prentice (ed). Can. Dep. Forest. and Rural Develop. Pub. 1180, p. 71–74, illus.

29. ——, Webb, F. E., and Fettes, J. J.
    1955–56. The use of aircraft in forest insect control. Forest. Abstr. 16 (4) and 17 (1 and 2), 31 p.

30. Balduf, W. V.
    Gory, in New Brunswick. Can. Entomol. 89 (1) :
    1928. Observations on the buffalo tree hopper, *Ceresa bubalus* Fabr. (Membracidae: Homoptera), and the bionomics of an egg parasite, *Polynema straticorne* Girault (Mymaridae, Hymenoptera). Entomol. Soc. Amer. Ann. 21 : 419–435, illus.

31. Banks, N., and Snyder, T. E.
    1920. A revision of the nearctic termites (Banks) with notes on biology and geographic distribution (Snyder). U.S. Nat. Mus. Bull. 108, 228 p., illus.

32. Baranowski, R. M.
    1958. Notes on the biology of the royal palm bug, *Xylastodoris luteolus* Barber (Hemiptera, Thaumastocoridae). Entomol. Soc. Amer. Ann. 51 (6) : 547–551, illus.

33. Barnes, W., and McDunnough, J.
    1918. Life histories of the North American species of the genus *Catocala*. Amer. Mus. Nat. Hist. 38 : 147–177, illus.

34. Barter, G. W.
    1957. Studies of the bronze birch borer, *Agrilus anxius* 12–36, illus.

35. ——
    1965. Survival and development of the bronze poplar borer, *Agrilus liragus* Barter and Brown (Coleoptera: Buprestidae). Can. Entomol. 97 (10) : 1063–1068, illus.

36. Barras, S. J., Clower, D. F., and Merrifield, R. G.
    1967. Control of the Nantucket pine tip moth on loblolly pine with systemic insecticides in Louisiana. J. Econ. Entomol. 60(1): 185–190, illus.
37. Batra, L. R.
    1963. Ecology of ambrosia fungi and their dissemination by beetles. Kans. Acad. Sci. Transl. 66(2): 213–236, illus.
38. Beal, J. A.
    1932. Controls of the turpentine borer in the naval stores region. U.S. Dep. Agr. Circ. No. 226, 19 p., illus.
39. ──────
    1933. Temperature extremes as a factor in the ecology of the southern pine beetle. J. Forest. 31(3): 329–336.
40. ──────, Haliburton, W., and Knight, F. B.
    1952. Forest insects of the Southeast: with special reference to species occurring in the Piedmont Plateau of North Carolina. Duke Univ., Sch. of Forest. Bull. 14, 168 p., illus.
41. ──────, and Massey, C. L.
    1945. Bark beetles and ambrosia beetles (Coleoptera: Scolytidae): with special reference to species occurring in North Carolina. Duke Univ., Sch. of Forest., Bull. 10, 178 p., illus.
42. ──────, and McClintick, K. B.
    1943. The pales weevil in southern pines. J. Econ. Entomol. 36(5): 792–794.
43. Beal, R. H.
    1967. Formosan invader. Pest Contr. Mag. 35(2): 13–17, illus.
44. Bean, J. L.
    1956. Red pine scale. U.S. Forest Service, Forest Pest Leafl. 10, 4 p., illus.
45. ──────, and Batzer, H. O.
    1956. A spruce budworm risk-rating for the spruce-fir types in the Lake States. U.S. Forest Service, Lake States Forest Exp. Sta., Tech. Note 453.
46. ──────, and Godwin, P. A.
    1955. Description and bionomics of a new red pine scale, *Matsucoccus resinosae*. Forest Sci. 1(2): 164–176, illus.
47. ──────, and Waters, W. E.
    1961. Spruce budworm in Eastern United States. U.S. Forest Service Forest Pest Leafl. 58, 8 p., illus.
48. Becker, G. C., Jr., and Benjamin, D. M.
    1964. Biology of the Swaine jack-pine sawfly in Wisconsin. Can. Entomol. 96(4): 589–599, illus.
49. ──────, and Benjamin, D. M.
    1967. The biology of *Neodiprion nigroscutum* (Hymenoptera: Diprionidae) in Wisconsin. Can. Entomol. 99(2): 146–159, illus.
50. Becker, W. B.
    1938. Leaf-feeding insects of shade trees. Mass. Agr. Exp. Sta. Bull. 353, p. 1–78.

51. Beckwith, R. C.
    1963. An oak leaf tier, *Croesia semipurpurpana* (Lepidoptera: Tortricidae) in Connecticut. Entomol. Soc. Amer. Ann. 56(6): 741–744, illus.
52. Bedard, W. D.
    1938. Control of the mountain pine beetle by means of chemicals. J. Forest. 36(1): 35–40, illus.
53. Behre, C. E., Cline, A. C., and Baker, W. L.
    1936. Silvicultural control of the gypsy moth. Mass Forest and Park Assn. Bull. 157, 16 p., illus.
54. Bellinger, P. F.
    1954. Studies of soil fauna with special reference to the Collembola. Conn. Agr. Exp. Sta. Bull. 583, 67 p., illus.
55. Belyea, R. M.
    1952. Death and deterioration of balsam fir weakened by spruce budworm defoliation in Ontario. Part II. An assessment of the role of associated insect species in the death of severely weakened trees. J. Forest. 50(10): 729–738, illus.
56. ———, and Sullivan, C. R.
    1956. The white pine weevil: A review of current knowledge. Forest. Chron. 32(1): 58–67.
57. Benedict, W. V.
    1959. Every Forester has a stake in forest insect spraying. J. Forest. 57(4): 245–249, illus.
58. Benjamin, D. M.
    1955. The biology and ecology of the red-headed pine sawfly. U.S. Dep. Agr. Tech. Bull. 1118, 57 p., illus.
59. Bennett, W. H
    1958. The Texas leaf-cutting ant. U.S. Forest Serv. Forest Pest Leafl. 23, 4 p., illus., (Rev. 1967).
60. ———
    1966. Pupal morphology of *Exoteleia chillicotti* Freeman (Lepidoptera, Gelechiidae). Entomol. Soc. Wash. Proc. 68(3): 181–183, illus.
61. Bergold, C. H.
    1953. On the nomenclature and classification of insect viruses. N.Y. Acad. Sci. Ann. 56: 495–516.
62. Berry, P. A.
    1938. *Tetrastichus brevistigma* Gahan, a pupal parasite of the elm leaf beetle. U.S. Dep. Agr. Circ. 485, 12 p., illus.
63. Bess, H. A.
    1961. Population ecology of the gypsy moth, *Porthetria dispar* L. (Lepidoptera: Lymantridae). Conn. Agr. Exp. Sta. Bull. 646, 43 p., illus.
64. ———, Spurr, S. H., and Littlefield, E. W.
    1947. Forest site conditions and the gypsy moth. Harvard Forest Bull. 22, 56 p., illus.
65. Billings, S. C.
    1965. Consolidated list of approved common names of insecticides and certain other pesticides. Entomol. Soc. Amer. Bull. 11(3): 204–213.

66. Bird, F. T.
    1953. The use of a virus disease in the biological control of the European pine sawfly, *Neodiprion sertifer* (Geoff.). Can. Entomol. 85: 437–446, illus.

67. ———
    1955. Virus diseases of sawflies. Can. Entomol. 87: 124–127.

68. Bishop, F. C.
    1923. The puss caterpillar and the effects of its sting on man. U.S. Dep. Agr. Circ. 288, 14 p., illus.

69. Blackman, M. W.
    1919. Notes on forest insects. II. Notes on several species of *Pityophthorus* breeding in the limbs and twigs of white pine. Psyche 26(5): 134–142, illus.

70. ———
    1922. Mississippi bark beetles. Miss. Agr. Exp. Sta. Tech. Bull. 11, 130 p., illus.

71. ———
    1928. The genus *Pityophthorus* Eichh. in North America. N.Y. State Coll. Forest., Syracuse Univ. Tech. Pub. 25, 159 p., illus.

72. ———
    1931a. Revisional study of the genus *Pseudopityophthorus* Swaine in North America. Wash. Acad. Sci. J. 21: 223–236, illus.

73. ———
    1931b. Revisional study of the genus *Gnathotrichus* Eichh. in North America. Wash. Acad. Sci. J. 21: 264–276, illus.

74. ———
    1934. A revisional study of the genus *Scolytus* Geoffroy *Eccoptogaster* Herbst) in North America. U.S. Dep. Agr. Tech. Bull. 431, 30 p.

75. ———
    1938. The genus *Chramesus* LeConte in North America (Coleoptera: Scolytidae). Wash. Acad. Sci. J. 28: 534–545, illus.

76. ———
    1941. Bark beetles of the genus *Hylastes* Erichson in North America. U.S. Dep. Agr. Misc. Bull. 417.

77. ———
    1942. Revision of the genus *Phloesinus* Chapuis in North America (Coleoptera, Scolytidae). U.S. Nat. Mus. Proc. 92(3154): 397–474, illus.

78. ———
    1943. New genera and species of bark beetles of the sub-family Micracinae. U.S. Nat. Mus. Proc. 93: 341–365, illus.

79. Blais, J. R.
    1960. Spruce budworm parasite investigations in the lower St. Lawrence and Gaspe regions of Quebec. Can. Entomol. 92(5): 384–396.

80. ———
    1965. Parasite studies in two residual spruce budworm (*Choristoneura fumiferana* (Clem.)) outbreaks in Quebec. Can. Entomol. 97(2): 129–136.

81. Blatchley, W. S.
1910. An illustrated descriptive catalog of the Coleoptera, or beetles (exclusive of the Rhynchophora), known to occur in Indiana. 2 vol., 1385 p., illus., Indianapolis: Nature Pub. Co.

82. ———
1920. Orthoptera of Northeastern America. 784 p., Indianapolis: The Nature Pub. Co.

83. ———
1926. Heteroptera, or true bugs of eastern North America, with especial reference to the faunas of Indiana and Florida. 1116 p., illus., Indianapolis: The Nature Pub. Co.

84. ———, and Leng, C. W.
1916. Rhynchophora or weevils of northeastern North America. 682 p., illus., Indianapolis: The Nature Pub. Co.

85. Blickenstaff, C. C., chairman, Comm. Common Names of Insects.
1965. Common names of insects—Approved by the Entomological Society of America. Entomol. Soc. Amer. Bull. 11(4): 287–320.

86. Bobb, M. L.
1965. Insect parasite and predator studies in a declining sawfly population. J. Econ. Entomol. 58(5): 925–926.

87. Bohart, R. M.
1951. Family Vespidae. In Hymenoptera of America North of Mexico. U.S. Dep. Agr., Agr. Monogr. No. 2: 875–907.

88. Bongberg, J. W.
1958. Forest Insect Surveys in the United States. Tenth Int. Cong. Entomol. Proc. 1956, 4: 193–199.

89. Borkovec, A. B.
1962. Sexual sterilization of insects by chemicals. Sci. 137: 1034–1037.

90. Borror, D. J., and DeLong, D. M.
1960. An introduction to the study of insects. 1030 p., illus. New York: Holt, Rinehart and Winston.

91. Boving, A. G., and Champlain, A. B.
1921. Larvae of North American beetles of the family Cleridae. U.S. Nat. Mus. Proc. 57: 575–649, illus.

92. ———, and Craighead, F. C.
1930–31. An illustrated synopsis of the principal larval forms of the order Coleoptera. Entomol. Amer. (n.s.) 11: 1–349, illus.

93. Bracken, D. F.
1961. The external morphology of two eastern species of the genus Anoplonyx (Hymenoptera: Tenthredinidae), with special reference to Anoplonyx luteipes (Cresson). Can. Entomol. 93(7): 573–593, illus.

94. Bradley, J. C.
1930. A manual of the genera of beetles of America north of Mexico. 360 p. Ithaca, N.Y.

95. Bramble, W. C., and Holst, E. C.
    1940. Fungi associated with *Dendroctonus frontalis* in killing shortleaf pines and their effect on conduction. Phytopathology 30: 881–99.
96. Braun, A. F.
    1917. Nepticulidae of North America. Amer. Entomol. Soc. Trans. 43(2): 155–209.
97. ———
    1963. The genus *Bucculatrix* in America north of Mexico (Microlepidoptera). Amer. Entomol. Soc. Mem. No. 18, 208 p.
98. Brezner, Jr.
    1960. Biology, ecology, and taxonomy of insects infesting acorns. Mo. Agr. Exp. Sta. Res. Bull. 726, 40 p., illus.
99. Bright, D. E., Jr.
    1963. Bark beetles of the genus *Dryocoetes* (Coleoptera, Scolytidae) in North America. Entomol. Soc. Amer. Ann. 56(1): 103–115, illus.
100. ———
    1968. Review of the tribe Xyleborini in America north of Mexico (Coleoptera: Scolytidae). Can. Entomol. 100(12): 1288–1323, illus.
101. Brimley, C. S.
    1938. The insects of North Carolina. N. C. State Dep. Agr., Div. of Entomol., Raleigh, 560 p.
102. Britton, W. E.
    1913. The apple-tree tent caterpillar. Conn. Agr. Exp. Sta. Bull. 177, 19 p., illus.
103. ———
    1923. Guide to the insects of Connecticut. Part IV. The Hemiptera or sucking insects of Connecticut. Conn. Geol. and Nat. Hist. Surv. Bull. 34, 807 p.
104. Brooks, F. E.
    1926. Life history of the hickory spiral borer, *Agrilus arcuatus* Say. J. Agr. Res. 33(4): 331–338, illus.
105. ———, and Cotton, R. T.
    1924. The cambium curculio, *Conotrachelus anaglypticus* Say. J. Agr. Res. 28: 377–386, illus.
106. ———
    1929. The chestnut curculios. U. S. Dep. Agr. Tech. Bull. 130, 23 p., illus.
107. Brower, A. E.
    1940. The arborvitae leaf miners (Yponomeutidae and Gelechiidae). Soc. Amer. Forest., New Engl. Sect., Tree Pest Leafl. No. 46, 4 p., illus.
108. Brown, A.W.A.
    1940. A note on the gross estimate of forest insect damage in Canada. 71st Ann. Rep. Entomol Soc. Ontario, p. 52.
109. ———
    1951. Insect control by chemicals. New York: John Wiley & Sons, Inc., 817 p.
110. ———
    1962. Effects of insecticides on wildlife. Conservationist (N.Y.) 17(3): 8–11, 40.

111 Brown, C. E.
    1962. The life history and dispersal of the Bruce span-
        worm *Operophtera bruceata* (Hulst.) (Lepidop-
        tera: Geometridae). Can. Entomol. 94(10):
        1103-1107, illus.

112. Brown, N. R., and Clark, R. C.
    1959. Studies of predators of the balsam woolly aphid,
        Adelges piceae (Ratz.) (Homoptera:Adelgidae).
        VI. *Aphidecta obliterata* (L.) (Coleoptera: Coc-
        cinellidae), an introduced predator in eastern
        Canada. Can. Entomol. 91(9): 596-599.

113. ———
    1962. Studies of predators of the balsam wooly aphid,
        Adelges piceae (Ratz.) (Homoptera:Adelgidae).
        X. Field identification of *Laricobius erichsonii*
        Rosen (Coleoptera: Derodontidae). Can. Ento-
        mol. 94(2): 191-193, illus.

114. Brues, C. T., Melander, A. L., and Carpenter, F. M.
    1954. Classification of insects: keys to the living and
        extinct families of insects and to the living fami-
        lies of other terrestrial arthropods. Mus. Comp.
        Zool., Harvard Univ. Bull. 108: 1-917, illus.

115. Buchanan, W. D.
    1941. Experiments with an ambrosia beetle, *Xylosandrus
        germanus* (Blfd.). J. Econ. Entomol. 34(3):
        367-369.

116. ———
    1958. The small oak bark beetle transmits the oak wilt
        disease. J. Forest. 56(6): 414-415, illus.

117. ———
    1960. Biology of the oak timberworm *Arrhenodes minutus*.
        J. Econ. Entomol. 53(4): 510-513, illus.

118. Buckner, C. H.
    1966. The role of vertebrate predators in the biological con-
        trol of forest insects. Ann. Rev. of Entomol. 11:
        449-470, illus.

119. Burdick, D. J.
    1961. A taxonomic and biological study of the genus *Xyela*
        Dalman in North America. Univ. Calif. Pub. in
        Entomol. 17(3): 285-356, illus.

120. Burgess, A. F.
    1921. The satin moth—an introduced enemy of poplars
        willows. U.S. Dep. Agr. Circ. 167, 16 p., illus.

121. ———, and Baker, W. L.
    1938. The gypsy and brown-tail moths and their control.
        U.S. Dep. Agr. Circ. 464, 38 p., illus.

122. ———, and Collins, C. W.
    1915. The Calosoma beetle (*Calosoma sycophanta*) in New
        England. U.S. Dep. Agr. Bull. No. 251, 40 p., illus.

123. ———, and Crossman, S. S.
    1927. The satin moth, a recently introduced pest. U.S. Dep.
        Agr., Dep. Bull. 1469, 23 p., illus.

124. ———
    1929. Imported insect enemies of the gypsy moth and the
        brown-tail moth. U.S. Dep. Agr. Tech. Bull. 86,
        148 p., illus.

125. Burks, B. D.
    1943. The North American parasitic wasps of the genus *Tetrastichus*—a contribution to biological control of insect pests. U.S. Nat. Mus. Proc. 93(3170): 508–608.
126. Burns, D. P., and Gibson, L. P.
    1968. The leaf-mining weevil of yellow-poplar. Can. Entomol. 100(4): 421–429, illus.
127. Busck, A.
    1915. The European pine-shoot moth: A serious menace to pine timber in America. U. S. Dep. Agr. Bull. 170, 11 p., illus.
128. Bushing, R. W.
    1965. A synoptic list of the parasites of Scolytidae (Coleoptera) in North America north of Mexico. Can. Entomol. 97(5): 449–492.
129. Bushland, R. C.
    1960. Male sterilization for the control of insects. pp. 1–25. (ed.) Metcalf, R. L. *In* Advances in Pest Control Research, v. III, Interscience Pub(s), Inc., New York, London.
130. ———, and Hopkins, D. E.
    1951. Experiments with screw-worm flies sterilized by X-rays. J. Econ. Entomol 44(5): 725–731.
131. ———
    1953. Sterilization of screw-worm flies with x-rays and gamma rays. J. Econ. Entomol. 46(4): 648–656.
132. Butcher, J. W. and Hodson, A. C.
    1949. Biological and ecological studies on some lepidopterous bud and shoot insects of jack pine (Lepidoptera-Olethreutidae). Canad. Ent. 81(7): 161–173, illus.
133. Campbell, R. W.
    1967. The analysis of numerical change in gypsy moth populations. Forest Sci. Monog. 15, 33 p., illus.
134. Capps, H. W.
    1964. Description of a new species of *Euzophora* Zeller attacking magnolias and note on two related species (Lepidoptera, Phycitidae). Fla. Entomol. 47(1): 49–52, illus.
135. Carolin, V. M., Klein, W. H., and Thompson, R. M.
    1962. Eradicating European pine shoot moths on ornamental pines with methyl bromide. U. S. Dep. Agr., Forest Serv., Pacific Northwest Forest and Range Exp. Sta. Res. Pap. 47, 16 p., illus.
136. Carroll, W. J., and Waters, W. E.
    1967. Eastern hemlock looper (*Lambdina fiscellaria fiscellaria* (Guen.). p. 120–122, illus., *In* Davidson and Prentice (eds.), Important forest insects and diseases of mutual concern to Canada, the United States, and Mexico. Dept. Forest. and Rural Develop. Can., Pub. 1180.

137. Chapman, J. W.
    1910. The introduction of a European scolytid (the smaller elm bark-beetle, *Scolytus multistriatus* Marsh) into Massachusetts. Psyche 17: 63–68, illus.

138. Christian, M. B.
    1939. Experiments on the prevention of ambrosia beetle damage in hardwoods. S. Lumberman 159: 110–112, illus.

139. ———
    1940–41. Biology of the powder-post beetles, *Lyctus planicollis* Leconte and *Lyctus parallelo-pipedus* (Melsh.). Part I. La. Conserv. Rev. 9(4): 56–59, illus.; 10(1): 40–42.

140. Ciesla, W. M.
    1964. The feeding preference for hardwoods by elm spanworm in the southern Appalachian Mountains. J. Econ. Entomol. 57(4): 604.

141. ———
    1965. Observations on the life history of *Telenomus alsophilae,* an egg parasite of the elm spanworm. *Ennomos subsignarius.* J. Econ. Entomol. 58(4): 702–704, illus.

142. ———, Bell, J. C. Jr., and Curlin, J. W.
    1967. Color photographs and the southern pine beetle. Photogram. Eng. 33(8): 883–888, illus.

143. Clausen, C. P.
    1956. Biological control of insect pests in the continental United States, U.S. Dep. Agr. Tech. Bull. 1139, 151 p.

144. ———
    1962. Entomophagous insects. McGraw-Hill Book Co., Inc. 688 p.

145. Cole, M. M., Clark, P. H., and Smith, C. N.
    1960. Toxicants for body lice control. Soap and Chemical Specialties (May, 1960), 5 p., illus.

146. Collier, C. W., and Downey, J. E.
    1967. Laboratory and field evaluations of chemosterilants for the gypsy moth in 1964, 1965. J. Econ. Entomol. 60(1): 265–268.

147. Collins, C. W.
    1915. Dispersion of gypsy-moth larvae by the wind. U.S. Dep. Agr. Bull. No. 273, 23 p., illus.

148. ———
    1926. Observations on a recurring outbreak of *Heterocampa guttivitta* Walker and natural enemies controlling it. J. Agr. Res. 32(7): 689–699.

149. ———
    1933. The oriental moth (*Cnidocampa flavescens* Walk.) and its control. U.S. Dep. Agr. Circ. 277, 8 p., illus.

150. Collins, C. W., Buchanan, W. D., Whitten, R. R., and Hoffman, C. H.
    1936. Bark beetles and other possible vectors of the Dutch elm disease, *Ceratostomella ulmi* (Schwarz) Buisman. J. Econ. Entomol. 29: 167–176.

151. Collins, C. W., and Potts, S. F.
    1932. Attractants for the flying gypsy moths as an aid in locating new infestations. U.S. Dep. Agr. Tech. Bull. 336, 43 p., illus.
152. Comstock, J. H.
    1947. An introduction to entomology. Ed. 9, revised, 1064 p., illus. Ithaca, N. Y.: Comstock Pub. Co., Inc.
153. ——, and Gertsch, W. J.
    1940. The spider book. 729 p., illus. New York: Doubleday & Co., Inc.
154. Condrashoff, S. F.
    1964. Bionomics of the aspen leaf miner, *Phyllocnistis populiella* Cham. (Lepidoptera: Gracillariidae). Can. Entomol. 96(6): 857–874, illus.
155. Connell, W. A.
    1956. Nitidulidae of Delaware. Del. Agr. Exp. Sta. Bull. 318 (Tech.): 67 p. illus.
156. ——, and Beacher, J. H.
    1947. Life history and control of the oak lacebug. Del. Agr. Exp. Sta. Bull. 265, Tech No. 37, 28 p., illus.
157. Connola, D. P., Waters, W. E., and Nason, E. R.
    1959. A sequential sampling plan for red- pine sawfly, *Neopridon nanulus* Schedl. J. Econ. Entomol. 52(4): 600–602.
158. ——, Waters, W. E., and Smith, W. E.
    1957. The development and application of a sequential sampling plan for forest tent caterpillars in New York. N. Y. State Mus. & Sci. Serv. Bull. No. 366, 22 p., illus.
159. ——, and Wixson, E. C.
    1963. White pine weevil attack in relation to soils and other environmental factors in New York. N. Y. State Mus. & Sci. Serv. Bull. No. 389, 80 p., illus.
160. Coppel, H. C., and Benjamin, D. M.
    1965. Bionomics of the nearctic pine-feeding Diprionids. Ann. Rev. Entomol. 10: 69–96.
161. ——, Casida, J. E., and Dauterman, W. C.
    1960. Evidence for a potent sex attractant in the introduced pine sawfly, *Diprion similis* (Hymenoptera: Diprionidae). Entomol. Soc. Amer. Ann. 53(4): 510–512, illus.
162. Coyne, J. F.
    1959. *Neodiprion taedae linearis,* a sawfly pest of loblolly and shortleaf pines. U.S. Forest Serv., Forest Pest Leafl. 34 (Rev. 1968), 4 p., illus.
163. ——
    1968. *Laspeyresia ingens,* a seedworm infesting cones of longleaf pine. Entomol. Soc. Amer. Ann. 61(5): 1116–1122, illus.
164. Craighead, F. C.
    1915. Contributions toward a classification and biology of the North American Cerambycidae. Larvae of the Prioninae. U.S. Dep. Agr. Sect. Rep. 107, 24 p., illus.

165. ———
1923. North American Cerambycid larvae. A classification and the biology of North American Cerambycid larvae. Can. Dept. Agr. Entomol. Br. Bull. 27, 238 p., illus.

166. ———
1928. Interrelation of tree-killing bark beetles (*Dendroctonus*) and blue stains. J. Forest. 26(7): 886–887.

167. ———
1950. Insect Enemies of Eastern Forests. U.S. Dep. Agr., Misc. Pub. 657, 679 p., illus.

168. ———, and Hofer, G.
1921. Protection of mesquite cordwood and posts from borers. U.S. Dep. Agr. Farmers' Bull. 1197, 12 p., illus.

169. ———, and Miller, J. M.
1949. Insects in the forest: A survey. U.S. Dept. Agr. Yearbook "Trees," pp. 407–413.

170. ———, and Morris, C. L.
1952. A progress report: possible importance of insects in transmission of oak wilt. Pa. Forests and Waters, Nov.-Dec. 1952, p. 1–6, illus.

171. ———, and St. George, R. A.
1938. Experimental work with the introduction of chemicals into the sap stream of trees for the control of insects. J. Forest. 36(1): 26–34.

172. Crandall, B. S., and Baker, W. L.
1950. The wilt disease of American persimmon, caused by *Cephalosporium diospyri*. Phytopathology 40(4): 307–325, illus.

173. Creighton, J. T.
1937. *Homaledra sabalella* Chambers, the major pest of palms in Florida. J. Econ. Entomol. 30(4): 590–595.

174. Creighton, W. S.
1950. The ants of North America. Harvard Univ., Bull. of the Mus. of Comp. Zoo., Vol. 104, 585 p., illus.

175. Crossman, S. S.
1925. Two imported egg parasites of the gypsy moth, *Anastatus bifasciatus* Fonsc. and *Schedius kuvanae* Howard. J. Agr. Res. 30: 643–675, illus.

176. Crumb, S. E.
1956. The larvae of the Philaenidae. U.S. Dep. Agr. Tech. Bull. 1135, 356 p., illus.

177. Culver, J. J.
1919. A study of *Compsilura concinnata,* an imported tachinid parasite of the gipsy moth and the brown-tail moth. U.S. Dep. Agr. Bull. 766, 27 p., illus.

178. Cuming, F. G.
1961. The distribution, life history, and economic importance of the winter moth, *Operophtera brumata* (L.) (Lepidoptera, Geometridae) in Nova Scotia. Can. Entomol. 93(2): 135–142, illus.

179. Cumming, M. E. P.
    1959. The biology of *Adelges cooleyi* (Gill.) (Homoptera: Phylloxeridae). Can. Entomol. 91(10): 601–617, illus.
180. ———
    1968. The life history and morphology of *Adelges lariciatus* (Homoptera: Phylloxeridae). Can. Entomol. 100(2): 113–126, illus.
181. Curran, C. H.
    1934. The families and genera of North American Diptera. 512 p., illus. New York: J. D. Sherman, Jr.
182. Daviault, L.
    1956. The red pine web-spinning sawfly, *Cephalcia marginata* Middlekauff (Hymenoptera, Pamphiliidae). Can. Entomol. 88(8): 488–492, illus.
183. ———, and Ducharme, R.
    1966. Life history and habits of the green spruce leaf miner, *Epinotia nanana* (Treitschke) (Lepidoptera, Tortricidae). Can. Entomol. 98(7): 693–699, illus.
184. Davidson, R. H., and Landis, B. J.
    1938. *Crabro davidsoni* Sandh., a wasp predaceous on adult leafhoppers. Entomol. Soc. Amer. Ann. 32: 5–8, illus.
185. Davis, D. R.
    1964., Bagworm moths of the Western Hemisphere (Lepidoptera: Psychidae). U.S. Nat. Mus. Bull. 244, 233 p., illus.
186. Dean, G. A.
    1946. The elm *Calligrapha* (*Calligrapha scalaris* LeC.) Kans. State Coll. Agr. Exp. Sta. Circ. 234, 7 p., illus.
187. DeBach, P. (ed.)
    1964. Biological Control of Insect Pests and Weeds. 844 p., illus. New York: Reinhold Publishing Corp.
188. DeBarr, G. L.
    1967. Two new sucking insect pests of seed in southern pine seed orchards. U.S. Forest Serv. Res. Note SE-78, 3 p., illus.
189. DeLong, D. M.
    1948. The leafhoppers, or Cicadellidae, of Illinois (Eurymelinae-Balcluthinae). Ill. Nat. Hist. Surv. Bull. 24 (Art. 2), 376 p., illus.
190. Denmark, H. A.
    1960. Some observations on the biology of *Anchyloptera platanana* Clemens (Lepidoptera, Olethreutidae) in Florida. Fla. Entomol. 43(2): 81–87, illus.
191. Denton, R. E.
    1958. The larch casebearer in Idaho—a new defoliator record for western forests. U.S. Forest Serv. Intermount. Forest & Range Exp. Sta. Res. Note 51, 6 p., illus.
192. Dietrich, H.
    1945. The Elateridae of New York State. Cornell Univ. Agr. Exp. Sta. Mem. 269, 79 p.

193. Dillon, E. S., and Dillon, L. S.
1961. A manual of common beetles of eastern North America. 884 p., illus. Evanston, Ill.: Row, Peterson & Co.

194. Dixon, J. C., and Osgood, E. A.
1961. Southern pine beetle—a review of present knowledge. U.S. Forest Serv., Southeast. Forest Exp. Sta., Pap. 128, 34 p., illus.

195. Doane, C. C.
1959. *Beauveria bassiana* as a pathogen of *Scolytus multistriatus*. Entomol. Soc. Amer. Ann. 52(1): 109–111.

196. Doane, R. W., Van Dyke, E. C., Chamberlain, W. J., and Burke, H. E.
1936. Forest Insects. 463 p., illus. New York: McGraw-Hill Co., Inc.

197. Dodge, H. R.
1938. The bark beetles of Minnesota (Coleoptera: Scolytidae). Minn. Agr. Exp. Sta. Tech. Bull. 132, 60 p., illus.

198. Donley, D. E.
1964a. Mimosa webworm and its control on individual honeylocusts with systemic insecticides. Arborists' News 29(3): 17–20, illus.

199. ———
1964b. Season-long webworm control for honeylocust. Amer. Nurseryman, June 1, 1964., 2 p., illus.

200. ———, and Burns, D. P.
1965. The tuliptree scale. U.S. Forest Serv. Forest Pest Leafl. 92, 5 p., illus.

201. Dorsey, C. K., and Leach, J. G.
1956. The bionomics of certain insects associated with oak wilt with particular reference to the Nitidulidae. J. Econ. Entomol. 49(2): 219–230, illus.

202. Dowden, P. B.
1935. *Brachymeria intermedia* (Nees), a primary parasite, and *B. compsilurae* (Crawford), a secondary parasite of the gypsy moth. J. Agr. Res. 50(6): 495–523, illus.

203. ———
1939. *Schizonotus sieboldi*, an imporant parasite of the imported willow leaf beetle. J. Agr. Res. 58: 581–592, illus.

204. ———
1941. Parasites of the birch leaf-mining sawfly (*Phyllotoma nemorata*). U.S. Dep. Agr. Tech. Bull. 757, 56 p., illus.

205. ———
1962. Parasites and predators of forest insects liberated in the United States through 1960. U.S. Dep. Agr. Handbook No. 226, 70 p.

206. ———, Buchanan, W. D., and Carolin, V. M.
1948. Natural control factors affecting the spruce budworm. J. Econ. Entomol. 41(3): 457–464.

207. ———, Carolin, V. M., and Dirks, C. O.
    1950. Natural control factors affecting the spruce bud-worm in the Adirondacks during 1946–48. J. Econ. Entomol. 43(6) : 744–783.
208. Drooz, A. T.
    1956. The larch sawfly. U.S. Forest Serv., Forest Pest Leafl. 8 (Rev. 1967), 4 p., illus.
209. ———
    1960a. White-pine shoot borer (*Eucosma gloriola* Heinrich). J. Econ. Entomol. 53(2) : 248–251, illus.
210. ———
    1960b. The larch sawfly—its biology and control. U.S. Dep. Agr. Tech. Bull. No. 1212, 52 p., illus.
211. Duncan, D. R., Hodson, A. C., Schneider, A. E., and others
    1956. Influence of the forest tent caterpillar (*Malacosoma disstria* Hbr.) upon the aspen forests of Minnesota. 45 p., illus., St. Paul, Minn.: Office of Iron Range Resources and Rehabil.
212. Dutky, S. R.
    1940. Two new spore-forming bacteria causing milky diseases of Japanese beetle larvae. J. Agr. Res. 61: 57–68.
213. Dyar, H. G.
    1902. A list of North American Lepidoptera and key to the literature of this order of insects. U.S. Nat. Mus. Bull. No. 52, 723 p.
214. Eaton, C. B., Beal, J. A., Furniss, R. L., and Speers, C. F.
    1949. Airplanes and helicopter spraying with DDT for spruce budworm control. J. Forest. 47(10) : 823–827, illus.
215. ———, and Yuill, J. S.
    1960. Gouty pitch midge. U.S. Forest Serv., Forest Pest Leafl. 46, 8 p., illus.
216. Ebel, B. H.
    1961. Thrips injure slash pine female flowers. J. Forest. 59(5) : 374–375.
217. ———
    1965. The *Dioryctria* coneworms of North Florida pines (Lepidoptera: Phycitidae). Entomol. Soc. Amer. Ann. 58(5) : 623–630, illus.
218. ———
    1966. Rearing and occurrence of Xyelid sawflies on slash and long leaf pines in North Florida (Hymenoptera: Xyelidae). Entomol. Soc. Amer. Ann. 59(1) : 227–229, illus.
219. ———, and Merkel, E. P.
    1967. *Hylobius* weevil larvae attack roots of young slash pines. Forest Sci. 13(1) : 97–99, illus.
220. Eddy, G. W., and Bushland, R. C.
    1946. Control of human lice. U.S. Dep. Agr., Bur. Entomol. and Plant Quar., E-685, 5 p.
221. Edwards, J. G.
    1949. Coleoptera or beetles, east of the Great Plains. San Jose State Col., Dep. of Biol., San Jose, Calif., 181 p., illus.

222. Edwards, W. H.
　　1879–97. The butterflies of North America. 3 Vol. Boston: Houghton Mifflin Co.
223. Ehrlich, J.
　　1934. The beech bark disease, a *Nectria* disease of *Fagus*, following *Cryptococcus fagi* (Baer). Can. J. Res. (Spec. No.) 10: 593–692, illus.
224. Eidt, D. C.
　　1965. The life history of a web-spinning sawfly of spruce, *Cephalcia fascipennis* (Cresson) (Hymenoptera: Pamphiliidae). Can. Entomol. 97(2): 148–153, illus.
225. Ely, C. R.
　　1917. A revision of the North American Gracillariidae from the standpoint of venation. Wash. Entomol. Soc. Proc. 19: 29–77.
226. Embree, D. G.
　　1958. The external morphology of the immature stages of the beech leaf tier, *Psilocorsis faginella* (Chamb.) with notes on its biology in Nova Scotia. Can. Entomol. 90(3): 166–174, illus.
227. ———
　　1965. The population dynamics of the winter moth in Nova Scotia, 1954–62. Entomol. Soc. Can. Mem. 46, 57 p., illus.
228. ———
　　1966. The role of introduced parasites in the control of the winter moth in Nova Scotia. Can. Entomol. 98(11): 1159–1168, illus.
229. Emerson, A. E.
　　1926. Development of soldier termites. Zool. (N.Y. Zool. Soc.), 7(2): 69–100, illus.
230. Engelhardt, G. P.
　　1946. The North American clear-wing moths of the family Aegeriidae. U.S. Nat. Mus. Bull. 190, 222 p., illus.
231. Esenther, G. R., Allen, T. C., Casida, J. E., and Shenefelt, R. D.
　　1961. Termite attractant from fungus-infested wood. Science 134 (3471): 50.
232. Essig, E. O.
　　1942. College Entomology. 900 p., illus. New York: The Macmillan Co.
233. Ewan, H. G.
　　1957. Jack-pine sawfly. U.S. Forest Serv., Forest Pest Leafl. 17, 4 p., illus.
234. ———
　　1960. The poplar borer in relation to aspen stocking. Lake States Forest Exp. Sta. Tech. Note No. 580, illus.
235. ———
　　1961. The Saratoga spittlebug. U.S. Dep. Agr. Tech. Bull. 1250, 52 p., illus.
236. Ewing, H. E.
　　1929. A manual of external parasites. 225 p. Springfield, Ill.: C. C. Thomas, Publ.

237. Fattig, P. W.
      1947. Cerambycidae or long-horned beetles of Georgia. Emory Univ. Mus. Bull. 5, 48 p.
238. Fedde, G. F.
      1963. Elm spanworm. U.S. Forest Serv., Forest Pest Leafl. 81, 7 p., illus.
239. Felt, E. P.
      1904. Monograph of the genus *Saperda*. N.Y. State Mus. Bull. 74, 86 p., illus.
240. ———
      1905–06. Insects affecting park and woodland trees. N.Y. State Mus. Mem. 8, vol. 1: 1–322; vol. 2: 333–887.
241. ———
      1925. Key to gall midges. N.Y. State Mus. Bull. 257, 239 p., illus.
242. Fenton, F. A.
      1942. The flatheaded apple tree borer (*Chrysobothris femorata* (Olivier)). Okla. Agr. Exp. Sta. Bull. No. B-259, 31 p., illus.
243. Ferris, G. F.
      1951. The sucking lice. Pacific Coast Entomol. Soc. Mem., Vol. 1, 320 p., illus.
244. Finnegan, R. J.
      1958. The pine weevil, *Pissodes approximatus* Hopk. in southern Ontario. Can. Entomol. 90(6): 348–354, illus.
245. ———
      1959. The pales weevil, *Hylobius pales* (Herbst.) in southern Ontario. Can. Entomol. 91(10): 664–670, illus.
246. ———
      1962. The pine root-collar weevil, *Hylobius radicis* Buch. in southern Ontario. Can. Entomol. 94(1): 11–17, illus.
247. ———
      1963. The storage of ambrosia fungus spores by the pitted ambrosia beetle, *Corthylus punctatissimus* Zimm. (Coleoptera: Scolytidae). Can. Entomol. 95(2): 137–139, illus.
248. ———
      1965. The pine needle miner, *Exoteleia pinifoliella* (Chamb.) (Lepidoptera: Gelechiidae) in Quebec. Can. Entomol. 97(7): 744–750, illus.
249. ———
      1967. Notes on the biology of the pitted ambrosia beetle, *Corthylus punctatissimus* (Coleoptera: Scolytidae) in Ontario and Quebec. Can. Entomol. 99(1): 49–54, illus.
250. ———, and Godwin, P. A.
      1967. Northern pine weevil, *Pissodes approximatus* Hopk. p. 145–147, illus., *In* Davidson and Prentice (eds.), Important forest insects and diseases of mutual concern to Canada, the United States, and Mexico. Dept. Forest. and Rural Develop. Can., Pub. 1180.

251. ————, and Stewart, K. E.
  1962. Control of the pine root collar weevil, *Hylobius radicis*. J. Econ. Entomol. 55(4): 483–486.
252. Fisher, R. C., Thompson, G. H., and Webb, W. E.
  1953–54. Ambrosia beetles in forest and sawmill, their biology, economic importance, and control. Forest. Abstr. 14(4): 381–389 and 15(1): 3–5.
253. Fisher, W. S.
  1942. A revision of the North American species of Buprestid beetles belonging to the tribe Chrysobothrini. U.S. Dep. Agr. Misc. Pub. No. 470, 271 p., illus.
254. ————
  1950. A revision of the North American species of beetles belonging to the family Bostrichidae. U.S. Dep. Agr. Misc. Pub. No. 698, 155 p.
255. Fleming, W. E.
  1963. The Japanese beetle in the United States. U.S. Dep-Agr., Handbook No. 236, 30 p., illus.
256. Foote, R. H.
  1965. Family Cecidomyiidae. P. 241–295, *in* Stone, A., Sabrosky, C. W., Wirth, W. W., and others. A catalog of the Diptera of America north of Mexico. U.S. Dep. Agr. Handbook No. 276.
257. Forbes, R. S., and Daviault, L.
  1964. The biology of the mountain-ash sawfly, *Pristiphora geniculata* (Htg.) (Hymenoptera: Tenthredinidae) in eastern Canada. Can. Entomol. 96(8): 1117–1133, illus.
258. Forbes, W. T. M.
  1923. The Lepidoptera of New York and neighboring states. N.Y. (Cornell) Agr. Exp. Sta. Mem. 68, 729 p., illus.
259. Forbush, E. H., and Fernald, C. H.
  1896. The gypsy moth, *Porthetria dispar* Linn. 495 p., illus. Boston: State Board of Agr.
260. Fowler, M. E.
  1958. Oak wilt. U.S. Forest Serv., Forest Pest Leafl. 29, 5 p., illus.
261. Fox, I.
  1940. Fleas of eastern United States. 191 p., illus. Ames Iowa: Iowa State Col. Press.
262. Fracker, S. B.
  1915. The classification of lepidopterous larvae, with ten plates. Ill. Biol. Monog. 2(1): 1–169, illus.
263. Francke-Grossmann, H.
  1963. Some new aspects in forest entomology. Ann. Rev. Entomology 8: 415–438.
264. Franklin, R. T., and Lund, H. O.
  1956. The Buprestidae (Coleoptera) of Georgia. Ga. Agr. Exp. Sta. Tech. Bull. (n.s.) 3, 48 p., illus.
265. Freeman, T. N.
  1953 The spruce budworm, *Choristoneura fumiferana* (Clem.) and an allied new species on pine (Lepidoptera, Tortricidae). Can. Entomol. 85(4): 121–127, illus.

266. ———
1958. The Archipinae of North America (Lepidoptera, Tortricidae). Can. Entomol. Suppl. 7, 89 p., illus.

267. ———
1960. Needle-mining Lepidoptera of pine in North America. Can. Entomol. Suppl. 16, 51 p., illus.

268. ———
1967a. Annotated keys to some nearctic leaf-mining Lepidoptera on conifers. Can. Entomol. 99 (4) : 419–435, illus.

269. ———
1967b. On coniferophageous species of *Choristoneura* (Lepidoptera: Tortricidae) in North America. I. Some new forms of *Choristoneura* allied to *C. fumiferana*. Can. Entomol. 99 (5) : 449–455, illus.

270. Frick, K. E.
1959. Synopsis of the species of the agromyzid leaf miners described from North America. U.S. Nat. Mus. Proc. 108: 347–465, illus.

271. Friend, R. B.
1933. The birch leaf-mining sawfly, *Fenusa pumilla* Klug. Conn. Agr. Exp. Sta. Bull. 348: 291–364, illus.

272. ———, and Carlson, A. B.
1937. The control of carpenter ants in telephone poles. Conn. Agr. Exp. Sta. Bull. 403, 912–929, illus.

273. ———, and West, A. S.
1933. The European pine shoot moth (*Rhyacionia buoliana* Schiff.) with special reference to its occurrence in the Eli Whitney Forest. Yale Univ., Sch. of Forest. Bull. 37: 1–65, illus.

274. Froeschner, R. C.
1954. The grasshoppers and other Orthoptera of Iowa. Iowa State Col., J. Sci. 29 (2) : 163–354, illus.

275. Fulton, B. B.
1915. The tree crickets of New York: life history and bionomics. N.Y. Agr. Exp. Sta. Tech. Bull. 42, 47 p., illus.

276. Funkhouser, W. D.
1923. Family Membracidae. P. 163–206, illus. *In* Hemiptera or sucking insects of Connecticut. Part IV. Conn. Geol. and Nat. Hist. Surv. Bull. 34.

277. Furniss, R. L., and Every, R. W.
1957 Carpenter ant control. Ore. State Coll. Ext. Circ. 627, illus.

278. Gahan, A. B.
1918. An interesting new hymenopterous parasite. Can. Entomol. 50: 151–52.

279. Gardiner, L. M.
1960. Descriptions of immature forms and biology of *Xylotrechus colonus* (Fab.) (Coleoptera: Cerambycidae). Can. Entomol. 92 (11) : 820–825, illus.

280. Garman, H.
1916. The locust borer (*Cyllene robiniae*) and other insect enemies of the black locust. Kentucky Agr. Exp. Sta, State Univ. Bull. 290, 135 p., illus.

281. Garman, P.
1940. Tetranychidae of Connecticut. Conn. Agr. Exp. Sta. Bull. 431: 67–88, illus.

282. Gates-Clark, J. F.
1941. Revision of the North American moths of the family Oecophoridae, with descriptions of new genera and species. U.S. Nat. Mus. Proc. 90 (3107): 33–286, illus.

283. Genung, W. J.
1959. Notes on the Syntomid moth, *Lymire edwardsii* (Grote) and its control as a pest of *Ficus* in south Florida. Fla. Entomol. 42 (1): 39–42.

284. George, J. L., and Mitchell, R. T.
1948. Calculations on the extent of spruce budworm control by insectivorous birds. J. Forest. 46: 454–455.

285. Gerberg, E. J.
1957. A revision of the new world species of powder-post beetles belonging to the family Lyctidae. U.S. Dep. Agr. Tech. Bull. 1157, 69 p., illus.

286. Gerhold, Henry D., Schreiner, E. J., McDermott, R. E., and Winieski, J. A. (editors)
1966. Breeding pest-resistant trees. Oxford, Pergamon Press, 505 pp., illus.

287. Gibbons, C. F., and Butcher, J. W.
1961. The oak skeletonizer, *Bucculatrix ainsliella,* in a Michigan wood lot. J. Econ. Entomol. 54 (4): 681–684, illus.

288. Gibson, L. P.
1964. Biology and life history of acorn-infesting weevils of the genus *Conotrachelus* (Coleoptera: Curculionidae). Entomol. Soc. Amer. Ann. 57 (5): 521–526.

289. ———
1965. Systematics of acorn-infesting weevils, *Conotrachelus naso, C. carinifer,* and *C. posticatus* (Coleoptera: Curculionidae). Entomol. Soc. Amer. Ann. 58 (5): 705–712, illus.

290. ———
1969. Monograph of the genus *Curculio* in the new world (Coleoptera: Curculionidae). Part I. U.S. and Can. Entomol. Soc. Amer. Misc. Pub. 6 (5): 241–285.

291. Giese, R. L.
1966. The bioecology of *Corthylus columbianus* Hopk. Purdue Univ. Agr. Expt. Sta. J. Pap. No. 2597, 8 p., illus. (Presented at Internationales Symposium Berlin-Dahlem (1965) Uber Holz und Organismen. Material und Organismen. Beiheft 1: 361–370).

292. ──────
1967. The Columbian timber beetle, *Corthylus columbianus* (Coleoptera: Scolytidae). V. A description of the mycetangia. Can. Entomol. 99(1): 54–58, illus.

293. ──────, and Benjamin, D. M.
1959. The biology and ecology of the balsam gall midge in Wisconsin. Forest Sci. 5(2): 193–208, illus.

294. ──────
1964. Studies of maple blight. Part II. The insect complex associated with maple blight. Univ. Wisc. Res. Bull. 250, p. 21–58, illus.

295. Gill, J. B.
1917. The pecan leaf case-bearer. U.S. Dep. Agr. Bull. 571, 28 p., illus.

296. Gillette, C. F., and Palmer, M. A.
1931. Aphidae of Colorado. Part I. Entomol. Soc. Amer. Ann 24: 827–934, illus., 1931.

297. ──────
1932. Aphidae of Colorado. Part II. Etomol. Soc. Amer. Ann. 25: 369–496, illus., 1932.

298. ──────
1934. Aphidae of Colorado. Part III. Entomol. Soc. Amer. Ann. 27: 133–255, illus., 1934.

299. Girth, H. B., and McCoy, E. E.
1946. *Neodiprion sertifer,* a sawfly injurious to pines in New Jersey, and parasite work for its control. N.J. Dep. Agr. Circ. No. 363: 18 p., illus.

300. Godwin, P. A., Rule, H. D., and Waters, W. E.
1964. Some effects of gamma irradiation on the gypsy moth, *Porthetria dispar.* J. Econ. Entomol. 57(6): 986–990.

301. Gorham, J. R.
1961. Aquatic insects and DDT forest spraying in Maine. Me. Forest Serv. Bull. 19, 49 p., illus.

302. Graham, K.
1963. Concepts of forest entomology. 388 p., illus. New York: Reinhold Publishing Corp.

303. Graham, S. A.
1926. The biology and control of the white pine weevil, *Pissodes strobi* Peck. Cornell Univ. Agr. Exp. Sta. Bull. 449, 32 p., illus.

304. ──────
1937. The walking stick as a forest defoliator. Mich. Univ. Sch. of Forest, and Conserv. Circ. 3, 28 p., illus.

305. ──────
1939. Principles of forest entomology. Ed. 2, 410 p. New York and London: McGraw-Hill Book Co., Inc.

306. ──────
1956a. Hazard rating of stands containing balsam fir according to expected injury by spruce budworm. Mich. Univ. Dept. of Forest., Mich. Forest. 13, 2 p.

307. ———
1956b. The larch sawfly in the Lake States. Forest Sci. 2(2): 132–160, illus.
308. ———, and Baumhofer, L. G.
1927. The pine tip moth in the Nebraska National Forest. J. Agr. Res. 35: 323–333, illus.
309. ———, and Knight, F. B.
1965. Principles of Forest Entomology. Ed. 4, 417 p., illus. New York: McGraw-Hill Book Co.
310. ———, and Orr, L. W.
1940. The spruce budworm in Minnesota. Minn. Agr. Expt. Sta. Tech. Bul. 142, 27 pp., illus.
311. Gray, I. E.
1946. Observations on the life history of the horned *passalus*. Amer. Midland Nat. 35(3): 728–746, illus.
312. Green, H. B.
1952. Biology and control of the imported fire ant in Mississippi. J. Econ. Entomol. 45(4): 593–597.
313. Greenbank, D. O.
1956. The role of climate and dispersal in the initiation of outbreaks of the spruce budworm in New Brunswick. I. The role of climate. Can. J. Zool. 34: 453–476, illus.
314. Griswold, C. L.
1956. Transmission of the oak wilt fungus by *Pseudopityophthorus minutissimus* (Zimm.). J. Econ. Entomol. 49(4): 560–561.
315. ———
1958. Transmission of the oak wilt fungus by certain woodland-inhabiting Drosophilidae. J. Econ. Entomol. 51(5): 733–735.
316. Gurney, A. B.
1951. Praying mantids of the United States, native and introduced. Smithsn. Inst. Ann. Rep. 1949/50: 339–362.
317. Haliburton, W.
1951. On the habits of the elm borer, *Physocnemum brevilineum* (Say); (Coleoptera: Cerambycidae). Can. Entomol. 83(2): 36–38.
318. Hall, R. C.
1942. Control of the locust borer. U.S. Dep. Agr. Circ. 626, 19 p., illus.
319. Hamilton, C. C.
1948. The pin oak sawfly. The Shade Tree 21(9): 4.
320. Hanson, J. B., and Benjamin, D. M.
1967. Biology of *Phytobia setosa,* a cambium miner of sugar maple. J. Econ. Entomol. 60(5): 1351–1355, illus.
321. Harman, D. M., and Kulman, H. M.
1967. An Annotated List—Parasites and Predators of the white pine weevil, *Pissodes strobi* (Peck). Md. Univ., Nat. Resources Inst. Contrib. 323, 35 p.

322. Hartzell, A.
　　1957. Red pine scale with special reference to its host plants and cold hardiness. Boyce Thompson Inst. Contrib. 18: 421–428, illus.
323. Haseman, L.
　　1940. The walnut caterpillar. Mo. Agr. Expt. Sta. Bull. 418, 14 p., illus.
324. ———, and McLane, S. R.
　　1940. The history and biology of the juniper midge (*Contarinia juniperina* Felt). Amer. Entomol. Soc. Ann. 33(4): 612–615, illus.
325. Hay, C. J.
　　1958. Life history and control of a root collar borer (*Euzophera ostricolorella* Hulst) in yellow-poplar. J. Econ. Entomol. 51(2): 251–252.
326. ———
　　1962. Reduce red oak borer damage silviculturally. U.S. Forest Serv., Central States Forest Exp. Sta., Sta. Note 154.
327. ———, and Morris, R. C.
　　1961. Carpenterworm. U.S. Forest Serv. Forest Pest Leafl. 64, 8 p., illus.
328. Haynes, D. L., and Butcher, J. W.
　　1962. Studies on the ecology of European pine shoot moth larvae in Michigan. Ecology 43(1): 96–107, illus.
329. Hebard, M.
　　1931. The Orthoptera of Kansas. Acad. Nat. Sci. Phila. Proc. 83: 119–227.
330. ———
　　1932. The Orthoptera of Minnesota. Minn. Agr. Exp. Sta. Tech. Bull. 85, 61 p.
331. ———
　　1934. The Dermaptera and Orthoptera of Illinois. Ill. Nat. Hist. Surv. Bull. 20: 125–279, illus.
332. ———
　　1936. Orthoptera of North Dakota. N. Dak. Agr. Exp. Sta. Tech. Bull. 284, 69 p.
333. Heimpel, A. M.
　　1967. A critical review of *Bacillus thurigiensis* var. *thurigiensis* Berliner and other crystalliferous bacteria. Ann. Rev. Entomol. 12, p. 287–322.
334. ———, and Angus, T. A.
　　1963. Diseases caused by certain spore-forming bacteria, p. 21–73, illus., *in* E. A. Steinhaus (ed.). Insect Pathology, An Advanced Treatise, Vol. 2. New York: Academic Press.
335. Heinrich, C.
　　1923. Revision of the North American moths of the subfamily Eucosminiae of the family Olethreutidae. U.S. Nat. Mus. Bull. 123, 298 p., illus.
336. ———
　　1956. American moths of the subfamily Phycitinae. U.S. Nat. Mus. Bull. 207, 581 p., illus.

337. Heinrichs, E. A., and Thompson, H. E.
    1968. The biology of *Choristoneura houstonana* (Lepidoptera: Tortricidae), a pest of Juniperus species. Can. Entomol. 100(7): 750–763, illus.
338. Heller, R. C., Aldrich, R. C., and Bailey, W. F.
    1959. An evaluation of aerial photography for detecting southern pine beetle damage. Photogram. Eng., Sept. 1959, p. 595–600, illus.
339. ————, R. C., Bean, J. L., and Marsh, J. W.
    1952. Aerial survey of spruce budworm damage in Maine in 1950. J. Forest. 50: 8–11, illus.
340. ————, Lowe, J. H., Aldrich, R. C., and Weber, F. P.
    1967. A test with large scale aerial photographs to sample balsam woolly aphid damage in the northeast. J. Forest. 65(1): 10–18, illus.
341. ————, and Schmiege, D. C.
    1962. Aerial survey techniques for the spruce budworm in the Lake States. J. Forest. 60(8): 525–532, illus.
342. Hendee, E. C.
    1934. The association of termites and fungi, p. 105–114, illus. *In* C. A. Kofoid (ed.). Termites and Termite Control. Berkeley, Calif.: Univ. Calif. Press.
343. Herrick, G. W.
    1910. The snow-white linden moth. Cornell Univ. Agr. Exp. Sta. Bull. 286, p. 51–64, illus.
344. Hess, A. D.
    1940. The biology and control of the round-headed apple-tree borer, *Saperda candida* Fabricus. N.Y. State Agr. Exp. Sta. Bull. 688, 93 p., illus.
345. Hetrick, L. A.
    1941. Life history studies of *Neodiprion americanum* (Leach). J. Econ. Entomol. 34(3): 373–380.
346. ————
    1956. Life history studies of five species of *Neodiprion* sawflies. Forest Sci. 1(3): 181–185.
347. ————
    1959. Ecology of the pine sawfly, *Neodiprion excitans* (Rohwer) (Hymenoptera, Diprionidae). Fla. Entomol. 42(4): 159–162.
348. ————
    1960. *Nepytia semiclusaria* (Walker) as a defoliator of pine (Lepidoptera: Geometridae). Fla. Entomol. 43(4): 205–206.
349. ————
    1961. *Kalotermes approximatus* Snyder infests roseaceous trees (Isoptera: Kalotermitidae). Fla. Entomol. 44(1): 53–54.
350. Hickey, J. J.
    1961. Some effects of insecticides on terrestrial wildlife in the middle west. Wilson Bull. 73: 398–424.
351. Highland, H. A.
    1946. The biology of *Ferrisiana virgata*, a pest of azaleas. J. Econ. Entomol. 49(2): 276–277.

352. ————
1964. Life history of *Asphondylia ilicicola* (Diptera, Cecidomyiidae), a pest of American holly. J. Econ. Entomol. 57 (1) : 81–83.
353. Hildahl, V., and Reeks, W. A.
1960. Outbreaks of the forest tent caterpillar, *Malacosoma disstria* Hbn., and their effects on stands of trembling aspen in Manitoba and Saskatchewan. Can. Entomol. 92 (3) : 199–209, illus.
354. Hite, J. M., Gladney, W. J., Lancaster, Jr., J. L., and Whitcomb, W. H.
1966. Biology of the brown recluse spider. Ark. Agr. Exp. Sta. Bull. 711, 26 p., illus.
355. Hodson, A. C.
1939. *Sarcophaga aldrichi* Parker as a parasite of *Malacosoma disstria* Hbn. J. Econ. Entomol. 32 (3) : 396–401, illus.
356. ————
1941. An ecological study of the forest tent caterpillar, *Malacosoma disstria* Hbn. in northern Minnesota. Minn. Agr. Exp. Sta. Tech. Bull. 148, 55 p., illus.
357. ————
1942. Biological notes on the basswood leaf-miner, *Baliosus ruber* (Weber). J. Econ. Entomol. 35 (4) : 570–573, illus.
358. ————, and Weinman, C. J.
1945. Factors affecting recovery from diapause and hatching of eggs of the forest tent caterpillar, *Malacosoma disstria* Hbn. Minn. Univ. Agr. Exp. Sta. Tech. Bull. 170, 31 p., illus.
359. ————, and Zehngraff, P. J.
1946. Budworm control in jack pine by forest management. J. Forest. 44 (3) : 198–200.
360. Hoff, C. C.
1949. The pseudoscorpions of Illinois. Ill. Nat. Hist. Surv. Bull. 24 (4) : 419–498, illus.
361. Hoffman, C. H., and Linduska, J. P.
1949. Some considerations of the biological effects of DDT. Sci. Monthly 69 (2) : 104–114, illus.
362. ————, and Merkel, E. P.
1948. Fluctuations in insect populations associated with aerial applications of DDT to forests. J. Econ. Entomol. 41 (3) : 464–473.
363. ————, Townes, H. K., Swift, H. H., and Sailer, R. I.
1949. Field studies on the effects of airplane application of DDT on forest invertebrates. Eco. Monog. 19 (1) : 1–46, illus.
364. Holland, W. J.
1898. The butterfly book. Revised ed. 1931, 424 p., illus. New York: Doubleday & Co., Inc.
365. ————
1903. The moth book. 479 p., illus. New York: Doubleday & Co., Inc.

366. Hood, C. E.
   1949. Life history and control of the imported willow leaf beetle. U.S. Dep. Agr. Circ. 572, 9 p., illus.
367. Hopkins, A. D.
   1899 Report on investigations to determine the cause of unhealthy conditions of the spruce and pine from 1880–1893. W. Va. Agr. Exp. Sta. Bull. 56, 461 p., illus.
368. ———
   1909. Practical information on the Scolytid beetles of North American forests. I. Barkbeetles of the genus *Dendroctonus*. U.S. Bur. Entomol. Bull. 83, 169 p., illus.
369. Hopping, G. R.
   1963a. The natural groups of species of the genus *Ips* DeGeer (Coleoptera: Scolytidae) in North America. Can. Entomol. 95(5): 508–516, illus.
370. ———
   1963b. The North American species in Group I of *Ips* DeGeer (Coleoptera: Scolytidae). Can. Entomol. 95(10): 1091–1096, illus.
371. ———
   1963c. The North American species in Groups II and III of *Ips* DeGeer (Coleoptera: Scolytidae). Can. Entomol. 95(11): 1202–1210, illus.
372. ———
   1964. The North American species in Groups IV and V of *Ips* DeGeer (Coleoptera: Scolytidae). Can. Entomol. 96(7): 970–978, illus.
373. ———
   1965a. The North American species in Group VII of *Ips* DeGeer (Coleoptera: Scolytidae). Can. Entomol. 97(2): 193–198, illus.
374. ———
   1965b. The North American species in Group VIII of *Ips* DeGeer (Coleoptera: Scolytidae). Can. Entomol. 97(2): 159–172, illus.
375. ———
   1965c. The North American species in Group IX of *Ips* DeGeer (Coleoptera: Scolytidae). Can. Entomol. 97(4): 422–434, illus.
376. ———
   1965d. The North American species in Group VI of *Ips* DeGeer (Coleoptera: Scolytidae). Can. Entomol. 97(5): 533–541, illus.
377. ———
   1965e. The North American species in Group X of *Ips* DeGeer (Coleoptera: Scolytidae). Can. Entomol. 97(8): 803–809, illus.
378. Hopping, R.
   1921. A review of the genus *Monochamus* Serv. (Cerambycidae: Coleoptera). Can. Entomol. 53: 252–258, illus.

379. Horsfall, W. R.
    1943. Biology and control of common blister beetles in Arkansas. Ark. Agr. Exp. Sta. Bull. 436, 55 p., illus.
380. Hottes, F. C., and Frison, T. H.
    1931. The plant lice or Aphidae of Illinois. Ill. Nat. Hist. Surv. Bull. 19 (Art. 3), p. 121–447, illus.
381. Houser, J. S.
    1918. Destructive insects affecting Ohio shade and forest trees. Ohio Agr. Exp. Sta. Bull. 332, 486 p.
382. Howard, L. O.
    1897. A study of insect parasitism: A consideration of the white-marked tussock moth, with descriptions of new species. U.S. Dep. Agr., Div. Entomol. Bull. 5 (Tech. Serv.), 57 p., illus.
383. ———
    1899. Three insect enemies of shade trees. U.S. Dep. Agr. Farmers' Bull. 99, 29 p., illus.
384. ———, and Chittenden, F. H.
    1916a. The bagworm, an injurious shade tree insect. U.S. Dep. Agr. Farmers' Bull. 701, 11 p., illus.
385. ———
    1916b. The catalpa sphinx. U.S. Dep. Agr. Farmers' Bull. 705, 9 p., illus.
386. ———
    1916c. The leopard moth: A dangerous imported insect enemy of shade trees. U.S. Dep. Agr. Farmers' Bull. 708, 10 p., illus.
387. ———, and Fiske, W. F.
    1911. The importation into the United States of the parasites of the gypsy moth and the brown-tail moth: A report of progress, with some consideration of previous and concurrent efforts of this kind. U.S. Bur. Entomol. Bull. 91, 344 p., illus.
388. Hubbard, H. G.
    1897. The ambrosia beetles of the United States. U.S. Dep. Agr. Entomol. Bull. (n.s.) 7, p. 9–35, illus.
389. Hughes, K. M.
    1957 An annotated list and bibliography of insects reported to have virus diseases. Hilgardia 26: 597–629.
390. Ignoffo, C. M., and Granovsky, A. A.
    1961. Life history and gall development of *Mordwilkoja vagabunda* (Homoptera: Aphidae) on *Populus deltoides*. Entomol. Soc. Amer. Ann. 54(4): 486–499, illus.
391. Imms, A. D.
    1948. A general textbook of entomology; including the anatomy, physiology, development, and classification of insects. 7th ed., 727 p., illus. New York: E. P. Dutton & Co., Inc.
392. Isler, D. A., and Yuill, J. S.
    1956. Research on the control of forest insects by aircraft. J. Econ. Entomol. 49(1): 92–94.

393. Ives, W. G. H., and Prentice, R. M.
      1958. A sequential sampling technique for surveys of the larch sawfly. Can. Entomol. 90 (6) : 331–338, illus.
394. ———, and Warren, G. L.
      1965. Sequential sampling for white grubs. Canad. Ent. 97 (6) : 596–604, illus.
395. Jacobson, M.
      1965. Insect sex attractants. 154 p., illus. New York, London, Sydney: Interscience Publishers.
396. ———
      1966. Chemical insect attractants and repellents. Ann. Rev. Entomol. 11: 403–422.
397. ———, Beroza, M., and Jones, W. A.
      1960. Isolation, identification, and synthesis of the sex attractant of gypsy moth. Science 132: (3433) 1011–1012.
398. ———
      1961. Insect sex attractants. I. The isolation, identification, and synthesis of the sex attractant of the gypsy moth. J. Amer. Chem. Soc. 83, 4819.
399. ———, and Jones, W. A.
      1962. Insect Sex Attractants. II. Synthesis of a highly potent gypsy moth sex attractant and some related compounds. J. Org. Chem. 27, 2523.
400. Jaynes, H. A., and Drooz, A. T.
      1942. The importance of parasites in the spruce budworm infestations in New York and Maine. J. Econ. Entomol. 45 (6) : 1057–1061.
401. ———, and Godwin, P. A.
      1957. Sterilization of the white-pine weevil with gamma radiation. J. Econ. Entomol. 50 (4).
402. Jensen, D. C.
      1957. Parasites of the Psyllidae. Hilgardia 27 (2) : 71–99.
403. Johnson, P. C.
      1958. Spruce spider mite infestations in northern Rocky Mountain Douglas-fir forests. U.S. Dep. Agr. Intermountain Forest and Range Exp. Sta. Res. Pap. 55, 14 p., illus.
404. Johnston, H. R.
      1952. Insect control—Practical methods for the control of insects attacking green logs and lumber. S. Lumberman, May 15, 1952, 3 p., illus.
405. ———, and Kowal, R. J.
      1949. New insecticides for the prevention of attack by ambrosia beetles on logs and lumber. S. Lumberman, Dec. 15, 1949, 6 p., illus.
406. Jones, F. M., and Parks, H. B.
      1928. The bagworms of Texas. Texas Agr. Exp. Sta. Bull. No. 382, 36 p., illus.
407. Kabir, A. K. M. F., and Giese, R. L.
      1966a. The Columbian timber beetle, *Corthylus columbianus*, (Coleoptera: Scolytidae). I. Biology of

the beetle. Entomol. Soc. Amer. Ann. 59(5): 883–894, illus.

408. ———
1966b. The Columbian timber beetle, *Corthylus columbianus* (Coleoptera: Scolytidae). II. Fungi and staining associated with the beetle in soft maple. Entomol. Soc. Amer. Ann. 59(5): 894–902, illus.

409. Kapler, J. E., and Benjamin, D. M.
1960. The biology and ecology of the red pine sawfly in Wisconsin. Forest Sci. 6(3): 253–268, illus.

410. Kaston, B. J.
1939. The native elm bark beetle, *Hylurgopinus rufipes* (Eichhoff), in Connecticut. Conn. Agr. Exp. Sta. Bull. 420, 39 p., illus.

411. Kearby, W. H., and Benjamin, D. M.
1964. The biology and ecology of the red-pine needle midge and its role in fall browning of red pine foliage. Can. Entomol. 96(10): 1313–1322, illus.

412. Keen, F. P.
1938. Insect enemies of western forests. U.S. Dep. Agr. Misc. Pub. No. 273 (rev. 1952), 280 p., illus.

413. ———
1943. Ponderosa pine tree classes redefined. J. Forest. 41(4): 249–253, illus.

414. Keifer, H. H.
1946. A review of North American economic Eriophyid mites. J. Econ. Entomol. 39(5): 563–570.

415. Kerr, T. W.
1949. The arborvitae weevil, *Phyllobius intrusus* Kono. R. I. Agr. Exp. Sta. Bull. 305, 30 p., illus.

416. Kilgore, W. W., and Doutt, R. L. (editors)
1967 Pest control; biological, physical, and selected chemical methods. New York and London, Academic Press, 477 pp.

417. King, W. V., Bradley, G. H., and McNeel, T. E.
1939. The mosquitoes of the southeastern states. U.S. Dep. Agr. Misc. Pub. 336, (Slightly rev. 1944) 96 p., illus.

418. Kinsey, A. C.
1920a. Life histories of American Cynipidae. Amer. Mus. Nat. Hist. Bull. 42: 319–357, illus.

419. ———
1920b. Phylogeny of Cynipid genera and biological characteristics. Amer. Mus. Nat. Hist. Bull. 42: 357–402, illus.

420. ———
1935. The economic importance of the Cynipidae. J. Econ. Entomol. 28(1): 86–91.

421. Kirby, H., Jr.
1934. Protozoa in termites. P. 89–98, illus., Ed. 2, rev., *In* C. A. Kofoid (ed.). Termites and termite control. Berkeley, Calif.: Univ. Cal. Press.

422. Klots, A. B.
1951. A field guide to the butterflies of North America, east of the Great Plains. 349 p., illus. Boston: Houghton Mifflin Co.

423. Knight, F. B.
1958. The effects of woodpeckers on populations of the Engelmann spruce beetle. J. Econ. Entomol. 51(5): 603–607.

424. Knight, H. H.
1941. The plant bugs, or Miridae, of Illinois. Ill. Nat. Hist. Surv. Bull. 22 (Art. 1), 234 p., illus.

425. Knipling, E. F.
1955. Possibilities of insect control or eradication through the use of sexually sterile males. J. Econ. Entomol. 48(4): 459–462.

426. ———
1959. Sterile-male method of population control. Science 130(3380): 902–904.

427. ———
1959. Screwworm eradication: concepts and research leading to the sterile-male method. Smithsonian Rep. 1958, Pub. 4365: 409–418, illus.

428. ———
1960. Use of insects for their own destruction. J. Econ. Entomol. 53(3): 415–420.

429. ———
1963. A new era in pest control: the sterility principle. U.S. Dep. Agr., Agr. Sci. Rev. 1(1): 2–12, illus.

430. ———, and McGuire, J. U.
1966. Population models to test theoretical effects of sex attractants used for insect control. U.S. Dep. Agr., ARS, Agr. Inc. Bull. 308, 20 p.

431. Knull, J. F.
1946. The long-horned beetles of Ohio (Coleoptera, Cerambycidae). Ohio. Biol. Bull. 39 (Vol. VII, No. 4): 133–354, illus.

432. ———
1951. The checkered beetles of Ohio (Coleoptera: Cleridae). Ohio Biol. Survey Bull. 42 (Vol. VIII, No. 2): 269–350, illus.

433. Knutson, H.
1944. Minnesota Phalaenidae (Noctuidae). Minn. Agr. Exp. Sta. Tech. Bull. 165, 128 p., illus.

434. Koerber, T. W.
1963. *Leptoglossus occidentalis* (Hemiptera, Coreidae), a newly discovered pest of coniferous seed. Entomol. Soc. Amer. Ann. 56(2): 229–234, illus.

435. Kofoid, C. A. (ed.)
1934. Termites and termite control. Ed. 2, revised. 795 p., illus. Berkeley, Calif.: Univ. Calif. Press.

436. Kosztarab, M.
1963. The armored scale insects of Ohio (Homoptera: Coccidea: Diaspididate). Ohio Biol. Surv. Bull., New Series, Vol. II, No. 2, 120 p., illus.

437. Kotinsky, J.
    1921. Insects injurious to deciduous shade trees and their control. U.S. Dep. Agr. Farmers' Bull. 1169, 100 p.
438. Kowal, R. J.
    1960. Southern pine beetle. U.S. Forest Service Forest Pest Leafl. 49 (revised, 1966), 8 p., illus.
439. Kraft, K. J.
    1968. Ecology of the cone moth, *Laspeyresia to reuta,* in *Pinus banksiana* stands. Entomol. Soc. Amer. Ann. 61(6): 1462–1465.
440. Krause, N. L. H.
    1937. A study of the genus *Glyptosceles* Lec. in America north of Mexico (Coleoptera, Chrysomelidae). Univ. of Calif. Pub. Entomol. 7(2): 21–32, illus.
441. Krishna, K.
    1966. Key to eight termite genera. U.S. Dep. Agr. Coop. Econ. Insect Surv. Rep. 16(47): 1087–1098, illus.
442. Krombein, K. V.
    1958. Hymenoptera of America north of Mexico, Synoptic Catalog. First Suppl. U.S. Dep. Agr. Monogr. No. 2, 305 p.
443. ———, and Burks, B. D.
    1967. Hymenoptera of America north of Mexico, Synoptic Catalog. Second Suppl. U.S. Dep. Agr. Monogr. No. 2, 584 p.
444. Kulman, H. M.
    1965a. Natural control of the bagworm and notes on its status as a forest pest. J. Econ. Entomol. 58(5): 863–866.
445. ———
    1965b. Natural control of the eastern caterpillar and notes on its status as a forest pest. J. Econ. Entomol. 58(1): 66–70.
446. ———
    1967. Biology of the hard maple bud miner, *Obrussa ochrefasciella,* and notes on its damage (Lepidoptera: Nepticulidae). Entomol. Soc. Amer. Ann. 60(2): 387–391, illus.
447. ———, and Dorsey, C. R.
    1962. Granular application of systemics for control of European pine shoot moth. J. Econ.. Entomol. 55(3): 304–305.
448. Langford, G. S., and McConnell, H. S.
    1935. Biology of *Tomostethus multicinctus* (Roh.), a sawfly attacking ash. J. Econ. Entomol. 28(1): 208–210, illus.
449. Langlois, T. H., and Langlois, M. H.
    1964. Notes on the life-history of the hackberry butterfly, *Asterocampa celtis* (Bdvl. & Lec.) on South Bass Island, Lake Erie (Lepidoptera, Nymphalidae). Ohio J. Sci. 64(1): 1–11, illus.

450. Leach, J. G., Orr, L. W., and Christensen, C.
    1937. The interrelations of bark beetles and blue-staining fungi in felled Norway pine timber. J. Agr. Res. 55: 129–140, illus.

451. Leng, C. W.
    1920. Catalogue of the Coleoptera of America north of Mexico. 470 p. Mount Vernon, New York: John D. Sherman, Jr.

452. ———, and Mutchler, A. J.
    1927. Supplement, 1919 to 1924, inclusive, to catalogue of the Coleoptera of America, north of Mexico. 78 p.

453. ———
    1933. Second and third supplements, 1925–1932 (inclusive) to catalogue of the Coleoptera of America, North of Mexico. 112 p.

454. Leonard, M. D., editor-in-chief
    1928. A list of insects of New York. N. Y. (Cornell) Agr. Exp. Sta. Mem. 101, 1011 p.

455. Lewis, F. B., and Connola, D. P.
    1966. Field and laboratory investigations of *Bacillus thuringiensis* as a control agent for gypsy moth, *Porthetria dispar* (L.) U.S. Forest Serv., Northeast. Forest Exp. Sta. Res. Pap. NE-50, 38 p., illus.

456. Lindquist, A. W.
    1965. The use of gamma radiation for control or eradication of the screw-worm. J. Econ. Entomol. 48(4): 467–469.

457. ———
    1959. Use of sexually sterile males for eradication of screwworms. 2nd Inter-Amer. Symposium on Peaceful Application of Nuclear Energy, Buenos Aires, June 1959, Proc. 229–235.

458. Lindquist, O. H., and Bowser, R. L.
    1966. A biological study of the leaf miner, *Chrysopeleia ostryaealla* Chambers (Lepidoptera: Cosmopterygidae), on ironwood in Ontario. Can. Entomol. 98(3): 252–258, illus.

459. ———, and Trinnell, J. R.
    1967. The biology and description of immature stages of *Exoteleia nepheos* (Gelechiidae) on pine in Ontario. J. Lepidopterists' Soc. 21(1): 15–21, illus.

460. Linsley, E. G.
    1943. The recognition and control of deathwatch, powderpost, and false powderpost beetles. Pests 11(3): 11–14, 23–26, illus.

461. Lowe, R. E., Giese, R. L., and McManus, M. L.
    1967. Mycetangia of the ambrosia beetle, *Monarthrum fasciatum*. J. Invert. Pathol. 9(4): 451–458, illus.

462. Luginbill, P., Sr., and Painter, H. R.
    1953. May beetles of the United States and Canada. U.S. Dep. Agr. Tech. Bull. 1060, 102 p., illus.

535

463. Lyons, L. A.
    1956. Insects affecting seed production in red pine. Part I. *Conopthorus resinosae* Hopk. (Coleoptera: Scolytidae). Can. Entomol. 88(10): 599–608, illus.

464. ———
    1957a. Insects affecting seed production in red pine. Part II. *Dioryctria disclusa* Heinrich, *D. abietella* (D. & S.), and *D. cambiicola* (Dyar) (Lepidoptera, Phycitidae). Can. Entomol. 89(2): 70–79, illus.

465. ———
    1957b. Insects affecting seed production in red pine. Part III. *Eucosma monitorana* Heinrich, *Laspeyresia toreuta* Grote (Lepidoptera: Olethreutidae), *Rubsaamenia* sp. (Diptera: Cecidomyiidae), and other insects. Can. Entomol. 89(4): 150–164, illus.

466. ———
    1964. The European pine sawfly, *Neodiprion sertifer* (Geoff.) (Hymenoptera: Diprionidae). Entomol. Soc. Ontario Proc. 94(1963): 5–37, illus.

467. MacAloney, H. J.
    1930. The white pine weevil (*Pissodes strobi* Peck)—Its biology and control. N.Y. State Coll. Forest., Syracuse Univ., Tech. Pub. 28, 87 p., illus.

468. ———
    1958. White-pine weevil. U.S. Forest Serv. Forest Pest Leafl. 21 (revised 1967), 7 p., illus.

469. ———
    1961. Pine tortoise scale. U.S. Forest Serv. Forest Pest Leafl. 57, 7 p., illus.

470. ———
    1967. The hemlock borer. U.S. Forest Serv. Forest Pest Leafl. 109, 4 p., illus.

471. ———
    1968. The bronze birch borer. U.S. Forest Serv. Forest Pest Leafl. 111, 4 p., illus.

472. ———, and Ewan, H. G.
    1964. Identification of hardwood insects by type of tree injury, North-central region. U.S. Forest Serv., Lake States Forest Exp. Sta. and No. Cent. Reg., Res. Pap. LS-11, 71 p., illus.

473. ———, and Schmiege, D. C.
    1962. Identification of conifer insects by type of tree injury. U.S. Forest Serv., Lake States Forest Exp. Sta. and N. Cent. Reg., Sta. Pap. No. 100, 42 p., illus.

474. ———, and Wilson, L. F.
    1957. The red-headed pine sawfly. U.S. Forest Serv. Forest Pest Leafl. 14, (rev. 1964), 4 p., illus.

475. McCambridge, W. F., and Downing, G. L.
    1960. Black-headed budworm. U.S. Forest Serv., Forest Pest Leafl. 45, 4 p., illus.

476. McConnell, H. S., and Davidson, J. A.
    1959. Observations on the life history and morphology of *Kermes pubescens* Bogue (Homoptera: Coccoi-

dea: Dactyiopiidae). Entomol. Soc. Amer. Ann.
52(4) 463–468, illus.

477. MacCreary, D.
1945. Ticks of Delaware—with special reference to *Dermacantor variabilis* (Say), vector of Rocky Mountain spotted fever. Univ. Del. Agr. Exp. Sta. Bull. No. 252, Tech. No 32, 22 p., illus.

478. McDunnough, J.
1938. Check list of the Lepidoptera of Canada and the United States of America. Part I, Macrolepidoptera. S. Calif. Acad. Sci. Mem. 1: 272 p., 1938.

479. ——————
1939. Check list of the Lepidoptera of Canada and the United States of America. Part II, Microlepidoptera. S. Calif. Acad. Sci. Mem. 2(1): 171 p., 1939.

489. McGregor, E. A.
1950. Mites of the family Tetranychidae. Amer. Midland Nat. 44(2): 257–420, illus.

481. McGugan, B. M.
1958. The Canadian Forest Insect Survey. Tenth Int. Cong. of Entomol. Proc. 1956(4): 219–231, illus.

482. —————— (compiler)
1958. Forest Lepidoptera of Canada. Vol. I. Papilionidae to Arctiidae. Forest Biol. Div., Can. Dep. Agr., Pub. 1034, 76 p. illus.

483. ——————, and Blais, J. R.
1959. Spruce budworm parasite studies in northwestern Ontario. Can. Entomol. 91(12): 758–783, illus.

484. ——————, and Coppel, H. C.
1962. Biological control of forest insects, 1910–1958, p, 35–216, illus. *In* A review of the biological control attempts against insects and weeds in Canada. Part II. Commonwealth Inst. of Biol. Contr., Tech. Commun. No. 2.

485. McIntyre, T., and Dutky, S. R.
1961. Aerial application of virus for control of a pine sawfly, *Neodiprion pratti pratti*. J. Econ. Entomol. 54(4): 809–810.

486. ——————, and St. George, R. A.
1961. The old house borer. U.S. Dep. Agr., Leafl. No. 501, 8 p., illus.

487. MacKay, M. R.
1959. Larvae of the North American Olethreutidae (Lepidoptera). Can. Entomol. Suppl. 10 (Vol. 91), 338 p., illus.

488. ——————
Additional larvae of the North American Olethreutinae (1) (Lepidoptra: Totricidae). Can. Entomol. 94(6); 626–643, illus.

489. ——————
1968. The North American Aegeridae (Lepidoptera): A revision based on late-instar larvae. Entomol. Soc. Can. Mem., No. 58, 112 p., illus.

490. McKenzie, H. L.
    1967. Mealybugs of California. Calif. Univ. Press, 525 p., illus.

491. McKnight, M. E.
    1968. A literature review of the spruce, western, and 2-year-cycle budworms. U.S. Forest Serv., Rocky Mountain Forest and Range Exp. Sta. Res Pap. RM-44, 35 p.

492. MacLean, D. B., and Giese, R. L.
    1967. The life history of the ambrosia beetle, *Xyloterinus politus* (Coleoptera: Scolytidae). Can. Entomol. 99(3): 285–299, illus.

493. ———
    1968. Fungi associated with *Xyloterinus politus* (Say) (Coleoptera: Scolytidae). J. Invertebrate Pathol. 10(2): 185–189, illus.

494. McLeod, J. M.
    1966. Notes on the biology of a spruce needle-miner, *Pulicalvaria piceaella* (Kearfott) (Lepidoptera: Gelechiidae). Can. Entomol. 98(3): 225–236, illus.

495. ———, and Daviault, L.
    1963. Notes on the life history and habits of the spruce coneworm, *Dioryctria reniculella* (Grote) (Lepidoptera: Pyralidae). Can. Entomol. 95(3): 309–316, illus.

496. McLintock, T. F.
    1947. Silvicultural practices for control of spruce budworm. J. Forest. 45(9): 655–658.

497. ———
    1948. Evaluation of tree risk in the spruce-fir region of the Northeast. Iowa State Coll. J. Sci. 22(4): 415–419.

498. ———
    1949. Mapping vulnerability of spruce-fir stands in the Northeast to spruce budworm attack. U.S. Forest Serv. , Northeast. Forest Exp. Sta. Pap. 21, 20 p., illus.

499. McManus, M. L., and Giese, R. L.
    1968. The Columbian timber beetle, *Corthylus columbianus*. VII. The effect of climatic integrants on historic density fluctuations. Forest Sci. 14(3): 242–253.

500. Marlatt, C. L.
    1903. Scale insects and mites on citrus trees. U.S. Dep. Agr. Farmers' Bull. 172, 42 p., illus.

501. Martignoni, M. E., and Langston, R. L.
    1959. Supplement to an annotated list and bibliography of insects reported to have virus diseases. Hilgardia 30: 1–40.

502. Martin, J. L.
    1956. The bionomics of the aspen blotch miner, *Lithocolletis salicifoliella* Cham. (Lepidoptera: Gracillariidae). Can. Entomol. 88(4): 155–168, illus.

503. ———
 1958. Observations on the biology of certain tortricids in
       young coniferous plantations in Southern Ontario.
       Can. Entomol. 90(1): 44–53, illus.

504. ———
 1959. The bionomics of the pine bud moth, *Exoteleia do-
       decella* L. (Lepidoptera: Gelechiidae) Ontario.
       Can. Entomol. 91(1): 5–14, illus.

505. ———
 1960a. The bionomics of *Profenusa thomsoni* (Konow)
        (Hymenoptera: Tenthredinidae), a leaf-mining
        sawfly on *Betula* spp. Can. Entomol. 92(5):
        376–384, illus.

506. ———
 1960b. Life history of the pine tip moth, *Rhyacionia adana*
        Heinrich, in Ontario (Lepidoptera: Olethreutii-
        dae). Can. Entomol. 92(10): 725–728, illus.

507. Marty, R., and Mott, D. G.
 1964. Evaluating and scheduling white pine weevil con-
       trol in the Northeast. Northeastern Forest Expt.
       Sta., Forest Service, Res. Paper NE-19, 56 p.,
       illus.

508. Massey, C. L.
 1966. The influence of nematode parasites and associates
       on bark beetles in the United States. Bull. Ento-
       mol. Soc. Amer. 12(4): 384–386.

509. Matheson, R.
 1917. The poplar and willow borer. Cornell Agr. Exp. Sta.
       Bull. 388: 455–483, illus.

510. ———
 1951. Entomology for introductory courses. Ed. 2, 629 p.,
       illus. Ithaca, New York: Comstock Pub. Assoc.,
       Inc.

511. Mattoon, W. R.
 1930. Growing black locust trees. U.S. Dep. Agr. Farmers'
       Bull. No. 1628 (revised 1937), 30 p., illus.

512. Maynard, E. A.
 1951. A monograph of the Collembola or springtail in-
       sects of New York State. Thesis 339 p., illus.
       (Published in association with Cornell Univ.
       Press) Ithaca, New York: Comstock Publishing
       Co., Inc.

513. Merkel, E. P.
 1962. The number of larval instars of *Dioryctria abietella*
       (D. & S.) (Lepidoptera: Phycitidae) in Florida.
       Can. Entomol. 94(9): 1005–1007.

514. ———
 1967. Life history of the slash pine seedworm, *Laspey-
       resia anaranjada* Miller (Lepidoptera: Oleth-
       reutidae). Fla. Entomol. 50(3): 141–149, illus.

515. ———
 1969. Control of insects in slash pine cones with trunk
       implantations of Bidrin ® systemic insecticide—
       first year result. U.S. Forest Serv., Southeast.
       Forest Exp. Sta. Res. Note SE-109, 4 p., illus.

516. Metcalf, C. L.
    1913. The Syrphidae of Ohio. Ohio Biol. Surv. Bull. 1:
        1–122, illus.
517. Metcalf, Z. P.
    1922. The gloomy scale. N. C. Agr. Exp. Sta. Tech. Bull.
        p. 21, 23, illus.
518. Mickel, C. E.
    1928. Biological and taxonomic investigations on the
        Mutillid wasps. U.S. Nat. Mus. Bull. 143, 351 p.,
        illus.
519. Middlekauff, W. W.
    1958. The North American sawflies of the genera *Acantholyda, Cephalica* and *Neurotoma* (Hymenoptera, Pamphiliidae), Univ. Calif. Pub. Entomol.
        14(2) : 51–174, illus.
520. Middleton, W.
    1923. The imported pine sawfly. U.S. Dep. Agr. Bull. No.
        1182, 21 p., illus.
521. Miller, C. A.
    1963. Parasites and the spruce budworm, p. 228–244, illus.
        In R. F. Morris (ed.) The Dynamics of epidemic
        spruce budworm population. Entomol. Soc. Can.
        Mem. 31.
522. Miller, J. M.
    1950. Resistance of pine hybrids to the pine reproduction
        weevil. U.S. Forest Serv., Calif. Forest and Range
        Exp. Sta., Forest Res. Note 68, 17 p., illus.
523. Miller, W. E.
    1955. Biology of *Anacampsis innocuella* (Teller), a leaf-
        roller on aspen. J. Econ. Entomol. 48(5) : 622–
        623, illus.
524. ———
    1960. A new pine tip moth (Olethreutidae) from the Gulf
        of Mexico region. J. Lepidopterists Soc. 14(4) :
        231–236.
525. ———
    1963. The shore-leaf pitch-blister moth, *Petrova houseri*
        Miller. Ohio J. Sci. 63(6) : 297–301, illus.
526. ———
    1965. Protecting Christmas tree plantations. J. Forest.
        63(11) : 849–852.
527. ———
    1967a. The European pine shoot moth—ecology and con-
        trol in the Lake States. Forest Sci. Monogr. 14,
        72 p., illus.
528. ———
    1967b. Taxonomic review of the *Rhyacionia frustrana*
        group of pine-tip moths, with description of a
        new species (Olethreutidae). Can. Entomol.
        99(6) : 590–596, illus.
529. ———, Hastings, A. R. and Wootten, J. F.
    1961. European pine shoot moth. U.S. Forest Serv., For-
        est Pest Leafl. 59 (revised 1966), 8 p., illus.

530. ———, and Neiswander, R. B.
    1955. Biology and control of the European pine shoot moth. Ohio Agr. Exp. Sta. Res. Bull. 760: 31, illus.

531. ———
    1956. The pitch twig moth and its occurrence in Ohio. Ohio Agr. Exp. Sta. Res. Bull. 779, 24 p., illus.

532. Millers, I., Benjamin, D. M., and Warner, R. E.
    1963. A new *Hylobius* weevil associated with jack pine stand deterioration (Coleoptera: Curculionidae). Can. Entomol. 95(1): 18–22, illus.

533. Milliken, F. B.
    1916. The cottonwood borer. U.S. Dep. Agr. Bull. No. 424 (Prof. Pap.): 8 p., illus.

534. Milliron, H. E.
    1958. Economic importance and control of the loblolly mealybug, *Dysmicoccus obesus* Lob. J. Econ. Entomol. 51(4): 555–556, illus.

535. Mitchell, R. T.
    1952. Consumption of spruce budworm by birds in a Maine spruce-fir forest. J. Forest. 50: 387–389.

536. Morris, C. L., Schroeder, W. J., and Bobb, M. L.
    1963. A pine sawfly, *Neoiprion pratti pratti*, in Virginia. Va. Div. Forest. Dep. Conserv. & Econ. Develop. 42 p., illus.

537. Morris, R. C.
    1960. Control of cottonwood insects with a systemic insecticide. J. Forest. 58(9): 718, illus.

538. ———
    1963. Trunk borers in cottonwood. Miss. Agr. Exp. Sta. Inform. Sheet 826, 2 p., illus.

539. ———
    1964. "Grease spot" in oak—blemish or beauty? S. Lumberman 208(2592): p. 23, 26, illus.

540. ———
    1967. Biology of *Gypsonoma haimbachiana* (Lepidoptera: Olereuthidae), a twig borer in eastern cottonwood. Entomol. Soc. Amer. Ann. 60(2): 423–427, illus.

541. Morris, R. F.
    1951. The larval elateridae of eastern spruce forests and their role in the natural control of *Gilpinia hercyniae* (Htg.) (Hymenoptera: Diprionidae). Can. Entomol. 83(6): 133–147, illus.

542. ———
    1955. The development of sampling techniques for forest insect defoliators with particular reference to the spruce budworm. Can. J. Zool. 33: 225–294, illus.

543. ——— (ed.)
    1963. The dynamics of epidemic spruce budworm populations. Can. Entomol. Soc. Mem. 31, 332 p., illus.

544. Morrison, H.
1928. A classification of the higher groups and genera of the coccid family Margarodidae. U.S. Dep. Agr. Tech. Bull. 52, 240 p., illus.
545. ———, and Morrison, E.
1927. The Maskell species of scale insects of the subfamily *Asterolecaniinae*. U.S. Nat Mus. Proc. 71 (Art. 17) No. 2689: 1–65, illus.
546. Morse, A. P.
1920. Manual of the Orthoptera of New England. Boston Soc. Nat. Hist. Proc. 35: 197–556, illus.
547. Moser, J. C.
1965. The interrelationships of three gall makers and their natural enemies, on hackberry (*Celtis occidentalis* L.) N. Y. State Mus. and Sci. Serv. Bull. 402, 95 p., illus.
548. Mosher, F. H.
1915. Food plants of the gypsy moth in America. U.S. Dep. Agr. Bull. 250: 39, illus.
549. Muesebeck, C. F. W.
1918. Two important introduced parasites of the brown-tail moth. J. Agr. Res. 14: 191–206.
550. ———, Krombein, K. V., and Townes, H. K.
1951. Hymenoptera of America north of Mexico—Synoptic Catalog. U.S. Dep. Agr. Monogr. No. 2, 1420 p.
551. Munroe, E.
1959. Canadian species of *Dioryctria* Zeller (Lepidoptera: Pyralidae). Can. Entomol. 91 (2): 65–72, illus.
552. Nagel, R. H., McComb, D., and Knight, F. H.
1957. Trap tree method for controlling the Engelmann spruce beetle. J. Forest. 55: 894–898.
553. Nash, R. W.
1934. The willow flea weevil, *Orchestes rufipes* LeC., and its control in Maine. J. Econ. Entomol., 27: 236–239.
554. ———
1939. The yellow-headed spruce sawfly in Maine. J. Econ. Entomol. 32: 330–334, illus.
555. Nat. Acad. of Sci., Nat. Res. Counc.
1962–63. Evaluation of pesticide-wildlife problems. Natl. Acad. of Sciences—Natl. Res. Council Pub. 920–A, 28 pp; 920–B, 53 pp., 1962; Pub. 920–C, 28 pp. 1963.
556. ———
1966. Scientific aspects of pest control. Natl. Acad. Sci.-Natl. Res. Counc. Pub. 1402: 470.
557. ———, Subcomm. on Insect Pests.
1969. Insect-pest management and control. Princ. Plant and Anim. Pest Contr., Vol. 3, pub. 1695, 508 p., illus.
558. Needham, J. G., and Claasen, P. W.
1925. A monograph of the Plecoptera or stoneflies of America north of Mexico. Thomas Say Foundation, Entomol. Soc. Amer. II: 397 p., illus.

559. ――――, Frost, S. W., and Tothill, B. H.
    1928. Leaf-mining insects. 351 p., illus. Baltimore: The Williams and Wilkins Co.

560. ――――, Traver, J. R., and Hsu, Yin-Chi
    1935. The biology of mayflies. 759 p., illus. Ithaca, New York: Comstock Publishing Co., Inc.

561. Neilson, M. M., and Morris, R. F.
    1964. The regulation of European spruce sawfly numbers in the maritime provinces of Canada from 1937 to 1963. Can. Entomol. 96(5): 773–784, illus.

562. Neiswander, R. B.
    1949. The grape mealybug on *Taxus* in Ohio. J. Econ. Entomol. 42(1): 41–44, illus.

563. Nelson, R. M.
    1934. Effect of blue stain fungi on southern pine attacked by bark beetles. Phytopathol. Z. 7(4): 327–353, illus.

564. ――――, and Beal, J. A.
    1929. Experiments with blue stain fungi in southern pine. Phytopathol. 19: 1101–1106.

565. Neunzig, H. H. and Merkel, E. P.
    1967. A taxonomic study of the pupae of the genus *Dioryctria* in the southeastern United States (Lepidoptera: Phycitidae). Entomol. Soc. Amer. Ann. 60(4): 801–808, illus.

566. ――――, Raab, R. L., Ebel, B. H., and Merkel, E. P.
    1964. Larvae of the genus *Dioryctria* (Lepidoptera: Phycitidae) in the southeastern United States. Entomol. Soc. Amer. Ann. 57(6): 693–707, illus.

567. Nichols, H. W.
    1966. Texas leafcutting ant controlled with pelleted Mirex bait. J. Econ. Entomol. 59(3): 628–631.

568. Nord, J. C., Knight, F. B., and Vogt, G. B.
    1965. Identity and biology of an aspen root girdler, *Agrilus hornii*. Forest Sci. 11(1): 33–41, illus.

569. Nordin, G. L., and Appleby, J. E.
    1969. Bionomics of the juniper webworm. Entomol. Soc. Amer. Ann. 62(2): 287–292, illus.

570. Norris, D. M.
    1967. Systematic insecticides in trees, Ann. Rev. Ent. Vol. 12: 127–148.

571. Oatman, E. R., Legner, E. F., and Brooks, R. F.
    1962. Bionomics of the eye-spotted bud moth, *Spilonota ocellana*, on cherry in Wisconsin. J. Econ. Entomol. 55(6): 930–934, illus.

572. Odell, T. M., and Godwin, P. A.
    1964. White-pine cone beetle. U. S. Forest Serv., Forest Pest Leafl. 83, 7 p., illus.

573. Oliver, A. D.
    1964. Studies on the biological control of the fall webworm, *Hyphantria cunea*, in Louisiana. J. Econ. Entomol. 57(3): 314–318, illus.

574. Osborn, H.
    1938. The Fulgoridae of Ohio. Ohio Biol. Surv. Bull. 35,
        Vol. 6(6): 283–357, illus.

575. ———
    1940. The Membracidae of Ohio. Ohio Biol. Surv. Bull.
        37, Vol. 7(2): 51–101, illus.

576. Parker, D. E.
    1936. *Chrysis shanghaiensis* Smith, a parasite of the Ori-
        ental moth. J. Agr. Res. 52: 449–458, illus.

577. Parker, D. L.
    1935. *Apanteles solitarius* (Ratzeburg), an introduced
        braconid parasite of the satin moth. U. S. Dep.
        Agr. Tech. Bull. 477, 18 p., illus.

578. Parr, T. J.
    1937. Notes on the golden or pit-making oak scale. J.
        Forest. 35(1): 51–58, illus.

579. ———
    1939. *Matsucoccus* sp., a scale insect injurious to certain
        pines in the northeast (Hemiptera-Homoptera).
        J. Econ. Entomol. 32(5): 624–230, illus.

580. ———
    1940. *Asterolecanium variolosum* Ratzezurg, a gall-form-
        ing coccid, and its effects upon the host trees.
        Yale Univ. Sch. Forest. Bull. No. 46, 49 p., illus.

581. Parrott, P. J., and Glasgow, H.
    1916. The leaf-weevil. (*Polydruses impressifrons* Gyll.)
        N.Y. Agr. Exp. Sta. Tech. Bull. No. 56, 24 p.,
        illus.

582. Patch, E. M.
    1908. The saddled prominent, *Heterocampa guttivitta*
        Walker. Maine Agr. Exp. Sta. Bull. 161, p. 311–
        350, illus.

583. ———
    1910. Gall species of the elm. Maine Agr. Exp. Sta. Bull.
        181, p. 193–240, illus.

584. ———
    1912. Aphid pests of Maine. Maine Agr. Exp. Sta. Bull.
        202, p. 159–178, illus.

585. ———
    1923. Family Aphididae. *In* Conn. State Geol. and Nat.
        Hist. Surv. Bull. 34, 250–256, illus.

586. ———
    1938. Food plant catalogue of the aphids of the world in-
        cluding the Phylloxeridae. Maine Agr. Exp. Sta.
        Bull. 393: 35–431.

587. Pechuman, L. L.
    1940. Notes on the feeding and breeding habits of *Saperda*
        tridentata Oliv. Brooklyn Entomol. Soc. Bull.
        35(4): 113–116.

588. Peck, O.
    1963. A catalogue of the Nearactic Chalcidoidea (Insecta:
        Hymenoptera). Can. Entomol. Suppl. 39: 1092.

589. Peirson, H. B.
    1921. The life history and control of the pales weevil

(*Hylobious pales*). Harvard Forest Bull. 3, 33 p., illus.

590. ———
1922. Mound-building ants in forest plantations. J. Forest. 20 (4) : 325–336.

591. ———, and Brower, A. E.
1936. Biology and control of the birch leaf-mining sawfly. Me. Forest Serv. Bull. 11, 37 p., illus.

592. Perry, C. C.
1955. Gypsy moth appraisal program and proposed plan to prevent spread of the moths. U. S. Dep. Agr. Tech. Bull. 1124, 27 p., illus.

593. Peterson, A.
1959. A leaf skeletonizer, *Lobesia liriodendrana* (Kearfott), Olethreutidae, on *Magnolia grandiflora* in Florida. Fla. Entomol. 43 (3) : 105–114, illus.

594. Peterson, L. O. T.
1958. The boxelder twig borer, *Proteoteras willingana* (Kearfott), (Lepidoptera : Olethreutidae). Can. Entomol. 90 (11) : 639–646, illus.

595. Pilon, J. G.
1965. Bionomics of the spruce bud moth, *Zeiraphera ratzeburgiana* (Ratz.) (Lepidoptera : Olethreutidae). Phytoprotection 46 (1) : 5–13, illus.

596. Plumb, G. H.
1950. The adult feeding habit of some conifer-infesting weevils. Can. Entomol. 82 (3) : 53–57, illus.

597. ———
1953. The formation and development of the Norway spruce gall caused by *Adelges abietis* L. Conn. Agr. Exp. Sta. Bull. 566, 77 p., illus.

598. Plummer, C. C., and Pillsbury, A. E.
1929. The white pine weevil in New Hampshire. Univ. N.H. Exp. Sta. Bull. 247, 31 p., illus.

599. Pointing, P. J., and Green, G. W.
1962. A review of the history and biology of the European pine shoot moth, *Rhyacionia buoliana* (Schiff.) (Lepidoptera : Olethreutidae), in Ontario, Entomol. Soc. Ont. Proc. 92 (1961) : 58–69, illus.

600. Porter, B. A.
1958. The eastern tent caterpillar. U. S. Dep. Agr. Leafl. No. 161 (slightly revised 1968), 6 p., illus.

601. Potts, S. F.
1958. Concentrated spray equipment, mixtures, and application methods. 598 p. Caldwell, New Jersey : Dorland Books.

602. ———, and Friend, R. B.
1946. Mist blowers for applying concentrated spray. 45th Rep. Conn. State Entomol. : 47–60, illus.

603. Powell, J. A.
1968. Host associations and taxonomy of nearctic conifer cone moths of the genus *Eucosma* (Lepidoptera : Torticidae). Hilgardia 39 (1) : 36.

604. Prebble, M. L.
1941. The diapause and related phenomena in *Gilpinia polytoma* (Hartig). Can. J. Res. 19(10): 295–322, 323–346, illus.; (11): 350–362, illus.; (12): 437–454.

605. ———
1951. Forest entomology in relation to silviculture in Canada. Forest. Chron. 27: 1–32.

606. Prentice, R. M.
1955. The life history and some aspects of the ecology of the large aspen tortrix, *Choristoneura conflictana* (Wlkr.) (N. Camb.) (Lepidoptera: Tortricidae). Can. Entomol. 87(11): 461–473, illus.

607. Prentice, R. M. (Co-ordinator)
1962. Forest Lepidoptera of Canada. Vol. II. Nyteolidae, Noctuidae, Notodontidae, Liparidae. Can. Dep. Forest., Ottawa. II: 77–281, 1962.

608. ———
1963. Forest Lepidoptera of Canada. Vol. III. Lasiocampidae, Thyatiridae, Drepanidae, Geometridae. Can. Dept. Forest., Ottawa. III: 283–543, 1963.

609. ———
1965. Forest Lepidoptera of Canada. Vol. IV. Microlepidoptera. Can. Dep. Forest., Ottawa. IV: 545–840, 1965.

610. Raske, A. G., and Hodson, A. C.
1964. The development of *Pineus strobi* (Hartig) (Adelginae, Phylloxeridae) on white pine and black spruce. Can. Entomol. 96(4): 599–616, illus.

611. Readio, P. A.
1927. Studies on the biology of the Reduviidae of America north of Mexico. Univ. Kans. Sci. Bull. 17(11): 291 p., illus.

612. Reeks, W. A.
1956. Sequential sampling for larvae of the winter moth, *Operophtera brumata* (Linn.) (Lepidoptera: Geometridae). Can. Entomol. 88(6): 241–246, illus.

613. Rehn, J. A. G., and Grant, Jr., H. J.
1961. A monograph of the Orthoptera of North America (north of Mexico). Acad. Nat. Sci. Phila. Monogr. 12(1): 257, illus.

614. Rennels, R. G.
1960. The Zimmerman pine moth. Ill. Agr. Exp. Sta. Bull. 660, 39 p., illus.

615. Rexrode, C. O., Kulman, H. M., and Dorsey, C. K.
1965. Bionomics of the bark beetle, *Pseudopityophthorus pruinosus*, with special reference to its role as a vector of oak wilt, *Ceratocystis fagacearum*. J. Econ. Entomol. 58(5): 913–920, illus.

616. Ritcher, P. O.
1940. Kentucky white grubs. Ky. Agr. Exp. Sta. Bull. 401, 157 p., illus.

617. Rollinson, W. D., Lewis, F. B., and Walters, W. E.
    1965. The successful use of a nuclear-polyhedrosis virus against the gypsy moth. J. Invertebrate Pathol. 7(4): 515–517, illus.
618. Rose, A. H.
    1957. Some notes on the biology of *Monochamus scutellatus* (Say) (Coleoptera: Cerambycidae). Can. Entomol. 89(12): 547–553, illus.
619. ———
    1958. The effect of defoliation on foliage production and radial growth of quaking aspen. Forest Sci. 4(4): 335–342, illus.
620. Ross, D. A.
    1962. Bionomics of the maple leaf cutter, *Paraclemensia acerifoliella* (Fitch), (Lepidoptera: Incurvariidae). Can. Entomol. 94(10): 1053–1063, illus.
621. Ross, H. H.
    1937. A generic classification of the nearctic sawflies (Hymenoptera, Symphata). Ill. Biol. Monogr. 15(2): 173 p., illus.
622. ———
    1951. Superfamily Tenthredinoidea, P. 12–82, *In* C. F. W. Muesbeck, K. V. Krombein, and H. K. Townes (dir.). Hymenoptera of America north of Mexico —Synoptic Cat. U. S. Dep. Agr. Monogr. No. 2, 1420 p.
623. ———
    1955. Taxonomy and evolution of the sawfly genus *Neodiprion*. Forest Sci. 1(3): 196–209, illus.
624. ———
    1956. A textbook of entomology. Ed. 2, 519 p., illus. New York: John Wiley & Sons, Inc.
625. Rudd, R. L., and Genelly, R. E.
    1956. Pesticides: their use and toxicity in relation to wildlife. Calif. Dep. of Fish and Game, Game Manag. Br. Bull. 7, 209 p.
626. Rumbold, C. T.
    1932. Two blue-staining fungi associated with bark-beetle infestations of pines. J. Agr. Res. 43: 847–873, illus.
627. Russell, L. M.
    1941. A classification of the scale insect genus *Asterolecanium*. U. S. Dep. Agr., Misc. Pub. 424, 322 p., illus.
628. Sabrosky, C. W.
    1952. How many insects are there? U. S. Dep. Agr. Yearbook 1952: 1–7.
629. ———, and Arnaud, Jr., P. H.
    1965. Family Tachinidae (Larvaevoridae). *In* A Catalog of the Diptera of America north of Mexico. U. S. Dep. Agr., Agr. Handbook No. 276: 961–1108.
630. St. George, R. A., Johnson, H. R., and Kowal, R. J.
    1960. Subterranean termites, their prevention and control

in buildings. U. S. Dep. Agr., House and Garden Bull. 64 (slightly revised 1963), 30 p., illus.

631. Salman, K. A., and Bongberg, J. W.
    1942. Logging high-risk trees to control insects in the pine stands of northeastern California. J. Forest. 40(7): 533–539.

632. Sanders, C. J.
    1964. The biology of carpenter ants in New Brunswick. Can. Entomol. 96(6): 894–909, illus.

633. Saylor, L. W.
    1945. Revision of the scarab beetles of the genus *Dichelonyx*. Bull. Brooklyn Entomol. Soc. 40(5): 137–158.

634. Schaefer, C. H.
    1964. Studies on the life history of the Virginia pine sawfly (*Neodiprion pratti* Dyar). U. S. Forest Serv. Res. Pap. WO-2, 8 p., illus.

635. Schaffner, J. F., Jr.
    1936. European sawfly *Pristiphora geniculata* attacks mountain ash in the United States. J. Econ. Entomol. 29(2): 469.

636. ———
    1939. *Neodiprion sertifer* (Geoff.), a pine sawfly accidentally introduced into New Jersey from Europe. J. Econ. Entomol. 32(6): 887–888.

637. ———
    1944. *Diprion frutetorum* (F.). 43rd Report, 1943, Conn. State Entomol. Bull. 481, p. 307–313, illus.

638. ———
    1959. Microlepidoptera and their parasites reared from field collections in the northeastern United States. U. S. Dep. Agr., Misc. Pub. 767, 97 p.

639. ———, and Griswold, C. L.
    1934. Macrolepidoptera and their parasites reared from field collections in the northeastern part of the United States. U. S. Dep. Agr., Misc. Pub. 188, 160 p.

640. ———, and McIntyre, H. L.
    1944. The pine root-collar weevil. J. Forest. 42(4): 269–275, illus.

641. Schenk, J. A., and Benjamin, D. M.
    1969. Notes on the biology of *Ips pini* in eastern Wisconsin jack-pine forests. Entomol. Soc. Amer. Ann. 62(3): 480–485, illus.

642. Schoof, H. F.
    1942. The genus *Conotrachelus* Dejean (Coleoptera, Curculionidae) in the north central United States. Ill. Biol. Monogr. 19(3): 170 p., illus.

643. Shaw, F. R., and Weidhaas, J. W.
    1956. Distribution and habits of the giant hornet in North America. J. Econ. Entomol. 49(2): 275.

644. Shenefelt, R. D., and Benjamin, D. M.
    1955. Insects of Wisconsin forests. Wisc. Coll. Agr. Ext.

548

Serv. and Wisc. Conserv. Dep. Cir. 500, 110 p., illus.

645. Shigo, A. L.
1962. Another scale insect on beach. U. S. Forest Serv., Northeast. Forest Exp. Sta. Pap. 168, 13 p., illus.

646. ———
1963. Beech bark disease. U. S. Forest Serv., Forest Pest Leafl. 75, 7 p., illus.

647. Silver, G. T.
1957. Studies on the aborvitae leaf miners in New Brunswick (Lepidoptera: Yponomeutidae and Gelechiidae). Can. Entomol. 89 (4) : 171–182, illus.

648. Silverstein, R. M., Brownlee, R. G., Bellas, T. E., and others.
1968. Brevicomin: Principal sex attractant in the frass of the western pine beetle. Science 159 (3817) : 889–891.

649. Simeone, J. B.
1954. Carpenter ants and their control. State Univ. N.Y., Coll. of Forest., Syracuse, Bull. 34, 19 p., illus.

650. ———
1961. An introduced species of *Ptilinus* from New York (Coleoptera: Anobiidae). Can. Entomol. 93 (6) : 428–430, illus.

651. ———
1962. Survey of wood-feeding Anobiidae in northeastern United States, including a study of temperature and humidity effects on egg development of *Hadrobregmus carinatus* Say. Eleventh Int. Cong. Entomol., Vienna Proc. 2nd Sect. 1960: 326–335.

652. ———, and Engelken, J. H.
1959. Injury to coniferous tree seedlings by the obliquebanded leaf roller. J. Forest. 57 (7) : 492–494, illus.

653. Sloop, K. D.
1937. A revision of the North American buprestid beetles belonging to the genus *Melanophila* (Coleoptera, Buprestidae). Univ. Calif. Pub. Entomol. 7 (1) : 1–20, illus.

654. Smirnoff, W. A., Fettes, J. J., and Haliburton, W.
1962. A virus disease of Swaine's jack pine sawfly, *Neodiprion swainei* Midd. sprayed from an aircraft. Can. Entomol. 94 (5) : 477–486.

655. Smith, D. R.
1966. A new *Profenusa* (Hymenoptera: Tenthredinidae) from red oak with keys to the adults and known larvae of the nearctic species. Entomol. Soc. Ann. 59 (4) : 719–723, illus.

656. Smith, F. F.
1932. Biology and control of the black vine weevil. U. S. Dep. Agr. Tech. Bull. No. 325, 45 p., illus.

657. Smith, H. S.
1912. The Chalcidoid genus *Perilampus* and its relation to the problem of parasite introduction. Technical

results from the gypsy moth laboratory. U. S. Bur. Entomol. Tech Ser. 19, Part 4, p. 33–69, illus.

658. Smith, J. B., and Dyar, H. G.
1899. Contributions toward a monograph of the lepidopterous family Noctuidae of boreal North America; a revision of the species of Acronycta (Ochsenheimer) and of certain allied genera. U. S. Nat. Mus. Proc. 21, No. 1140, p. 1–194, illus.

659. Smith, M. R.
1947. A generic and subgeneric synopsis of the United States ants, based on workers (Hymenoptera: Formicidae). Amer. Midland Nat. 37(3): 521–647, illus.

660. ———
1965. House-infesting ants of the eastern United States— their recognition, biology and economic importance. U. S. Dep. Agr., Tech. Bull. No. 1326, 105 p., illus.

661. Smith, R. C.
1922. The biology of the Chrysopidae. Cornell Univ. Agr. Exp. Sta. Mem. 58: 1285–1376.

662. ———, and Taylor, R. S.
1953. The biology and control of the hackberry psyllids in Kansas. Kans. Entomol. Soc. 26(3): 103–115, illus.

663. Smith, R. H.
1960. Resistance of pines to the pine reproduction weevil, *Cylindrocopturus eatoni*. J. Econ. Entomol. 53(6): 1044–1048, illus.

664. ———
1961. Red turpentine beetle. U. S. Forest Serv. Forest Pest Leafl. 55, 8 p., illus.

665. ———
1963. Toxicity of pine resin vapors to three species of *Dendroctonus* bark beetles. J. Econ. Entomol. 56: 827–831, illus.

666. ———
1965. Effect of Monoterpene vapors on the western pine beetle. J. Econ. Entomol. 58(3): 509–510, illus.

667. ———
1966. The Monoterpene composition of *Pinus ponderosa* xlyem resin and of *Dendroctonus brevicomus* pitch tubes. For. Sci. 12(1): 63-68, illus.

668. ———, and Lee, R. E.
1957. Black turpentine beetle. U. S. Forest Serv. Forest Pest Leafl. 12 (revised 1967), 7 p., illus.

669. Synder, T. E.
1916. Termites, or "white ants", in the United States: their damage and methods of prevention. U. S. Dep. Agr. Bull. No. 333, 32 p., illus.

670. ———
1926a. The biology of the termite castes. Quart. Rev. Biol. 1(4): 522–552, illus.

671. ────
    1926b. Preventing damage by lyctus powder-post beetles. U. S. Dep. Agr. Farmer's Bull. 1477 (revised 1936, 1938), 14 p., illus.

672. ────
    1934. The dry-wood termites of eastern and southern United States. P.269–272, illus. *In* C. A. Kofoid (ed.). Termites and termite control. Ed 2, revised Berkeley: Univ. Calif. Press.

673. ────
    1948. Our enemy, the termite. 257 p., illus. Rev. ed. Ithaca, New York: Comstock Publishing Co., Inc.

674. ────
    1949. Catalog of the termites (Isoptera) of the world. Smithsonian Inst. Misc. Collect. 112: 490 p.

675. ────
    1950. Control of non-subterranean termites. U.S. Dep. Agr. Farmers' Bull. 2018, 16 p., illus.

676. ────
    1954. Order Isoptera. The termites of the United States and Canada. 64 p., illus. New York: Nat. Pest Contr. Assn.

677. ────
    1965. Our native termites. Smithsonian Inst. Pub. 4633: 497–506, illus.

678. Solomon, J. D.
    1968. Cerambycid borer in mulberry. J. Econ. Entomol. 61(4): 1023–1025, illus.

679. ────, and Morris, R. C.
    1965. White oak borer in Mississippi. Miss. Agr. Exp. Sta. Inform. Sheet 908, 2 p., illus.

680. ────
    1966. Clearwing borer in red oaks. U. S. Forest Serv., South. Forest Exp. Sta. Res. Note SO–39, 3 p., illus.

681. Speers, C. F.
    1941. The pine spittlebug (*Aphrophora parallela* Say). N.Y. State Coll. Forest., Tech. Pub. 54, 65 p., illus.

682. ────
    1955. Pales weevil rapidly becoming a serious pest of pine reproduction in the south. J. Forest. 56: 723–726, illus.

683. ────
    1967. Pales weevil. U. S. Forest Serv., Forest Pest Leafl. 104, 4 p., illus.

684. ────, and Schmiege, D. C.
    1961. White grubs in forest tree nurseries and plantations. U. S. Forest Serv., Forest Pest Leaflet 63, 4 pp., illus.

685. Stairs, G. R.
    1965. Artificial initiation of virus epizootics in forest tent caterpillar populations. Can. Entomol. 97(10): 1059–1062, illus.

686. Stearns, L. A.
    1923. Family Cercopidae. Conn. State Geol. and Nat. Hist. Surv. Bull. 34: 206–238, illus.

687. Stehr, F. W., and Cook, E. F.
    1968. A revision of the genus *Malacosoma* (Hubner) in North America (Lepidoptera: Lasiocampidae): Systematics, biology, immatures, and parasites. U.S. Nat. Mus. Bull. 276, 321 p., illus.

688. Stehr, G. W.
    1967. On coniferophagous species of *Choristoneura* (Lepidoptera: Tortricidae) in North America. II. Geographic distribution in accordance with forest regions. Can. Entomol. 99(5): 456–463.

689. Stehr, W. C.
    1930. The Coccinellidae (ladybird beetles) of Minnesota (Coleoptera) Univ. of Minn. Agr. Exp. Sta., Tech. Bull. 75, 54 p., illus.

690. Steinhaus, E. A.
    1949. Principles of insect pathology. 757 p., illus. New York: McGraw-Hill Co., Inc.

691. Stern, V. M., Smith, R. F., van den Bosch, R., and Hagen, K. S.
    1959. The integration of chemical and biological control of the spotted alfalfa aphid. I. The integrated control concept. Hilgardia 29: 81–101, illus.

692. Stevens, R. E. and Stark, R. W.
    1962. Sequential sampling for the lodgepole needle miner, *Evagora milleri.* Jour. Econ. Ent. 55(4): 491–494, illus.

693. Stone, A.
    1965a. Family Culicidae. *In* A. Stone, C. W. Sabrosky, W. W. Wirth, and others (dir.). A catalog of the Diptera of America north of Mexico. U. S. Dep. Agr., Handbook No. 276, p. 105–120.

694. ――――
    1965b. Family Simuliidae. *In* A. Stone, C. W. Sabrosky, W. W. Wirth, and others (dir.). A catalog of the Diptera of America north of Mexico. U. S. Dep. Agr. Handbook No. 276, p. 181–189.

695. ――――, Sabrosky, C. W., Wirth, W. W., and others.
    1965. A catalog of the Diptera of America north of Mexico. U. S. Dep. Agr., Agr. Handbook No. 276, 1696 p.

696. Sublette, J. E., and Sublette, M. S.
    1965. Family Chironomidae. *In* A. Stone, C. W. Sabrosky, W. W. Wirth, and others (dir.). A catalog of the Diptera of America north of Mexico. U. S. Dep. Agr. Handbook No. 276, p. 142–181.

697. Summers, J. N.
    1922. Effect of low temperature on the hatching of gypsymoth eggs. U. S. Dep. Agr. Bull. No. 1080, 14 p.

698. Swaine, J. M.
    1918. Canadian bark-beetles. II. A preliminary classification with an account of the habits and means of

control. Can. Dep. Agr. Entomol. Br. Bull. 14 (pt. 2), 143 pp., illus.

699. ———
1924. The control of the destructive spruce bark beetle in eastern Canada. Can. Dep. Agr. Entomol. Br. Pam. (n.s.) 48, 29 p., illus.

700. ———, Craighead, F. C., and Bailey, I. W.
1924. Studies of the spruce budworm (*Cacoecia fumiferana* Clem.). Can. Dep. Agr. Entomol. Br. Tech. Bull. (n.s.) 37, 91 p., illus.

701. Sweetman, H. L.
1958. The principles of biological control. 560 p. Dubuque, Iowa: Wm. C. Brown Co.

702. Swingle, R. U.
1942. Phloem necrosis, a virus disease of the American elm. U. S. Dep. Agr. Circ. 640, 8 p., illus.

703. Talerico, R. L.
1962. A study of damage caused by the sugar maple borer. J. Forest. 60(3): 178–180, illus.

704. ———, McComb, C. W., and Garrett, W. T.
1967. *Fiorinia externa* Ferris, a scale insect of hemlock. U. S. Forest Serv., Forest Pest Leafl. 107, 4 p., illus.

705. Taylor, R. L.
1929. The biology of the white pine weevil, *Pissodes strobi* Peck), and a study of its insect parasites from an economic viewpoint. Entomol. Amer. (n.s.) 9(4): 167–246.

706. ———
1930. The biology of the white pine weevil, *Pissodes strobi* Peck), and a study of its insect parasites from an economic viewpoint. Entomol. Amer. (n.s.) 10(1): 1–86.

707. Thatcher, R. C.
1960. Bark beetles affecting southern pines: A review of current knowledge. U. S. Forest Serv., Southern Forest Exp. Sta. Occas. Pap. 180, 25 p.

708. ———
1960. Influence of the pitch-eating weevil on pine regeneration in east Texas. Forest Sci. 6(4): 354–361, illus.

709. ———
1967. Pine sawfly *Neodiprion excitans* Roh. U. S. Forest Serv. Forest Pest Leafl. 105, 4 p., illus.

710. ———, and Pickard, L. S.
1966. The clerid beetle, *Thanasimus dubius,* as a predator of the southern pine beetle. J. Econ. Entomol. 59(4): 955–957, illus.

711. Thatcher, T. O.
1961. Forest entomology. 225 p. Minneapolis, Minn.: Burgess Pub. Co.

712. Thompson, H. E.
1962a. European elm scale control investigations. J. Econ. Entomol. 55(4): 430–434.

713. ———
　　　1962b. Control of the hackberry-nipple-gall maker with new organic insecticides. J. Econ. Entomol. 55(4): 555–56.
714. Thompson, W. R.
　　　1956. The fundamental theory of natural and biological control. Ann. Rev. Entomol. 1: 379–402.
715. Tothill, J. D.
　　　1922. Natural control of the fall webworm, *Hyphantria cunea* (Drury), in Canada together with an account of its several parasites. Can. Dep. of Agr. Bull. No. 3 (n.s.), p. 1–107, illus.
716. Townes, H.
　　　1958. Some biological characteristics of the Ichneunionidae (Hymenoptera) in relation to biological control. J. Econ. Entomol. 51(5): 650–652.
717. Townes, H. K., Jr.
　　　1944. A catalogue and reclassification of the nearctic Ichneumonidae (Hymenoptera). Part I, 1944, The subfamilies Ichneumoninae, Tryphoninae, Cryptivae, Phaeogeninae, and Lissonotinae. Amer. Entomol. Soc. Mem. 11: 1–477.
718. ———
　　　1945. A calatogue and reclassification of the nearctic Ichneumonidae (Hymenoptera). Part II, 1945, The subfamilies Mesoleiinae, Plectisciniae, Orthocentrinae, Diplazoninae, Melopiinae, Ophioninae, Mesochorinae. Amer. Entomol. Soc. Mem. 11: 480–925.
719. Trimble, F. M.
　　　1925. Scale insects injurious in Pennsylvania. Pa. Dep. Agr. Gen. Bull. 398, 21 p., illus.
720. Triplehorn, C. A.
　　　1955. The Asiatic oak weevil in Delaware. J. Econ. Entomol. 48(3): 289–293, illus.
721. Tripp, H. A.
　　　1954. Description and habits of the spruce seedworm, (*Laspeyresia youngana* (Kft.) (Lepidoptera: Olethreutidae). Can. Entomol. 86(9): 385–402, illus.
722. Turnbull, A. L., and Chant, D. A.
　　　1961. The practice and theory of biological control of insects in Canada. Can. J. Zool. 39: 697–753.
723. Turnock, W. J.
　　　1953. Some aspects of the life history and ecology of the pitch nodule maker, *Petrova albicapitana* (Busck) (Lepidoptera—Olethreutidae). Can. Entomol. 85(7): 233–243, illus.
724. United States Department of Agriculture
　　　1939. Cankerworms. U. S. Dep. Agr. Leafl. No. 183 (revised 1953, 1965), 7 p., illus.
725. ———
　　　1939. The elm leaf beetle. U. S. Dep. Agr. Leafl. No. 184 revised 1964), 4 p., illus.

726. ──────
      1955. Wood ticks—how to control them in infested places
            U. S. Dep. Agr. Leafl. No. 387 (revised 1963),
            illus.
727. ──────
      1966. Periodical cicadas. U. S. Dep. Agr. Leafl. No. 540,
            8 p., illus.
728. ──────
      1967. Oriental wood borer (*Heterobostrychus aequalis*
            (Waterhouse). Coop. Econ. Insect Rep. 17(7):
            95.
729. U. S. Forest Service
      1958. Timber resources for America's future. Forest Re-
            source Rep. No. 14, 713 p., illus.
730. Uvarov, B. P.
      1928. Locusts and grasshoppers. 352 p., illus. London:
            Imp. Bur. Entomol.
731. Van Duzee, E. P.
      1923. Family Fulgoridae. Conn. State Geol. and Nat. Hist.
            Surv. Bull. 34: 24–55, illus.
732. Van Leeuwen, E. R.
      1952. Life history and habits of chestnut weevils. J. Econ.
            Entomol. 45(6): 1089–1091.
733. Verrall, A. F.
      1941. Dissemination of fungi that stain logs and lumber.
            J. Agr. Res. 63: 549–558.
734. ──────
      1943. Fungi associated with certain ambrosia beetles. J.
            Agr. Res. 66(3): 135–144, illus.
735. Wade, O.
      1917. The sycamore lacebug (*Corythucha ciliata* Say).
            Okla. Agr. Exp. Sta. Bull. 116, 16 p., illus.
736. Walgenbach, D. D., and Benjamin, D. M.
      1964. Biology of the pine tussock moth. N. Cent. Br.,
            Entomol. Soc. Amer. Proc. 19: 21–22.
737. Wallace, P. P.
      1945. Biology and control of the dogwood borer, *Syanthe-
            don scitula* Harris. Conn. Agr. Exp. Sta. Bull.
            488: 373–395, illus.
738. Wallesz, D. P., and Benjamin, D. M.
      1960. The biology of the pine webworm, *Tetralopha ro-
            bustella,* in Wisconsin. J. Econ. Entomol. 53(4):
            587–589, illus.
739. Walton, B. C. J.
      1960. The life cycle of the hackberry gall-former, *Pachyp-
            sylla celtidisgemma* (Homoptera: Psyllidae).
            Entomol. Soc. Amer. Ann. 53(2): 265–277, illus.
740. Warner, R. E.
      1966. A review of the *Hylobius* of North America with a
            new species injurious to slash pine (Coleoptera:
            Curculionidae). Coleopterists' Bull. 20(3): 65–
            81, illus.
741. Warren, G. L.
      1960. External anatomy of the adult of *Hylobius warreni*

Wood (Coleoptera: Curculionidae) and comparison with *Hylobius pinicola* (Couper). Can. Entomol. 92(5): 321–341, illus.

742. Warren, L. O., and Coyne, J. F.
1958. The pine sawfly—*Neodiprion taedae linearis* Ross—in Arkansas. Ark. Agr. Exp. Sta. Bull. 602, 23 p., illus.

743. Waters, W. E.
1955. Sequential sampling in forest insect surveys. Forest Sci. 1(1): 68–79, illus.

744. ———, McIntyre, T., and Crosby, D.
1955. Loss in volume of white pine in New Hampshire caused by the white pine weevil. J. Forest. 53(4): 271–274, illus.

745. Wear, J. F. and Bongberg, J. W.
1951. Use of aerial photographs in forest insect surveys. J. Forest. 49(8): 632–633.

746. ———, Pope, R. B., and Orr, P. W.
1966. Aerial photographic techniques for estimating damage by insects in western forests. U. S. Forest Serv., Pacific Northwest Forest and Range Exp. Sta., 79 p., illus.

747. Weaver, J. E., and Dorsey, C. K.
1965. Parasites and predators associated with five species of leaf-mining insects in black locust. Entomol. Soc. Amer. Ann. 58(6): 933–934.

748. ———, and Sommers, R. A.
1969. Life history and habits of the short-tailed cricket *Anurogryllus muticus* in central Louisiana. Entomol. Soc. Amer. Ann. 62(2): 337–342, illus.

749. Webb, F. E., and Forbes, R. S.
1951. Notes on the biology of *Pleroneura borealis* Felt (Xyelidae: Hymenoptera). Can. Entomol. 83(7): 181–183, illus.

750. Webb, J. L.
1909. Some insects injurious to forests. The southern pine sawyer. U. S. Bur. Entomol. Bull. 48, Part IV, p. 41–56, illus.

751. Webber, R. T., and Schaffner, Jr., J. V.
1926. Host relations of *Compsilura concinnata* Meigen, an important tachnid parasite of the gipsy moth and the brown-tail moth. U. S. Dep. Agr. Bull. 1363, 31 p.

752. Weiss, F., and St. George, R. A.
1940. Culture, diseases, and pests of the box tree. U. S. Dep. Agr. Farmers' Bull. No. 1855 (revised 1959), 21 p., illus.

753. Welch, H. E.
1963. Nematode infections. *In* E. A. Steinhaus (ed.) Insect pathology, an advanced treatise. Vol. 2, p. 363–392, illus. New York, London: Academic Press.

754. Weld, L. H.
1951. Superfamily Cynipoidea. *In* Hymenoptera of America north of Mexico. P. 594–654. U. S. Dep. Agr. Monogr. No. 2.

755. West, Jr., A. S.
 1936. Winter mortality of larvae of the European pine shoot moth, *Rhyaciona buoliana* Schiff., in Connecticut. Entomol. Soc. Amer. Ann. 29: 438–448.

756. Wester, H. V., and St. George, R. A.
 1947. Life history and control of the webworm. *Homadaula albizziae*. J. Econ. Entomol. 40(4): 546–553, illus.

757. Westveld, M.
 1946. Forest management as a means of controlling the spruce budworm. J. Forest. 44(11): 949–953.

758. ———
 1954. A budworm vigor-resistance classification for spruce and balsam fir. J. Forest. 52(1): 11–24, illus.

759. Wheeler, W. M.
 1910. Ants, their structure, development, and behavior. 663 p., illus. New York: Columbia Univ. Press.

760. White, R. E.
 1962. The Anobiidae of Ohio (Coleoptera). Bull. Ohio Biol. Surv. (n.s.), vol. 1, no. 4, 58 p., illus.

761. Whitten, Jamie L.
 1966. That we may live. Princeton, New Jersey, Van Nostrand Co., Inc. 251 p.

762. Whitten, R. R.
 1941. The internal application of chemicals to kill elm trees and prevent bark beetle attack. U. S. Dep. Agr. Circ. No. 605, 11 p.

763. ———, and Swingle, R. U.
 1958. The Dutch elm disease and its control. U. S. Dep. Agr., Inform. Bull. 193 (revised 1964), 12 p., illus.

764. Wilcox, J. A.
 1954. The leaf beetles of Ohio (Chrysomelidae: Coleoptera). Ohio Biol. Surv. Bull. 43, 8(3): 353–506, illus.

765. Wilford, B. H.
 1937. The spruce gall aphid (*Adelges abietis* Linnaeus) in southern Michigan. Mich. Univ. Sch. Forest. and Conserv. Circ. 2, 34 p., illus.

766. ———
 1940. The seed corn maggot, a pest of red cedar seedlings. J. Forest. 38: 658–659.

767. Wilkinson, R. C., Becker, G. C., and Benjamin, D. M.
 1966. The biology of *Neodiprion rugifrons* (Hymenoptera: Diprionidae), a sawfly infesting jack pine in Wisconsin. Entomol. Soc. Amer. Ann. 59(4): 768–792, illus.

768. Williams, S. R., and Hefner, R. A.
 1928. The millipedes and centipedes of Ohio. Ohio Biol. Surv. Bull. 18, 4(3): 91–146, illus.

769. Williston, S. W.
 1908. Manual of North American Diptera. Ed. 3, 405 p., illus. New Haven, Conn.: J. T. Hathaway.

770. Wilson, L. F.
 1961a. Grasshoppers—A major defoliator of trees and

shrubs in the northern Great Plains. U. S. Forest Serv. Lake States Forest Exp. Sta. Tech. Notes No. 596, 2 p., illus.

771. ———

1961b. Variable oak leaf caterpillar. U. S. Forest Serv., Forest Pest Leafl. 67, 4 p., illus.

772. ———

1962a. Yellow-headed spruce sawfly, U.S. Forest Serv., Forest Pest Leafl. 69, 4 p., illus.

773. ———

1962b. White-spotted sawyer. U. S. Forest Serv., Forest Pest Leafl. 74, 7 p., illus.

774. ———

1963. The green-striped maple-worm. U. S. Forest Serv., Forest Pest Leafl. 77, 4 p., illus.

775. ———

1964. Walkingstick. U. S. Forest Serv., Forest Pest Leafl. 82, 4 p., illus.

776. ———

1965. Life history and some habits of the pine gall weevil, *Podapion gallicola,* in Michigan. Can. Entomol. 97(9): 962–969, illus.

777. ———

1966a. Effects of different population levels of the European pine sawfly on young Scotch pine trees. J. Econ. Entomol. 59(5): 1043–1049.

778. ———

1966b. Introduced pine sawfly. U. S. Forest Serv., Forest Pest Leafl. 99, 4 p., illus.

779. ———

1966c. Life history, habits, and damage of the boxelder leaf gall midge, *Contarinia negundifolia* Felt (Diptera: Cecidomyiidae), in Michigan. Can. Entomol. 98(7): 777–784, illus.

780. ———

1967. Effects of pruning and ground treatments on populations of the pine root collar weevil. J. Econ. Entomol. 60(3): 823–827, illus.

781. ———

1968a. Life history and habits of the willow beaked gall midge, *Mayetiola rigidae* (Diptera: Cecidomyiidae), in Michigan. Can. Entomol. 100(2): 202–206, illus.

782. ———

1968b. Life history, habits, and damage of a gall midge, *Oligotrophus papyriferae* (Diptera: Cecidomyiidae), injurious to paper birch in Michigan. Can. Entomol. 100(6): 663–669, illus.

783. ———, and Kennedy, P. C.

1968. Suppression of the Saratoga spittlebug in the nymphal stage by granular Baygon[R]. J. Econ. Entomol. 61(3): 839–840.

784. ———, and Millers, I.

1966. Suppression of Saratoga spittlebug with helicopter

application of low- and high-volume malathion. J. Econ. Entomol. 59(6): 1456–1458.

785. ———, and Schmiege, D. C.
1959. Pine root collar weevil. U. S. Forest Service, Forest Pest Leafl. 39, (revised 1965), 7 p., illus.

786. Wirth, W. W.
1965. Family Ceratopogonidae. *In* A. Stone, C. W. Sabrosky, W. W. Wirth, and others (dir.). A catalog of the Diptera of America north of Mexico. U. S. Dep. Agr., Agr. Handbook No. 176, p. 121–142.

787. ———, Sedman, Y. S., and Weems, Jr., H. V.
1965. Family Syrphidae. *In* A. Stone, C. W. Sabrosky, W. W. Wirth, and others (dir.). A catalog of the Diptera of America north of Mexico. U. S. Dep. Agr., Agr. Handbook No. 276, p. 557–625.

788. Wolcott, G. N.
1914. Notes on the life history and ecology of *Tiphia inornata* Say. J. Econ. Entomol. 7: 382–389.

789. Wollerman, E. H.
1962. The locust borer. U. S. Forest Serv., Forest Pest Leafl. 71 (revised 1967), 7 p., illus.

790. ———
1965a. Bagworm. U. S. Forest Serv., Forest Pest Leafl. 97, 7 p., illus.

791. ———
1965b. The boxelder bug. U. S. Forest Serv., Forest Pest Leafl. 95, 6 p., illus.

792. Wood, D. E., Browne, L. E., Bedard, W. D., and others.
1968. Response of *Ips confusus* to synthetic sex pheromones in nature. Science 159(3821): 1373–1374.

793. Wood, S. L.
1963. A revision of the bark beetle genus *Dendroctonus* Erichson (Coleoptera: Scolytidae). The Great Basin Nat. 23(1–2): 117, illus.

794. Woods, W. C.
1917. The biology of the alder flea beetle. *Altica bimarginata* Say. Maine Agr. Exp. Sta. Bull. 265: 249–284, illus.

795. Wright, C. G.
1960. Biology of the southern Lyctus beetle, *Lyctus planicollis*. Entomol. Soc. Amer. Ann. 53(3): 285–292, illus.

796. Wright, J. W., and Gabriel, W. J.
1959. Possibilities of breeding weevil-resistant white pine strains. U. S. Forest Serv., Northeast. Forest Exp. Sta., Sta. Pap. No. 115, 35 p., illus.

797. Yates, III, H. O.
1967. Key to nearctic parasites of the genus *Rhyacionia:* with species annotations. U. S. Forest Serv., Southeast. Forest Exp. Sta., (May 1967), 127 p., illus.

798. ———, and Beal, R. H.
1962. Nantucket pine tip moth. U. S. Forest Serv., Forest Pest Leafl. 70, 4 p., illus.

559

799. Yearian, W. C., and Warren, L. O.
  1964. Insects of pine cones in Arkansas. J. Kans. Entomol.
    Soc. 37 (3) : 259–264.
800. Young, H. C., App, B. W., Gilland, J. B., and Hollingsworth,
  H. S.
  1950. White-fringed beetles and how to combat them.
    U. S. Dep. Agr., Circ. 850, 15 p., illus.
801. Yuasa, H.
  1922. A classification of the larvae of the Tenthredinoidea.
    Ill. Biol. Monogr. 7 (4) : 172 p., illus.
802. Zappe, M. P.
  1921. Notes on the life history of a sawfly feeding on
    Austrian pine, *Itycorsia Zappei*. Conn. State Agr.
    Exp. Sta. Ann. Rep. 1920, Bull. 226 : 179–182,
    illus.

INDEX TO INSECTS BY HOST PLANTS

This index should enable foresters and others not trained in entomology to identify many of the insects causing damage to particular species of trees or shrubs. Only those insects having definite host plants are included. The common names of insects, where known, are used; otherwise, the scientific name is given. Where more than one page reference is given for an insect, the page on which the insect is discussed is in boldface type.

569

Douglas-fir—Continued
  borers, wood—
    old house borer, 206
    Semanotus litigiosus, 198
    Stephanopachys substriatus, 136
  leaf feeders—
    European chafer, 150
    spruce budworm, 25, **378**, 472, 477
  sucking insect—
    Cooley spruce gall aphid, **87**, 91

Elder:
  Desmocerus spp., 193
  elder borer, 193
  Phlyctaenia coronata, 351
Elm (*Ulmus* spp.):
  bark feeders—
    elm bark borer, 197
    elm sawfly, **438**, 472
  borers, bark and phloem—
    black elm bark weevil, **224**, 478
    elm borer, 188
    flat-headed apple tree borer, **165**, 478
    native elm bark beetle, **250**, 499
    Neoclytus scutellaris, 184
    peach bark beetle, 240
    red elm bark weevil, **224**, 478
    Scolytus mali, 237
    shot-hole borer, 238
    smaller European elm bark beetle, 10, 19, 24, 29, 154, **235**, 475, 499
  borers, wood—
    beetles:
      Anoplodera minnesotana, 197
      banded-ash borer, 184
      Buprestis rufipes, 165
      Columbian timber beetle, 265
      dogwood twig borer, 189
      elm borer, 188
      flat-headed apple tree borer, **165**, 478
      Goes spp., 182
      Hylocurus langstoni, 253
      ivory-marked beetle, 192
      Lichenophanes bicornis, 136
      living-beech borer, 183
      Magdalis barbicornis, 225
        pandura, 225
      Neoclytus scutellaris, 184
      Oberea tripunctata, 189
        ulmicola, 190
      Platybregmus canadensis, 134
      Platypus compositus, 273
      powder-post beetle, 17, 21, **126**, 128, 155
      Saperda lateralis, 188
      Scobicia bidentata, 136
      Thysanoes berschemiae, 253
      twig girdler, **191**, 502
      twig pruner, 192
      Xylosandrus germanus, 271
    horntails:
      pigeon tremex, 466

Elm—Continued
  borers, wood—Continued
    horntails—Continued
      Xiphydra abdominalis, 467
        hicoriae, 467
        tibialis, 467
    moths and butterflies:
      carpenterworm, 388
      leopard moth, 386
  leaf feeders—
    beetles:
      Altica carinata, 142
      Anomoea laticlavia, 145
      Brachys aeriguinosa, 169
      elm calligrapha, 140
      elm leaf beetle, **138**, 431, 474
      European snout beetle, 219
      flat-headed apple tree borer, **165**, 478
      Japanese beetle, 19, **151**, 485, 486
      larger elm leaf beetle, 141
      locust leaf miner, **143**, 472, 478
      Pachybrachys othonus, 145
      Phyllophaga drakei, 146
        forsteri, 148
        implicta, 148
        prunina, 147
        tristis, 148
      willow flea weevil, 222
      Xanthonia decimnotata, 145
    mites:
      Eotetranychus matthyssei, 7
      Tetranychus canadensis, 7
        schoenei, 7
    moths and butterflies:
      Acronicta funeralis, 308
        interrupta, 308
        morula, 308
      American dagger moth, 308
      Argyrotaenia mariana, 385
      bagworm, 21, **411**, 472, 475, 477, 478
      brown-tail moth, 24, **325**, 430, 431, 469, 472, 476
      Canarsia ulmiarrosorella, 359
      cecropia moth, **298**, 477
      Charadra deridens, 309
      Choristoneura fractivittana, 384
      Coleophora ulmifoliella, 404
      dark tussock moth, 320
      Deuteronomos magnarius, 346
      elm casebearer, 404
      elm spanworm, **343**, 484
      elm sphinx, 295
      fall cankerworm, 21, **334**, 339, 472, 483
      fruit-tree leaf roller, 377
      gypsy moth, 12, 18, 19, 24, 25, 28, 62, 65, 117, 123, **320**, 430, 431, 469, 472, 474, 475, 476, 483
      Hemerocampa definita, 319
      hemlock looper, 344, 478, 483
      Heterocampa bilinecta, 316
      hickory tussock moth, 304

573

Fir, balsam—Continued
　borers, wood—Continued
　　beetles—Continued
　　　northeastern sawyer, 205
　　　old house borer, 206
　　　Pityokteines sparsus, 263
　　　Semanotus litigiosus, 198
　　　spruce timber beetle, 268
　　　Stephanopachys substriatus,
　　　　136
　　　white-spotted sawyer, 203
　　　Xylotrechus undulatus, 203
　　horntails, *Sirex juvencus*, 466
　　sawflies, *Pleroneura brunneicornis*, 433
　bud and flower feeders—
　　spruce bud moth, 369
　　spruce budworm, 25, **378**, 472,
　　　477
　　spruce coneworm, 355
　gall insect, balsam gall midge, 418
　leaf feeders—
　　beetles:
　　　white-spotted sawyer, 203
　　moths and butterflies:
　　　Anomogyna eliminata, 309
　　　Argyrotaenia occultana, 385
　　　black-headed budworm, **385**,
　　　　472
　　　Campaea perlata, 346
　　　chain-spotted geometer, 345
　　　Eufidonia notataria, 338
　　　Eupethecia filmata, 337
　　　　luteata, 337
　　　　transcanadata, 337
　　　false hemlock looper, 344
　　　filament bearer, 342
　　　Griselda radicana, 374
　　　hemlock looper, **344**, 478, 483
　　　Hyperetis amicaria, 342
　　　Lexis bicolor, 307
　　　Palthis angulalis, 309
　　　Pero morrisonarius, 344
　　　pine tussock moth, 320
　　　Protobarmia porcelaria, 346
　　　red-banded leaf roller, 384
　　　Semiothisa granitata, 338
　　　spruce budworm, 25, **378**, 472,
　　　　477
　　　white-marked tussock moth,
　　　　318, 476, 478, 483
　　sawflies:
　　　Acantholyda maculiventris,
　　　　435
　　　balsam fir sawfly, **446**, 473
　　　Pleroneura brunneicornis, 433
　nesting insects—
　　black carpenter ant, 484, **486**
　seed insects—
　　Megastigmus specularis, 476
　sucking insects—
　　balsam twig aphid, 83
　　balsam woolly aphid, 12, 24, **88**,
　　　90, 123, 124
　　Cinara curvipes, 80
　　Fiorinia externa, 111
　　hemlock scale, 108
　　pine spittlebug, 71

Fir, balsam—Continued
　sucking insects—Continued
　　Saratoga spittlebug, **72**, 472
Fir, Fraser:
　balsam gall midge, 418
　balsam twig aphid, 83
　balsam woolly aphid, 12, 24, **88**,
　　90, 123, 124
　Dryocoetes autographus, 263
　Taenioglyptes fraseri, 259
Fir, Siberian, see Balsam Fir
Fringe tree:
　Sphinx kalmiae, 296
Fruit trees, various:
　borer, bark and phloem—
　　shot-hole borer, 238
　borer, root—
　　Prionus spp., 200
　borers, wood—
　　apple twig borer, 136
　　carpenterworm, 388
　　dogwood twig borer, 189
　　New York weevil, 209
　　pear blight beetle, 269
　　twig girdler, **191**, 502
　bud and flower feeders—
　　eye-spotted budmoth, 365
　　fruit-tree leaf roller, 377
　fruit feeders—
　　fruit-tree leaf roller, 377
　　plum curculio, 227
　leaf feeders—
　　Datana ministra, 311
　　eastern tent caterpillar, **328**,
　　　476, 477, 483
　　eye-spotted budmoth, 365
　　fruit-tree leaf roller, 377
　　Oriental moth, **347**, 349, 431, 484
　　red-humped caterpillar, 316

Gingko:
　American plum borer, 359
Gum, black or sour, see Tupelo
Gum, red, see Sweetgum

Hackberry:
　borers, bark and phloem—
　　Agrilus celti, 163
　　　lecontei, 163
　　Chramesus chapuisii, 239
　　flat-headed apple tree borer,
　　　165, 478
　　hackberry engraver, 239
　　Phloeotribus dentifrons, 240
　　Pseudothysanoes lecontei, 253
　　Scolytus fagi, 238
　borer, root—
　　Archodontes melanopus, 206
　borers, wood—
　　flat-headed apple tree borer,
　　　165, 478
　　Hylocurus langstoni, 253
　　　rudis, 252
　　Lichenophanes bicornis, 136
　　painted hickory borer, 178
　　pear blight beetle, 269
　　red-headed ash borer, 184
　　Scobicia bidentata, 136

577

Hemlock—Continued
  borers, cone—
    Eucosma tocullionana, 368
  borers, root—
    pales weevil, 213
    strawberry root weevil, 221
  borers, wood—
    Anoplodera canadensis, 196
    black-horned juniper borer, 195
    black-horned pine borer, 194
    Buprestis maculipennis, 165
          striata, 165
    Chrysobothris pusilla, 167
          scabripennis, 167
          sexsignata, 167
    hemlock borer, **168**, 483
    Melanophila drummondi, 169
    Monarthrum fasciatum, 267
          mali, 267
    old house borer, 206
    pales weevil, 213
    spruce timber beetle, 268
    Stephanopachys substriatus, 136
    striped ambrosia beetle, 267
    Trypodendron scabricollis, 268
    Xyleborus saxeseni, 269
    Xyloterinus politus, 264, **267**
    Xylotrechus undulatus, 203
  gall formers—
    Nalepella tsugifoliae, 8
  leaf feeders—
    beetles:
      Asiatic garden beetle, 149,
          485
      Japanese weevil, 219
      pales weevil, 213
    moths and butterflies:
      Abbottana clemataria, 346
      Anacamptodes ephyraria, 338
      black-headed budworm, **385**,
          472
      Campaea perlata, 346
      *Coleotechnites apicitripunc-
          tella*, 390
      false hemlock looper, 344
      Feralia jocosa, 309
      filament bearer, 342
      gypsy moth, 12, 18, 19, 24, 25,
          28, 62, 65, 117, 123, **320**, 430,
          431, 469, 472, 474, 475, 476,
          483
      hemlock looper, **344**, 478, 483
      *Lambdina athasaria atha-
          saria*, 345
      Melanolophia canadaria, 338
      Neptyia semiclusaria, 344
      Semiothisa granitata, 338
      spruce budworm, 25, **378**, 472,
          477
  root feeders—
    Japanese weevil, 219
    strawberry root weevil, 221
  sucking insects—
    Fiorinia externa, 111
    hemlock scale, 108
    pine spittlebug, 71

Hickory (*Carya* spp.) :
  bark feeders—
    Cryptocleptus dislocatus, 253
    Hypothenemus spp.
    New York weevil, 209
  borers, bark and phloem—
    Chramesus hicoriae, 239
    Conotrachelus anaglypticus, 227
    flat-headed apple tree borer,
          165, 478
    hickory bark beetle, **237**, 270
    hickory spiral borer, 163
    mulberry bark borer, 193
    Neoclytus mucronatus, **184**, 186
          scutellaris, **184**
    oak bark scaler, 199
    Phymatodes varius, 197
    Pseudopityophthorus pruinosus,
          256
  borers, nut—
    Conotrachelus affinis, 227
          hicoriae, 227
    hickory shuckworm, 372, 472,
          477, 485
    pecan nut casebearer, 354
    pecan weevil, 226
    Valentinia glandulella, 396
  borers, shoot and leaf petiole—
    Acrobasis caryivorella, 353
    apple twig borer, 136
    Chramesus hicoriae, 239
    Conotrachelus aratus, 227
    hickory bark beetle, **237**, 270
    pecan carpenterworm, 387
    pecan nut casebearer, 354
  borers, wood—
    beetles:
      Actenodes acornis, 169
      Agrilus otiosus, 163
      Anoplodera minnesotana, 197
          proxima, 197
          vagans, 197
      banded-ash borer, 184
      banded-hickory borer, 178
      Buprestis rufipes, 165
      Chramesus hicoriae, 239
      Chrysobothris adelpha, 167
          sexsignata, 167
      Cryptocleptus dislocatus,
          253
      Dicerca lurida, 168
      Dryophthorus americanus,
          223
      flat-headed apple tree borer,
          165, 478
      flat powder-post beetle, 199
      hickory spiral borer, 163
      Hylocurus bicornus, 252
          biorbis, 252
          harnedi, 252
          rudis, 252
          spadix, 252
      Hypothenemus dissimilis, 254
          eruditus, 254
          interstitialis, 254
          quercus, 254
          rotundicollis, 254
      ivory-marked beetle, 192
      Lichenophanes bicornis, 136

Hickory—Continued
  sucking insects—Continued
    Myzocallis caryaefoliae, 84
    obscure scale, 108
    periodical cicada, 74
    Phylloxera spp., 91
    plant bugs, 65
    scurfy scale, 108
    sycamore lacebug, 63
Holly (*Ilex* spp.) :
  borers, wood—
    pear blight beetle, 269
    Xyleborus saxeseni, 269
  gall insect—
    Asphondylia ilicicola, 418
  leaf feeders—
    Epicauta torsa, 121
    holly leaf miner, 426
    Tolype velleda, 333
  sucking insects—
    Chrysomphalus   dictyospermi,
      112
    Comstock mealybug, 100
    Fiorinia theae, 112
    holly scale, 101
    mulberry whitefly, 92
    Prosapia bicincta, 73
Honeylocust:
  borers, bark and phloem—
    Agrilus difficilis, 163
    Hypothenemus dissimilis, 254
                quercus, 254
  borers, seed—
    Amblycerus robiniae, 137
  borers, wood—
    Hylocurus langstoni, 253
    Hypothenemus dissimilis, 254
                quercus, 254
    ivory-marked beetle, 192
    painted hickory borer, 178
    pear blight beetle, 269
    twig girdler, 191, 502
    Xyleborus saxeseni, 269
  gall insects—
    Dasineura gleditchiae, 418
  leaf feeders—
    beetles:
      Anomoea laticlavia, 145
      Epicauta cinerea, 121
    mites:
      *Platytetranychus   multidigi-
        tuli,* 7
      Tetranychus ellipticus, 7
    moths and butterflies:
      imperial moth, 303
      locust leaf roller, 358
      Machimia tentoriferella, 395
      mimosa webworm, 396
      oriental moth, 347, 349, 431,
        484
      Semiothisa ocellinata, 338
      Sparganothis sulfureana, 375
      yellow-necked caterpillar, 311
  sucking insects—
    cottony maple scale, 101
    European fruit lecanium, 105,
      475

Honeylocust—Continued
  sucking insects—Continued
    Macropsis spp., 69
    Micrutalis calva, 71
    periodical cicada, 74
Hophornbeam:
  borers, bark and phloem—
    Pseudopityophthorus pruinosus,
      256
    Pseudothysanoes lecontei, 253
  borers, wood—
    Hypothenemus dissimilis, 254
                quercus, 254
    pitted ambrosia beetle, 266
  leaf feeders—
    beetles:
      basswood leaf miner, 141
      Epicauta cinerea, 121
      Thysanoes fimbricornis, 253
    mite:
      Oligonychus letchworthi, 6
    moths and butterflies:
      Depressaria betulella, 395
      gypsy moth, 12, 18, 19, 24, 25,
        28, 62, 65, 117, 123, 320,
        430, 431, 469, 472, 474, 475,
        476, 483
      maple leaf cutter, 143
      walnut sphinx, 297
      winter moth, 336
      yellow-necked caterpillar, 311
    sawfly, *Nematus ostryae,* 461
  sucking insects—
    Corythucha pallipes, 63
    Phenacoccus acericola, 22, 99
Hornbeam, see Hophornbeam
Hornbeam, American (blue beech) :
  borers, bark and phloem—
    Pseudopityophthorus pruinosus,
      256
    pubescens, 256
    two-lined chestnut borer, 160
  borers, wood—
    banded hickory borer, 178
    birch and beech girdler, 201
    Dicerica lurida, 168
    pitted ambrosia beetle, 266
    Xiphydria tibialis, 467
    Xylotrechus   quadrimaculatus,
      201
Huisache:
  Oncideres pustulatus, 192

Incense-cedar, see Pine, incense-
  cedar
Ironwood, (see also Hophornbeam;
  Hornbeam, American) :
  borers, wood—
    Cinyra gracilipes, 170
    two-lined chestnut borer, 160
  leaf feeders—
    Acleris chalybeana, 385
    Aenea ostryaealla, 390
    luna moth, 298
    Pandemis lamprosana, 375
    Tymnes tricolor, 145

589

593

594

Pine, shortleaf—Continued
 borers, wood—
  beetles:
   Chrysobothris dentipes, 167
              pusilla, 167
   Gnathotrichus materiarius, 268
   Monochamus titillator, 203
   northern pine weevil, 211
   pales weevil, 213
   Pityoborus comatus, 258
   Trypodendron scabricollis, 268
   turpentine borer, 164
   Xyleborus saxeseni, 269
  horntail:
   Sirex nigricornis, 466
 gall insects—
  Pleuroneura sp., 433
  Xyela sp., 432
 leaf feeders—
  beetles:
   Glyptoscelis pubescens, 145
   pine colaspis, 142
   turpentine borer, 164
  moths and butterflies:
   Lambdina athasaria pellucidaria, 345
   Nantucket pine tip moth, **363**, 472, 475, 477, 478, 485
   pine needle miner, 391
   pine webworm, 65, **351**
  sawflies:
   European pine sawfly, 12, 19, 24, **447**, 470, 471, 473
   Neodiprion abbotii, 447
        excitans, 19, **449**
        pinirigidae, **450**, 473
        pratti paradoxicus, **443**, 473
        pratti pratti, 441
        taedae linearis, **443**, 445
        warreni, 450
   red-headed pine sawfly, 446
   white-pine sawfly, 446
 pollen feeder—
  Pomphopoea polita, 121
 shoot feeder—
  Pleuroneura sp., 433
  Xyela sp., 432
 sucking insects—
  Cinara carolina, 83
        pini, 83
        watsoni, 83
  Eulachnus rileyi, 83
  pine twig gall scale, 65, **96**
Pine, slash:
 bark feeders—
  pales weevil, 213
 borers, bark and phloem—
  beetles:
   black turpentine beetle, 244
   Ips spp., 260
   pales weevil, 213
   Pityoborus comatus, 258
   Pityophthorus spp., 255
   red turpentine beetle, 246
   southern pine beetle, **240**, 477, 502

Pine, slash—Continued
 borers, bark and phloem—Con.
  moth, *Dioryctria abietella*, 23, **355**
 borers, bud and shoot—
  beetle:
   Pityophthorus spp., 255
  moths and butterflies:
   Dioryctria abietella, 23, **355**
            clarioralis, 354
   Holcocera lepidophaga, 396
   Nantucket pine tip moth, **363**, 472, 475, 477, 478, 485
   Rhyacionia rigidana, **363**, 477, 478
            subtropica, 365
 borers, cone—
  Dioryctria abietella, 23, **355**
        amatella, 356
        clarioralis, 354
  Holcocera lepidophaga, 396
  Laspeyresia anaranjada, 372
            ingens, 373
 borers, gall—
  Dioryctria amatella, 356
  Moodna ostrinella, 359
 borers, root—
  Hylobius aliradicis, 217
 borers, wood—
  pales weevil, 213
  Pityoborus comatus, 258
  southern pine sawyer, 263
  turpentine borer, 164
 cone feeders—
  Gnopothrips fuscus, 42
  Holcocera lepidophaga, 396
 flower feeders—
  Holcocera lepidophaga, 396
  thrips spp., **41**, 43
  Xyela bakeri, 432
        minor, 432
        obscura, 432
 gall insects—
  Pleroneura sp., 433
  Xyela sp., 432
 leaf feeders—
  ant, Texas leaf-cutting, 490
  beetles:
   pine colaspis, 142
  cricket, short-tailed cricket, 60
  moths and butterflies:
   Apantesis radians, 307
   Nantucket pine tip moth, **363**, 472, 475, 477, 478, 485
   pine webworm, 65, **351**
  sawflies:
   Neodiprion obbotii, 447
        excitans, 19, **449**
        merkeli, 450
   red-headed pine sawfly, 19, 431, **439**, 473
 shoot feeder—
  Pleroneura sp., 433
  Xyela sp., 432
 sucking insects—
  Brochymena carolinensis, 62

610

611

Yellow-poplar—Continued
  borers, wood—
    Ambrosiodmus   tachygraphus,
      269
    Buprestis rufipes, 165
    Chalcophorella campestris, 168
    Columbian timber beetle, 265
    flat-headed apple tree borer, **165**,
      478
    Orchesia castanea, 125
    pear blight beetle, 269
    sapwood timberworm, 126
    Xyleborus saxeseni, 269
  leaf feeders—
    beetles:
      flat-headed apple tree borer,
        165, 478
      Odontopus calceatus, 221
    mite, *Tetranychus magnoliae,* 7
    moths:
      Epimecis virginiara, 339
      Paralobesia liriodendrana, 373
      Phyllocnistis   liriodendrella,
        408

Yellow-poplar—Continued
  leaf feeders—Continued
    moths—Continued
      polyphemus moth, 299
      promethea moth, 298
  sucking insects—
    Abgrallaspis townsendi, 108
    Chionaspis salicisnigrae, 109
    European fruit lecanium, **105**,
      475
    Macrosiphum liriodendri, 84
    periodical cicada, 74
    tuliptree scale, 103
Yew:
  leaf and root feeders—
    Asiatic garden beetle, **149**, 485
    black vine weevil, 220
    strawberry root weevil, 221
  sucking insects—
    Comstock mealybug, 100
    cottony maple leaf scale, **101**
    Dysmicoccus cuspidatae, 99
    Fiorinia externa, 111
    Fletcher scale, **106**
    grape mealybug, 100

INSECT INDEX

This is an alphabetical listing of the insect species, both scientific and common names. Bold face numbers indicate page where the insect is discussed.

620

622

624

625

626

629

632

634

642